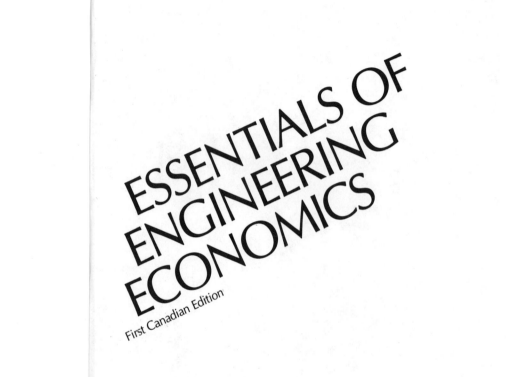

# ESSENTIALS OF ENGINEERING ECONOMICS

First Canadian Edition

# ESSENTIALS OF ENGINEERING ECONOMICS

First Canadian Edition

James L. Riggs
Professor and Department Head
Industrial and General Engineering
Oregon State University

William F. Rentz
Faculty of Administration
University of Ottawa

Alfred L. Kahl
Faculty of Administration
University of Ottawa

McGraw-Hill Ryerson Limited

Toronto  Montréal  New York  St. Louis
San Francisco  Auckland  Bogotá  Guatemala
Hamburg  Johannesburg  Lisbon  London  Madrid
Mexico  New Delhi  Panama  Paris  San Juan
São Paulo  Singapore  Sydney  Tokyo

To Our Families.
JLR
WFR
ALK

Acknowledgement: The assistance of
Joseph Ting is appreciated.

ESSENTIALS OF ENGINEERING ECONOMICS
First Canadian Edition

ISBN 0-07-548580-X

3456789 D 21098765

Printed and bound in Canada

Canadian Cataloguing in Publication Data

Riggs, James L.
  Essentials of engineering economics

Includes index.
ISBN 0-07-548580-X

1. Engineering economy.  2. Managerial economics.
I. Rentz, William F.  II. Kahl, Alfred L.  III. Title.

TA177.4.R532 1983  620'.0068'1  C83-094048-0

# CONTENTS

# PREFACE

The curricula of most professional schools include a course in applied economics under titles such as *engineering economy, financial management*, and *managerial economics*. Practicing professionals usually rate their "econ" course as one of the most useful subjects taken in college. This book is written to make that econ experience as rewarding as possible and to provide a comprehensive reference for future applications.

Engineering economics is a fascinating subject. Its core is decision making based on comparisons of the worths of alternative courses of action with respect to their costs. Decisions vary from personal investments to corporate capital budgeting, and occur at all organizational levels in both the public and private sectors of the economy. Tools for decision making stretch from standardized worksheets for discounted cash-flow evaluations to refinements for sensitivity and risk analysis. The practices followed are grounded in classical economic theory, yet rely on techniques adapted from financial accounting, decision theory, operations research, and other disciplines. Most of the applications are intuitively logical and computationally simple, but the underlying principles are conceptually demanding.

# CONTENTS

The following brief tour through *Essentials of Engineering Economics* indicates how the diverse characteristics described above are coordinated into a logical flow of subjects that is both comprehensive and comprehensible.

- An introductory chapter traces the history of engineering economic thought to show how the generic title — engineering economics — represents a blend of subjects that builds on the traditional engineering concern for operating economies to include *financial considerations, management concepts*, and *decision-analysis techniques*.

- The conventional mathematics of money is presented in Section One. Five chapters are devoted to the *mechanics of time-value calculations* and comparisons of alternatives based on their *equivalent annual worth, present worth*, and *rate of return*. Interest factors follow ASEE-suggested functional notations, and interest calculations are displayed on cash flow diagrams. A wide variety of examples and exercises is provided.

- Applications of discounted cash flow comparisons are detailed in Section Two. Chapters 7 and 8 present ways to structure evaluations to determine a *preferred investment alternative* or *replacement policy. Financial considerations* for private investments and *benefit-cost analyses* for government projects are discussed in the following two chapters.

- After the examination of standard and specialized formulations, Section Three focuses on the practicalities of money management. *Basic accounting* and *depreciation methods* direct attention to *corporate income taxation*. These subjects are followed by a pair of timely chapters on the *effects of inflation* and *sensitivity analysis*. Chapter 15 concludes the section with a discussion of procedures used by industries to select and justify *investment proposals*.

- Readily applicable decision models are introduced in Section Four. Chapter 16 shows how and why *breakeven analyses are used*. The fundamental *expected-value criterion* is described in the next chapter and is applied to a variety of decision situations. The expected-value concept is extended to *decision trees* in Chapter 18. Chapter 19 addresses the controversial subject of "intangibles" and suggests procedures for accommodating both convenient- and difficult-to-quantify data in *economic decision making*.

- Section Five contains Chapter 20 on estimating and forecasting. It makes the first 19 chapters operational.

# FEATURES

A text on engineering economy is expected to have plenty of detailed examples, comprehensive interest tables, and an ample assortment of practice exercises. This book has them. Realistic examples are interspersed throughout each chapter, and a collection of worked-out review exercises at the end of each chapter further expands on solution techniques. There are almost 600 questions and problems, with answers provided for over half of them.

*Essentials of Engineering Economics* is drawn from the second U.S. edition of *Engineering Economics*. It benefits from suggestions made by users of the first edition, which led to shorter chapters, reorganization of subject flow, amplified discussions of troublesome concepts, and expanded coverage of timely topics such as inflation and sensitivity analysis. The informal prose is retained. Overly elaborate theoretical developments are avoided.

The subjects included in "Essentials" are designed for a one-term course. They comprise all the conventional topics – and many more. *Extensions* at the end of each chapter provide added flexibility. These are supplementary topics that can be treated as study cases because questions are included for each one; or, they may be considered as readings because they are outside the regular flow of subject matter. Some of them deal with personal finances and socioeconomic situations (creativity, pollution control, noncorporate taxation, value of a human life), whereas others introduce analysis methods that complement those in the chapters (geometric series, life-cycle costing, financial statements, causes and consequences of inflation, investments to avoid risk, fault trees, etc.). Extension 12B provides a microcomputer model for the analysis of investment decisions. A glossary of terms is included.

## TRIBUTE

Money is the modern equivalent of the long-sought "philosopher's stone." For centuries, alchemists vainly sought the "stone" that could transform one type of metal into another. Now we have that capacity, indirectly. With money as the medium of exchange, we can convert one type of resource into other types easily and rapidly, but not always wisely. The worthiness of this transformation is a subtle aspect of the mission of engineering economists. Telltale analyses of alternatives reveal the innermost workings of a project and burden the analyst with ethical responsibilities atop fiscal obligations. Prerequisite to bearing the burden is a thorough knowledge of accepted economic principles and practices. This knowledge facilitates putting a legitimate monetary value on the transformation of each resource and, combined with technical expertise about the subject, allows an accurate and conscientious appraisal of worthiness. Resource commitments monetized as cash flows set a quantitative framework for ensuing qualitative value considerations. This book is dedicated to the economic analysts who contribute to resource-allocation decisions. May you do so wisely.

It can be said that those who manage people manage people who manage works, but those who manage money manage all. We hope you accept the challenge and enjoy a satisfying and profitable experience from *Engineering Economics.*

*James L. Riggs*
*William F. Rentz*
*Alfred L. Kahl*

# CHAPTER 1

# INTRODUCTION TO ENGINEERING ECONOMICS

OVERVIEW

Engineers are planners and builders. They are also problem solvers, managers, and decision makers. Engineering economics touches each of these activities. Plans and production must be financed. Problems are eventually defined by dollar dimensions, and decisions are evaluated by their monetary consequences. Much of the management function is directed toward economic objectives and monitored by economic measures.

Engineering economics is closely aligned with conventional microeconomics, but it has a history and a special flavor of its own. It is devoted to problem solving and decision making at the operations level. It is subject to suboptimization—a condition in which a solution satisfies tactical objectives at the expense of strategic effectiveness—but careful attention to the collection and analysis of data minimizes the danger.

An engineering economist draws upon the accumulated knowledge of engineering and economics to identify alternative uses of limited resources and to select the preferred course of action. Evaluations rely mainly on mathematical models, but judgment and experience are pivotal inputs. Many accepted models are available for analyses of short-range projects when the time value of money is not relevant, and of long-range proposals when discounting is required for input data assumed to be known or subject to risk. Familiarity with these models, gained from studying subsequent chapters, should guide your passage through the engineering economic decision maze.

## ENGINEERING DECISION MAKERS

Which one of several competing designs should be selected?

Should the machine in use be replaced with a new one?

With limited capital available, which investment alternative should be funded?

Would it be preferable to pursue a safer, conservative course of action or follow a riskier one that offers higher potential returns?

Among several proposals for funding that yield substantially equivalent worthwhile results but have different cash flow patterns, which is preferable?

Are the benefits expected from a public-service project large enough to make its implementation costs acceptable?

Two characteristics of the above questions should be apparent. The first is that each deals with a choice among alternatives, and the second is that all of them involve economic considerations. Less obvious are the requirements of adequate data and an awareness of technological constraints, to define the problem and to identify legitimate solutions. These considerations are embodied in the decision-making role of engineering economists to

**1**  Identify alternative uses for limited resources and obtain appropriate data
**2**  Analyze the data to determine the preferred alternative

The breadth of problems, depth of analysis, and scope of application that a practicing engineer encounters vary widely. Newly graduated engineers are regularly assigned to cost-reduction projects and are expected to be cost conscious in all their operations. As they gain more experience, they may become specialists in certain application areas or undertake more general responsibilities as managers. Beginners are usually restricted to short-range decisions for low-budget operations, while engineering managers are confronted with policy decisions that involve large sums and are influenced by many factors with long-range consequences. Both situations are served by the principles and practices of engineering economics.

A decision is simply a selection from two or more courses of action, whether it takes place in construction or production operations, service or manufacturing industries, private or public agencies. Some choices are trivial or largely automatic, but other decisions can be challenging, exciting experiences. Most major decisions, even personal ones, have overtones of economy. This consistent usage makes the subject of engineering economics especially challenging *and rewarding.*

## ENGINEERING AND ECONOMICS

Prior to about 1940, engineers were mainly concerned with the design, construction, and operation of machines, structures, and processes. Less attention was given to the resources, human and physical, that produced the final products. Many factors have since contributed to expanded engineering responsibilities and concerns.

Besides the traditional work with scientists to develop new discoveries about nature into useful products, engineers now are expected not only to generate novel technological solutions but also to make skillful financial analyses of the effects of implementation. In today's close and tangled relationships among industry, the public, and government, cost and value analyses are supposed to be more detailed and inclusive (e.g., worker safety, environmental effects, consumer protection) than ever before. Without these analyses, an entire project can too easily become more of a burden than a boon.

Most definitions of engineering recognize the mission of engineers to transform the resources of nature for the benefit of the human race. The types of resources susceptible to engineering enrichment include everything from ores and crops to information and energy. A growing awareness of finite limits for earth's resources has added a pressing dimension to engineering evaluations. The focus on scarce resources welds engineering to economics.

Dr. Paul A. Samuelson, Nobel laureate in economics, says that

> Economists today agree on a general definition something like the following: Economics is the study of how men and society end up *choosing*, with or without the use of money, to employ *scarce* productive resources that would have alternative uses, to produce various commodities and distribute them for consumption, now or in the future, among various people and groups in society. It analyzes the costs and benefits of improving patterns of resource allocation.*

The relationship of engineering to economics can be likened to that of engineering to physics. The sciences are devoted to the discovery and explanation of nature's laws. Engineers work with the scientists and extend the revelations to practical applications. The "laws" of economics are not as precise as those of physics, but their obvious application to production and the utilization of scarce resources assures increasing attention from engineers.

## ECONOMICS: A CAPSULE VIEW

Economics, like engineering, has informal roots deep in history. The construction of the pyramids is considered an engineering marvel; it was also a significant economic accomplishment to have funneled all the necessary resources into monuments rather than consuming them in commerce. The formal roots of economics stretch back two centuries to the publication (in 1776) of Adam Smith's *The Wealth of Nations*.

Early writings deplored government intervention in commerce and promoted a "laissez-faire" policy. Thomas Malthus, in *An Essay on the Principles of Population* (1798), conjectured about the causes of economic crises, saying population tends to increase geometrically and the means of subsistence only arithmetically; his forecasts of misery for most of the population predisposed the "dismal science" nickname for economics. Later, John Stuart Mill, in *Treatise on Political Economy* (1800), argued against Malthus' pessimism by suggesting that the laws of distribution are not as immutable as the laws of production. Modern "doomsday" scenarios indicate the issue is still in doubt.

Karl Marx, in *Das Kapital* (1867), argued that capitalism would be superseded by socialism, which would then develop into communism. According to his views, workers

*P.A. Samuelson & A. Scott, *Economics*, 5th Canadian Edition, McGraw-Hill Ryerson, Toronto, 1980, p. 3.

produce more value than they receive in wages. The surplus takes the form of profit and allows capital accumulation, but the capitalist system will eventually fail, owing to cyclic depressions and other inherent weaknesses. About one-third of the world's population agrees with Marx.

"New Economics" evolved from the work of John Maynard Keynes in the 1930s. In his *General Theory of Employment, Interest, and Money,** Keynes clashed with classical economic theory by proclaiming, for example, that interest rates and price-wage adjustments are not adequate mechanisms for controlling unemployment in capitalistic economies. Refinements and extensions of the original work are collectively called "Keynesian economics," which is just one of many current schools of economic thought.

Keynes' and Marx' theories deal with the entire economic system in terms of national income, flow of money, consumption, investment, wages, and general prices. This level of analysis, concerned with the economy as a whole, is called *macroeconomics*. It produces economywide statistical measures such as the national cost of living index and total employment figures.

*Microeconomics* is the study of economic behavior in very small segments of the economy, such as a particular firm or household. It is generally assumed that the objective of a firm is to maximize profit, and the objective of a household is to maximize satisfaction. Measurement statistics for a small economic unit might be the number of workers employed by a firm and income or expenditures of a given firm or family.

Alfred Marshall, in *Principles of Economics*, (1890), was the first economist to clearly state these principles. He showed that prices reflect the marginal cost of producing goods and the marginal benefits that consumers receive. The Marshallian model is known as *partial equilibrium analysis* because it considers only one market at a time.

Engineering economics, with its focus on economic decision making in an individual organizational unit, is closely aligned with microeconomics.


# ENGINEERING ECONOMY: A SHORT HISTORY

*The Economic Theory of the Location of Railways*, written by Arthur M. Wellington in 1887, pioneered engineering interest in economic evaluations. Wellington, a civil engineer, reasoned that the capitalized cost method of analysis should be utilized in selecting the preferred lengths of rail lines or curvatures of the lines. He delightfully captured the thrust of engineering economy as

> It would be well if engineering were less generally thought of, and even defined, as the art of constructing. In a certain important sense it is rather the art of not constructing; or, to define it rudely but not inaptly, it is the art of doing that well with one dollar which any bungler can do with two after a fashion.†

---

*J. M. Keynes, *General Theory of Employment, Interest, and Money*, Harcourt, Brace & World, New York, 1936.

†A. M. Wellington, *The Economic Theory of the Location of Railways*, Wiley, New York, 1887.

In the 1920s, J. C. L. Fish and O. B. Goldman looked at investments in engineered structures from the perspective of actuarial mathematics. Fish* formulated an investment model related to the bond market. Goldman, in his book *Financial Engineering*, proposed a compound-interest procedure for determining comparative values, and said

> It seems peculiar and is indeed very unfortunate that so many authors in their engineering books give no, or very little, consideration to costs in spite of the fact that the primary duty of the engineer is to consider costs in order to obtain real economy – to get the most possible number of dollars and cents: to get the best financial efficiency.**

The confines of classical engineering economy were staked out in 1930 by Eugene L. Grant in his text, *Principles of Engineering Economy*.† Professor Grant discussed the importance of judgment factors and short-term investment evaluation as well as conventional comparisons of long-run investments in capital goods based on compound-interest calculations. His many contributions resulted in the recognition that "Eugene L. Grant can truthfully be called the father of engineering economy."‡

Modern approaches to discounted cash flow and capital rationing were influenced by the work of Joel Dean.§ He incorporated the theories of Keynes and other economists to develop ways to analyze the effects of supply and demand for investment funds in allocating resources.

Current developments are pushing the frontiers of engineering economics to encompass new methods of risk, sensitivity, and intangible analysis. Traditional methods are being refined to reflect today's concerns for resource conservation and effective utilization of public funds.

---

### Example 1.1    Economics of Energy

The divergent missions of classical economics and engineering economics are apparent when a specific application is examined. Consider the energy problem. How serious is it? What are its dimensions? What can be done about it?

Energy supply and demand relationships fit familiar economic concepts. The collection of data about who uses how much energy falls in the province of economic demographics, a growing branch of economics that deals with the consequence of changes in the characteristics of a nation's population. An optimal energy mix that best utilizes the national energy supply can be determined according to market prices and market risks, economic principles that give priority to energy sources that are cheapest and carry the least risk, other things being equal.

From an understanding of supply-demand relationships, engineering effort can be unleashed to overcome technological constraints. If solar or geothermal energy

---

*J. C. L. Fish, *Engineering Economics*, 2d ed., McGraw-Hill, New York, 1923.

**O. B. Goldman, *Financial Engineering*, Wiley, New York, 1920.

†E. L. Grant, *Principles of Engineering Economy*, Ronald, New York, 1930.

‡A. Lesser, Jr., "Engineering Economy in the United States in Retrospect – An Analysis," *The Engineering Economist*, vol. 14, no. 2, 1969.

§J. Dean, *Capital Budgeting*, Columbia, New York, 1951.

appears to be the most promising source, engineers must provide the means to convert the promise into reality. Engineering economics is applied to evaluate alternative solutions.

It is estimated that Canadian consumption could be almost halved by eliminating avoidable energy losses. Actions suggested to plug the leaks in our economic machine include correcting heat losses in offices and homes, better building designs, more energy-efficient machines and automobiles, and co-generation of electricity and steam. Estimating cash flows, comparing investment proposals, and testing the sensitivity of specific energy-conservation actions are tasks for engineering economists.

# PROBLEM SOLVING AND DECISION MAKING

An engineering economist draws upon the accumulated knowledge of engineering and economics to fashion and employ tools to identify a preferred course of action. The tools developed so far are not perfect. There is still considerable debate about their theoretical bases and how they should be used. This concern is wholesome because it promises improved procedures, but the variety of analysis techniques can frustrate practitioners, especially inexperienced ones: There are many aspects to consider, and many ways to consider them.

The fundamental approach to economic problem solving is an elaboration of the time-honored "scientific method." The method is anchored in two worlds: the real, everyday working world and the abstract, scientifically oriented world. As depicted in Figure 1.1, *problems* in engineering and managerial economy originate in the real world of economic planning, management, and control. The problem is confined and clarified by *data* from the real world. This information is combined with scientific principles supplied by the analyst to formulate a *hypothesis* in symbolic terms. The symbolic language aids the digestion of data. By manipulating and *experimenting* with the abstractions of the real world, the analyst can simulate multiple configurations of reality which otherwise would be too costly or too inconvenient to investigate. From this activity a *prediction* emerges, usually.

The predicted behavior is converted back to reality for testing in the form of hardware, designs, or commands. If it is valid, the problem is solved. If not, the cycle is repeated with the added information that the previous approach was unsuccessful. Fortunately, a host of successful approaches have been discovered and validated for economic analyses; the challenge now is to use them wisely.

## Intuition and Analysis

Because engineers generally attack practical problems with solution deadlines instead of engaging esoteric issues for long-term enlightenment, their mission might appear relatively simple. Engineering economic evaluations could even seem mundane, since they usually rely on data from the marketplace and technology from the shelf: Just grab prices from a catalog, plug them into a handy formula, and grind out an answer. Occasionally, such a

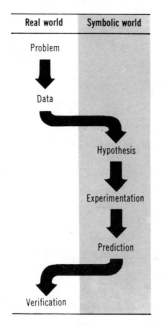

**FIGURE 1.1** Problem-solving process.

routine works. Spectacular workbench discoveries and overnight fortunes attest to the fact that plungers sometimes win. There are also innumerable instances where rule-of-thumb, skin-deep evaluations are absolutely unsatisfactory.

As represented in Figure 1.2, a decision made now is based on data from past performances and establishes a course of action that will result in some future outcome. When the decision is shallow and the outcomes are unnotable, a reflex response based upon intuition is feasible. Intuition, immediate knowledge without conscious reasoning, is oriented in the present but informally embraces memories of the past and estimates of what may happen in the future. It is a valid tool for a decision maker's repertoire provided the logic is not flawed by fads and unrecognized bias.

Instinctive judgments are often formalized by *standard operating procedures* (SOPs). In economic analyses, SOPs often take the form of worksheets for the justification of investments. Such short-form justifications are typically limited to smaller investments, say $2000, which can be recaptured from savings generated by the investment within 6 months or 1 year. These forms or similar SOPs represent collective intuition derived from experience. They have a secure place in economic evaluations, but their use should be tempered by economic principles and a continuing audit to verify that previous judgments are appropriate for current decisions.

Most significant problems require both analysis and personal judgment. Initially, the analyst settles on which evaluation technique to utilize and how to apply it. As the solution procedures progress, factors that are difficult to quantify often arise. These are called *intangibles;* they represent aspects of a problem that cannot be translated readily into monetary values. Intuitive ratings are frequently assigned to intangibles to allow them to be included in the decision process. Judgment also enters the process in determining whether

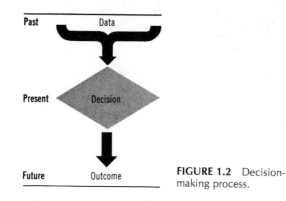

**Past** Data

**Present** Decision

**Future** Outcome

**FIGURE 1.2** Decision-making process.

a solution is well enough founded to be accepted. Thus intuition and judgment complement analysis methods by contributing to better decisions.

## Example 1.2 To Intuit or to Analyze

Most decision makers informally set boundaries for routine responses to noncritical problems of a personal and professional nature. Three possible parameters to identify routine responses are shown in Figure 1.3. The level that separates an automatic decision from a problem that requires more investigation varies among decision makers.

Since there are limits to a decision maker's time and energy whereas the reservoir of problems often seems infinite, guidelines are necessary to confine involvement. SOPs do save time. An intuitive response is quick. Both draw upon experience to yield a reasonable solution. However, handy answers may mask better solutions that could have been exposed by analysis. What was good for yesterday's operations may not be adequate for tomorrow's. Difficulties can occur when the scale of current operations changes without a corresponding revision in the cutoff levels for routine decisions.

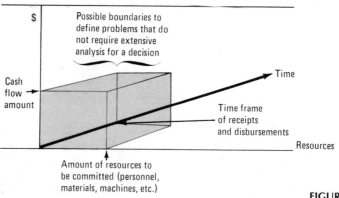

$ 

Possible boundaries to define problems that do not require extensive analysis for a decision

Time

Cash flow amount

Time frame of receipts and disbursements

Resources

Amount of resources to be committed (personnel, materials, machines, etc.)

**FIGURE 1.3** Criteria for routine responses to an economic problem.

## Tactics and Strategy

About the only thing more frustrating than a wrong decision for an important problem is the right decision for the wrong problem. Some problems are virtually handed to an analyst on a platter, complete with data trimmings. More commonly, a problem is ill defined, and the analyst is forced to seek the intent of a solution before applying analytical tools. Recognizing the difference between tactical and strategic considerations may clarify the purpose.

*Strategy* and *tactics* historically are military terms respectively associated with broad plans from the high command and specific schedules from lower echelons. Strategy sets ultimate objectives, and the associated tactics define the multiple maneuvers required to achieve the objectives. Strategic and tactical considerations have essentially the same meaning for economic studies.

There are usually several strategies available to an organization. A strategic decision ideally selects the overall plan that makes the best use of the organization's resources in accordance with its long-range objectives. A strategic industrial decision could be a choice from among several different designs to develop or products to promote. In government, strategic evaluations could take the form of benefit-cost analyses to select the preferred method of flood control or development of recreational sites. The measure of merit for strategic alternatives is *effectiveness*—the degree to which a plan meets economic targets.

A strategic plan can normally be implemented in a number of ways. For example, each industrial design or product has tactical alternatives such as which kind of machine to employ or materials to use; tactics for flood control might involve choices among dams, levees, dredging, etc. The relative values of tactical choices are rated according to their *efficiency*—the degree to which an operation accomplishes a mission within economic expectations.

The relationship between strategies and tactics offers some constructive insights. The effectiveness of each strategy is initially estimated from the effect it will have on system objectives. It thus serves as a guide to the area in which tactics will produce the highest efficiency. The actual efficiency of each tactic is determined from a study of the activities required to conduct the tactical operation.

Two strategies, each with three apparent means of accomplishment, are depicted in Figure 1.4. The average efficiency for the tactics associated with strategy 1 (tactics 1-1, 1-2, and 1-3) has a higher value than that for strategy 2. However, it could happen that a strategy with a lower effectiveness possesses the tactic with the highest efficiency. Tactic 2-1 is close to the most efficient tactic of strategy 1. If it were the highest on the efficiency scale, it would be the leading candidate for selection, regardless of its strategic origin.

## Sensitivity and Suboptimization

The decision situation related by Figure 1.4 has high sensitivity; that is, it is vulnerable to small changes in the controlling conditions. With tactics 1-1 and 2-1 so close on the efficiency scale, a slight change in operating conditions or external influencing factors could switch the positions of the top tactics, or even the strategies. An insensitive situation

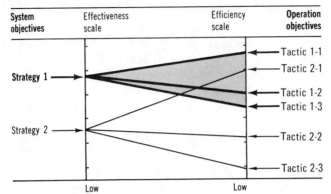

| System objectives | Effectiveness scale | Efficiency scale | Operation objectives |
|---|---|---|---|

**FIGURE 1.4**
Relationship of tactics and strategies.

occurs when all the tactics for a given strategy have a higher efficiency than the best tactic of any other strategy. The consequence of high sensitivity is to force a complete investigation to assure the validity of the data being evaluated.

A *sensitivity analysis* can be conducted on any problem to explore the effects of deviations from the original problem conditions. Since most engineering economic problems extend over a period of years, future cash flows are necessarily estimated. These estimations may be quite reliable, but it is often enlightening to observe how the attractiveness of alternatives varies as the initial estimates are altered.

Whenever multiple objectives are present in a decision situation, it is probable that there is no single course of action that will optimize all the objectives simultaneously. This conflict situation could lead to *tactical suboptimization*—a solution that optimizes tactical efficiency with little or no regard for strategic effectiveness. "You don't understand the big picture" is a common complaint from harried managers to seemingly sound proposals to alleviate an operating problem, proposals that would, if adopted, clash with policies established for the overall benefit of the organization.

In general, suboptimization occurs when there is a larger problem than the analyst has visualized. It is always tempting to employ intact a classical textbook solution to a real-world problem, whether or not it truly fits the actual conditions. The availability of "canned" computerized solutions to complex problems increases the temptation. Another cause of suboptimal solutions is the legitimate analysis technique of partitioning a large problem into parts during a preliminary investigation to avoid being bogged down in a deluge of details. Trouble enters when tentative solutions to the problem's parts are not integrated. Advances in computer science and operations research may eventually allow analysis of an entire complex system in a single evaluation, but until then it helps to be aware of the areas in which suboptimization is most likely to occur. Three regularly encountered perspectives that lead to suboptimization are described below.

## 1  CROSS-EYED VIEW

Both organizations and individuals can be confused by opposing objectives. An example of the danger inherent in focusing on just one parameter while blurring others is what would happen to a company that redeployed its resources to save its ailing flagship

**FIGURE 1.5** Symbolic world strategy and real-world tactics.

product at the expense of the rest of the product line. The rescue could boost sales for the previously eminent product while total sales declined owing to the drain on resources suffered by the rest of the company's products; thus, the battle could be won but the war lost.

Individuals seeking "the good life" also get caught by conflicting goals. If "good" is interpreted as "long and full," then unlimited pleasure seeking for a full life would undoubtedly jeopardize the health needed for a long life. Moderation, however, should produce a temperate plan to satisfy both goals, resulting in a life less full but longer. Of course, there are also irreconcilable objectives such as those pictured in Figure 1.5.

## 2 SHORTSIGHTEDNESS

Tactics based on a planning horizon of 1 or 2 years may not have the same efficiency as those based on a longer span of years. Suppose a manufacturer anticipates using a fixed number of containers each year. The containers can be purchased or the manufacturer can make them by acquiring new production equipment. Costs for the choices are displayed by the breakeven chart in Figure 1.6. A planning horizon under 2 years would indicate that purchasing is the preferable alternative; beyond 2 years it is more attractive to make the containers. Individuals face the same danger of suboptimization in lease-or-buy decisions for housing and transportation.

## 3 TUNNEL VISION

Organizations are very susceptible to situations in which departments understand the common goal but individually go about working toward the goal in ways that hurt each

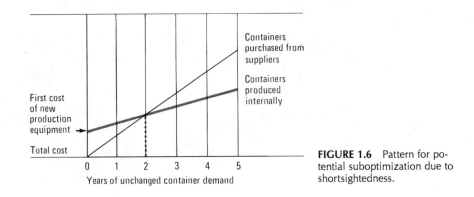

**FIGURE 1.6** Pattern for potential suboptimization due to shortsightedness.

other. A typical example is the goal to reduce material and inventory costs, as viewed by

- *Purchasing*    "Buy in large quantities to get quantity discounts."
- *Comptroller*    "Buy in smaller quantities to avoid paying interest on the capital required for purchases."
- *Production*    "Larger inventories allow longer production runs which reduce manufacturing costs."
- *Warehousing*    "Larger inventories cost more to store and increase the cost of material handling."

If each of the involved departments acts independently, inventory levels will behave like a yo-yo. Obviously, a workable plan will be a compromise, probably satisfying no one completely, but still producing lower total material costs for the organization as a whole.

## THE ENGINEERING ECONOMIC DECISION MAZE

Most important decisions in engineering economics entail consideration of future events. A focus on the future has always had a special and irresistible appeal, but it also encumbers the mission of engineering economists. Not only must they search the past to understand the present and survey the present for hints about the future, but they must consolidate the accumulated results into a pattern that is susceptible to analysis and then select a decision rule to yield a verdict. An indication of the complexities involved is apparent from the maze shown in Figure 1.7.

It would take a much larger maze to portray all the pitfalls and challenges of economic analyses, but enough are included to expose the anatomy of engineering economics and to map the contents of this book. All the channels in the maze represent subjects treated in the chapters that follow. As is apparent in the decision labyrinth, there are many paths by which to progress from a problem to a solution. Which path is utilized depends on the nature of the problem and the type of analysis that is most appropriate. Because problems come in such profuse variety and there are so many ways to evaluate them, engineering economics is rich in application opportunities and offers rewarding challenges to its practitioners.

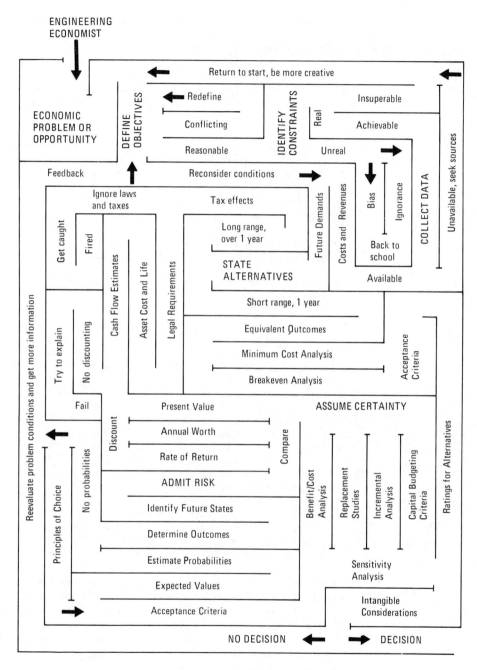

**FIGURE 1.7**
Engineering economic decision maze.

## Review Exercises and Discussions

**Exercise 1** The past few years have witnessed a remarkable number of events and activities that will undoubtedly have far-reaching effects on engineering practices. Some of the most prominent areas of activity include:

1 The passage of national, provincial and local legislation that regulates industrial operations and developments
2 The formation of public pressure groups whose efforts are directed toward improving the quality of life
3 The increasing world market values for some raw materials
4 The closer scrutiny of government programs

Select a specific example that illustrates activity in each of the above areas, and relate it to the work of engineers with particular reference to engineering economic considerations.

**Solution 1** Numerous examples can be cited to show how changing societal interests direct the practices of engineers.

1 *Laws* The Ontario Occupational Health and Safety Act established stricter standards for worker safety. Many provinces and communities have passed zoning laws that set tighter design requirements for new plants. Most legislative actions require added investments, and engineers are called upon to devise ways to meet new standards with minimal expenditures.
2 *Pressure groups* Consumer-protection groups successfully compaigned for automobile modifications and control of waste discharges. New technologies have to be developed to protect the quality of air, water, and land; the relationship between control costs and quality levels is largely an engineering function.
3 *Scarce resources* Higher prices for energy, especially gas and oil, sparked worldwide alarm over the future availability of raw materials. Higher prices for certain materials suggest design changes for greater economy. Some resource conservation measures have yielded surprising savings.
4 *Government programs* The abandonment of plans for supersonic transports and declining budgets for space exploration exemplify critical assessments of government activities. Engineers are intimately involved in assessing the effectiveness of government programs. Benefit-cost analyses are routinely conducted by government agencies to determine the acceptability of projects.

**Exercise 2** A subassembly line has been giving the production manager nightmares for months. All kinds of minor modifications have been tried, and all failed to improve output. The current per-unit cost is $4.20, which seems reasonable, but output has failed to reach the required 10,000 units per year. A check with the purchasing department reveals that supplementary units are now being purchased for $4.75 each, but one vendor agrees to provide them at $4.50 each if the entire annual demand is ordered.

The subassembly-line supervisor suggests acquiring three new machines to mechanize successive stages of the production process. Engineers calculate that the machines' purchase price of $100,000 would make their discounted annual cost over a 10-year machine life, coupled with yearly operating costs, amount to $27,000. If needed, the machines have the capacity to double the present output. At the present output level, the remaining subassembly costs using the new machines will annually total $18,000.

While investigating the problem, the engineers uncovered another alternative: All three successive operations could be combined and handled by a single machine. This one combination machine would have the same capacity, speed, life, and remaining production costs as the three-machine alternative, but ownership and operating costs would be reduced by $3000 per year.

Which alternative should be accepted, and why?

**Solution 2** Apparently, it has been decided that something must be done to improve subassembly production, so the "do-nothing" alternative is eliminated. The single machine is obviously more attractive than the three-machine alternative because the combined operation costs $3000 less. The unit cost for the one-machine alternative is

$$\frac{\$27,000 + \$18,000 - \$3000}{10,000 \text{ subassemblies}} = \$4.20/\text{subassembly}$$

This unit cost is the same as the current cost but promises more reliability. It is also $0.30 per unit less expensive ($4.50 − $4.20) than purchasing all the subassemblies from a supplier. However, more information is needed about the long-range (10-year) expected demand for the subassemblies. Without this information, the decision is subject to the make-or-buy pattern of suboptimization shown in Figure 1.6.

# PROBLEMS

**1.1** There are many general definitions of engineering, and specific ones for different branches of engineering. Look up one of them, and comment on the explicit and/or implied attention paid to economic considerations.

**1.2** It has been said that economists are very busy people because they have to spend full time telling what's going to happen and full time explaining why it didn't. Engineering economists also work with forecasts of the future but are not usually subjected to such joking comments. Why?

**1.3** Efficiency is defined as output divided by input (times 100 percent). Engineering efficiency is commendable when it approaches 100 percent, but financial efficiency must exceed 100 percent before it is considered adequate. Explain.

**1.4** "In the 1930's many economists maintained that the United States economy had reached the apogee of its growth; in the period just after World War II, many predicted an immediate depression; and in late 1969, some economists predicted without qualification that there would be no recession in 1970; but all these assertions proved to be erroneous. This is not to deny, of course, that the predictions made by economists often are accurate; indeed, at a given moment reputable economists make so many conflicting forecasts that one is almost certain to be correct. (To give one illustration, in December of 1969 Milton Friedman said that a recession on the order of that in 1960 seems to be in the cards for 1970; Raymond J. Saulnier said there was a 50-50 chance of a recession; and Pierre A. Rinfret said that 'There ain't gonna be no recession in 1970, period.')"[*]

[*]R. Handy and E. C. Harwood, *A Current Appraisal of the Behavioral Sciences*, rev. ed., Behavioral Research Council, Great Barrington, Mass., 1973.

**1.4a**   Why do economic projections for a future event tend to vary more widely than engineering estimates of performance for a new design?

**1.4b**   Why might there be less confidence in the economic performance than the operating performance of a new machine?

*The following four cases illustrate everyday situations in which individuals are required to decide the most advantageous use of limited resources. Identify the strategic or tactical nature of each decision situation, and discuss the factors that should be considered (including sensitivity, if appropriate).*

**1.5**   A fisherman stands in his crowded cabin and studies a map. Three fishing grounds are circled on the map. He mentally compares recent reports and gossip concerning the grounds. He also considers the market demands, the weather forecasts, the condition of his ship, and the supplies on board. He has to decide where to fish.

**1.6**   An engineer contemplates the bulging walls of a large concrete culvert under a highway. The collapsing culvert is the result of thousands of tons of rock recently stockpiled on the roadbed above in preparation for new construction. In a few days the spring thaw will soak the ground and send torrents of water through the culvert. The engineer speculates on possible designs in terms of the conditions and the restrictions imposed by available equipment, materials and time.

**1.7**   The owner of a wholesale distribution center seeks to improve his delivery service in order to meet competition. To do so he can buy or rent more trucks, subcontract his deliveries, open additional outlets, and/or improve his handling facilities. His capital is limited, and the outlook for increased volume is uncertain. First he must decide if any action is needed. If it is, he must select the most suitable alternative.

**1.8**   The manager of a large manufacturing company surveys a collection of proposals laid out neatly on the long table in the board room. Each proposal represents many hours of staff work. Each is a detailed plan for the development of a new product. She must select the proposal which best serves the interests of the company within the constraints of restricted physical and human resources, competition, legal requirements, available capital, and corporate objectives. Her decision will affect the activities of hundreds of people.

**1.9**   Since engineering economics has been compared to a maze in Figure 1.7, it is consistent to use a word puzzle to review some of the terminology associated with the discipline.

*Across*

  **4**   Science concerned with the economy as a whole
 **12**   Selection from two or more courses of action
 **13**   Pioneer in engineering economic evaluations
 **14**   Rating scale for tactical operations
 **17**   Fifth step in the problem-solving process
 **18**   _____ analysis explores the effects of deviations from original conditions
 **19**   Perfection of a part at the expense of the whole

*Down*

  **1**   "Father of engineering economy"
  **2**   Key contributor to economics in the 1930s
  **3**   Critical resource that fuels economic concern
  **4**   Made his mark with *Das Kapital*
  **5**   Science concerned with specific economic units

**6** Standard operating procedure
**7** View that could lead to suboptimization
**8** Limited _____ attract attention of engineering economists
**9** Measure of merit for strategic alternatives
**10** Examination of the components of a problem
**11** Overall plan for a major accomplishment
**12** Information
**15** Immediate knowledge without conscious reasoning
**16** Mode of operation to achieve an operational objective

# EXTENSIONS

*1A  Creativity*  Creativity is essentially the ability to produce new and interesting results. Pure, basic research seeks new enlightenment from nature. Innovation discovers a novel relationship. The ability to relate things, sometimes in odd yet striking fashion, is the heart of creativity, no matter what the field or discipline. An innovative engineering economist has the ability to identify more productive uses of capital within the problem-solving process.

Originality enters the problem-solving sequence of Figure 1.1 more as an attitude than a procedure. The first five steps could be replaced by the personal outlooks *We* want: →*Who else?* →*What if?* →*Maybe . . . maybe . . .* →*Aha! Eureka!* Many techniques have been proposed to expedite this chain. Some involve groups of participants, to take advantage of shared experiences and the snowball effect of one person's idea triggering many more ideas from others in the group. "Brainstorming" is the most famous group approach.*

There are also ways to improve solo ideation. Since economic analyses are often individual exercises, methods to enhance individual inventiveness are emphasized below.

*Analogies*  A structured approach that attempts to make the strange familiar and the familiar strange is called *synectics* (a Greek word for combining diverse elements).† It achieves an "out of focus" look at some aspect of the known world by employing analogical mechanisms to tap the subconscious mind. A *direct* analogy can be made between objects or systems which are not usually associated (e.g., an ant hill and an urban development). By identifying oneself with a nonhuman entity a *personal* analogy is formed (e.g., "if I were a rudder" or "how would I behave if I were a rat in a maze?"). Images may be formed by *symbolic* or *fantasy* analogies (e.g., a rope stiff enough to climb, or if we could train bees . . .).

*Triggers*  Several techniques rely on words or phrases to stir innovation. The *modifier* approach fuels imagination by progressing through a list of modifiers that pertain to a key characteristic of a problem. For instance, if size were a key factor, the list could include bigger, shorter, thinner, flatter, etc. *Checklists* can be developed for regularly encountered types of problems. They can be categorized by actions (e.g., what is done, where, when, and by whom?), changes (e.g., combine, substitute, rearrange, use differently, alter quantity), and functions (e.g., bottlenecks? waste? delays? duplication?).

*Matrices*  *Morphological synthesis*‡ involves listing the major variables of a problem in a two- or three-dimensional matrix so that interrelationships can be systematically examined (e.g., a 3 × 3 matrix for the solution to a project-management problem could have rows labeled organization, facilities, and operations, and columns labeled personnel, money, and time. The operations-time cell might have an entry such as "speed up services"). *Trigger cards* are strips of paper on which are vertically listed possible factors that pertain to the parameters of a problem. For instance, parameters for a design could be locomotion, structure, power, and material. Factors listed under material could include wood, plastic, metal, fiberglass, paper, rubber, and foam. Ideas are generated by placing all the cards side by side and slipping them vertically, one at a time, to reveal different combinations of factors across each row. Five parameter cards, each with seven factors, would suggest 16,807 combinations, many of which would be infeasible or even ridiculous, but which nonetheless might spark an inspiration.

*Alex Osborn, *Applied Imagination*, Scribner, New York, 1957.
†W. J. J. Gordon, *Synectics*, Harper & Row, New York, 1961.
‡M. S. Allen, *Morphological Creativity*, Prentice-Hall, Englewood Cliffs, N.J., 1962.

The relationship between decision making and creativity is clarified by classifying people who deal with problems. *Problem recognizers* can detect when a problem exists, and this certainly requires intelligence. *Problem solvers* need a higher order of intelligence to develop and implement the best solution. *Problem anticipators* combine extraordinary intelligence with creativity to sense an approaching obstacle and devise means to avoid trouble before it happens.

## QUESTIONS

**1A.1** It has been said that the universal idea killer is silence. But vocal putdowns are effective too. Negative phrases include: It's against company policy. Has anyone else ever tried it? Write it up on one sheet of paper. It's not new; it reminds me of . . . .
**a** What other idea killers have you heard?
**b** What idea-boosting phrases can you suggest?

**1A.2** The challenge is to suggest labor-intensive products suitable for production in cottage industries, but which require no outstanding talent. They also have to be salable. The products will be manufactured in homes and therefore must be produced with hand tools, and these tools cannot be expensive. Materials must also be inexpensive and readily available. Since finished products will be sold at booths in supermarkets, fairs, and craft shows, the units must be easy to transport. They should be designed to sell for less than $25 apiece, and materials should not cost over 25 percent of the selling price.

Develop a set of trigger cards to stimulate ideas. Some of the parameters might be material, use, construction, and market. Use the trigger cards to generate a list of possible products. Evaluate the list according to the economic criteria, to select the five most promising products.

*1B  Perpetual-Motion Mystique*  The idea of perpetual motion—something for nothing—seems to be a persistent, insidious dream of humans. It has been around a long time. Over 2000 years ago the Chinese searched for an unpowered "everlasting going." Archimedes tried to find it through hydraulics, and da Vinci experimented with gravity-powered mechanisms. In 1670, John Wilkens, the Bishop of Chester, designed a ramp leading to a pedestal where a magnet was mounted. The magnet was supposed to attract an iron ball up the ramp until it fell off onto a chute that returned it to the bottom of the ramp, again and again and. . . . (What was wrong with the bishop's reasoning?)

A perpetual-motion machine was exhibited in New York in 1813. People paid to see little carriers ceaselessly moving up and down inclined planes to drive a wheel which offered free energy. Robert Fulton, of steamboat fame, exposed the hoax by showing that the contraption was connected by a hidden strand of catgut to a handpowered crank in an adjacent room.

The infamous John E. W. Keely perpetual-motion machine, unveiled in 1875, enriched its inventor for years without disclosing any practicality. "Whatever other laws he may have violated in his long career," wrote Stanley W. Angrist in *Scientific American*, "Keely had left the first and second laws of thermodynamics inviolate."

The mystique of perpetual-motion machines has a counterpart in economic ventures—rewards without inputs.

**QUESTIONS**

**1B.1**  Cite an example of a get-rich-quick scheme or a similar hoax that promises a lot for a little.

**1B.2**  How could a trip through the engineering economic decision maze expose a financial hoax or at least make a potential investor wary of a scheme such as that cited in answer to Question 1B.1?

# SECTION ONE

# DISCOUNTED CASH
# FLOW MECHANICS

*Interest* is the cost of using capital. Its history extends as far back as the recorded transactions of mankind. In earliest times, before money was coined, capital was represented by wealth in the form of personal possessions, and interest was paid in kind. For example, a loan of seed to a neighbor before planting was returned after harvest with an additional increment. We can surmise that the concept of interest in its modern sense arose from such loans for productive purposes.

Capital and credit have been important to human progress since about 5000 B.C. At that time Neolithic man was engaged in agriculture and animal culture to provide his own food. Capital was counted by seeds, tools, and herds of animals. Cattle were probably the first true productive assets and are the origin of many financial terms. *Pecuniary* stems from *pecus* meaning "flock" in Latin, and the Egyptian term *ms,* meaning "interest," is derived from the verb *msj,* which means "to give birth." Early Greeks measured wealth in terms of cattle; in the Odyssey, Ulysses was promised a contribution "of bronze and gold to the value of twenty oxen."

By the time the Greek and Roman empires were in their ascendancies, interest rates were somewhat standardized and occasionally legislated. The amount charged for loans to the most reliable borrowers was around 10 percent, with the range from 4 percent in first-century Rome to about 50 percent for grain loans in Egypt during the same period.*

Along with the development of money and credit came abuses. Aristotle pointed out that money was "barren," and it was unfair to charge interest for loans. Early Israelites did not permit lending at interest. Romans permitted credit but limited the rate of interest to about 5 to 12 percent. Greeks encouraged credit without limit but forbade personal bondage for debt. Biblical utterances against usury were aimed at loans for consumption rather than production, yet interest was forbidden by canon law through the Middle Ages.

The concept of interest has not changed much through the centuries, but the modern credit structure differs markedly from that of antiquity. Lending or investing was relatively inconvenient in ancient days because transactions were made directly between individuals. There were no banking organizations to act as intermediaries, and no credit instruments in the money market. Governments were not often able to float loans since they could not pledge the private resources of their people. And they had not discovered the practice of deficit financing.

Today there are many credit instruments, and most people use them. Business and government are the biggest borrowers. Businesses seek the use of capital goods to increase productivity. Governments borrow against future tax revenues to finance highways, welfare programs, and public services. Households also borrow to make purchases in excess of their current cash resources. Such borrowers, and the corresponding lenders, must acknowledge the time value of their commitments.

The following examples reveal the significance of interest in economic transactions and confirm the importance of understanding how it operates, whether it pertains to personal finances or to professional practices:

- The purchase of a home is the largest investment most people make. The table below vividly portrays the impact of interest rates and loan periods: A shorter repayment period at a given interest rate or a lower interest rate for a given loan period begets a conspicuous saving.

Monthly Payments on $100,000 Mortgage*

| Interest Rate | 12% | 15% | 18% | 21% |
|---|---|---|---|---|
| Repayment Period | | | | |
| 15 yrs. | $1,182 | $1,369 | $1,565 | $1,766 |
| 20 yrs. | $1,081 | $1,284 | $1,494 | $1,710 |
| 25 yrs. | $1,032 | $1,246 | $1,466 | $1,689 |
| 30 yrs. | $1,006 | $1,229 | $1,455 | $1,682 |

*Interest compounded semi-annually, not in advance. Compounding is discussed in Chapter 2.

*S. Homer, *History of Interest Rates*, Rutgers, New Brunswick, N.J., 1963.

Laws have been passed requiring standardized statements of interest charges. The need for such laws arises from the many ways interest can be calculated and the unique vocabulary associated with the subject. The profusion breeds confusion.

In this section we shall explore interest vocabulary and discounted cash flow calculations (Chapters 2 and 3), and then consider three methods for comparing the economic time value of alternatives: present worth (Chapter 4), equivalent annual worth (Chapter 5), and rate of return (Chapter 6). From the economic decision maze in Chapter 1 we observed the prominent position of these comparison methods in the problem-solving process; they are the foundation for refinements that ration capital to the most rewarding projects. The mechanics of discounted cash flow are straightforward, relatively simple mathematical operations, but they are absorbing because they have so many practical applications.

# CHAPTER 2

# TIME VALUE OF MONEY

OVERVIEW

Nearly everyone is directly exposed to interest transactions occasionally, and is indirectly affected regularly. Credit cards are a mainstay of commerce; they have an interest load for delayed payments. Key parts of a contract for purchasing an automobile or home are the interest stipulations. The rate of interest paid on municipal bonds directly affects tax rates for property in the affected area. Businesses borrow to expand or just maintain operations, and the cost of their borrowing must be repaid from more profitable operations allowed by loans. All this borrowing, taken together, adds up to an enormous debt, and it all has interest charges.

To fully appreciate interest charges, one must comprehend the reasons for the charges, how they are calculated, and their effect on cash flows. Interest represents the earning power of money. It is the premium paid to compensate a lender for the administrative cost of making a loan, the risk of nonrepayment, and the loss of use of the loaned money. A borrower pays interest charges for the opportunity to do something now that would otherwise have to be delayed or never done. *Simple interest I* is a charge directly proportional to the capital (principal $P$) loaned at rate $i$ for $N$ periods, so that $I = PiN$. *Compound interest* includes charges for the accumulated interest as well as the amount of unpaid principal.

A *nominal interest rate r* of 8 percent compounded quarterly, for example, indicates an interest charge of 2 percent per period compounded four times a year. If $m$ is the number of compounding periods per year, the equivalent *effective interest rate i* of a nominal rate

25

is $i = (1 + r/m)^m - 1$. *Continuous interest* is the nominal interest rate as $m$ approaches infinity, and its equivalent effective interest rate is $i = e^r - 1$.

Time-value mechanics involves the use of compound-interest factors to translate payments of various amounts occurring at various times to a single equivalent payment. Interest factors are symbolized by notations based on $i, N, P$ = present worth, $F$ = future worth, and $A$ = annuity payment. An ordinary annuity is a series of equal payments, at equal intervals, with the first payment at the end of the first period. When payments in an annuity increase by a constant increment $G$ each period, an equivalent ordinary annuity is determined through use of the arithmetic-gradient factor.

Seven discrete interest factors are commonly used to evaluate cash flows and convert them into summary statements that define alternative uses for capital. These factors are represented by functional symbols that assist calculations; the values of the factors for different interest rates and numbers of compounding periods are tabulated in Appendix B.

The fundamental concepts of interest and the basic constructs of interest calculation introduced in this chapter are the foundations for discounted cash flow applications developed in the next four chapters.

# REASONS FOR INTEREST

### Example 2.1   All You Have to Do to Be Rich Is Live Long Enough

The famous purchase of Manhattan Island from the Indians for $24 is often referred to as an exceptional bargain. This incident reputedly occurred in 1626, when Peter Minuit of the Dutch West India Company bought the rights to the island from local residents. Was it a bargain? For the sake of argument, suppose the Indians could have invested the money at a reasonable interest rate of 6 percent compounded annually. Over the years since then, the original $24 investment would have grown by the following proportions:

| Year | Value of the Original $24 Investment |
|------|----------------------------------:|
| 1626 | $24.00 |
| 1676 | 442.08 |
| 1726 | 8,143.25 |
| 1776 | 149,999.92 |
| 1826 | 2,763,021.69 |
| 1876 | 50,895,285.76 |
| 1926 | 937,499,015.11 |
| 1976 | 17,268,876,484.38 |

The significance of interest is obvious in the above example. The reasons for this effect become more apparent when we examine the uses of capital. In our economic environment, capital is the basic resource. It can be converted into production goods, consumer goods, or services. It has the power to earn and to satisfy wants.

From a lender's viewpoint, capital is a fluid resource. Capital can be spent on goods expected to produce a profit or on personal satisfaction. It can be hoarded or given away. It can also be loaned. If it is loaned, the lender will normally expect some type of compensation. The common compensation is interest. Interest compensates for the administrative expense of making the loan, for the risk that the loan will not be repaid, and for the loss of earnings which would have been obtained if the money had been invested for productive purposes.

From a borrower's viewpoint, a loan is both an obligation and an opportunity. A borrower must expect to repay the loan. Failure to repay leads to a damaged reputation, loss of possessions, and other consequences. The loan offers an opportunity to do something immediately that would otherwise have to be delayed. In some cases an objective would no longer exist after a delay. In order to take advantage of an existing course of action or to fulfill a current need, the borrower agrees to pay a certain amount in addition to the sum immediately received. This premium is the interest paid to avoid waiting for the money.

Implied in both the lender's and borrower's viewpoints is the earning power of money. For money to earn something, the owner or user must wait (*waiting-earning* is obviously opposed to the *spending-owing* use of money to gratify immediate desires. Interest payments have been likened to the reward for waiting, but it is more appropriate for engineering economists to view interest as the productive gain from efficient use of the money resource. The prevailing interest rate is essentially a measure of the productivity to expect from the resource. An owner of money can lend it at the prevailing rate and wait to be repaid the original amount plus an extra increment. Equivalently, the borrower could reloan the money at a higher rate to acquire a gain larger than the amount to be repaid, or the money could be converted to productive goods that would be expected to earn more than the amount needed to repay the loan. In both cases the prevailing interest rate sets the minimum level of expected productivity, and both cases involve time between receipt and return of the loan to secure the earnings: the *time value of money*.

---

### Example 2.2   Borrowers Be Aware

"One/ten-a-week" loans are offered by shadowy characters to tide borrowers over until the next paycheck. The lenders charge $1 for each $10 borrowed for a week. Thus, $140 would have to be repaid for the use of $100 for 4 weeks. The simple interest rate for this arrangement, based on a 52-week year, is an exorbitant 520 percent: A $10 debt held for a year would accumulate $1/week $\times$ 52 weeks = $52 interest expense, so that the simple interest rate is $52/$10 $\times$ 100 percent = 520 percent.

---

# SIMPLE INTEREST

When a *simple interest rate* is quoted, the interest earned is directly proportional to the capital involved in the loan. Expressed as a formula, the interest earned $I$ is calculated by

$$I = PiN$$

*where* $P$ = present amount or principal
$i$ = interest rate/period
$N$ = number of interest periods

Since the principal or amount borrowed $P$ is a fixed value, the annual interest charged is constant. Therefore, the total amount a borrower is obligated to pay a lender is

$$F = P + I = P + PiN = P(1 + iN)$$

where $F$ is a future sum of money. When $N$ is not a full year, there are two ways to calculate the simple interest earned during the period of the loan. Using *ordinary simple interest,* the year is divided into twelve 30-day periods, or a year is considered to have 360 days. In *exact simple interest* a year has exactly the calendar number of days, and $N$ is the fraction of the number of days the loan is in effect that year.

An example of simple interest as the rental cost of money is a loan of $1000 for 2 years at 10 percent, where interest is charged only on the principal. Then the interest owed at the end of the 2 years is $1000 × 0.10 × 2 = $200, and the total amount due after 2 years is $1000 + $200 = $1200. Note that the principal has earned $1000 × 10% = $100 at the end of 1 year, but no interest is charged on this $100 increment.

# COMPOUND INTEREST

Again we use the example of $1000 loaned for 2 years, this time at an interest rate of 10 percent compounded annually; the pattern of interest compounding is shown in Table 2.1.

**TABLE 2.1** Future value of a $1000 loan when interest is due on both the principal and unpaid interest.

| Year | Amount Owed at Beginning of Year | Interest on Amount Owed | Amount Owed at End of Year |
|---|---|---|---|
| 1 | $1000 | $1000 × 0.10 = $100 | $1000 + $100 = $1100 |
| 2 | 1100 | $1100 × 0.10 = $110 | $1100 + $110 = $1210 |

The amount to be repaid for the given loan is thus $1210 − $1200 = $10 greater for compound than for simple interest. The $10 difference accrues from the interest charge on the $100 earned during the first year that was not accounted for in the simple-interest calculation. The formula approach for the calculations in Table 2.1, using previously defined symbols, is

$$\frac{\text{Compound amount}}{\text{due in 2 years}} = \frac{\text{amount}}{\text{borrowed}} + \frac{\text{year-1}}{\text{interest}} + \left(\begin{array}{c}\text{amount bor-}\\ \text{rowed plus}\\ \text{interest due}\end{array}\right)\left(\begin{array}{c}\text{interest}\\ \text{rate}\end{array}\right)$$

$$
\begin{aligned}
F_2 &= P + Pi + (P + Pi)i \\
&= P(1 + i + i + i^2) \\
&= P(1 + i)^2 \\
&= \$1000(1 + 0.10)^2 \\
&= \$1000(1.21) = \$1210
\end{aligned}
$$

The key equation in the above development is $F_2 = P(1 + i)^2$. Generalized for any number of interest periods $N$, this expression becomes $F = P(1 + i)^N$, and $(1 + i)^N$ is known as the *compound-amount factor*. It is one of several interest factors derived in this chapter for which numerical values are tabulated in Appendix B.

---

### Example 2.3    The Timing Tells the Value

Let the interest on a $1000 loan for 2 years at an interest rate of 10 percent compounded annually be paid when it comes due. That is, at the end of the first year an interest payment of $1000 × 0.10 = $100 is paid, and at the end of the second year the principal ($1000) plus the interest earned during the second year ($100) is paid. The total interest charge is thus $100 + $100 = $200 at 10 percent compounded annually, which is the same as the interest charge at 10 percent simple interest ($I = PiN = $1000 × 0.10 × 2 = $200). How come?

The mirage that the two interest payment plans are equal is dispelled by noting the difference in the timing of the payments. When compounded annually, interest is calculated and charged to the account each year. If the interest so calculated is not physically withdrawn from the account, it is added to the balance, and it earns interest during the next period.

The cited payment plans appear to produce the same interest because no mention is made of what was done with the $100 received after the first year. If the $100 interest payment were reinvested at the given 10 percent rate, it would earn $100 × 0.10 = $10, making the total amount due at the end of two years $200 + $10 = $210. The sum of the principal ($P$ = $1000) and interest is then $1210, which is the expected compound amount due in 2 years.

---

## Nominal Interest Rates

Interest rates are normally quoted on an annual basis. However, agreements may specify that interest will be compounded several times per year: monthly, quarterly, semiannually, etc. For example, a year divided into four quarters with interest at 2 percent per quarter is typically quoted as "8 percent compounded quarterly." Stated in this fashion, it is called a *nominal interest rate*. The future value at the end of 1 year for $200 earning interest at 8 percent compounded quarterly is developed as

$$F_{3 \text{ mo}} = P + Pi = \$200 + (\$200)(0.02)$$
$$= \$200 + \$4 = \$204$$
$$F_{6 \text{ mo}} = \$204 + (\$204)(0.02)$$
$$= \$204 + \$4.08 = \$208.08$$
$$F_{9 \text{ mo}} = \$208.08 + (\$208.08)(0.02)$$
$$= \$208.08 + \$4.16 = \$212.24$$
$$F_{12 \text{ mo}} = \$212.24 + (\$212.24)(0.02)$$
$$= \$212.24 + \$4.24 = \$216.48$$

The result of the nominal interest rate is to produce a higher value than might be expected from the 8 percent figure stated in its expression. At 8 percent compounded annually, the $200 mentioned above would earn, in 1 year, $F_{12 \text{ mo}} =$

$200 + $200(0.08) = $216, which is 48 cents less than the amount accrued from the nominal rate of 8 percent compounded quarterly. An interest of 1½ percent per month is also a nominal interest rate that could appear to the uninitiated as being quite reasonable. Using the compound-amount factor to calculate how much would have to be repaid on a 1-year loan of $1000 at a nominal interest rate of 18 percent compounded monthly (1½ percent per period with 12 interest periods per year) gives

$$F_{12} = \$1000(1 + 1\tfrac{1}{2}\%)^{12} = \$1000(0.015)^{12}$$
$$= \$1000(1.1956) = \$1196$$

This can be compared to the future value of the same loan at 18 percent compounded semiannually (9 percent per period with 2 interest periods per year):

$$F_{12} = \$1000(1 + 9\%)^2 = \$1000(1.09)^2$$
$$= \$1000(1.1881) = \$1188$$

Thus, more frequent compounding within a nominally stated annual rate does indeed increase the future worth.

## Effective Interest Rates

Confusion about the acutal interest earned is eliminated by stating the charge as an *effective interest rate*. The effective interest rate is simply the ratio of the interest charge for one year to the principal (amount loaned or borrowed). For the $1000 one-year loan at a nominal interest rate of 18 percent compounded monthly,

$$\text{Effective interest rate} = \frac{F - P}{P} = \frac{\$1196 - \$1000}{\$1000}$$
$$= \frac{\$196}{\$1000} \; 100\% = 19.6\%$$

For the same loan at 18 percent compounded semiannually,

$$\text{Effective interest rate} = \frac{\$1188 - \$1000}{\$1000}$$
$$= \frac{\$188}{\$1000} \; 100\% = 18.8\%$$

The effective interest rate can be obtained without reference to the principal. Based on the same reasoning utilized previously, and with

$i$ = effective interest rate
$r$ = nominal interest rate
$m$ = number of compounding periods per year

the effective interest rate for a nominal interest rate of 18 percent compounded semiannually is

$$i = \left(1 + \frac{r}{m}\right)^m - 1 = \left(1 + \frac{0.18}{2}\right)^2 - 1$$

$$= (1 + 0.09)^2 - 1 = 1.188 - 1$$
$$= 0.188 \quad \text{or} \quad 18.8\%$$

which means that a nominal interest rate of 18 percent compounded semiannually is equivalent to a compound interest rate of 18.8 percent on an annual basis.

The ultimate limit for the number of compounding periods in a year is called *continuous compounding*. Under this accrual pattern, $m$ approaches infinity as interest compounds continuously, moment by moment. The effective interest rate for continuous compounding is developed as follows:

The interest periods are made infinitesimally small:

$$i = \lim_{m \to \infty} \left(1 + \frac{r}{m}\right)^m - 1$$

The right side of the equality is rearranged to include $r$ in the exponent:

$$\left(1 + \frac{r}{m}\right)^m - 1 = \left[\left(1 + \frac{r}{m}\right)^{m/r}\right]^r - 1$$

The bracketed term is recognized as the value of the mathematical symbol $e$ [$e$ = 2.718 is the value of $(1 + 1/n)^n$ as $n$ approaches infinity]:

$$\lim_{m \to \infty} \left(1 + \frac{r}{m}\right)^{m/r} = e$$

By substitution,

$$i = \lim_{m \to \infty} \left[\left(1 + \frac{r}{m}\right)^{m/r}\right]^r - 1 = e^r - 1$$

As an example of continuous compounding, when the interest rate is $r = 18.232$ percent,

$$i = e^r - 1 = e^{0.18232} - 1 = 0.20 \quad \text{or} \quad 20\%$$

and, correspondingly, when the effective interest rate is $i = 22.1$ percent,

$$0.221 = e^r - 1$$
$$1.221 = e^r$$
$$r = 20\%$$

---

### Example 2.4  Relative Effects of Nominal Interest Rates

A loan can be arranged at a nominal rate of 12 percent compounded monthly, or 13 percent compounded semiannually. Which arrangement provides the lower debt at the end of the loan period?

The more attractive arrangement is the one with the lowest effective interest rate. At 12 percent compounded monthly, $r = 0.12$ and $m = 12$, and

$$\text{Effective interest rate} = \left(1 + \frac{0.12}{12}\right)^{12} - 1$$
$$= (1.01)^{12} - 1 = 1.127 - 1 = 0.127$$

At 13 percent compounded semiannually, $r = 0.13$ and $m = 2$, and

$$\text{Effective interest rate} = \left(1 + \frac{0.13}{2}\right)^2 - 1$$
$$= (1.065)^2 - 1 = 1.134 - 1 = 0.134$$

The loan at 12 percent compounded monthly is thus seen to have the lower $F$ value.

## Continuous Compounding

Occasionally, economic studies are conducted with continuous compounding rather than conventional discrete interest rates. The most obvious computational effect of using continuous interest is that a given nominal rate, say 20 percent, produces a significantly larger future amount than the same figure as an effective interest rate; as demonstrated above, a continuously compounded $r$ of 20 percent compared to $i = 20$ percent yields an annual return greater by

$$\frac{0.221 - 0.20}{0.20} 100\% = 10.5\%$$

The rationale for using continuous interest in economic analyses is that the cash flow in certain situations is best approximated by a continuous pattern; that is, cash transactions tend to be spread out over a year in more or less of an even distribution, rather than being concentrated at particular dates. Some mathematical models are also facilitated by the assumption of continuous compounding rather than periodic compounding.

In actual practice, however, interest rates are seldom quoted on a continuous basis, and the vast majority of organizations use discrete compounding periods in their economic studies. The reason for this is probably custom or the familiarity that makes it easier to understand periodic interest charges. Accounting practices that categorize receipts and disbursements as end-of-year values, and financial experiences with annual tax, insurance, or mortgage payments, contribute to thinking in terms of discrete periods. Yet continuous and discrete compounding are both only approximations of true cash flow, because cash neither flows like a free stream of water nor gushes like a geyser at given intervals. Receipts and disbursements are irregular in amount and in timing.

In the following discussion of the time value of money and in subsequent chapters on economic comparison methods, end-of-year compounding is utilized. All interest statements are for effective rates unless specified otherwise. Tables of interest factors are provided in Appendix B only for discrete compounding. However, the development of comparable interest factors for continuous compounding is explained in Chapter 3, as they might be needed for special applications; continuous-compounding interest tables are provided in Appendix C.

## TIME-VALUE EQUIVALENCE

Two things are equivalent when they produce the same effect. The effective interest rate computed for a nominally stated interest rate is an equivalent expression of the interest charge. Both interest charges produce the same effect on an investment. In considering time-value conversions, the equivalent numerical values of money are determined, *not* values with equivalent *purchasing power*. The amount of goods that can be purchased with a given sum of money varies up and down (more often down) as a function of special localized circumstances and nationwide or worldwide economic conditions. Ways to include inflation effects are discussed in Chapter 13. In this chapter about time-value mechanics, attention is directed toward calculations based on the *earning power* of money, which relates time and earnings to locate time-equivalent money amounts.

If $1000 were sealed and buried today, it would have a cash value of $1000 when it was dug up 2 years from now. Regardless of changes in buying power, the value remains constant because the earning power of the money was forfeited. It was observed earlier that $1000 deposited at 10 percent interest compounded annually has a value of $1000(1 + 0.10)^2 = $1210$ after 2 years. Therefore, $1000 today is equivalent to $1210 in 2 years from now if it earns at a prevailing rate of 10 percent compounded yearly. Similarly, to have $1000 in 2 years from now, one need only deposit

$$\$1000 \frac{1}{(1 + 0.10)^2} = \$826.44$$

today. In theory then, if 10 percent is an acceptable rate of return, an investor would be indifferent between having $826.44 in hand or having a trusted promise to receive $1000 in 2 years.

The $1000 could also be used to pay two equal annual $500 installments. The buried $1000 could be retrieved after 1 year, an installment paid, and the remaining $500 interred again until the second payment became due. If, instead, the $1000 is deposited at 10 percent, there would be $1100 available at the end of the first year. After the first $500 installment was paid, the remaining $600 would draw interest until the next payment. Paying the second $500 installment would leave

$$\$600(1.10) - \$500 = \$660 - \$500 = \$160$$

in the account. Because of the earning power of money, the initial deposit could have been reduced to $868 to pay out $500 at the end of each of the two years:

*First year:*     $868(1.10) - $500 \doteq $955 - $500 = $455
*Second year:*    $455(1.10) \doteq $500 =$ second installment

Thus, $868 is equivalent to $500 received 1 year from now plus another $500 received 2 years from now:

*First year:*     $\dfrac{\$500}{1.10} \doteq \$455$

*Second year:*    $\$455 + \dfrac{\$500}{(1.10)^2} = \$455 + \dfrac{\$500}{1.21}$

$$\doteq \$455 + \$413 \doteq \$868$$

The concept of equivalence is the cornerstone for time-value-of-money comparisons. To have a precise meaning, income and expenditures must be identified with time as well as with amount. A decision between alternatives having receipts and disbursements spread over a period of time is made by comparing the equivalent outcomes of the alternatives at a given date. Figure 2.1 shows the translation of $1000 at time zero (now) into equivalent alternative expressions of cash flow.

**FIGURE 2.1**
Equivalent outcomes with an interest rate of 6 percent compounded annually.

$1000 today is equivalent to $1791 received 10 years from now.

$1000 today is equivalent to $237.40 received at the end of each year for the next 5 years.

$1000 today is equivalent to $317.70 received at the end of years 6, 7, 8, 9, and 10.

$237.40 received at the end of each year for the next 5 years is equivalent to a lump sum of $1791 received 10 years from now.

$317.70 received at the end of years 6, 7, 8, 9, and 10 is equivalent to $1791 received 10 years from now.

$237.40 received at the end of each year for the next 5 years is equivalent to $317.70 received at the end of years 6, 7, 8, 9, and 10.

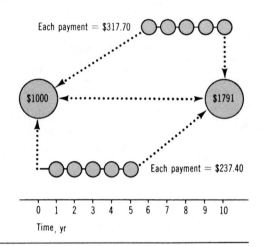

# COMPOUND-INTEREST FACTORS

Cash flow is translated to a given point in time by determining either its present worth or its future worth. A present-worth calculation converts a single future sum or a series of future values to an equivalent amount at an earlier date. This date is not necessarily the present time. Future-worth calculations convert values occurring at any time to an equivalent amount at a later date.

Equivalent values could be determined by calculating the compound amount of each sum for each period. This tedious routine is avoided by using compound-interest tables for different present- and future-worth factors. There are two basic types of factors. The one we have already considered converts a single amount to a present or future value. The other type is for a series of uniform values called an *annuity*. The tables in Appendix B are based on an annuity characterized by (1) *equal payments A,* (2) *equal periods between payments N,* and (3) *the first payment occurring at the end of the first period.* Annuity factors are used to convert a series of payments to a single future or present sum and to translate single sums into a series of payments occurring in the past or future.

## Conversion Symbols

There are seven basic interest factors for discrete compounding. Names and notations for these factors are those suggested by the Engineering Economy Division of the American

Society for Engineering Education.* Each factor is described by a name (for instance, one is the "compound-amount factor" used previously to find the future worth of a single payment) and two notational forms: (1) a mnemonic symbol (to assist memory by association) as in $(CA\text{-}i\%\text{-}N)$ for the compound-amount factor, and (2) a functional symbol (to suggest the use of the interest factor) as in $(F/P, i\%, N)$, again for the compound-amount factor which is used to find $F$ given $P$. Since the functional notation is most descriptive of the operation to be performed, it will be utilized for all the interest factors. Time-value conversions and associated factors are summarized in Table 2.2.

| *Factor* | *To Find* | *Given* | *Symbol* |
|---|---|---|---|
| Compound amount | Future worth, $F$ | Present amount, $P$ | $(F/P, i\%, N)$ |
| Present worth | Present worth, $P$ | Future amount, $F$ | $(P/F, i\%, N)$ |
| Sinking fund | Annuity amounts, $A$ | Future amount, $F$ | $(A/F, i\%, N)$ |
| Series compound amount | Future worth, $F$ | Annuity amounts, $A$ | $(F/A, i\%, N)$ |
| Capital recovery | Annuity amounts, $A$ | Present amount, $P$ | $(A/P, i\%, N)$ |
| Series present worth | Present worth, $P$ | Annuity amounts, $A$ | $(P/A, i\%, N)$ |
| Arithmetic gradient conversion | Annuity amounts, $A$ | Uniform increase in amount, $G$ | $(A/G, i\%, N)$ |

**TABLE 2.2**  Interest factors for discrete cash flow with end-of-period compoundings.

The symbols for the first six time-value conversions are abbreviations for the equivalent values sought (future worth $F$, present worth $P$, or uniform series amounts $A$) and the data given ($F$, $P$, or $A$ with its associated interest rate $i$ and number of compounding periods $N$). The arithmetic gradient conversion factor is used to convert a constantly increasing or decreasing series into a uniform series of amounts $A$ which can then be an input to other interest factors. In the equation

$$F = \$1000(F/P, 10, 2)$$

$1000 is the known present amount, the interest rate is 0.10 per period ($i$ is 10 percent), and $F$ is the equivalent future worth after two periods ($N = 2$). The whole symbol stands for the numerical expression $(1 + 0.10)^2$, and the numerical value is found in Appendix B. To find the value for $(F/P, 10, 2)$, look for 2 in the $N$ column of the 10 percent table, and then read across to the compound-amount factor column to find 1.2100.

The conversion descriptions and symbols connote that certain factors are reciprocals of one another:

$$(F/P, i, N) = \frac{1}{(P/F, i, N)}$$

$$(A/F, i, N) = \frac{1}{(F/A, i, N)}$$

$$(A/P, i, N) = \frac{1}{(P/A, i, N)}$$

Other relationships are not so apparent from the abbreviations but are useful in understand-

*See *The Engineering Economist*, vol. 14, no. 2, Winter 1969.

ing conversion calculations. The following equalities are verified during the development of the conversion symbols:

$$(F/P, i, N) \times (P/A, i, N) = (F/A, i, N)$$
$$(F/A, i, N) \times (A/P, i, N) = (F/P, i, N)$$
$$(A/F, i, N) + i = (A/P, i, N)$$

## Development of Interest Formulae

A better understanding of the conversion process is achieved by studying the development of the interest-factor formulas. The symbols employed in the following discussion of the seven interest factors are the same as those described previously. It should be remembered that these factors are for discrete compounding, and their numerical values are tabulated in Appendix B; corresponding factors for continuous compounding are presented in the next chapter.

Additional sample applications of the interest factors are provided in the review exercises at the end of this chapter.

### 1  COMPOUND-AMOUNT FACTOR (SINGLE PAYMENT)

*Use: To find F, given P*
*Symbols: (F/P, i%, N)*
*(CA-i%-N)*
*Formula: $F = P(1 + i)^N$*
*$= P(F/P, i, N)$*

The effect of compound interest on an investment was demonstrated in previous examples. The future worth of a present amount when interest is accumulated at a specific rate $i$ for a given number of periods $N$, where $F1$ is the future worth at the end of the first period and $F_N$ is the future worth at the end of $N$ years, is

$$F1 = P + Pi = P(1 + i)$$
$$F2 = P[(1 + i) + (1 + i)i]$$
$$= P(1 + i)(1 + i) = P(1 + i)^2$$
$$F3 = P[(1 + i)^2 + (1 + i)^2 i]$$
$$= P(1 + i)^2(1 + i) = P(1 + i)^3$$
$$F_N = P(1 + i)^N$$

The ratio of future worth to present amount is then expressed as

$$\frac{F}{P} = (F/P, i, N) = (1 + i)^N$$

### 2  PRESENT-WORTH FACTOR (SINGLE PAYMENT)

*Use: To find P, given F*
*Symbols: (P/F, i%, N)*
*(PW-i%-N)*
*Formula: $P = \dfrac{1}{(1 + i)^N}$*
*$= F(P/F, i, N)$*

$P$ is the present worth of a sum $N$ periods in the future. Rearranging the single-amount future-value formula $F = P(1 + i)^N$ to express $P$ in terms of $F$ gives

$$P = F\frac{1}{(1 + i)^N}$$

Then the ratio of present worth to future value is

$$\frac{P}{F} = (P/F, i, N) = \frac{1}{(1 + i)^N}$$

That the present-worth factor is simply the reciprocal of the compound-amount factor is confirmed by applying it to the data given in Table 2.1, where the future worth of $1000 at 10 percent compounded annually was shown to be $1210. Equivalently, $P = F(P/F, i, N)$ is the expression for the present worth when the future worth is known. The numerical value of the present-worth factor ($P/F$, 10, 2) is found in the 10 percent table of Appendix B at $N = 2$: 0.82645. Then,

$$P = \$1210(0.82645) = \$1000$$

## 3  SINKING-FUND FACTOR

*Use: To find A, given F*
*Symbols: (A/F, i%, N)*
*(SF-i%-N)*

*Formula:* $A = F \dfrac{i}{(1 + i)^N - 1}$
$= F(A/F, i, N)$

A fund established to accumulate a given future amount through the collection of a uniform series of payments is called a *sinking fund*. Each payment has a constant value $A$ and is made at the end of an interest period.

The growth pattern of a sinking fund is illustrated in Table 2.3. Each end-of-year payment $A$ is equal to $1000, and payments continue for 5 years. Interest is 8 percent compounded annually. It is assumed that each payment begins to draw interest as soon as it is deposited in the sinking-fund account. Thus, the first payment draws interest for 4 years, and the last payment receives no interest.

| Time of Payment (end of year) | Amount of Payment, A | Future Worth at the End of Each Year |
|---|---|---|
| 1 | $1000 | $1000(1.08)^4 = \$1360$ |
| 2 | 1000 | $1000(1.08)^3 = 1260$ |
| 3 | 1000 | $1000(1.08)^2 = 1166$ |
| 4 | 1000 | $1000(1.08)^1 = 1080$ |
| 5 | 1000 | $1000(1.08)^0 = 1000$ |
| | | Annuity value $F$ at the end of year 5 = $5866 |

**TABLE 2.3** Compound amount of a uniform series of payments.

A more general expression for the future worth of an annuity develops from the use of symbols to represent the values in Table 2.3. The first payment, earning interest for $N - 1$ periods, where $N$ is 5 years in the example, increases to a future worth of

$$F = A(1 + i)^{N-1}$$

Each of the payments is treated in the same manner and collected to obtain the total amount $F$:

$$F = A(1 + i)^{N-1} + A(1 + i)^{N-2} + A(1 + i)^{N-3} + A(1 + i)^{N-4} + A(1 + i)^{N-N}$$

Factoring out $A$ and letting the exponent $N - N = 0$, we have

$$F = A[(1 + i)^{N-1} + (1 + i)^{N-2} + (1 + i)^{N-3} + (1 + i)^{N-4} + 1]$$

Multiplying this equation by $1 + i$ results in

$$F(1 + i) = A[(1 + i)^N + (1 + i)^{N-1} + (1 + i)^{N-2} + (1 + i)^{N-3} + (1 + i)]$$

Subtracting the original equation from the last equation gives

$$F(1 + i) - F = -A + A(1 + i)^N$$
$$Fi = A[(1 + i)^N - 1]$$

Solving for $A$,

$$A = F \frac{i}{(1 + i)^N - 1}$$

we see the sinking-fund factor expressed as

$$(A/F, i, N) = \frac{i}{(1 + i)^N - 1}$$

Then, applying the sinking-fund factor to the data in Table 2.3, we have

$$A = \$5866(A/F, 8, 5)$$
$$= \$5866(0.17046) = \$1000$$

## 4   SERIES COMPOUND-AMOUNT FACTOR (UNIFORM SERIES)

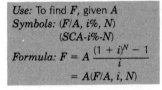

*Use:* To find $F$, given $A$
*Symbols:* $(F/A, i\%, N)$
  $(SCA\text{-}i\%\text{-}N)$
*Formula:* $F = A \dfrac{(1 + i)^N - 1}{i}$
  $= A(F/A, i, N)$

From the development of the sinking-fund-factor formula,

$$Fi = A(1 + i)^N - 1$$

which is expressed in terms of $F$ as

$$F = A \frac{(1 + i)^N - 1}{i}$$

Then the time value for the future worth of an annuity is

$$(F/A, i, N) = \frac{(1 + i)^N - 1}{i}$$

and the future worth of the annuity composed of five annual payments of $1000 each invested at 8 percent compounded annually, as portrayed in Table 2.3, is

$$F = \$1000(F/A, 8, 5)$$
$$= \$1000(0.58665) = \$5866$$

## 5   CAPITAL-RECOVERY FACTOR

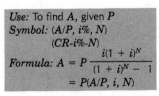

*Use:* To find $A$, given $P$
*Symbol:* $(A/P, i\%, N)$
  $(CR\text{-}i\%\text{-}N)$
*Formula:* $A = P \dfrac{i(1 + i)^N}{(1 + i)^N - 1}$
  $= P(A/P, i, N)$

The capital-recovery factor is used to determine the amount of each future annuity payment required to accumulate a given present value when the interest rate and number of payments are known. For instance , the amount of each annual payment made for 5 years in order to repay a debt of $3993 bearing 8 percent annual interest can be determined through the use of the capital-recovery factor. Table 2.4 shows that it would take five $1000 payments to repay the $3993 debt.

| Time of Payment (end of year) | Amount of Payment, A | Present Worth of Payments at End of Year |
|---|---|---|
| 1 | $1000 | $1000(1.08)^{-1} = \$\ 926$ |
| 2 | 1000 | $1000(1.08)^{-2} =\ \ \ \ 857$ |
| 3 | 1000 | $1000(1.08)^{-3} =\ \ \ \ 794$ |
| 4 | 1000 | $1000(1.08)^{-4} =\ \ \ \ 735$ |
| 5 | 1000 | $1000(1.08)^{-5} =\ \ \ \ 681$ |
| | | Present worth $P$ of the 5-year annuity $= \$3993$ |

**TABLE 2.4** Present worth of a uniform series of payments.

Using symbols to represent the conversions shown in Table 2.4, the present worth of an annuity is

$$P = A[(1 + i)^{-1} + (1 + i)^{-2} + (1 + i)^{-3} + (1 + i)^{-4} + (1 + i)^{-N}]$$

and multiplying both sides of the equation by $(1 + i)^{-1}$ results in

$$P(1 + i)^{-1} = A[(1 + i)^{-2} + (1 + i)^{-3} + (1 + i)^{-4} + (1 + i)^{-N} + (1 + i)^{-N-1}]$$

Subtracting the first equation from the second equation gives

$$P[(1 + i)^{-1} - 1] = A[(1 + i)^{-N-1} - (1 + i)^{-1}]$$

Converting $(1 + i)^{-1} - 1$ to $-i/(1 + i)$, multiplying both sides by $-(1 + i)$, and rearranging yields

$$P\frac{i(1 + i)}{1 + i} = A[(1 + i)(1 + i)^{-1} - (1 + i)(1 + i)^{-N-1}]$$

$$Pi = A[1 - (1 + i)^{-N}]$$

$$= A\frac{(1 + i)^N - 1}{(1 + i)^N}$$

*or* $$A = P\frac{i(1 + i)^N}{(1 + i)^N - 1}$$

from which comes the expression for the capital-recovery factor,

$$(A/P, i, N) = \frac{i(1 + i)^N}{(1 + i)^N - 1}$$

As applied to the data in Table 2.4 where $P = \$3993$,

$$A = \$3993(A/P, 8, 5)$$
$$= \$3993(0.25046) = \$1000$$

The relationship among time-value annuity factors is apparent from the way the capital-recovery factor can be converted to the sinking-fund factor by substituting $P = F(1 + i)^{-N}$ in the capital-recovery formula, as

$$A = P(A/P, i, N) = \frac{F}{(1 + i)^N}(A/P, i, N) = \frac{F}{(1 + i)^N}\frac{i(1 + i)^N}{(1 + i)^N - 1}$$

$$A = F \frac{i}{(1 + i)^N - 1} = F(A/F, i, N)$$

or

$$(A/P, i, N) = (A/F, i, N) + i$$

as indicated by

$$\frac{i(1 + i)^N}{(i + i)^N - 1} = \frac{i}{(1 + i)^N - 1} + i = \frac{i + i(1 + i)^N - i}{(1 + i)^N - 1} = \frac{i(1 + i)^N}{(1 - i)^N - 1}$$

## 6 SERIES PRESENT-WORTH FACTOR (UNIFORM SERIES)

*Use:* To find *P*, given *A*
*Symbols:* (*P/A, i%, N*)
  (*SPW-i%-N*)
*Formula:* $P = A \frac{(1 + i)^N - 1}{i(1 + i)^N}$
  $= A(P/A, i, N)$

The present value of a series of uniform end-of-period payments can be calculated in the cumbersome fashion shown in Table 2.4. The present worth is more readily determined by use of the series present-worth factor.

Expressing the known relationship

$$A = P \frac{i(1 + i)^N}{(1 + i)^N - 1}$$

in terms of *P* yields

$$P = A \frac{(1 + i)^N - 1}{i(1 + i)^N} = A(P/A, i, N)$$

which is the time value expression of the present worth of an annuity.

The reciprocal relationship between the capital-recovery factor and the series present-worth factor is demonstrated by the data from Table 2.4:

$$P = \$1000(P/A, 8, 5)$$
$$= \$1000(3.9926) = \$3993$$

which indicates the equivalence of having $3993 in hand and a firm contract to receive five year-end payments of $1000 each when the interest rate is 8 percent.

## 7 ARITHMETIC-GRADIENT CONVERSION FACTOR (TO UNIFORM SERIES)

*Use:* To find *A*, given *G*
*Symbols:* (*A/G, i%, N*)
  (*GUS-i%-N*)
*Formula:* $A = G\left[\frac{1}{i} - \frac{N}{(1 + i)^N - 1}\right]$
  $= G(A/G, i, N)$

Enough situations occur in which series of payments increase at equal increments to warrant a special conversion factor. A series of payments that increases at a rate of $200 per year is illustrated in Figure 2.2. The $200 periodic change is the gradient *G*, and the payment at the end of the first period is the base annuity value *A'*. The pattern of an arithmetic gradient is then

$$A', A' + G, A' + 2G, \ldots, A' + (N - 1)G$$

where *N* is the duration of the series (*N* = 5 in Figure 2.2).

A uniformly increasing series can be evaluated by calculating *F* or *P* for each individual payment and summing the collection. Calculation time is reduced by converting the series

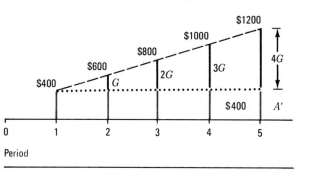

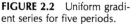

**FIGURE 2.2** Uniform gradient series for five periods.

into an equivalent annuity of equal payments $A$. The formula for this translation is developed by separating the series shown in Figure 2.2 into two parts: a base annuity designated $A'$ and an arithmetic-gradient series increasing by $G$ each period. The future worth of the $G$ values in Figure 2.2 is calculated as

$$F = \$200(F/P, i, 3) + \$400(F/P, i, 2) + \$600(F/P, i, 1) + \$800$$

or

$$F = G(1 + i)^3 + 2G(1 + i)^2 + 3G(1 + i)^1 + 4G$$

Multiplying the latter expression by $(1 + i)^1$ gives

$$F(1 + i) = G(1 + i)^4 + 2G(1 + i)^3 + 3G(1 + i)^2 + 4G(1 + i)^1$$

Subtracting the last equation from the one above it yields

$$F - F(1 + i) = -G(1 + i)^4 - G(1 + i)^3 - G(1 + i)^2 - G(1 + i)^1 + 4G$$

Letting $4G = (N - 1)G$ and multiplying both sides of the equation by $-1$ give

$$F(1 + i) - F = G[(1 + i)^4 + (1 + i)^3 + (1 + i)^2 + (1 + i) + 1] - NG$$

We have, in brackets, the series compound-amount factor $(F/A, i, 5)$, so

$$Fi = G(F/A, i, N) - NG$$

To convert $F$ to an annuity, both sides of the equation are multiplied by the sinking-fund factor $(A/F, i, N)$, which is the reciprocal of $(F/A, i, N)$, to get

$$Fi(A/F, i, N) = G - NG(A/F, i, N)$$

and since $A = F(A/F, i, N)$,

$$A = \frac{G}{i} - \frac{NG}{i}(A/F, i, N)$$

or

$$A = G\left[\frac{1}{i} - \frac{N}{i}(A/F, i, N)\right]$$

in which the bracketed expression is called the *arithmetic gradient conversion factor* with the symbol $(A/G, i, N)$.

For the cash flow diagramed in Figure 2.2, the equivalent uniform annuity calculated at an effective interest rate per period of 10 percent is

$$A = A' + G(A/G, i, N)$$
$$= \$400 + \$200(A/G, 10, 5)$$
$$= \$400 + \$200(1.8100) = \$762$$

which means that five end-of-period payments of $762 are equivalent to five payments starting at $400 and increasing by $200 each period.

The gradient factor may also be applied to a pattern of payments that decrease by a constant increment each period. The formula would then be

$$A = A' - G(A/G, i, N)$$

As an example, assume an endowment was originally set up to provide a $10,000 first payment with payments decreasing by $1000 each year during the 10-year endowment life. What constant annual payment for 10 years would be equivalent to the original endowment plan if $i = 8$ percent? We have

$$A = \$10,000 - \$1000(A/G, 8, 10)$$
$$= \$10,000 - \$1000(3.8712) = \$6128.80$$

# Review Exercises and Discussions

**Exercise 1**  The money earned from making a loan is evident in the contract (sometimes in fine print). A loan of $10,000 for 1 year at an interest rate of 10 percent earns the lender $10,000 × 0.10 = $1000. A borrower usually does not know in advance exactly how much will be gained from a loan to buy productive goods. It is often impossible to segregate precisely the receipts due a certain production operation when that operation is a small part of a much larger production system. In such cases an evaluation study may be made on the amount production costs of the system are decreased by improvements to the given operation, assuming the operation must be performed to maintain the total process. Then the earnings are in the form of "cost savings" in the system which are compared to the investment cost of acquiring and using assets to improve the operation.

Assume a machine is purchased for $10,000 with the loan mentioned above. The machine will be completely worn out by the end of the year, and its operating costs will be $100 per month more than the costs of the present operation. How large a cost reduction must be provided by the machine for its purchase to earn a 15 percent return for the borrower?

**Solution 1**  The costs involved include repaying the loan plus interest charges for the loan, extra operating costs, and investment earnings resulting from the purchase of the machine.

| | |
|---|---:|
| Loan repayment (purchase price of the machine) | $10,000 |
| Interest paid on the loan for 1 year = $10,000 × 0.10 | 1000 |
| Additional operating cost incurred = $100/month × 12 | 1200 |
| 15% earnings on the $10,000 borrowed = $10,000 × 0.15 | 1500 |
| Necessary cost reduction to support the investment | $13,700 |

If the cost reduction turned out to be only $13,700 − $1500 = $12,200, it would just cover expenses and nothing would be gained from the machine's purchase. However, if the company could afford $10,000 of its own money for the machine rather than borrowing it, a cost reduction of $12,200 would yield a 10 percent return on the investment, which is the rate the company could earn by simply lending its money at the "going" interest rate of 10 percent. A cost reduction of $13,700 would produce a return of

$$\frac{\$13,700 - \$10,000 - \$1200}{\$10,000} = \frac{\$2500}{\$10,000} \; 100\% = 25\%$$

which is attractive to the company because it provides an added 15 percent beyond the cost capital to support the project.

---

**Exercise 2**   A loan of $200 is made for a period of 13 months, from January 1 to January 31 the following year, at a simple interest rate of 8 percent. What future amount is due at the end of the loan period?

**Solution 2**   Using ordinary simple interest, the total amount to be repaid after 13 months is

$F = P + PiN$
$= \$200 + (\$200)(0.08)(1 + 1/12)$
$= \$200 + (\$200)(0.0867)$
$= \$200 + \$17.34 = \$217.34$

If exact simple interest is used, the future value (assuming the year in question is not a leap year) is

$F = P + PiN$
$= \$200 + (\$200)(0.08)\left(1 + \frac{31}{365}\right)$
$= \$200 + (\$200)(0.0868)$
$= \$200 + \$17.36 = \$217.36$

---

**Exercise 3**   A credit plan charges interest at the rate of 36 percent compounded monthly. What is the effective interest rate?

**Solution 3**   The nominal 36 percent rate comprises monthly charges of 3 percent. From this statement we know that $r = 0.36$ and $m = 12$, so the effective interest rate can be calculated as

$$i = \left(1 + \frac{r}{m}\right)^m - 1 = \left(1 + \frac{0.36}{12}\right)^{12} - 1$$

$$= (1.03)^{12} - 1 = 1.4257 - 1 = 42.57\%$$

The same result can be obtained by recognizing that

$$(1.03)^{12} - 1 = (F/P, 3, 12) - 1$$

Then the tables in Appendix B can be used to find the value of the compound-amount factor at $i = 3$ percent and $N = 12$:

$$(F/P, 3, 12) = 1.4257$$

so

$$1.4257 - 1 = 42.57\%$$

---

**Exercise 4**   How much would a person have had to invest 1 year ago to have $2500 available today, when the investment earned interest at the nominal rate of 12 percent compounded monthly?

**Solution 4**   It is first necessary to convert the nominal rate to its corresponding periodic rate: 12 percent compounded monthly means an investment earns 1 percent per month. Next, it must be recognized that today's worth is a future worth in terms of when the investment $P$ was made, one year previously. It is known that $F = \$2500$, $i = 1$ percent, and $N = 12$ (12 months have passed since the original investment); therefore,

$$P = F(P/F, 1, 12) = \$2500(0.88746) = \$2219$$

---

**Exercise 5**   What annual year-end payment must be made each year to have $10,000 available 4 years from now? The compound annual interest rate is 10 percent.

**Solution 5**   The 4-year annuity is a sinking fund which has a value at maturity of $F = \$10,000$. The necessary annual deposits equal

$$A = F(A/F, 10, 4) = \$10,000(0.21547) = \$2155$$

---

**Exercise 6**   If you deposit $10,000 today, what equal amounts can you withdraw at the end of each year for the next 4 years when the interest rate is 10 percent?

**Solution 6**   The withdrawals form an ordinary annuity where $N = 4$ and $i = 10$ percent. Given $P = \$10,000$, the capital invested is recovered by payments of

$$A = \$10,000(A/P, 10, 4) = \$10,000(0.31547) = \$3158$$

---

**Exercise 7**   A teenager plans to deposit $2000 in a savings account starting 1 year from now and to increase annual deposits by $1000 each year for the next 6 years. Assuming deposits earn 9 percent annually, what equal-payment annuity would accumulate the same amount over the 7-year period?

**Solution 7**   The first step in using the arithmetic-gradient conversion factor is to identify the base annuity $A'$ and the gradient $G$. $A'$ is the first payment of $2000, and $G$ is the amount by which the payments increase each year, $1000. Then,

$$A = A' + G(A/G, i, N) = \$2000 + \$1000(A/G, 9, 7)$$
$$= \$2000 + \$1000(2.6572) = \$2000 + \$2657 = \$4657$$

Thus seven equal payments of $4657 are equivalent to seven payments increasing by $1000 increments from $2000 for the first one to $8000 for the last one.

---

**Exercise 8**   Receipts from an investment will decline by $150 each year for 5 years from a level of $1000 at the end of the first year. For an interest rate of 7 percent, calculate a constant annual series amount that is equivalent to the gradient over the 6 year period.

**Solution 8**   The base amount ($A' = $1000$) is decreased by a uniform amount each year ($G = -$150$). Given $i = 7$ percent and $N = 6$,

$$A = \$1000 - \$150(A/G, 7, 6) = \$1000 - \$150(2.3030) = \$654.55$$

---

# PROBLEMS

*Problems 2.1 through 2.11 are adapted from Mathematics of Finance by L. L. Smail (McGraw-Hill, New York). This college text was published in 1925, and it shows that basic interest problems have not changed much over the years.*

**2.1**   What sum must be loaned at 6 percent simple interest to earn $47 in 2 years?
*($391.67)*

**2.2**   How long will it take $800 to yield $72 in simple interest at 4 percent?
*(2¼ years)*

**2.3**   At what rate will $65.07 yield $8.75 in simple interest in 3 years, 6 months?
*(3.8%)*

**2.4**   How long will it take any sum to double itself at a 5 percent simple interest rate?

**2.5**   Find the ordinary and exact simple interest on $3300 at 6 percent for 56 days.
*($30.80; $30.38)*

**2.6**   If the interest on a certain sum for 3 months is $63.87 at 5 percent simple interest, what would it be at 6 percent?

**2.7**   Find the compound amount of $100 for 3 years at 5 percent compounded annually.
*($115.76)*

**2.8**   What is the compound amount of $750 for 5 years at 6 percent compounded quarterly?

**2.9**   Accumulate a principal of $600 for 5 years, 9 months at 6 percent compounded monthly. How much interest is earned?
*($246.42)*

**2.10**   Find the difference between the amount of $100 at simple interest and at compound interest for 5 years at 5 percent.
*($2.62)*

**2.11**   Find the compound amount of $5000 at 6 percent for 4, 6, 8, and 10 years, and compare the results. Does doubling the time double the amount?

**2.12**  What is the effective interest rate for:
**2.12a**  12 percent compounded semiannually?
**2.12b**  12 percent compounded quarterly?
**2.12c**  12 percent compounded monthly?

*(i = 12.7%)*

**2.13**  A personal loan is made at an interest rate of 3/4 percent per month on the unpaid balance.
**2.13a**  What is the effective interest rate?
**2.13b**  How much interest is earned if the duration of the loan is 18 months?

*(Interest earned = 14.4%)*

**2.14**  How is it possible to determine the numerical value of a capital-recovery factor $(A/P)$ if the only table available is:
**2.14a**  $(P/F)$?
**2.14b**  $(A/F)$?
**2.14c**  $(F/A)$?

**2.15**  Determine the value of $(F/A, 4, 8)$ using only the table for $(P/A)$.

**2.16**  Develop a formula for the present worth of an annuity due (see Example 3.5).

**2.17**  For a finance charge stated as 1.75 percent per month, what are the corresponding nominal and effective interest rates?

*(r = 21%; i = 23.14%)*

**2.18**  A loan of $5000 is scheduled to be repaid in equal monthly installments over 2½ years. The nominal interest rate is 6 percent. How large is each payment?

*($179.95)*

**2.19**  How much will a piece of property have to increase in value over the next 5 years if it is to earn 10 percent per year on the purchase price?

**2.20**  What simple interest rate must be applied to earn the same interest over 5 years as earned by an investment at 5 percent compounded semiannually?

*(5.6%)*

**2.21**  How much could you spend now to avoid spending $10,000 three years from now, if your money earns 12 percent per year?

*($7118)*

**2.22**  Compare the effective interest rates for 16 percent compounded quarterly and 15 percent compounded monthly.

**2.23**  How much less would it cost to pay off a $3000 loan in 1 year with 12 equal payments when interest is 12 percent compounded monthly, as opposed to making a single payment when the effective interest rate is 12 percent?

**2.24**  How much money could you borrow if you agreed to pay back $1000 at the end of each year for 5 years? The lender expects to earn 10 percent per year.

**2.25**  The net income from a newly purchased piece of construction equipment is expected to be $12,000 the first year and to decrease by $1500 each year as maintenance costs increase. The equipment will be used for 4 years. What annual annuity would produce an equivalent income when the interest rate is 8 percent?

**2.26**   Calculate the equivalent annual cost of a series of expenses in which no cost is incurred in the first year but thereafter costs rise by $700 per year until they reach $5600 annually. Use $i$ = 6 percent.

# EXTENSION

**2A   *Geometric Series*** A geometric series is a nonuniform progression that grows or declines at a *constant percentage rate* per period. The most familiar example is the effect of inflation or deflation on a cash flow stream. For instance, the rate of growth during a period of inflation could be 10 percent per period. An item priced at $1000 during the first year would then increase by 10 percent per year as shown in Figure 2.3(a). A decline of 10 percent per year, starting from the same $1000 figure, would take the pattern shown in Figure 2.3(b).

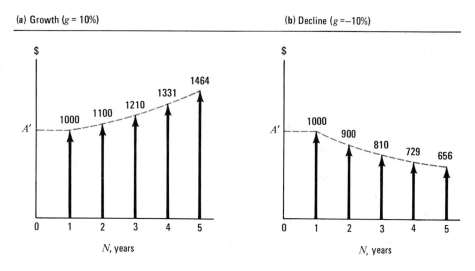

(a) Growth ($g$ = 10%)     (b) Decline ($g$ = −10%)

**FIGURE 2.3**
Compound growth and decline patterns. Changes in cash flows occur at a constant *rate* in a geometric series, in contrast to changes of equal *increments* in an arithmetic series.

The present worth of such series could be calculated by bringing each payment back to its present value by multiplying individual amounts by their appropriate ($P/F$, $i$, $N$). For many applications it is more convenient to apply geometric gradient formulas. These formulas are based on the cash flow in period 1 ($A'$). Thus the cash flow $N$ periods from time zero is $A'(1 + g)^N$, where $g$ is the rate of growth or decline.

Three different formulae are necessary to calculate the present worth $P$ of a geometric series. Which one to use depends on the relationship between the percentage rate $g$ and the interest rate $i$.

*Case 1:* When $g$ is greater than $i$, define a special interest rate $i^*$ as

$$i^* = \frac{1 + g}{1 + i} - 1$$

and calculate the present value as

$$P = \frac{A'}{1 + i}(F/A, i^*, N)$$

Consider the cash flow in Figure 2.3(a), where $g = 0.10$ and $A' = \$1000$. For $i = 0.08$, case 1 ($g > i$) applies and

$$i^* = \frac{1 + 0.10}{1 + 0.08} - 1 = \frac{1.10}{1.08} - 1 = 1.0185 - 1 = 1.85\%$$

which is the special interest rate that is used in the series compound-amount factor with $N = 5$. Since there are no tables in Appendix B for 1.85 percent, it is necessary to interpolate between tables to obtain a value for $(F/A, 1.85, 5)$.

$$P = \frac{\$1000}{1 + 0.08}(F/A, 1.85, 5) = \$926(5.1882) = \$4804$$

*Case 2:* When $g$ equals $i$, the growth and discount rates cancel each other to produce a present-value equation of

$$P = \frac{NA'}{1 + i}$$

If the interest rate for the 10 percent growth pattern in Figure 2.3(a) is also 10 percent ($i = g$), then

$$P = \frac{5(\$1000)}{1 + 0.10} = \frac{\$5000}{1.10} = \$4545$$

*Case 3:* When $g$ is less than $i$, the special interest rate is

$$i^* = \frac{1 + i}{1 + g} - 1$$

and

$$P = \frac{A'}{1 + g}(P/A, i^*, N)$$

Again using the cash flow pattern in Figure 2.3(a), but this time assuming $i = 12$ percent ($g < i$), we have

$$i^* = \frac{1 + 0.12}{1 + 0.10} - 1 = \frac{1.12}{1.10} - 1 = 1.0182 - 1 = 1.82\%$$

and

$$P = \frac{\$1000}{1 + 0.10}(P/A, 1.82, 5) = \$909(4.7408) = \$4309$$

Case 3 applies to all declining cash flow streams because $g$ is always negative during deflation. As applied to the cash flow pattern in Figure 2.3(b), where $g = -10$ percent, $A' = \$1000$, $N = 5$, and $i$ is assumed to be 8 percent,

$$i^* = \frac{1 + 0.08}{1 + -0.10} - 1 = \frac{1.08}{0.90} - 1 = 1.20 - 1 = 20\%$$

$$P = \frac{\$1000}{1 - 0.10}(P/A, 20, 5) = \$1111(2.991) = \$3323$$

In summary, cases 1 and 3 require the calculation of a special interest rate $i^*$ that depends on the growth rate $g$ and regular interest rate $i$. This special rate is used just like any other interest rate in obtaining the values for applicable interest factors, $F/A$ or $P/A$. After applying the appropriate formula for the case where $g$ is greater than, equal to, or less than $i$, the present value of the geometric series is obtained. The value thus calculated can be converted to an equivalent cash flow by applying any other discrete compound-interest formula using the regular interest rate $i$.

### QUESTIONS

**2A.1**  Tuition costs are expected to inflate at the rate of 8 percent per year. The first year's tuition is due 1 year from now and will be $2000. A fund is to be set up today to cover tuition costs for 4 years in an account that will earn interest at rate $i$. How large must the fund be if

**a**   $i = 5\%$                                                                                   ($7952)
**b**   $i = 8\%$                                                                                   ($7407)
**c**   $i = 10\%$                                                                                  ($7077)

**2A.2**  Today's price for materials used in a production process is expected to hold constant for this year at $100,000. What is the present worth of 5 years' supply for the same amount of material used each year when the interest rate is 8 percent, if the price changes at a constant annual rate of

**a**   $g = -5\%$                                                                                  ($364,205)
**b**   $g = 0\%$                                                                                   ($399,260)
**c**   $g = 5\%$                                                                                   ($437,904)
**d**   $g = 8\%$                                                                                   ($462,960)
**e**   $g = 15\%$                                                                                  ($526,990)

# CHAPTER 3

# DISCOUNTED CASH FLOW CALCULATIONS

OVERVIEW

Concepts concerning the time value of money from the last chapter become working tools in this chapter. Compound-interest factors for both discrete and continuous interest are applied to a variety of cash flows. The purpose of the calculations is to develop skills in converting cash flow patterns into equivalent sums that are more useful in comparing investments.

Receipts and disbursements associated with an economic situation can be portrayed on a cash flow diagram. When it is so diagramed, the timing of the cash flow is more apparent, and the chance of making careless errors is reduced. With practice, different cash flow patterns may be recognized and suggest the most direct approach for analysis.

Calculations made with either continuous or discrete interest factors rely on the same reasoning and rules; only the effect of interest on the cash flow varies. Both discount a cash flow to remove the time effect and thereby reveal its equivalent value at a specific point in time.

## CASH FLOW DIAGRAMS

During the construction of a cash flow diagram the structure of a problem often becomes distinct. It is usually advantageous to first define the time frame over which cash flows

*50*

occur. This establishes the horizontal scale, which is divided into time periods, frequently but not always years. Receipts and disbursements are then located on the time scale in adherence to problem specifications. Individual outlays or receipts are designated by vertical lines; relative magnitudes can be suggested by the heights of lines, but exact scaling wastes time. Whether a cash flow is positive or negative (positive above the axis, and negative below) depends on whose viewpoint is portrayed.

Figures 3.1(a) and (b) represent the same transaction: a loan paid off in three installments. From the borrower's viewpoint in Figure 3.1(a), the receipt of the loan is a positive inflow of cash, while subsequent installment payments represent negative outflows. Flows are reversed when viewed from the lender's perspective in Figure 3.1(b).

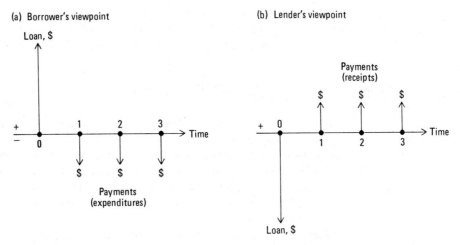

**FIGURE 3.1**
Perspectives for cash
flow diagrams.

Although cash flow diagrams are simply graphical representations of income and outlay, they should exhibit as much information as possible. It is useful to show the interest rate, and it may be helpful to designate the unknown that must be solved for in a problem. Figure 3.1 is redrawn in Figure 3.2 to represent specific problems. In Figure 3.2(a), the

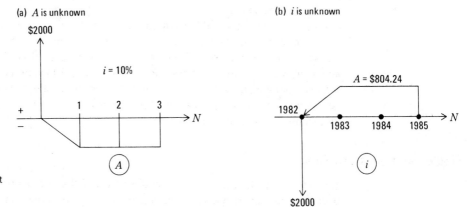

**FIGURE 3.2** Different
versions of cash flow
diagrams.

three equal payments are represented by a convenient convention that indicates a 3-year annuity in which the payment size $A$ is unknown. $A$ is circled to indicate the needed solution. The given interest rate ($i = 10$ percent) is entered in a conspicuous place, and the amount of the loan is placed on the arrow at time zero.

In Figure 3.2(b), numbered years are replaced with dates, and the size of $A$ is given. The problem is to find the interest rate that makes the annuity equivalent to the loan value; $i$ is circled. Sometimes it may clarify the situation to put in dashed lines for arrows that represent cash flows of unknown magnitude. This or a similar tactic is especially useful when a problem comprises several separate cash flow segments, each of which must be replaced by an equivalent value; these, in turn, are converted to a single sum representing all the segments.

The obvious requirements for cash flow diagraming are completeness, accuracy, and legibility. The measure of a successful diagram is that someone else can understand the problem fully from it. If it passes this test, you are unlikely to confuse yourself.

# CALCULATION OF TIME-VALUE EQUIVALENTS

The purpose of time-value calculations is to translate receipts and disbursements of various amounts occurring at various times to a cash flow pattern that assists an economic evaluation. The translation is essentially mechanical in the same fashion a vector is routinely decomposed into component forces; rules of geometry direct vector operations, and time-value relationships direct cash flow translations. Although errors in translation can arise from carelessness, mistakes due to incorrect problem formulations are the ones to guard against.

Cash flow diagrams assist problem formulation. They serve the same purpose as the free-body diagrams used to portray the effect of forces acting on a body. The intent is to isolate the factors pertinent to a problem and to display them clearly to observe what data are available and what calculations are needed.

The notable statements in a discounted cash flow problem are the interest elements: $P$, $F$, $A$, $N$, and $i$. Generally, three of the elements are known for each cash flow, and the problem entails solving for a fourth element. Several money-time translations may be required in one solution.

A variety of typical cash flow patterns are treated in the following pages. Examples are presented to put cash flow problems in a realistic setting, show different perspectives for the same type of problem, demonstrate the use of cash flow diagrams, and provide familiarity with the use of interest factors and tables. Although the examples all employ discrete compounding, the diagrams and solution formulations are equally applicable to continuous compounding. Specific applications of continuous interest factors are examined in the last section of this chapter.

## Single-Payment Cash Flow

Translation of a future amount to its present worth, or the reverse from present to future, has been demonstrated previously for both discrete and continuous compounding. Sometimes both present and future amounts are known, and the problem is to find the value of $i$ or $N$ that makes them equivalent.

---

### Example 3.1   Unknown Interest Rate
At what annual interest rate will $1000 invested today be worth $2000 in 9 years?

### Solution 3.1

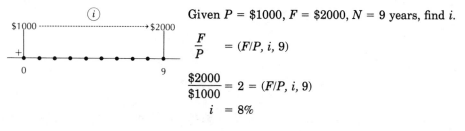

Given $P = \$1000$, $F = \$2000$, $N = 9$ years, find $i$.

$$\frac{F}{P} = (F/P, i, 9)$$

$$\frac{\$2000}{\$1000} = 2 = (F/P, i, 9)$$

$$i = 8\%$$

The interest rate $i$ is determined by locating the interest rate at which the single-payment compound-amount factor is equal to 2.0 at $N = 9$ (a reciprocal relationship using a present-worth factor could serve just as well). The numerical value of $i$ is found by leafing through the pages of interest rates and noting the appropriate factor values for the given number of periods.

---

It is usually necessary to interpolate from table values when $N$ or $i$ is unknown. The error introduced by linear interpolation is relatively insignificant for most practical applications. If the investment period for Example 3.1 had been 10 years instead of 9, the interest-rate calculation would have been

$$(F/P, i, 10) = \frac{F}{P} = \frac{\$2000}{\$1000} = 2.0$$

At $i = 7$ percent, $(F/P, 7, 10) = 1.9671$; at $i = 8$ percent, $(F/P, 8, 10) = 2.1589$. Then, by interpolation,

$$i = 0.07 + 0.01\,\frac{2.0000 - 1.9671}{2.1589 - 1.9671}$$

$$= 0.07 + 0.01\,\frac{0.0329}{0.1918}$$

$$= 0.07 + 0.0017 = 0.0717$$

or,

$$i \doteq 7.2\%$$

Most of the inconvenience of interpolation is avoided with calculators that can be programmed, or are preprogrammed, for the interest-factor formulas. Then it is a simple operation to punch in various values of the unknown element until matching values are obtained. Nonetheless, the mechanics of interpolation are presented because the origin of an element's value is more easily observed with numerical examples, and there may be occasions when the use of interest tables is unavoidable.

---

### Example 3.2  Unknown Number of Interest Periods

A loan of $1000 is made today under an agreement that $1400 will be received in payment some time in the future. When should the $1400 be received if the loan is to earn interest at a rate of 8 percent compounded quarterly?

### Solution 3.2

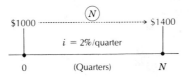

Given $P = \$1000$, $F = \$1400$, $i = r/m = 8\%/4 = 2\%$, find $N$ (in quarters).

$$\frac{F}{P} = \frac{\$1400}{\$1000} = 1.4 = (F/P, 2, N)$$

$N = 17$ quarters    or    4 years, 3 months

---

Example 3.2 is slightly deceptive because it involves a nominal interest rate. The problem is clarified by noting in the cash flow diagram that the time scale is in quarters of a year and that $i$ is given as the rate per quarter. The problem could also have been solved by converting the nominal rate to its equivalent effective interest rate,

$$i = \left(1 + \frac{0.08}{4}\right)^4 - 1 = 1.082 - 1 = 0.082$$

and solving the following equation by interpolation between the 8 percent and 9 percent interest tables and $N$ values between 4 and 5:

$$1.400 = (F/P, 8.2, N)$$
$$1.3604 + 0.2(1.4115 - 1.3604) = 1.3706 = (F/P, 8.2, 4)$$
$$1.4693 + 0.2(1.5386 - 1.4693) = 1.4831 = (F/P, 8.2, 5)$$

$$N = 4 + 1\,\frac{1.4000 - 1.3706}{1.4831 - 1.3706} = 4.265 \text{ years}$$

The result differs from 4 years, 3 months only by "round-off" errors in the interest factors.

## Multiple-Payment Cash Flows

Practical problems customarily involve both single payments and annuities. For instance, determining the equivalent present worth (cost) of owning a car for 3 years involves a series of payments to purchase the car and provide gas, repair, and maintenance costs at irregular intervals, and a single payment (receipt) when the car is sold. All these receipts and disbursements would be translated to "now" and summed to find the present worth—a single sum equivalent to ownership costs for 3 years.

## Example 3.3   More Compounding Periods than Payments

"Now" is June 30, 1982. Three payments of $500 each are to be received every 2 years starting 2 years from now and deposited in a bank where they will earn interest at 7 percent per year. How large will the bank account be on June 30, 1990?

### Solution 3.3

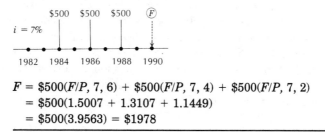

$F = \$500(F/P, 7, 6) + \$500(F/P, 7, 4) + \$500(F/P, 7, 2)$
  $= \$500(1.5007 + 1.3107 + 1.1449)$
  $= \$500(3.9563) = \$1978$

The equal payments in Example 3.3 do not constitute an ordinary annuity because there are fewer payments than compounding periods. Therefore, each payment must be translated individually to the 1990 date and added to the worth of the other payments at that date to obtain the equivalent future worth of all three payments.

## Example 3.4   Annuity with an Unknown $i$

A new machine that can be purchased for $8065 will annually reduce production costs by $2020. The machine will operate for 5 years, at which time it will have no resale value. What rate of return will be earned on the investment? (Alternative statement of the problem: At what interest rate will a cash flow of $2020 per year for 5 years equal a present value of $8065?)

### Solution 3.4

$$\frac{P}{A} = \frac{\$8065}{\$2020} = 3.993 = (P/A, i, 5)$$

$$i = 8\%$$

A series of payments made at the beginning instead of the end of each period is sometimes referred to as an *annuity due*. Rather than create a special factor for this annuity pattern, the series is divided into two parts. If the first payment is translated separately, the remaining payments fit the pattern for an ordinary annuity beginning at the time of the first payment. The present worth of the series is the sum of the first payment plus the product of one payment times the series present-worth factor, where $N$ is the number of payments minus 1.

## Example 3.5   Annuity Due

What is the present worth of a series of 15 year-end payments of $1000 each when the first payment is due today and the interest rate is 5 percent?

### Solution 3.5

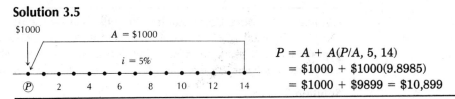

$P = A + A(P/A, 5, 14)$
$= \$1000 + \$1000(9.8985)$
$= \$1000 + \$9899 = \$10,899$

Another pattern for a series of payments, in which the first payment does not begin until some date later than the end of the first period, is called a *deferred annuity*. Like an annuity due, a deferred annuity is evaluated by dividing the time period into two parts. One portion is $N$, the number of payment periods, plus 1. This portion forms an ordinary annuity of $N$ periods. The second portion is the number of periods left after subtracting $N + 1$ periods. A solution results from determining the present worth of the ordinary annuity and then discounting this value through the deferred period.

---

### Example 3.6    Deferred Annuity

With interest at 6 percent, what is the worth on June 30, 1982, of a series of end-year payments of \$317.70 made on June 30 from 1987 through 1992?

### Solution 3.6

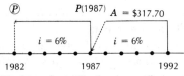

Starting from the known values of $A$, $i$, and $N$,

$P(1987) = A(P/A, 6, 5)$

$P(1987)$ becomes the $F$ value in calculating $P(1982)$:

$P(1982) = P(1987)(P/F, 6, 5)$

Collecting terms,

$P(1982) = A(P/A, 6, 5)(P/F, 6, 5)$
$= \$317.70(4.2123)(0.74726) = \$1000$

---

The results of Example 3.6 may be recognized as one of the equivalent outcomes presented without proof in Figure 2.1. Another of the outcomes from the same figure is shown in Figure 3.3.

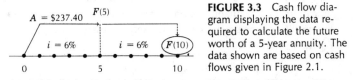

**FIGURE 3.3**   Cash flow diagram displaying the data required to calculate the future worth of a 5-year annuity. The data shown are based on cash flows given in Figure 2.1.

The value of the annuity after five payments of \$237.40 is labeled $F(5)$. By letting the end of the fifth year be "now," $F(5)$ is treated as a present value, and the compound-amount factor is used to find the future value at the end of year 10, or $F(10)$:

$F(5) = A(F/A, 6, 5)$ and $F(10) = F(5)(F/P, 6, 5)$
$F(10) = A(F/A, 6, 5)(F/P, 6, 5)$
$\qquad = \$237.40(5.6370)(1.3382) = \$1791$

## Example 3.7 Present Worth of an Arithmetic Gradient

A contract has been signed to lease a building at $20,000 per year with annual increases of $1500 for 8 years. Payments are to be made at the end of each year, starting 1 year from now. The prevailing interest rate is 7 percent. What lump sum paid today would be equivalent to the 8-year lease-payment plan?

### Solution 3.7

The base annuity $A'$ and the gradient $G$ per period are shown on the cash flow diagram.

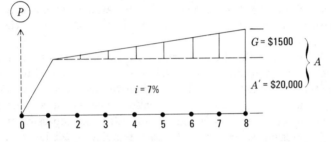

The first step in solving for the present worth of the lease-payment plan is to convert the increasing annual payments to a uniform series:

$A = A' + G(A/G, 7, 8) = \$20,000 + \$1500(3.1463)$
$\qquad\qquad\qquad\qquad = \$20,000 + \$4719.45 = \$24,719.45$

Then the annuity is translated to its present worth as

$P = A(P/A, 7, 8) = \$24,719.45(5.9712) = \$147,604.78$

which is the amount in today's dollars equivalent to the lease contract that provides yearly payments of $20,000 with annual increases of $1500 for 8 years.

More extensive economic situations often include both income and outlay. Such situations are evaluated by calculating the net outcome at a certain point in time. A cash flow diagram incorporates receipts and disbursements by displaying income above the time line and outlays below the line. Other payment categories can be handled similarly.

## Example 3.8 Income and Outlay

A boy is now 11 years old. On his fifth birthday he received a gift of $4000 from his grandparents which was invested in 10-year bonds bearing interest at 4 percent compounded semiannually. His parents plan to have $3000 available for the boy's nineteenth, twentieth, twenty-first, and twenty-second birthdays to help finance a college education. To assist the financing the grandparents' gift will be reinvested when the bonds mature. How much should the parents allocate to invest each year on the boy's twelfth through eighteenth birthdays to complete the education plan? All future investments will earn 6 percent annually.

### Solution 3.8

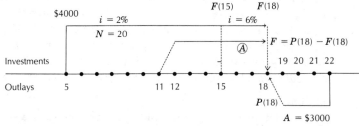

The cash-flow diagram for the problem is based on an evaluation date of the boy's eighteenth birthday. It would be equally valid to use any of his birthdays for the comparison date. The same value for the parents' payments, $A$, would result for any chosen date, but there is usually one time which reduces the number of required calculations.

As shown in the diagram, there are three payment plans involved: a series of outlays, a lump-sum investment, and a series of annual investments. After computing the difference between the amount available from the lump-sum investment and the amount required for the education expenses at a common date, the annual payment necessary to accumulate this difference can be determined.

The present worth of the education annuity on the boy's eighteenth birthday is

$$P(18) = A(P/A, 6, 4) = \$3000(3.4650) = \$10,395$$

The future worth of the grandparents' gift is a function of two investment rates: 2 percent per period for 20 periods (a nominal interest rate of 4 percent compounded semiannually for 10 years), followed by 6 percent per period for three periods:

$$F(18) = P(F/P, 2, 20)(F/P, 6, 3)$$
$$= \$4000(1.4859)(1.1910) = \$7079$$

The difference $F$ between the amount required and the amount available at year 18 is

$$F = P(18) - F(18) = \$10,395 - \$7079 = \$3316$$

which is the required future value for the series of $18 - 11 = 7$ payments of amount $A$ beginning on the boy's twelfth birthday:

$$A = F(A/F, 6, 7) = \$3316(0.11914) = \$395$$

# CALCULATIONS WITH CONTINUOUS INTEREST

In the discussion of nominal interest rates in Chapter 2, it was apparent that for a specific nominal rate, the effective interest rate gets larger as the compounding interval is shortened. The effective interest rate $i$ for a nominal interest rate of 18 percent ($r = 0.18$) compounded semiannually ($m = 2$) was shown to be

$$i = \left(1 + \frac{r}{m}\right)^m - 1 = \left(1 + \frac{0.18}{2}\right)^2 - 1 = 0.188 \qquad \text{or} \qquad 18.8\%$$

and that $i = e^r - 1$ when the interest periods are infinitesimally small. For the same 18 percent nominal interest compounded continuously,

$$i = e^{0.18} - 1 = 1.1972 - 1 = 0.1972 \qquad \text{or} \qquad 19.72\%$$

The result of using continuous compounding in place of discrete compounding is to increase the force of interest on the time value of money. A single payment earning continuous interest has a future value of

$$F = Pe^{rN}$$

where the continuous-interest compound factor $e^{rN}$ corresponds to the $(1 + i)^N$ used in the $F/P$ factor for discrete compounding.

---

### Example 3.9    Comparison of Continuous and Discrete Compounding
A sum of money doubles in size after 9 years when invested at 8 percent interest compounded annually:

$$F = P(1 + 0.08)^9$$
$$2P \doteq P(1.999)$$

At what rate of continuous compounding will an amount double in just half the time taken at the 8 percent effective rate?

### Solution 3.9
Given $F = 2P$ at $N = 9/2 = 4.5$ years. Substituting these values into the future-worth equation using continuous compounding gives

$$F = 2P = P(e^{rN}) \qquad \text{or} \qquad 2 = e^{4.5r}$$

The right-hand equation can be solved directly for $r$ to get $r = 15.4$ percent.

---

## Continuous-Compounding, Discrete Cash Flow

There are two versions of continuous interest. The *discrete cash flow* form applies continuous compounding to a payment whenever it is received, but the payment is assumed to be received in one lump sum. The other form assumes that cash flow is continuous. The future-worth formula $F = Pe^{rN}$ and its reciprocal, $P = Fe^{-rN}$, are discrete cash flows compounded continuously.

Continuous-compounding factors with *discrete payments* can be similarly developed from the end-of-period annuity formulas. First recall from the discussion of effective interest that $e^{rN}$ corresponds to $(1 + i)^N$, and that the effective interest rate is $i = e^r - 1$. Substitution of these expressions into the sinking-fund formula yields the fact that the discrete cash flow, end-of-period compounding, sinking-fund formula is equal to the discrete cash flow, continuous-compounding, *sinking-fund* formula when $i = e^r - 1$:

$$A = F \left[ \frac{i}{(1 + i)^N - 1} \right] = \left[ F \frac{e^r - 1}{e^{rN} - 1} \right]$$

and the reciprocal of the bracketed expression is the *series compound-amount factor* for continuous compounding.

By similar reasoning, the *capital-recovery* formula with continuous compounding and discrete payments is

$$A = P \left[ \frac{e^{rN} (e^r - 1)}{e^{rN} - 1} \right]$$

and the reciprocal of the bracketed expression is the continuous-compounding *series present-worth factor*.

In every formula the **A**, **F**, and **P** values resulting from computations using either end-of-period or continuous compounding are identical for discrete payments when the continuous interest rate is equivalent to the effective interest rate. This relationship is apparent when numbers are substituted into the sinking-fund formulas displayed above. Letting $i = 22.1$ percent, which corresponds to a nominal continuous interest rate of 20 percent ($0.221 = e^{0.2} - 1$), and applying the equivalent interest rates in the two sinking-fund formulas with $N = 2$, give

| *End-of-period compounding* | | *Continuous compounding* |
|---|---|---|
| $A = F \dfrac{0.221}{(1.221)^2 - 1}$ | $=$ | $F \dfrac{e^{0.2} - 1}{e^{(0.2)(2)} - 1}$ |
| $= F \dfrac{0.221}{1.491 - 1}$ | $=$ | $F \dfrac{1.221 - 1}{1.492 - 1}$ |
| $0.45$ | $=$ | $0.45$ |

This shows that the factors are equal when $i = e^r - 1$ and payments are discrete.

---

### Example 3.10   Continuous Compounding of a Discrete-Payment Annuity

Each year a single payment of $1766 is deposited in an account that earns 6 percent compounded continuously. What is the amount in the account immediately after the fifth payment?

**Solution 3.10**

Given $A = \$1766$, $r = 0.06$, and $N = 5$, $F$ is calculated as

$$F = A \frac{e^{rN} - 1}{e^r - 1} = \$1766 \frac{e^{(.06)(5)} - 1}{e^{(.06)} - 1}$$

$$= \$1766 \frac{1.3499 - 1}{1.0618 - 1} = \$1766(5.6618) = \$9999$$

This future worth is not notably higher than that earned by annual compounding of the same annuity

$$F = \$1766(F/A, 6, 5) = \$1766(5.6370) = \$9955$$

## Continuous-Compounding, Continuous Cash Flow

The other version of continuous compounding occurs when the *total payment for a period is received in continuous, small, equal payments during that period.* Letting $\overline{A}$ designate this total amount of each payment in the series, which continues for $N$ periods at interest rate $r$ per period, we find the future worth directly by integration as

$$F = \overline{A} \int_0^N e^{rt}\, dt = \overline{A} \left[ \frac{e^{rN} - 1}{r} \right]$$

The expression in brackets is called the *continuous-compounding series compound-amount factor* for continuous, uniform, payments.

Functional notations and formulas for the six basic continuous-compounding factors for continuous-flow payments are given in Table 3.1. The first two in the table are for a single continuous payment for one period, and the last four are annuity payments. Bars over the symbols for future, present, and annuity payments (respectively, $\overline{F}, \overline{P},$ and $\overline{A}$) represent the total amount accumulated from continuous small payments throughout each compounding duration.

**TABLE 3.1** Symbols and formulas for continuous compounding of a continuous flow. $\overline{F}$, $\overline{P}$, and $\overline{A}$ designate total amounts accumulated in small equal payments during one compounding period $N$ for $\overline{A}$, and over $N$ periods for $\overline{F}$ and $\overline{P}$. The continuous interest rate is $r$ per period.

| Functional Notation | Application Formula |
|---|---|
| $(F/\overline{P}, r\%, N)$ | $F = \overline{P}\, \dfrac{e^{rN}(e^r - 1)}{re^r}$ |
| $(P/\overline{F}, r\%, N)$ | $P = \overline{F}\, \dfrac{e^r - 1}{re^{rN}}$ |
| $(\overline{A}/F, r\%, N)$ | $\overline{A} = F\, \dfrac{r}{e^{rN} - 1}$ |
| $(F/\overline{A}, r\%, N)$ | $F = \overline{A}\, \dfrac{e^{rN} - 1}{r}$ |
| $(\overline{A}/P, r\%, N)$ | $\overline{A} = P\, \dfrac{re^{rN}}{e^{rN} - 1}$ |
| $(P/\overline{A}, r\%, N)$ | $P = \overline{A}\, \dfrac{e^{rN} - 1}{re^{rN}}$ |

The assumption of a continuous flow of disbursements and incomes throughout a year is rare as compared to the end-of-year payment pattern. However, the continuous-flow assumption is more revealing and applicable than continuous compounding of discrete payments because the main reason for using continuous interest in an economic evaluation is to determine the effects of continuous cash flows, not just the continuous interest on discrete payments. Consequently, tables are provided in Appendix C for continuous-compounding, continuous-flow interest factors. These factors follow the functional notations given in Table 3.1 and are applied to continuous cash flows according to the same logic and procedures that govern discrete compound-interest calculations.

---

### Example 3.11    Continuous Compounding of a Continuous-Payment Annuity

A savings plan offered by a company allows employees to set aside part of their daily wages and have them earn 6 percent compounded continuously. What annual amount withdrawn from pay will accumulate $10,000 in 5 years? (Alternative statement of the problem: What continuous-flow annual annuity will yeild a future value of $10,000 in 5 years when compounded continuously at 6 percent?)

### Solution 3.11

$$\overline{A} = F(\overline{A}/F, 6, 5) = F \frac{r}{e^{rN} - 1}$$

$$= F \frac{0.06}{e^{0.3} - 1} = \$10,000 \frac{0.06}{1.35 - 1}$$

$$= \$10,000(0.1714) = \$1714$$

The effect of continuous compounding of continuous flow can be judged by comparing Examples 3.10 and 3.11.

---

## Role of Continuous Compounding in Engineering Economic Studies

Some savings institutions advertise continuous compounding as an inducement to savers. The intent is to attract investors by paying higher effective interest than competitors while still adhering to the nominal interest rate set by regulation. This is an example of discrete continuous compounding.

Actual flows of funds in industry, minute-by-minute incoming receipts and outgoing disbursements, are essentially continuous. Since continuous cash flow closely approximates the pattern of business transactions, it would seem reasonable to compound that flow pattern in evaluating business proposals. It seldom is. Engineering economic studies primarily rely on discrete compounding because they typically focus on aggregate payments that are assumed to take place on specified dates. For instance, the gain or loss from owning an irregularly used machine is conventionally determined once a year from accounting records, and that summary figure is viewed as a single annual payment in evaluating the machine. Estimates of cash flow for the future use of a new machine would be even less precise than assessments of performance for existing machines; applying continuous compounding would add negligibly to the precision of the evaluation, even though cash flows are closer to being continuous than annual.

Discrete compounding is featured in this text because it is conceptually easier to grasp, provides adequate precision, and is the most widely applied method. Despite its lack of acceptance, continuous compounding is sometimes more appropriate, particularly when data show that the cash flow is indeed continuous. It is for these occasions that continuous-compounding, continuous cash flow calculations have been discussed. Furthermore, it is conceivable that continuous compounding may eventually be a prominent analytical tool for engineering economists.

# REVIEW EXERCISES AND DISCUSSIONS

**Exercise 1**   A manufacturing firm in a foreign country has agreed to pay $25,000 in royalties at the end of each year for the next 5 years for the use of a patented product design. If the payments are left with the foreign company, interest on the retained funds will be paid at an annual rate of 15 percent.

What total amount will be available in 5 years under these conditions?

How large would the uniform annual payments have to be if the patent owners insisted that a minimum of $175,000 must be accumulated in the account by the end of 5 years if they are to leave it with the company?

**Solution 1**   The annual payments form an annuity. Knowing that $A$ = $25,000 per period, $i$ = 15 percent per period, and there are five periods, the future worth $F$ is calculated as

$$F = A(F/A, 15, 5) = \$25,000(6.7423) = \$168,558$$

If the patent owners insisted on an accumulated value of $175,000, the five end-of-year royalty payments would have to be

$$A = F(A/F, 15, 5) = \$175,000(0.14832) = \$25,956$$

**Exercise 2**   The management of a wearing-apparel firm is considering a proposal from a consulting group to introduce a new method of training inexperienced sewing-machine operators. The consultants claim that their program will produce savings of $7000 per year over the planned 5-year life of the project. Immediate costs to implement the program are $12,000. Annual training expenses will be $4000. The company uses 6 percent annual interest for cost comparisons. Do the anticipated savings warrant the expense of hiring the training consultants?

**Solution 2**   Assuming that the costs and savings occur at the end of the year,

$A$ = annual savings − annual costs =$7000 − $4000 = $3000

For the proposal to be acceptable, the net return must be greater than the $12,000 initial cost. By translating the 5-year annuity to the present time, the initial cost and the present worth of savings $P$ are compared directly:

$$P = A(P/A, 6, 5) = \$3000(4.2123) = \$12,637$$

The indicated total net savings exceed the initial cost by

$12,637 − $12,000 = $637

which gives very little leeway for any error in cost or savings estimates.

The same conclusion results from a different approach with the same data. From the capital-recovery formula, the annual return on the gross savings $A$ required for 5 years to meet a current obligation of $12,000 is

$$A = P(A/P, 6, 5) = \$12,000(0.23740) = \$2849$$

Comparing the required return to the expected annual gross savings shows annual net savings of

$$\$3000 - \$2849 = \$151$$

---

**Exercise 3**    A very successful engineer plans to endow a chair of Engineering Economics at his alma mater. The endowment will last for 7 years at $20,000 per year, commencing 3 years from now. In addition, he wants to award annually a graduate Engineering Economist scholarship for the last 4 years of the endowment period. The 1-year scholarships will start at $5000 and increase by $500 each year. Funds for the endowment are to be provided by three equal payments starting 1 year from now, and the transfer to the university of a $90,000 bond the engineer owns that will mature in 6 years. How large will each of his payments be for the next 3 years to fund the Engineering Economics chair and scholarships, if all funds earn 7 percent interest?

**Solution 3**    Assuming the bond does not pay interest before its maturity and all university disbursements occur at the first of each funding year, the cash-flow diagram takes the pattern shown in Figure 3.4, where the engineer's investments are considered positive cash flows and the university's disbursements for the chair and scholarships are negative cash flows.

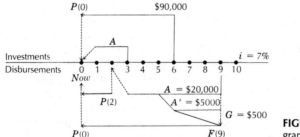

**FIGURE 3.4**    Cash flow diagram of multiple payments.

The future worth of the scholarships is calculated by determining the equivalent uniform annuity of the gradient and then its $F$ value:

$$F(9) = [A' + G(A/G, 7, 4)](F/A, 7, 4)$$
$$= [\$5000 + \$500(1.4153)](4.4398) = \$25,340.82$$

The equivalent cost at the end of the second year for the seven annual disbursements to the holder of the Engineering Economics chair is

$$P(2) = A(P/A, 7, 7) = \$20,000(5.3892) = \$107,784$$

The current present worth of the two annuities less the present worth of the bond is

$$P(0) = F(9)(P/F, 7, 9) + P(2)(P/F, 7, 2) - \$90,000(P/F, 7, 6)$$
$$= \$25,340.82(0.54394) + \$107,784(0.87344) - \$90,000(0.66635)$$
$$= \$13,774 + \$94,143 - \$59,972 = \$47,945$$

Then the annuity of three annual payments to get the endowment started is calculated as

$$A = P(0) \ (A/P, \ 7, \ 3) = \$47,948 \ (0.38105) = \$18,271$$

---

**Exercise 4**   The inventor of an automatic, coin-operated newstand, called "Automag," believes the economic evaluation of the invention should be based on continuous compounding of continuous cash flow because income from the Automag will be essentially continuous, and disbursements for services and purchases of materials (newspapers, paperbacks, news magazines, etc.) will occur regularly and frequently. The expected life of an Automag is 5 years. Annual income should average $132,000 at a good location, and total expenses for servicing materials are expected to average $105,000 per year. What initial price could be paid for an Automag (delivered and ready to operate) to allow a buyer to earn 15 percent on the investment if the income and disbursement estimates are accurate?

**Solution 4**   Net annual receipts from the Automag are expected to average $132,000 − $105,000 = $27,000. Since the cash flow is almost continuous, it is appropriate to apply continuous interest discounting. After recognition that the acceptable price of an Automag is the present-worth equivalent of a continuous annuity resulting from net receipts over 5 years, the value of the $P/\overline{A}$ factor at $r = 15$ percent and $N = 5$ is obtained from Appendix C:

$$P = \overline{A}(P/\overline{A}, \ 15, \ 5) = \$27,000(3.598) = \$97,146$$

---

# PROBLEMS

**3.1**   A company was incorporated for $50,000; at the end of 10 years the capital had increased to $90,000. What was the average rate of increase?                    *(6.052%)*

**3.2**   By the conditions of a will, a sum of $25,000 is left to a girl to be held in trust by her guardian until it amounts to $45,000. When will the girl receive the money if the fund is invested at 8 percent compounded quarterly?                    *(7.5 years)*

**3.3**   Find the amount of an annuity due of $240 per year payable annually for 5 years, money being worth 6 percent.                    *($1071.60)*

**3.4**   At the beginning of 10 successive years, a premium of $120 is paid on a certain insurance policy. What is the worth of the sum of these payments at the end of the tenth year if computed at 4 percent compound interest?                    *($1498.26)*

**3.5**   Find the present value of a deferred annuity of $500 per year for 12 years, deferred 6 years, if the current rate of interest is 5 percent annually.                    *($3306.91)*

**3.6**   What nominal interest, compounded quarterly, is required to provide a 6 percent effective interest rate? A 12 percent effective interest rate?                    *(11.49%)*

**3.7**   How long will it take for $1 to double in value (disregarding any change in the buying power of the dollar) if:
    **3.7a**   The interest rate is 10 percent compounded annually?                    *(7.3 years)*
    **3.7b**   The interest rate is 10 percent compounded semiannually?                    *(7.1 years)*
    **3.7c**   The interest rate is 10 percent ordinary simple interest?                    *(10 years)*

**3.8**    What is the future worth of each of the following investments?
**3.8a**    $6300 in 6 years at 15 percent compounded annually          *($14,572)*
**3.8b**    $2000 in 4 years at 4¼ percent compounded annually          *($2362)*
**3.8c**    $200 in 27 years at 6 percent compounded annually          *($964)*
**3.8d**    $4300 in 6 years at 7 percent compounded semiannually          *($6498)*
**3.8e**    $500 in 17 years at 9 percent compounded quarterly          *($2270)*

**3.9**    What annual interest rate increases an investment of $1400 to $2000 in 9 years?          *(4.037%)*

**3.10**    How many years will it take for the balance left in a savings account to increase from $1000 to $1500 if interest is received at a nominal rate of 6 percent compounded semiannually throughout the period?          *(6.86 years)*

*Solve Problems 3.11–3.18 with an annual interest rate of 5 percent.*

**3.11**    What amount must be invested today to secure a perpetual income of $6000 per year?          *($120,000)*

**3.12**    A present expenditure of $50,000 is justified by what annual saving for the next 12 years?          *($5641.50)*

**3.13**    What is the annual payment that will provide a sum of $20,000 in 20 years?          *($604.80)*

**3.14**    How much money can be loaned today on an agreement that $700 will be paid 6 years from now?          *($522.35)*

**3.15**    What payment can be made today to prevent a series of year-end expenses of $2800 lasting 15 years?          *($29,061.20)*

**3.16**    If the down payment on a piece of land is $7000 and the annual payments for 8 years are $2000 per year, what is the value of the land now?          *($19,926.20)*

**3.17**    What single payment 10 years from now is equivalent to a payment of $5500 in 3 years?          *($7738.50)*

**3.18**    If $12,000 must be accumulated by equal annual payments in 15 years, but the first end-of-year payment cannot be made until 4 years from now, how much will each payment be?          *($753.96)*

**3.19**    What semiannual cost beginning today is equivalent to spending lump sums of $2000 in 2 years, $4000 in 4 years, and $8000 in 8 years if the nominal interest rate is 8 percent compounded semiannually?          *($703.73)*

**3.20**    If investments of $2000 now, $2500 in 2 years, and $1000 in 4 years are all made at 4 percent effective interest, what will be the total in 10 years?          *($7647)*

**3.21**    An inventor has been offered $12,000 per year for the next 5 years and $6000 annually for the following 7 years for the exclusive rights to his invention. At what price could he afford to sell his rights to earn 10 percent, disregarding taxes?          *($63,625)*

**3.22**    A shady individual engaged in making small loans offers to lend $200 on a contract under which the borrower must pay $6.80 at the end of each week for 35 weeks in order to pay off the debt. What are:

**3.22a**  The nominal interest rate per annum?

**3.22b**  The effective interest rate?                                             *(67.8%)*

**3.23**  Three years ago a student borrowed $4000 to help pay for his education, agreeing to repay the loan in 100 payments at an interest rate of 12 percent compounded monthly. He has just received a bonus to play professional tennis and desires to pay the principal in a lump sum. How much does he owe?                                             *($2989)*

**3.24**  What annual expenditure for 10 years is equivalent to spending $1000 at the end of the first year, $2000 at the end of the fourth year, and $3000 at the end of the eighth year, if interest is at 8 percent per year?                                             *($598.62)*

*Solve Problems 3.25–3.29 using a continuous effective interest rate of 8 percent.*

**3.25**  What total amount must be invested each year to accumulate $10,000 in 10 years if cash flow is continuous?                                             *($664)*

**3.26**  What total amount invested continuously during the first year will be worth $10,000 in 10 years?                                             *($4812)*

**3.27**  What is the value of $A$ in Problem 3.25 if the cash flow is in discrete payments?                                             *($690)*

**3.28**  How long will it take a $10,000 single payment to double in amount? *(9 years)*

**3.29**  Continue the comparison in Problem 2.10 by finding the compound amount of $100 for 5 years. Also compare the answer to Problem 3.5 under the assumptions that:

**3.29a**  Cash flow is continuous.

**3.29b**  Cash flow is discrete.

**3.30**  If the population of a certain suburb is 29,000 in 1979 and the average annual rate of increase is estimated at 7 percent, what will its population be in 1989, if the growth rate remains constant?

**3.31**  Derive the equation for calculating the future worth of a series of discrete payments when interest is compounded continuously. Start from the expression

$$F = A + Ae^r + Ae^{2r} + \cdots + Ae^{(n-2)r} + Ae^{(n-1)r}$$

and follow the procedure used in developing the sinking-fund factor for end-of-period compounding.

**3.32**  Check the annual payments calculated for the engineer's endowment of an Engineering Economics chair in Review Exercise 3 to see whether they are adequate to cover the annual disbursement to the recipient of the chair, $20,000 payable at the first of each year starting on the day the final payment is received from the engineer.

**3.33**  Net receipts from a continuously producing oil well add up to $120,000 over 1 year. What is the present worth of the well if it maintains steady output until it runs dry in 8 years, if $r = 10$ percent?

**3.34**  A person owes debts of $3380 due in 4 years, with annual interest included at 9 percent, and $1200 plus interest due in 2 years on which the interest charge is 10 percent compounded annually. She now wishes to discharge these debts with two equal payments payable 1 and 2 years from now. What is the value of the installments if money is now worth 6 percent?

**3.35**  An orchard will come into full bearing in 6 years and is expected to yield a net income of $30,000 per annum. If it can be expected to maintain a constant average for 20 years, what is an equitable cash value for the orchard today if money is worth 8 percent?

**3.36**  A beachcomber bought a dune buggy, paying $1000 in cash and agreeing to pay $500 every 6 months for 3 years. As she was driving her buggy down the beach one day, she spotted a bottle that held five moldy but cashable $500 bills. She had not yet made her first semiannual installment for the dune buggy. When should she make a payment of $2500 to discharge her obligation for the purchase in a lump-sum settlement, if the interest rate is 12 percent compounded semiannually?

**3.37**  A family is planning to buy a vacation cabin for $19,000. They intend to keep the cabin for 6 years and expect the annual upkeep and taxes to amount to $900 per year. Without any major repairs, the cabin should have a resale price of $16,000. What is the equivalent annual cost of owning the cabin if the family's acceptable interest rate is 6 percent?

**3.38**  The family depicted in Problem 3.37 could also do some renovations on the cabin during their vacation periods which would increase the resale value to $26,000. How much could they afford to invest in materials each year if they hope to receive $500 per year for their labor?

**3.39**  Maintenance records of a certain type of machine indicate that the first-year maintenance cost of $80 increases by $30 per year over the 10-year replacement period of the machine. Answer the following, if the maintenance cost is considered to occur at the end of the year and the firm's interest rate is 12 percent:

**3.39a**  What equal annual payments could the firm make to a service organization to carry out the maintenance for 20 machines?

**3.39b**  How much additional could be paid for a new type of machine with the same service life that required no maintenance during its life?

**3.40**  The village hotshot borrowed $4000 to buy a chrome-plated peanut stand. He agreed to pay the loan back in 45 equal payments at 18 percent interest compounded monthly. A year after he took out the loan, he asked you to calculate how much of the $4000 debt he had paid off. Determine not only how much he has paid on the principal, but also how much interest he has paid so far.

**3.41**  A postal clerk wants to accumulate $20,000 in order to take a year's vacation 10 years from now. She now has $6000 in savings certificates which earn interest at 6 percent compounded semiannually. She plans to invest an equal amount each year in an account that earns 6 percent annual interest. How large should this amount be to give her $20,000 in 10 years when it is combined with the future value of the savings certificates?

**3.42**  The postal clerk in Problem 3.41 figures that in addition to the annuity calculated to give her $20,000 in 10 years, she will also be able to save part of her annual raises in pay. If the portion saved increases by $300 each year starting at the end of the second year from now (no additional increment is possible at the end of this year), how much extra money will she have when she is ready to take her year's vacation?

**3.43**  A lender offers loans under the following conditions: The total amount of interest owed is the difference between the future worth and the present worth of the loan, $I = P(F/P, i, N) - P$. This amount $I$ is then subtracted from the amount given to the borrower. That is, amount $P$ is borrowed, but only $P - I$ is received from the lender. If the interest rate used in the calculation is 9 percent and the duration of the loan is 3 years, what effective interest is charged?

**3.44** Office equipment can be purchased for $6000 cash or a down payment of $1000 followed by 24 end-of-month payments of $220 each. At what effective interest rate are these terms equivalent?

**3.45** If you invest $1000 at 10 percent compounded annually for the same length of time it takes an investment to triple in value at 12 percent simple interest, how much will you have?

**3.46** Assume that you sold property today for $2421 (net value), and that you had purchased the property 4 years ago with $2000 withdrawn from your savings account. During the 4-year period your savings would have earned 6 percent compounded quarterly. For a comparison of the investments, calculate the nominal interest rate received from your stock purchase.

**3.47** Forty monthly payments of $200 apiece are needed to repay a loan for which interest charges are 12 percent compounded monthly. What percentage of the amount borrowed has been repaid by the time the thirtieth payment is made?

**3.48** After taking an engineering economics course, an optimist decides she wants to be rich and that the way to do it is to make use of the earning power of money. If she is to be precisely a millionaire on her sixtieth birthday and she expects to start her millionaire-making plan on her twenty-second birthday, how much will she have to deposit on each birthday through her fifty-ninth (including her twenty-second), if her investment can earn 15 percent annually?

**3.49** Joshua Jones was born on January 1, 1899. On that day his grandfather deposited $1000 in his name in an account that paid 7 percent ordinary simple interest. Joshua graduated from high school on June 30, 1916. How much was in his account, assuming no withdrawals were made?

**3.50** Joshua had a monumental coming-of-age party, and when he awakened he found that he had volunteered for Navy service on his eighteenth birthday. While in the Navy for 28 months he had $10 per month deducted from his pay and deposited in a bank that paid interest at the rate of 6 percent compounded monthly. How much did he have in the bank when he was discharged from the Navy?

**3.51** Joshua used his savings, mustering-out pay, and other earnings to buy a business for $1500. It tripled in value by the time he sold it in 3 years. What nominal interest rate, compounded quarterly, did his investment earn?

**3.52** On his thirtieth birthday, Joshua designed a 10-year savings plan to produce $25,000 on his fortieth birthday. The first payment of $1500 was made on his thirty-first birthday. He enlarged each of the remaining 9 payments by an equal, increasing increment each year. The savings earned 8 percent compounded annually. How large was the increase each year?

**3.53** In 1942, Joshua bought a "war bond." It cost $18.75 and could be cashed in for $25 after 10 years. What interest rate was earned?

**3.54**   By his fifty-fifth birthday, Joshua had accumulated $75,000. He invested it in a 10-year bond that earned 9 percent compounded annually. He planned to retire at age 65 and to have enough saved so that he could draw out $25,000 from his savings each year for the next 15 years, starting on his sixty-sixth birthday. What equal payments into a savings account that paid annual interest at 7 percent did he have to make, starting on his fifty-fifth birthday with the last payment made on his sixty-fifth birthday, to fund his retirement? The amount accumulated, including the maturity value of the bond (first cost plus interest), will also earn 7 percent during the retirement period.

# EXTENSION

**3A *More Payments than Compounding Periods*** Many banks and financial institutions calculate the interest earned on savings accounts by applying the stated interest rate to the *minimum balance* maintained in the account during the interest period. This means that funds deposited during the interest period and funds withdrawn during the period receive no interest credit. Sometimes a grace period is allowed for the first 10 days of an interest period; deposits made during the grace period are considered to have been in the account for the full interest period.

A procedure that is somewhat the reverse of the interest-payment procedure is used to determine how much is owed on loans in which the balance changes between loan-charge calculations. The formulas used to determine the amount owed on credit account make a major difference in the financing charge. There are two basic methods of computing the interest owed on "revolving" accounts such as bank credit cards or charge accounts issued by stores. Actual practices and interest rates charged vary among lending institutions and the provinces within which they operate.

The first is called the *adjusted-balance* method. An example of how it works is as follows: Suppose you charge a purchase for $200 on March 1, and the billing date for your account is March 2. You are given 25 days from the billing date to pay your full bill without incurring any interest charges. If the bill is not paid in full, you are charged interest on the unpaid portion figured from the billing date. Assume you pay $100 on March 24, leaving a balance due of $100. On your April bill you will be charged interest, on the adjusted balance, which amounts to ($200 − $100)(0.015) = $1.50, if the monthly interest rate is 1½ percent.

The second method is the *average-daily-balance* system that works as follows: If the full bill is not paid in the 25-day grace period, then the purchase of $200 on March 1 and the $200 payment on March 24 with the billing date of March 2 are interpreted to mean that you owed $200 from March 1 to March 24 and $200 from the latter date until the next billing on April 2. That is 22 days at $200 and 9 days at $200, which result in

$$\text{Average daily balance} = \frac{22(\$200) - 9(\$100)}{31} = \$170.97$$

Again assuming an interest rate of 1½ percent per month,

Interest owed = $170.97 × 0.015 = $2.56

which is $2.56 − $1.50 = $1.06 greater than the interest charge using the adjusted-balance method, a significant difference.

Thus, with the adjusted-balance method, the interest charges are determined solely by the amount you pay. With the average-daily-balance system, the charges are also determined by when in the billing period you pay; the earlier you pay, the lower your interest. If you pay your entire bill within the first 25 days of the billing period, there is no interest charge in either system.

## QUESTIONS

**3A.1**  How much interest is credited to the account for the cash flow displayed in Figure 3.5, if the bank pays 8 percent compounded quarterly and a grace period is allowed during the first 10 days of each quarter?                    *($65.39 for the year)*

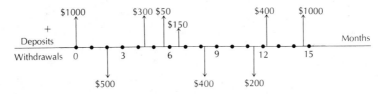

**FIGURE 3.5**

**3A.2**  Let interest be 18 percent compounded monthly, and the billing date be the second day of each month. Compare the total interest charges for April, May, and June, using both the adjusted-balance and average-daily-balance methods, for the following purchases on credit (−) and repayments (+):

| March 1  | −$200 | April 29 | −300 |
| March 24 | +100  | May 1    | +200 |
| March 29 | −300  | May 7    | −150 |
| April 1  | +200  | May 15   | +100 |
| April 14 | −150  | May 21   | −50  |
| April 21 | +200  | June 1   | +350 |

# CHAPTER 4

# PRESENT-WORTH COMPARISONS

OVERVIEW

A student once answered the question, "What is the present worth?" as, "The value the person receiving the present attaches to it." Though hardly apropos for an engineering economics class, the answer deserves at least some credit because it translates anticipation of future pleasures to the present's present worth. The answer even implies interest, albeit a personal value rather than a rate of return. This chapter answers "What is the present worth?" by presenting the reasons for and methods of calculating the equivalent present value of cash flow.

Present-worth comparisons are made only between coterminated proposals, to assure equivalent outcomes. Cotermination means that the lives of the involved assets end at the same time. When assets have unequal lives, the time horizon for an analysis can be set by a common multiple of asset lives or by a study period which ends with the disposal of all assets.

Net present worth, the difference between the present worths of benefits and cost, is the most widely used present-worth (PW) model. A capitalized cost model is used when an asset is assumed to have infinite life. Other PW models include deferred investments and valuation of property, stocks, and bonds.

Many economists prefer a present-worth analysis because it reveals the sum in today's dollars that is equivalent to a future cash flow stream, and PW models are less subject to misinterpretation. It is therefore important to become familiar with the assumptions upon which PW calculations are based and the types of comparisons that can be made.

# CONDITIONS FOR PRESENT-WORTH COMPARISONS

The previous chapter on discounted cash flow calculations introduced present-worth comparisons. A present worth resulted from each calculation of $P$. In this chapter, the present worth of a cash flow stream is distinguished by the designation PW—the present worth of receipts and disbursements associated with a particular course of action. Each alternative is thus represented by a PW, a measure of its economic merit.

The ingredients of a present-worth comparison are the amount (in dollars) and timing $(N)$ of cash flow, and the interest rate $i$ at which the flow is discounted. Interest factors are the obvious recipes for combining the ingredients, but there are many considerations that affect both the ingredients and the recipes for present-worth comparisons. Listed below are assumptions used in this and the next two chapters in introducing the basic comparison methods; also indicated are topics from subsequent chapters which make comparisons less restrictive.

1  *Cash flows are known.* The accuracy of cash flow estimates are always suspect because future developments cannot be anticipated completely. Transactions that occur now, at time zero, should be accurate, but future flows become less distinct as the time horizon is extended. Ways to evaluate riskier cash flows are discussed in Chapters 17 and 18.

2  *Cash flows are in constant-value dollars.* The buying power of money is assumed to remain unchanged during the study period. Ways to include the effect of inflation are presented in Chapter 13.

3  *The interest rate is known.* Different interest rates have a significant effect on the magnitude of the calculated present worth, as illustrated in Figure 4.1. The rate of return $i$ required by an organization is a function of its cost of capital, attitude toward risk, and investment policy. Alternative courses of action for the same proposal are normally compared using the same interest rate, but different proposals may be evaluated at different required rates of return. The sensitivity of interest rates is explored in Chapter 14.

4  *Comparisons are made with before-tax cash flows.* Inclusion of income taxes greatly expands the calculation effort for a comparison, and correspondingly increases reality. Since the workings of comparison methods are featured here and in the next few chapters, inclusion of income taxes is delayed until Chapter 12.

5  *Comparisons do not include intangible considerations.* "Intangibles" are difficult-to-quantify factors that pertain to a certain situation. For instance, the "impression" created by a design is an intangible factor in evaluating that design and an important one for marketing, but it would not be included in a present-worth comparison unless its economic consequence could be reasonably estimated (if a dollar value can be assigned, a factor is no longer intangible). Ways to include intangible factors in the decision-making process are considered in Chapter 19.

6  *Comparisons do not include consideration of the availability of funds to implement alternatives.* It is explicitly assumed that funds will be found to finance a course of action if its benefits are large enough. Although financing is not a direct input for

computations, the output computed can be appraised with respect to available funding. For instance, an old, inefficient machine could be kept in operation because there appears to be insufficient capital available in the organization to afford a replacement, but an engineering economic analysis might point out that the savings from replacing the bungling machine would be so great that the organization cannot afford not to find funds for a replacement. Such capital-budgeting considerations are examined in Chapter 9.

### Example 4.1    Present Worth by the 72-Rule

The present worth of a future amount drops off rapidly as the time between "now" and "then" increases, particularly at higher interest rates. The pattern of this decrease in present value is shown in Figure 4.1. Examination of the curves supports an interesting rule of thumb: the *72-rule* indicates the number of years $N^*$ over which a future value loses half its present worth at the annually compounded interest rate $i$:

*72-rule*:   $N^* = \dfrac{72}{i}$

Another way to view the 72-rule is that $(1 + i)^N$ doubles about every $N^*$ years. Thus, as is apparent in Figure 4.1, the present worth is halved in about 15 years at $i = 5$ percent, 7 years at $i = 10$ percent, and 4 years at $i = 20$ percent.

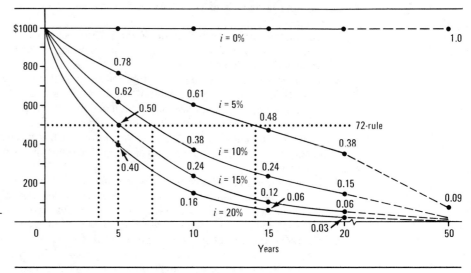

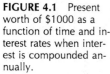

**FIGURE 4.1**   Present worth of $1000 as a function of time and interest rates when interest is compounded annually.

## BASIC PRESENT-WORTH COMPARISON PATTERNS

The present worth of a cash flow over time is its value today, usually represented as time zero in a cash flow diagram. Two general patterns are apparent in present-worth calculations.

## Present-Worth Equivalence

One pattern determines the present-worth equivalence of a series of future transactions. The purpose is to secure one figure that represents all the transactions. This figure can then be compared to a corresponding figure that represents transactions from a competing alternative, or it can be compared to the alternative of doing nothing. A *do-nothing alternative* is always possible, even if it results only from procrastination. More often there is a "go, no-go" situation where each alternative is selectively weighted to decide whether it is worth exercising. For instance, a series of expenses that will occur in the future can be discounted to obtain its PW, and then a decision can be made as to whether an investment of the PW amount should be made *now* to avoid the expenses. Similar reasoning guides the equivalence comparison in Example 4.2.

---

### Example 4.2   Equivalent PW of an Alternative

An investor can make three annual payments of $15,000, starting today, which will generate receipts of $10,000 at the end of year 4 and will increase annually by $2500 for the following 4 years. If the investor can earn a rate of return of 10 percent on alternative 8-year investments, is this alternative attractive?

### Solution 4.2

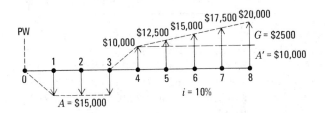

From the cash flow diagram, it is apparent that the receipts and disbursements each constitute an annuity, one positive and the other negative. Both are discounted to time zero at 10 percent:

PW = −$15,000(*P/A*, 10, 3) + [$10,000 + $2500(*A/G*, 10, 5)](*P/A*, 10, 5)(*P/F*, 10,3)

= −$15,000(2.4868) + [$10,000 + $2500(1.8100)](3.7907)(0.75132)

= −$37,302 + $41,368 = $4066

The interpretation of the $4066 present worth is that the transactions provide a return of 10 percent on the investment *plus* a sum of $4066. This investment is therefore preferable to one that would return exactly 10 percent over 8 years.

---

It is common practice to drop the negative sign when cash flow is predominately composed of costs. The calculated PW is then called the present worth of costs. This is purely a convention of convenience and is unlikely to cause confusion as long as the alternatives in a comparison are treated in the same way (see Example 4.6).

## Net Present Worth

The second general pattern for PW calculations has an initial outlay at time zero followed by a series of receipts and disbursements. This is the most frequently encountered pattern, and it leads to the fundamental relationship

Net present worth = PW(benefits) − PW(cost)

In choosing between alternatives, the criterion is to select the one that maximizes net present worth, or, simply, the one that yields the larger positive PW. A negative PW means the alternative does not satisfy the rate-of-return requirement. Applications of net present worth to benefits and costs of public projects are developed in Chapter 10. A typical industrial application is given in Example 4.3.

### Example 4.3   Net Present-Worth Comparison

Two devices are available to perform a necessary function for 3 years. The initial cost (negative) for each device at time zero and subsequent annual savings (positive) produced by the device are shown below. The required interest rate is 8 percent.

| Year | 0 | 1 | 2 | 3 |
|------|-----|-----|-----|-----|
| Device $A$ | −$9,000 | $4500 | $4500 | $4500 |
| Device $B$ | −$14,500 | $6000 | $6000 | $8000 |

### Solution 4.3

PW(device $A$) = −$9000 + $4500(P/A, 8, 3)
$\qquad$ = −$9000 + $4500(2.5770) = $2597
PW(device $B$) = −$14,500 + $6000(P/A, 8, 2) + $8000(P/F, 8, 3)
$\qquad$ = −$14,500 + $6000(1.7832) + $8000(0.79383)
$\qquad$ = $2594

Both alternatives meet the minimum acceptable rate of return, because both are positive, and their net present worths are almost equal. In this case other considerations must be involved in the choice, such as the availability of the extra $5500 needed to purchase device $B$.

In Examples 4.2 and 4.3 the alternatives were naturally coterminated. That is, in Example 4.2 the investment periods were identical and in Example 4.3 the lives of the two devices were equal. When the lives of assets being compared are unequal, special procedures must be applied to coterminate the analysis periods.

## COMPARISON OF ASSETS THAT HAVE UNEQUAL LIVES

The utilization of present-worth comparisons for *coterminated projects* implies that the lives involved have a common endpoint. The necessity for cotermination is readily apparent in considering a familiar decision such as the choice between paying $30 for a 3-year subscription to a magazine and paying $40 for a 5-year subscription to the same publication. A simple comparison of $30 to $40 for a subscription is inaccurate, because the extra $10 buys two more years of issues. *Alternatives must be compared on the basis of equivalent outcomes.*

Several variations have been proposed to accommodate present-worth comparisons of unequal-life assets.* Two prominent methods are described below.

1   *Common-multiple method.* Alternatives are coterminated by selecting an analysis period that spans a common multiple of the lives of involved assets. For instance, if assets had lives of 2, 3, 4, and 6 years, the least common multiple is 12 years, which means the asset with a life of 2 years would be replaced 6 times during the analysis period. The assets with the 3-, 4-, and 6-year lives would be replaced 4, 3, and 2 times, respectively.

   Legitimate use of a least common multiple of lives depends on the validity of the assumption that assets will be repeatedly replaced by successors having identical cost characteristics. This assumption is more often reasonable when the least common multiple is small. Then there is less likelihood that a technologically better asset will become available during the analysis period.

2   *Study-period method.* A more justifiable analysis is based on a specified duration that corresponds to the length of a project or the period of time the assets are expected to be in service. An appropriate study period reflects the replacement circumstances. Some of the possibilities are to set the study period as the length of

- *The shortest life of all competing alternatives*—a protection against technological obsolescence
- *The known duration of required service*—a project philosophy in which each new undertaking is considered to start with new assets, continue to use like replacements, and dispose of used assets when the project is completed
- *The time before a better replacement becomes available*—an attempt to minimize cost by purposely upgrading assets as improvements are developed

A study-period comparison presumes that all assets will be disposed of at the end of the time period. Therefore it is usually necessary to estimate the income that can be realized from the sale of an asset which can still provide useful service. This *salvage value* can be established somewhat arbitrarily by prorating the investment in the asset over its normal service life and then calculating the size of the unrecovered amount at the time of its disposal. A better estimate is obtained when it is possible to accurately appraise an asset's market value at the end of the study period. The most precise study would result from also having explicit knowledge of operating costs as a function of the asset's age and future capital costs for each successor. These conditions are explored more completely in Chapter 8.

---

## Example 4.4   PW Comparisons of Alternatives with Unequal Economic Lives

Assets $A1$ and $A2$ have the capability of satisfactorily performing the required function. $A2$ has an initial cost of $3200 and an expected salvage value of $400 at the

---

*D. J. Kulonda, "Replacement Analysis with Unequal Lives," *Engineering Economist*, Spring, 1978.

end of its 4-year economic life. Asset $A1$ costs $900 less initially, with an economic life 1 year shorter than that of $A2$, but it has no salvage value and its annual operating costs exceed those of $A2$ by $250. When the required rate of return is 15 percent, which alternative is preferred when compared by:

**a**   The least common-multiple method
**b**   A 2-year study period (assuming the assets are needed for only 2 years)

### Solution 4.4a

The least common-multiple method is based on the assumption that assets will be replaced by identical models possessing the same costs. Equivalent service results from comparing costs over a period divisible evenly by the economic lives of the alternatives; in this case the least common multiple is 12 years.

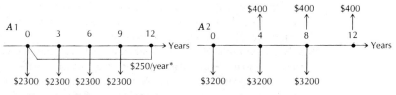

*Additional annual cost more than $A2$.

$$PW(A1) = -\$2300 - \$2300(P/F, 15, 3) - \$2300(P/F, 15, 6) - \$2300(P/F, 15, 9)$$
$$-\$250(P/A, 15, 12)$$
$$= -\$2300 - \$2300(0.65752) - \$2300(0.43233) - \$2300(0.28426)$$
$$-\$250(5.4206) = -\$6816$$
$$PW(A2) = -\$3200 - \$2800(P/F, 15, 4) - \$2800(P/F, 15, 12) + \$400(P/F, 15, 12)$$
$$= -\$3200 - \$2800(0.57175) - \$2800(0.3269) + \$400(0.18691) = -\$5642$$

The present-worth advantage of $A2$ over $A1$ for 12 years of service is $6816 $ - $ $5642 = $1174.

### Solution 4.4b

A service-period comparison is utilized when a limited period of ownership of assets is set by specific operational requirements. A 2-year study period for $A1$ and $A2$ indicates that the service required from either asset will be needed only 2 years, and it will be disposed of at that time. If possible, estimates of the worth of assets at the end of the study period should be secured. These salvage values may be quite large when the service period is only a small fraction of the economic life. When it is difficult to secure reliable estimates of worth after use during the ownership period, minimum resale levels can be calculated to make the alternatives equivalent. Then only a judgment is needed as to whether the market value will be above or below the minimum level.

For instance, assuming $S = 0$ for alternatives $A1$ and $A2$ after 2 years of service,

$$PW(A1) = -\$2300 - \$250(P/A, 15, 2) = -\$2300 - \$250(1.6257)$$
$$= -\$2707$$
$$PW(A2) = -\$3200$$

show that $A1$ has the lower present worth of costs for the 2-year service period. The salvage value for $A2$ that would make $PW(A1) = PW(A2)$ is

$$\$2707 = \$3200 - S(P/F, 15, 2)$$

$$S = \frac{\$3200 - \$2707}{(P/F, 15, 2)} = \frac{\$493}{0.75614} = \$652$$

which means that $A2$ is preferred to $A1$ when the resale value of $A2$ at the end of 2 years is more than \$652 greater than the resale value of $A1$ at the same time. The advantage of calculating this *aspiration level* is to avoid making an estimate of $S$; only a judgment is required about whether $S$ will exceed a certain amount, the aspiration value, which is \$652 in this case.

# COMPARISON OF ASSETS ASSUMED TO HAVE INFINITE LIFE

The sum of first cost plus the present worth of disbursements assumed to last forever is called a *capitalized cost*. This type of evaluation is essentially limited to long-lived assets. It is not used as extensively as it once was, but it is still favored by some for studies of dams, railway rights of way, tunnels, and similar structures which provide extended service.

The calculation of capitalized cost is conducted like a present-worth comparison, where $N$ equals infinity. This makes the analysis very sensitive to the selected rate of return. Like all present-worth calculations, the final figure is usually an impressive amount. As such, it could appear discouragingly high unless properly interpreted. Expressed as a formula,

Capitalized worth $= P + \dfrac{A}{i}$

where $A$ is the uniform difference between annual receipts and disbursements. When there is no revenue, the formula becomes

Capitalized cost $= P + \dfrac{\text{disbursements}}{i}$

---

### Example 4.5   An Asset that Lasts Forever

A \$500,000 gift was bequeathed to a city for the construction and continued upkeep of a music hall. Annual maintenance for a hall is estimated at \$15,000. In addition, \$25,000 will be needed every 10 years for painting and major repairs. How much will be left for the initial construction costs after funds are allocated for perpetual upkeep? Deposited funds can earn 6 percent annual interest, and the returns are not subject to taxes.

### Solution 4.5

The total capitalized cost is known to be \$500,000. From the capitalized-cost formula,

First cost $=$ capitalized cost $- \dfrac{\text{annual disbursements}}{i}$

The annual disbursements are $15,000 for maintenance plus the annual payments necessary to accumulate $25,000 every 10 years. The funds will earn interest at 6 percent, so we have

$$\text{First cost} = \$500,000 - \frac{\$15,000 + \$25,000(A/F, 6, 10)}{0.06}$$

$$= \$500,000 - \frac{\$15,000 + \$25,000(0.07587)}{0.06}$$

$$= \$500,000 - \$281,613 = \$218,387$$

which means that the interest earned on the amount left after allowing $218,387 for construction will cover all the anticipated upkeep indefinitely, provided the interest rate continues at 6 percent or more.

## COMPARISON OF DEFERRED INVESTMENTS

An occupational hazard for engineers is the habitual appeal to "get it done today, or preferably yesterday." The accustomed response to such an appeal is a workable solution that admittedly may not be the most economical long-run course of action. But keeping an operation going with a less-than-optimum solution is often less costly than the wait caused by a search for something better. For instance, suppose flooding at a construction site was the provocation for an engineer to remedy the situation quickly. An emergency purchase and installation of a pump plus sandbags for revetments cost $4000. The pumping facility was used off and on during the 2-year construction project for a total cost discounted to the time of purchase (assuming no salvage value and $i = 12$ percent) of

| | |
|---|---|
| First cost of pump and revetment | $4000 |
| Pumping cost and maintenance ($460/year): | |
| $460(P/A, 12, 2) = \$460(1.690)$ | 770 |
| PW of emergency pumping operation | $4770 |

A post-project review shows that a smaller pump could have been purchased to perform the same work adequately at

| | |
|---|---|
| First cost of smaller pump and revetment | $3100 |
| Pumping cost and maintenance ($640/year): | |
| $640(P/A, 12, 2) = \$640(1.690)$ | 1082 |
| PW of a lower-cost solution to flooding | $4182 |

However, if it had taken only a week longer to select and get delivery of the lower-cost pump, it is likely that the cost of 7 days of flooding would have exceeded the $4770 − $4182 = $588 potential saving.

A more typical analysis of deferred investments is to determine the timing of capital expenditures to meet anticipated activity increases. Piecemeal additions to existing capacity, infrequently of an emergency nature, almost promise to be an inefficient expansion program. It is a fine example of suboptimization due to shortsightedness. A planning horizon should extend far enough into the future to accommodate growth.

Designs to accommodate growth usually involve the question of whether to acquire a full-size facility now and absorb the temporary cost of unused assets, or to acquire a smaller facility with a later addition and accept the extra cost of duplicated effort and dislocation inconvenience. For a given capacity, one large facility inherently has a lower-per-unit cost because it is designed specifically for that level of operation, but it increases the chance of technical obsolescence and idleness, owing to changing future conditions. The economic analysis of a deferred addition is usually conducted by a present-worth comparison of the options.

---

### Example 4.6   Immediate and Deferred Investments for Identical Capacity

A small novelty manufacturing company needs to acquire storage space in order to reduce production costs by stabilizing employment. Ninety percent of the products produced are sold during the Christmas holiday season. A resource utilization study has shown that producing at a constant rate during the year and storing output will reduce the overall manufacturing costs.

The products produced by the novelty company have been well received, and sales have increased each year. Increased capacity will be needed in the future, and two alternatives have been identified. A large warehouse with sufficient space to meet all needs for 10 years can be leased for that period at $23,000 per year. Since there is some doubt about how much business will increase in the future, and the company is reluctant to go into debt deep enough to build a warehouse as large as the one available for leasing, the other feasible alternative is to build a small warehouse now for $110,000 and make an addition to it in 3 years for $50,000. Annual costs for taxes, insurance, maintenance, and repairs are expected to be $1000 for the first 3 years and $2000 for the next 7 years. The added-to warehouse should have a resale value of $50,000 in 10 years. Based on a study period equal to the lease contract and a 12 percent cost for capital, which alternative is preferable?

### Solution 4.6

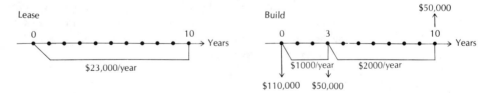

Where costs are considered to be positive,

$$\text{PW(lease)} = \$23{,}000(P/A,\ 12,\ 10) = \$23{,}000(5.6502) = \$129{,}955$$

$$\text{PW(build and add)} = \$110{,}000 + \$50{,}000(P/F,\ 12,\ 3) - \$50{,}000(P/F,\ 12,\ 10)$$
$$+ \$1000(P/A,\ 12,\ 3) + \$2000(P/A,\ 12,\ 7)(P/F,\ 12,\ 3)$$

$$= \$110,000 + \$50,000(0.71178) - \$50,000(0.32197)$$
$$+ \$1000(2.4018) + \$2000(4.5637)(0.71178)$$
$$= \$138,389$$

The analysis indicates that the present worth of storage costs for the next 10 years will be $138,389 − $129,955 = $8434 less from leasing than building the required warehousing facility.

This same problem is examined from a different perspective in Chapter 18, where it is no longer assumed future demands are known with certainty. If reliable probabilities for future capacity needs can be generated, they should be included in the analysis. The difficulty is in finding a reliable way to peek into the future.

# VALUATION

Value is a measure of the worth of something in terms of money or goods. A barter system uses a personally directed trade of goods to establish equivalent values. In an auction the measure of worth is established by competitive monetary bids. To some extent, selling price in an openly competitive market sets a value on goods as a result of the amount customers are willing to pay. Value is more difficult to determine before a transaction occurs. Expert appraisers are familiar with prices from previous transactions and interpolate to set values on goods that have not been exposed to the market. Works of art and land properties are subject to sometimes controversial evaluations.

Appraisals regularly encountered in financial practice are known by specific names. A *going value* is how much the assets of an organization are worth as an operating unit. It is opposed to a *liquidating value,* which is the amount that could be realized if the assets were sold separately from the organization that is using them. The going value is normally greater than the liquidating value, in recognition of the "organizational" value of a unit still in operating condition; accountants term this difference *goodwill.* The worth of an asset for accounting purposes is its *book value,* which may be quite different from its *market value,* the price at which it can be sold. Book value reflects historical cost, whereas market value is dependent upon earnings.

When the value of property depends upon its earning capacity, valuation results from discounting future probable earnings to their present worth. When risk is ignored, the "value" of such property is simply its present worth at the interest rate deemed appropriate by the appraiser. Examples of properties whose value tends to be a function of future cash flows are bonds, stocks, and rental assets.

## Bond Valuation

A bond is sold by an organization to raise money. Bonds represent a debt to the bondholders rather than a share of ownership in the organization. Most bonds bear interest semiannually and are redeemable for a specified maturity value at a give date. There are many variations designed to make bonds more attractive to purchasers, such as a provision to convert them to common stock under specified conditions, or to make the bond debt more manageable for the issuing organization, as in *callable (redeemable)* bonds that may be paid off prior to maturity.

Each bond has a *par value* which usually represents the amount borrowed. Generally, this par or face value is $1000. If the bond has a maturity date, as most bonds do, the par value is the amount the borrower promises to repay then.

The value of a bond of a given denomination depends on the size and timing of the periodic interest payments and the time until maturity. The bond valuation is thus the present worth* of the cash-flow stream of interest payments plus the discounted value of the face value. The key to the valuation is the rate of return expected by the bond purchaser. Lower rates are reasonable when there is very little risk of default. For instance, a government security would have less risk of nonrepayment than one issued by the Fly-by-Nite Corporation; consequently, a lower discount rate would be appropriate.

Bonds sell for less than their face value when buyers are not satisfied with the rate of interest promised, called the *coupon rate*. Interest is paid in the form of regular payments; the flow of which constitutes an annuity where

$$A = \text{payment} = (\text{face value})(\text{coupon rate})/n$$

and the number of payments (n) per year is a function of the bond rate structure (e.g., two payments per year for a semiannual bond). A present-worth purchase price for a bond that satisfies a buyer seeking a return greater than the coupon rate is calculated from the bond's maturity value $F$ and the annuity composed of interest payments $A$, both discounted at the buyer's desired rate of return.

---

## Example 4.7   To Buy a Bond

A 10-year corporate bond has a face value of $1000 and a coupon rate of 8 percent payable semiannually. A prospective buyer desires to earn a nominal rate of 12 percent on investments. What purchase price would the buyer be willing to pay?

## Solution 4.7

The bond matures for $1000 ten years from now. During that period, two interest payments will be paid each year in the amount of $A = \$1000(0.08/2) = \$1000(0.04) = \$40$. The buyer desires a return of $12/2 = 6$ percent per period. To meet the buyer's requirement, the purchase price must be the present worth of income from the bond discounted at 6 percent for 20 periods:

$$\begin{aligned} PW &= \$1000(P/F, 6, 20) + \$40\,(P/A, 6, 20) \\ &= \$1000(0.31181) + \$40\,(11.469) = \$770.57 \end{aligned}$$

---

Bonds are traded regularly through financial markets. Depending on the prevailing interest rate at a given time, a bond may sell for a price that is less than, more than, or equal to its face value. When the owner of a bond purchased previously seeks to sell it before maturity, the original purchase price and interest already received have no bearing on its market value; only future cash flow has consequence.

*The procedure for calculating a value is sometimes called *capitalization of income*.

### Example 4.8    Evaluation of a Bond Purchase

A utility company sold an issue of 4 percent bonds 26 years ago. Each bond has a face value (value at maturity) of $1000, is due in 4 years, and pays interest twice a year (2 percent per period). Because interest rates on savings have climbed in recent years, the bond can now be sold on the bond market for only $640. If buyers expect their money to earn 18 percent compounded semiannually and they must pay a brokerage charge of $20 to purchase each bond, is the current selling price reasonable?

### Solution 4.8

Semiannual interest payments amount to 2 percent of the face value of the bond, or 0.02 x $1000 = $20, and $1000 will be redeemed in 4 years, or 8 half-year periods. Therefore, the present value of the cash flow when the desired nominal interest rate is 9 percent per 6-month period is

$$\text{PW} = \$20(P/A, 9, 8) + \$1000(P/F, 9, 8)$$
$$= \$20(5.5347) + \$1000(0.50187) = \$612.56$$

Since the price of the bond is $640 + $20 = $660, prospective bond purchasers should look elsewhere to obtain their desired rate of return on investments.

---

The current market rate of interest strongly affects bond prices. Higher market rates tend to lower bond prices by decreasing the present worth of the future stream of payments promised by the bond. Figure 4.2 displays the valuation at different market rates of interest for a 20-year bond and a bond which pays the same interest rate but matures in 3 years.

As is apparent in Figure 4.2, the longer the maturity of a security, the greater its price change in response to a change in the market rate of interest. This pattern explains why short-

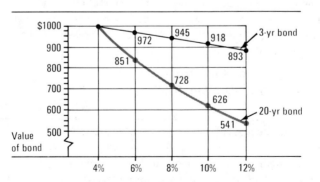

**FIGURE 4.2**  Value of $1000 long-term (20-year) and short-term (3-year) bonds at different market interest rates. Both bonds promise semiannual interest payments of $20.

term bonds with the same risk of default as long-term bonds usually have lower interest rates. Investments in short-term securities expose the investor to less chance of severe fluctuations in market value than comparable long-term investments.

## Stock Valuation

Stock in a company represents a share of ownership, as opposed to a bond which is a promissory note. There are many types of stocks and bonds, varying as to their degree of security and associated special privileges. In general, all bonds have claims on a company's assets before stock in case of a business failure. Stock is still a popular investment because it has the potential of increasing in value and may pay higher dividends than bonds when the company is very successful. Most shareholders have voting privileges which allow major investors to have some say in company policy.

*Preferred stocks* or *preference shares* usually entitle owners to regular, fixed dividend payments similar to bond interest. Characteristically, preferred stock has no voting rights. The *par value** of a preferred stock is the amount due the shareholder in the event of liquidation, and the annual yield is often expressed as a percentage of the par value. When preferred stock has no maturity date, it may be treated as a perpetuity whose value is

$$PW = \frac{\text{annual dividend on the preferred stock}}{\text{annual rate of return expected by the investor}}$$

*Common stocks,* the most common form of equity shares in a company, are more difficult to value than preferred stocks or bonds because dividends and prices of common stocks are not constant; investors hope they will increase over time. It is therefore necessary to forecast future earnings, dividends, and stock prices. If reliable forecasts could be made (and that is a highly questionable assumption), stock valuation would result from discounting the forecast cash flow.

To illustrate, suppose a share of Sumplex, Inc., has a current market price of $40. It is expected to pay a $3 dividend by the end of 1 year. Since the company went public in 1947, the value of its stock has been rising at an average rate of 4 percent. Using a 1-year study period,

$$\text{Present worth} = \frac{\text{dividend}}{(F/P, i, 1)} + \frac{\text{market price at end of year}}{(F/P, i, 1)}$$

$$\text{Present price} = \frac{\text{dividend}}{1 + i} + \frac{\text{Present price} \times 1.04}{1 + i}$$

Rearranging and substituting numerical data give

$$1 + i = \frac{\$3 + \$40(1.04)}{\$40} = \frac{\$44.60}{\$40} = 1.115$$

to reveal the discount rate

*The Canada Business Corporations Act proscribes par value for any shares of a corporation. Many firms, however, have provincial charters, and some provinces permit par value.

$i = 1.115 - 1 = 0.115$ or 11.5 percent

If an investor is satisfied with an 11.5 percent rate of return after considering the risk involved, shares in Sumplex, Inc., could be purchased. The same expected rate of return could be calculated as

$$i = \text{dividend rate} + \text{growth rate} = \frac{\$3}{\$40} + 0.04 = 0.075 + 0.04 = 0.115$$

The partition of expected returns into dividends and growth (*capital gains*) is important when taxes are considered. Capital gains, the increase in market value between the purchase and sale of a stock, are taxed at a different rate than ordinary income. Taxes are discussed in Chapter 12.

# Review Exercises And Discussions

**Exercise 1**  An entrepreneur intending to start a new business knows that the first few years are the most difficult. To lessen the chance of failure, a loan plan for start-up capital is proposed in which interest paid during the first 2 years will be at 3 percent, at 6 percent for the next 2 years, and at 12 percent for the final 2 years of the 6-year loan. How large a loan can be substantiated for proposed repayments at the end of years 2, 4, and 6 of, respectively, $20,000, $30,000, and $50,000?

**Solution 1**  It is not unusual for interest rates to change during a study. Time-value equivalence is calculated by translating individual cash flows through each time period at the interest rate applicable during that period. The procedure is illustrated by considering each loan repayment independently and calculating its present worth, as

PW($20,000 payment) $= \$20,000(P/F, 3, 2) = \$20,000(0.94260)$
    $= \$18,852$
PW($30,000 payment) $= \$30,000(P/F, 6, 2)(P/F, 3, 2)$
    $= \$30,000(0.89000)(0.94260) = \$25,167$
PW($50,000 payment) $= \$50,000(P/F, 12, 2)(P/F, 6, 2)(P/F, 3, 2)$
    $= \$50,000(0.79719)(0.89000)(0.94260)$
    $= \$33,439$

The loan that can be repaid by the given repayment amounts at the given interest rates is then

PW(total loan) = $18,852 + $25,167 + $33,439 = $77,458

A graph of the loan's balance over the 6-year period is shown in Figure 4.3. From an initial value of $77,458 at time zero, the amount owed increases to $82,175 in 2 years with interest at 3 percent. Then the $20,000 payment is recorded, dropping the amount owed to $62,175. The steeper rates of increase during the later stages of the loan result from greater earnings generated by higher interest rates.

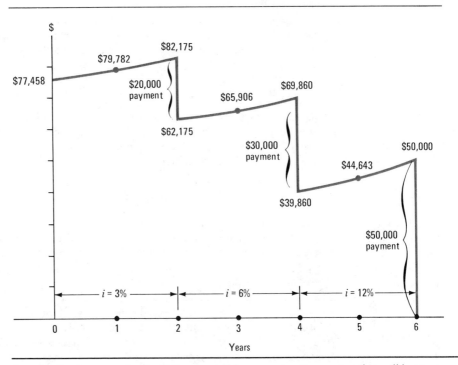

**FIGURE 4.3** Loan balance during the 6-year repayment period.

**Exercise 2**   A new rock pit will be operated for a construction project that will last 5 years. Rock can be loaded from an elevated box loader served by a conveyor from the pit, or by mobile shovel loaders. The box loader and conveyor have an initial cost of $264,000 and will have no salvage value at the end of the project. Two shovel loaders, each priced at $42,000, can provide the same capacity, but their operating costs together will be $36,000 per year more than the box loader. Normal service life for a shovel loader is 3 years with zero salvage value, but a 2-year-old machine can likely be sold for $10,000. Which alternative is preferred when the interest rate is 13 percent?

**Solution 2**   The study period is the duration of the project, 5 years. The present worth of the box-loader alternative is its initial cost: PW(box loader) = −$264,000.

Since the first two shovel loaders are replaced at the end of 3 years and the replacements will not be in service for their entire useful life, the estimated salvage value must be included as a cash inflow at the end of year 5. The additional operating costs incurred for the shovel-loader alternative form a 5-year annuity of annual $36,000 payments:

PW(shovel loaders) = $2(-\$42,000) + 2(-\$42,000)(P/F, 13, 3) - \$36,000(P/A, 13, 5)$
$$+\$20,000(P/F, 13, 5)$$
$$= -\$84,000 - \$84,000(0.69305) - \$36,000(3.5172)$$
$$+ \$20,000(0.54276)$$
$$= -\$84,000 - \$58,216 - \$126,620 + \$10,856$$
$$= -\$257,980$$

The shovel loaders appear to be more economical if the machines can be sold for the indicated salvage value after 2 years of use.

---

**Exercise 3**   A bank has offered to loan the novelty company described in Example 4.6 the sum of $145,000 at 8 percent interest compounded annually, to build a large warehouse immediately. The warehouse would be the same size as the small one plus the addition and would have annual expenses of $1500 per year. If its resale value at the end of 10 years is $50,000, would it be a better alternative than the other two in Example 4.6?

**Solution 3**   The interest rate offered by the bank should not be used in the comparison, because the required rate of return for an organization includes more than just the cost of borrowing. At $i = 12$ percent, the present worth of 10 years of storage from the construction of a large warehouse comparable in size to the other alternatives is

PW = $\$145,000 - \$50,000(P/F, 12, 10) + \$1500(P/A, 12, 10)$
$$= \$145,000 - \$50,000(0.32197) + \$1500(5.6502) = \$137,375$$

This cost is lower than that of the build-small-and-add alternative, but is more than the leasing cost. Note that the cost of construction in two phases of the same-sized building exhibits the typical relationship that the absolute cost (at $i = 0$ percent) of acquisition by parts is greater than acquisition all at one time. However, a deferral may make the time value of acquisition by parts less expensive.

---

**Exercise 4**   An investor has been investigating the stock performance of two companies: Withit and Righton. The Withit Corporation has consistently paid dividends that increase 10 cents per year while the selling price of the stock has averaged a 2 percent annual rise. Righton is a new glamour company that has paid no dividends because all earnings are retained for expansion, but its market price is expected to increase by $10 per year. Further, in about 5 years it is expected to start paying dividends equal to 2 percent of its price per share (a price-to-earnings ratio of 50:1). Current data about the two companies are summarized below.

|  | *Withit corporation* | *Righton Company* |
|---|---|---|
| Dividend | $2.25 (10¢/year increase) | 0 (2% of market price after 5 years) |
| Market price | $28 (2% annual increase) | $65 ($10/year increase) |
| Capitalization rate | 9% | 12% (risk adjusted) |

Since it is generally believed that Righton stock is less stable than Withit's, the extra risk of investing in Righton is recognized by requiring a higher rate of return for the valuation, 12 percent versus 9 percent.

Disregarding tax effects and brokerage commissions to buy or sell, which stock has the greater valuation for an anticipated 10-year ownership?

**Solution 4** A 10-year study period is used to calculate the present worth of each stock alternative, assuming dividends are paid at the end of the year. The valuation of Withit stock at $i = 9$ percent is

PW(Withit) = [$2.25 + $0.10($A/G$, 9, 10)]($P/A$, 9, 10) + $28($F/P$, 2, 10)($P/F$, 9, 10)
          = [$2.25 + $0.10(3.7976)](6.4176) + $28(1.2189)(0.42241)
          = $16.87 + $14.42 = $31.29

which makes the current market price of $28 appear attractive.

The valuation of Righton Company's stock based on a 12 percent desired rate of return and the assumption that dividends are paid annually after a 5-year wait is diagramed and calculated as

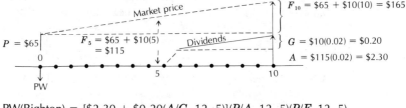

PW(Righton) = [$2.30 + $0.20($A/G$, 12, 5)]($P/A$, 12, 5)($P/F$, 12, 5)
            + $165($P/F$, 12, 10)
            = [$2.30 + $0.20(1.7745)](3.6047)(0.56743) + $165(0.32197)
            = $5.43 + $53.13 = $58.56

Since the $60 market price for Righton Stock exceeds the calculated valuation, it appears that Withit Stock is a better investment opportunity, assuming the risk-return ratings and forecast cash flows are reasonably accurate.

# PROBLEMS

**4.1** What is a contract worth today that promises you $50 per month for 20 months with the first payment to be received immediately, if 12 percent compounded monthly is expected on such contracts? *($911.30)*

**4.2** What would the contract in Problem 4.1 be worth if the amount received increased by $5 per month? *($1745)*

**4.3** Determine the present worth of the given end-of-year cash-flow stream for a discount rate of 15 percent. *(−$5379)*

| Year | Flow | Year | Flow |
|------|------|------|------|
| 0 | −$47,000 | 4 | −$2,000 |
| 1 | $12,000 | 5 | $12,000 |
| 2 | $10,000 | 6 | $10,000 |
| 3 | $8,000 | 7 | $8,000 |
|  |  | 8 | $19,000 |

**4.4** A company borrowed $100,000 to finance a new product. The loan was for 20 years at a nominal interest rate of 6 percent compounded semiannually. It was to be repaid in 40

equal payments. After half the payments were made, the company decided to pay the remaining balance in one final payment at the end of the tenth year. How much was owed? *($64,357.90)*

**4.5** A proposed improvement in an assembly line will have an initial purchase and installation cost of $67,000. The annual maintenance cost will be $3500; periodic overhauls once every 3 years, including the last year of use, will cost $6000 each. The improvement will have a useful life of 12 years, at which time it will have no salvage value. What is the present worth of the lifetime costs of the improvement at $i$ = 8 percent? *($107,304)*

**4.6** Machine $A$ has a first cost of $9000, no salvage value at the end of its 6-year useful life, and annual operating costs of $5000. Machine $B$ costs $16,000 new and has a resale value of $4000 at the end of its 9-year economic life. Operating costs for machine $B$ are $4000 per year. Compare the two alternatives on the basis of their present worths, using the repeated-projects assumption at 10 percent annual interest.

$$[PW(A) = \$57,954, PW(B) = \$53,175]$$

**4.7** A commercial rental property is for sale at $100,000. A prospective buyer estimates the property would be held for 12 years, at the end of which it could be sold for $90,000. During the ownership period, annual receipts from rentals would be $15,000, and average disbursements for all purposes in connection with ownership would be $6000. If a rate of return of 9 percent is expected, what is the maximum bid the prospective purchaser should make to buy the property? *($96,444)*

**4.8** A manufacturer requires an additional 10,000 square feet (929 square meters) of warehouse space. A reinforced-concrete building added to the existing main structure will cost $440,000, whereas the same amount of space can be constructed with a galvanized building for $310,000. The life of the concrete building is estimated at 50 years with a yearly maintenance cost of $19,200. The life of the galvanized building is estimated to be 30 years, and the annual maintenance cost is $48,000. Average annual property taxes are 1.2 percent for the concrete building or 0.5 percent for the metal building. Assume each type of warehouse would be replaced by the same model and that the salvage value equals the unrecovered balance of the purchase price at any time.

Compare the present worths of the two warehouse additions, using 12 percent interest, for a 50-year study period *[PW (concrete) = $643,249; PW(glavanized) = $731,073]*

**4.9** Two alternative structures are being considered for a specific service. Compare the present worth of the cost of 24 years' service, using an interest rate of 5 percent, when neither structure has a realizable salvage value. The pertinent data are as follows:

|  | *Structure I* | *Structure II* |
|---|---|---|
| First cost | $4500 | $10,000 |
| Estimated life | 12 years | 24 years |
| Annual disbursements | $1000 | $720 |

$$[PW(I) = \$20,805; PW(II) = \$19,935]$$

**4.10** Perpetual care for a small shrine in a cemetery is estimated to be available for $500 per year. The long-term interest rate is expected to average about 5 percent. If the capitalized cost is estimated at $15,000, what amount is anticipated for the first cost of the shrine? *($5000)*

**4.11** A proposed mill in an isolated area can be furnished with power and water by a gravity-feed system. A stream high above the mill will be tapped to provide flow for water needs and power requirements by connecting it to the mill with a ditch-and-tunnel system or with a wood-and-concrete flume that winds its way down from the plateau. Either alternative will meet current and future needs, and both will utilize the same power-generating equipment.

The ditch-and-tunnel system will cost $500,000 with annual maintenance of $2000. The flume has an initial cost of $200,000 and yearly maintenance costs of $12,000. In addition, the wood portion of the flume will have to be replaced every 15 years at a cost of $100,000.

Compare the alternatives on the basis of capitalized costs with an interest rate of 6 percent. *[CC(d&t) = $533,333; CC(flume) = $471,600]*

**4.12** What is the maximum amount you could afford to bid for a $3000 (face value) bond with a simple interest rate of 4 percent payable quarterly if your minimum attractive rate of return were 8 percent compounded quarterly? The bond matures in 5 years. *($2509)*

**4.13** A sum of $200,000 has been invested in bonds which yield a return of 2 percent of the face value every 6 months. The bonds mature in 20 years. The dividends received from the bonds are invested at a rate of 10 percent compounded semiannually. What amount invested today and earning 7 percent annual interest would produce a 20-year cash flow equivalent to the bond and its reinvested dividends?

**4.14** A $2 million school-bond issue bearing interest at 3 percent payable annually and maturing in 25 years was sold at a price which provided a 4 percent annual rate of return to the investors. The brokerage fee for handling the sale was 0.3 percent of the total bond issue. What amount was realized from the sale to actually use for school construction? *($1,681,500)*

**4.15** A corporation sold callable 10-year bonds with 5 percent semiannual interest payments (2½ percent per period). Each bond sold at the $500 face value was guaranteed a 10 percent premium if called before maturity. The extra $50 was added to the redemption value of the bonds bought back by the corporation 6 years from the time of the original issue. What was the yield to the bondholders of these bonds? *(3.2% per period)*

**4.16** Interest on a 3½ percent, $1000 bond due in 25 years is payable serniannually by clipped coupons, with the first payment possible 6 months from now. What must be the price of the bond to provide a rate of return to the buyer of 5 percent compounded semiannually, assuming the coupons are cashed promptly? *($787.30)*

**4.17** Bonds of the Overightors Corporation are perpetuities bearing 7 percent annual interest. Their par value is $1000.

    **4.17a** If bonds of this type currently are expected to yield 6 percent, what is the market price?

    **4.17b** If interest rates rise to the level at which comparable bonds return a yield of 8 percent, what would the market price be for Overightor bonds?

    **4.17c** How would the prices change in Problems 4.17*a* and 4.17*b* if the bonds had a definite maturity date in 20 years?

**4.18** The XX Company is currently earning $2 million per year after taxes. Shareholders own 1 million shares. If investors require a rate of return of 15 percent on stocks in the same risk class as XX stock, and the previous dividend was $1, what price will the stock sell for when future dividends are expected to grow at a constant rate of 5 percent per year? What is the price-to-earnings ratio? Since XX is not considered to be in a legitimate growth industry, any increases in price per share will result only from improved dividends.

**4.19** An engineer working on a construction project has reason to believe that the stock of one of the companies supplying materials to the project is undervalued at the current selling price of $60 per share. The last dividend was $2.50. She believes both the value of the stock and the dividends will double in 10 years. Assuming the increase occurs in constant increments each year, and the engineer requires a 10 percent return on such investments, how much could she afford to pay per share for the stock?

**4.20** A bond with a face value of $5000 pays quarterly interest of 1½ percent each period. Twenty-six interest payments remain before the bond matures. How much would you be willing to pay for this bond today if the next interest payment is due now and you want to earn 8 percent compounded quarterly on your money?

**4.21** The present worth of a bond is 70 percent of the face value when the total return to buyers is 12 percent compounded annually. What is the annual bond rate on this 10-year bond?

**4.22** A company is considering the purchase of a new piece of testing equipment which is expected to produce $8000 additional before-tax profit during the first year of operation; this amount will probably decrease by $500 per year for each additional year of ownership. The equipment costs $20,000 and will have an estimated salvage value of $3000 after 8 years of use. For a before-tax interest rate of 25 percent, determine the net present worth of this investment.                    *($3161.30)*

**4.23** A grant has been given by a corporation to support a summer music festival for 4 years. The first payment of $200,000 will be made a year from now, and payments will increase by 7 percent of the first payment each year to account for inflation. What is the present worth of this commitment today, if the corporation uses a 12 percent annual interest rate for discounting its transactions?

**4.24** To attract industry, a city has made an offer to a corporation. The city will install all roads and services for the plant site at no immediate cost to the corporation, but the corporation will be expected to bear the cost of operation and maintenance on a cost-sharing schedule whereby $65,000 is paid the first year and each subsequent payment will be $5000 less. The first payment will be made 2 years from now, and the corporation's obligation will end with the last $5000 payment. What is the present worth today of this agreement if the annual interest rate is 9 percent?

**4.25** A marina has two alternative plans for constructing a small-boat landing on a lake behind their sales building; one is a wooden dock, and the other is a metal and concrete wharf. Data for the two plans are as shown.

|  | *Wood* | *Metal and Concrete* |
|---|---|---|
| First cost | $25,000 | $50,000 |
| Period before replacement | 20 years | 30 years |
| Salvage value | $5000 | 0 |
| Annual maintenance | $5500 | $2800 |

Using a minimum attractive rate of return of 10 percent, compare the present worths of the two plans. Assume both will provide adequate service and that replacement costs will be the same as the original cost.

**4.26**  A refining company entered into a contract for raw materials with an agreement to pay $600,000 now and $150,000 per year beginning at the end of the fifth year. The contract was made for 10 years. At the end of the third year, because of unexpected profits, the company requested that it be allowed to make a lump-sum payment in advance for the rest of the contract. Both parties agreed that 7 percent compounded annually was a fair interest rate. What was the amount of the lump sum?

**4.27**  A machine can be repaired today for $2000. If repairs are not made, the operating expenses will increase by $200 each year for the next 5 years. Assume that the expenses will occur at the end of each year, and the machine will have no value under either alternative at the end of the 5-year period. The minimum acceptable rate of return is 12 percent. Compare the present worths of the two alternatives.

**4.28**  The following alternatives are available to accomplish an objective of 12 years' duration:

|  | Plan A | Plan B | Plan C |
|---|---|---|---|
| Life cycle | 6 years | 3 years | 4 years |
| First cost | $2000 | $8000 | $10,000 |
| Annual cost | $3200 | $700 | $500 |

Compare the present worths of the alternatives using an interest rate of 7 percent.

**4.29**  The lining of a chemical tank must be replaced every 3 years at a cost of $1800. A new type of lining is available that is more resistant to corrosion. The new lining costs $3100. If the minimum rate of return required is 12 percent, and taxes and insurance are 4 percent of the first cost annually, how long must the improved lining last to be more economical than the present lining?

**4.30**  A single underground transmission circuit is needed immediately, and load studies indicate the need for a second circuit in 6 years. If provision is made for a second conduit when the conduit for the first circuit is installed, there will be no future need for reopening, trenching, backfilling, and repaving. The cost of installing a single circuit with minimum preparation for the eventual second circuit is $850,000. The installation of the second circuit will be considered to cost $800,000 at the end of year 5, in order to be in operation by the end of year 6. If the second circuit is installed immediately, the total cost will be $1.4 million.

Levelized annual operating and maintenance costs of the circuits are 8 percent of the first cost and begin 1 year after the first costs are incurred. The average life of a circuit is 32 years. The required rate of return on such investments is 10 percent before taxes.

**4.30a**  Compare the deferred investment with the immediate investment using a 32-year study period.

**4.30b**  Compare the two conduit plans on a study period taken to eternity. Then compare this solution to the one in Problem 4.30a. Which is the most reasonable? Why?

**4.31**  Everwhite, a small community with big ideas, envisions development of a nearby winter recreational area. The idea seems reasonable, owing to the area's location near a major population center and because it normally has snow of exceptional quality. The provincial government has agreed to guarantee bonds, which pay 6 percent interest and mature in 20 years, to be sold to fund the project. The main decision remaining is whether to build a modest facility at first and enlarge it later or to acquire all the land and do all the construction at one time.

Costs for a small lodge with an open ice rink and two ski runs with lifts on 400 acres of land will be $2 million. Construction will take 2 years. Once the resort opens, net revenues from this size operation are expected to average $300,000 per year, exclusive of bond interest and debt retirement.

A year-round resort with provisions for golf, tennis, and two more ski runs will boost the first cost to $5 million, require 3 years to build, and will occupy 1500 acres. Net revenue (exclusive of debt payments) for a resort of this size should average $400,000 per year for the first four years of operation until the resort becomes well known, and then should increase by $100,000 per year for the next 13 years, at which time net revenue will level off.

The enlargement of the resort can be deferred 5 years, but the extra land required (1100 acres) should be purchased immediately for $500,000, to avoid the increased valuation expected when the resort opens. Construction can be done while the original facilities continue to operate. Money for the $3-million addition should be available at the end of the fifth year. When the additions are ready for use by the end of the seventh year, net revenue should at once jump annually by $150,000 over the revenue for the smaller version. This gradient increase should continue for 5 years and then drop to an annual increase of $100,000 over the previous year until the end of the twentieth year.

Depending on the development plan followed, bonds will be sold to accumulate $2, $2.5, or $5 million immediately, and $3 million at the end of year 5. Analyze the alternatives using a desired rate of return of 8 percent. Discuss your preferred solution with respect to the other alternatives available.

# EXTENSIONS

**4A Engineering, Economics, and Pollution** Life style in highly industrialized nations has been parodied as the "effluent society." The more developed countries do not have a monopoly on pollution problems. All large population concentrations face the danger of overloading nature's self-regenerating capacity to absorb and recycle wastes. However, pollution is acute and most obvious in industrialized countries because they process more resources per capita and use more advanced technologies that may damage the ecological system on a grand scale.

Alarming examples of pollution practices and frightening forecasts of eventual outcomes from continued contamination are regularly reported in the press. Progress toward cleansing some parts of our environment is also being reported. The Great Lakes cleanup has brought marine life back to "dead" Lake Erie. By 1979, exhaust from automobiles had 87 percent less carbon monoxide and hydrocarbons than did uncontrolled cars in the 1960s, and the level of smoke, soot, and dust in the air dropped by 14 percent from the levels of 5 years earlier. Advances have also been made in reducing discharges of untreated wastes into waterways, control of pesticides and industrial chemicals, and trash disposal. But the sweeping drive to clean up the environment appears to be slowing, owing in large part to related engineering and economic difficulties.

Technology to drastically curtail most pollutants is available, and it is expensive. Even if engineering advances can substantially cut the cost of pollution control, the remaining costs must be balanced against other national priorities. What is the the cost of a cleaner environment in terms of jobs lost or created, energy consumed, personal inconvenience, and changes in the standard of living – up, down, or just different? *The present worth of a pollution-control investment is the benefits from reducing pollution minus the costs of installing pollution-control equipment.* Examples of pollution-control costs include expenditures of public funds for municipal sewage-treatment plants, expenditures by industrial firms to remove contaminants from waste discharges, and expenditures by individuals for pollution-control devices on automobiles. Benefits from reducing pollution could include lower expenditures for water-purification systems, medical bills for illnesses due to polluted conditions, and remedies to combat mental and physical discomfort associated with pollution. The costs for pollution control are obviously easier to quantify than the benefits resulting from less pollution.

The relationship between pollution control costs and the benefits of reduced pollution generally follows the pattern shown in Figure 4.4. The message in this graph centers on the *economically feasible* level X of pollution control for a given state of technology and set of economic conditions. Ideally, the pollution level would be zero, but the sacrifice in terms of economic disruptions to reach that level is probably prohibitive. However, if the current level of pollution is Y, it would be economically sound to spend enough on pollution control to lower the level to X.

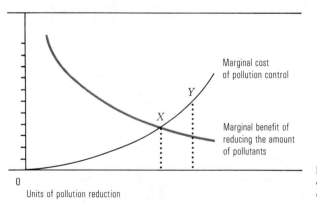

**FIGURE 4.4** Relationship of costs and benefits of pollution control.

Assume that Figure 4.4 represents a sewage-disposal situation in a certain locality. The pollution-prevention costs are expenditures to construct and operate a waste-treatment plant. The benefits of reduced pollution include reduced downstream water-purification expenses, reduced human health-care cost, and increased recreational activities.

**QUESTIONS**

**4A.1**  How could these costs be determined?

**4A.2**  Once the costs are obtained, how should they be used to convince the polluters to allocate resources for prevention when most of the benefits accrue downstream?

**4A.3**  Should the downstream beneficiaries contribute to the pollution-prevention costs?

*4B Future-Worth Comparisons*    It is evident from the equivalence concept that a present worth can be translated to a future worth at any given time at a given interest rate. The mechanics of the translation are elementary, but the change in perspective by the analyst can be significant. For certain situations the future worth of cash flow may be more meaningful to a decision maker than the present worth. The amount of debt or surplus accumulated at a future date could be a milestone in a financial plan or a goal that directs current activities.

Attention to future cash flows may yield more accurate estimates of receipts and disbursements because thinking tends to be in "then-current" dollars. As the purchasing power of a unit of currency is eroded by inflation, it may be advantageous to focus on how many currency units must be available to meet needs at a later date—the quantity of then-current dollars. Consequently, future-worth calculations are frequently utilized in escalation analyses, particularly for evaluating the effects of inflation.

The future-worth perspective can be illustrated by reference to the cash flow in Example 4.2. The 8-year cash flow in the example is composed of two annuities: annual $15,000 costs for the first 3 years followed by five equal-step receipts ranging from $10,000 to $20,000.

The future value of disbursements, treated as debts for which interest at 10 percent must be paid, builds in 8 years to a total indebtedness of

$$\text{FW(disbursements)} = -\$15,000(F/A, \ 10, \ 3)(F/P, \ 10, \ 5)$$
$$= -\$15,000(3.3099)(1.6105) = -\$79,959$$

A complementary future worth at the end of year 4 would show the accumulated indebtedness before any income is generated as

$$\text{FW(4)} = -\$15,000(F/A, \ 10, \ 3)(F/P, \ 10, \ 1) = -\$54,613$$

This amount is reduced by the receipt of $10,000 at the end of year 4, but it reveals the maximum liability level.

The positive arithmetic-gradient cash inflow reaches a maximum at the end of year 8, amounting to

$$\text{FW(receipts)} = [\$10,000 + \$2500(A/G, \ 10, \ 5)](F/A, \ 10, \ 5)$$
$$= [\$10,000 + \$2500(1.8100)](6.1050) = \$88,675$$

The balance on hand at the end of the study period is then

$$\text{Net FW} = \$88,675 - \$79,959 = \$8716$$

This same figure (differing only by rounding error from the interest tables) could be obtained from the previously calculated PW = $4066 as

Net FW = $4066($F/P$, 10, 8) = $4066(2.1435) = $8715

The relative usefulness of PW and FW comparisons depends on which figure is more valuable for decision making. If knowledge of the dollars available at some impending date is critical, then a future-worth calculation is called for. Knowing when to answer such a call marks a competent engineering economist.

**QUESTIONS**

**4B.1**  For the cash flow in Example 4.2, calculate the time at which the amount owed equals the amount received, including interest. This is the breakeven point for the cash flow.                                             *(7.54 years)*

**4B.2**  What is the future worth of the loan agreement made by the entrepreneur in Review Exercise 1?                                              *($115,821)*

# CHAPTER 5

# EQUIVALENT ANNUAL-WORTH COMPARISONS

OVERVIEW

Comparisons of investment proposals by the equivalent annual-worth method complement the more widely applied present-worth and rate-of-return methods. Sometimes it is most meaningful to structure a solution in terms of annual payments, but more often the annual-worth model is used because it is a more convenient way to arrive at a present worth or rate of return. All three methods of analysis indicate the same preference among investment alternatives.

An annual charge to account for the repayment of invested capital plus interest earnings on the unrecovered balance of the investment is obtained as

Equivalent annual cost = EAC = $(P - S)(A/P, i, N) + Si$

where $P$ = present value or purchase price
$S$ = salvage value or resale price
$N$ = study period or economic life of the asset
$i$ = interest rate expected on investments

Alternatives are compared on the basis of net equivalent annual worth (EAW) when both income and disbursements are known, or on their equivalent annual cost (EAC) when they serve the same function but income resulting from that function is not known.

When comparisons are made among assets that have different lives, a common-multiple assumption is usually made, but the study-period method can be used when enough information about replacements is known. Occasionally an assumption of perpetual life is appropriate.

A sinking fund may be established to protect investors by enforcing an orderly retirement of debt from current income. Periodic payments are made to an independent institution, where they earn interest at the institution's normal rate.

# UTILIZATION OF THE EQUIVALENT ANNUAL-WORTH COMPARISON METHOD

With an annual-worth method all the receipts and disbursements occurring over a period of time are converted to an equivalent uniform yearly amount. It is a popular method because of the widespread inclination to view a year's gains and losses as a yardstick of progress. Cost-accounting procedures, depreciation expenses, tax calculations, and other summary reports are annual in nature. These yearly cost tabulations generally make the annual-worth method easier to apply and comprehend than the other comparison methods.

Equivalent annual-worth comparisons produce results compatible with present-worth and rate-of-return comparisons. For a set of common assumptions, a preference for an alternative exhibited by one method will be mirrored by the other two. Annual-worth calculations are frequently a part of the computations required to develop present-worth and rate-of-return values, and parallel computations by different methods are useful for complementary comparisons that improve the clarity of an analysis.

The six conditions listed in Chapter 4 for basic present-worth comparisons also apply to basic annual-worth comparisons: cash flows and interest rates are known, cash flows are before taxes and in constant-value dollars, and comparisons include neither intangible considerations nor limits due to availability of financing. These restrictions are removed in later chapters, where equivalent annual-worth calculations are employed regularly to represent cash flow equivalents, especially in the analysis of capital-recovery patterns.

## Structure of a Capital-Recovery Annuity

The cornerstone of annual-worth calculations is the capital-recovery factor, which converts a lump sum into an equivalent annuity. This annuity usually represents an investment in an asset that is expected to generate a positive future cash flow, and the duration of the annuity is therefore the life of the asset. Since the cost of an asset is a cash outlay, the resulting annuity is a uniform series of negative payments. This negative cash flow is offset by the positive revenue produced by the asset in establishing the net equivalent annual worth of the investment.

The *capital-recovery factor* $(A/P, i, N)$ accounts for both the repayment of invested capital $P$ plus the interest earned on the unrecovered portion of the investment. Although the payments $A$ are uniform in size, the proportion of capital recovered and interest earned changes each period. The structure of an annuity, in which varying amounts from the equal payments are allocated to capital recovery and interest, is best revealed by examining a sample application.

Assume an asset is purchased for $40,000. It has an expected life of 4 years and no salvage value at the end of its life. The purchaser intends to recover the $40,000 investment over 4 years *plus* the interest the $40,000 would have earned if invested elsewhere. If an acceptable interest rate is 10 percent, the series of equal payments that would return the capital plus interest is computed as

$$\text{Equivalent annual payment} = A = P(A/P, 10, 4)$$
$$= \$40,000(0.31547) = \$12,619$$

Every year the proportion of a payment allotted to capital recovery and interest charges changes because interest is earned only on the amount of capital not yet recovered, and that amount changes each year. During year 1, before a payment is received, the $40,000 investment earns $40,000 × 0.10 = $4000 interest. The first payment of $12,619 then reduces the unrecovered capital by $12,619 − $4000 = $8619. During the second year, 10 percent interest is paid on $40,000 − $8619 = $31,381, amounting to $3138. Therefore, of the second payment, $3138 is interest and $12,619 − $3138 = $9481 is allocated to capital recovery. The complete sequence of changing proportions is given in Table 5.1.

**TABLE 5.1** Pattern of capital recovery and interest charges when the capital-recovery factor at $i$ = 10 percent is applied to the purchase of a $40,000 asset with a life of 4 years and no salvage value.

| End of Year | Capital Not Recovered by End of Year | Interest Due on Unrecovered Capital | Amount of Capital Recovered | Annual Capital-Recovery Charge |
|---|---|---|---|---|
| 0 | $40,000 | | | |
| 1 | 31,381 | $ 4000 | $ 8619 | $12,619 |
| 2 | 21,900 | 3138 | 9481 | 12,619 |
| 3 | 11,471* | 2190 | 10,429 | 12,619 |
| 4 | 0 | 1147 | 11,472* | 12,619 |
| Totals | | $10,476 | $40,001* | $50,476 |

*Differences are due to rounding errors.

## Capital-Recovery Calculations

As indicated in Table 5.1, the sum of the four annuity payments is $50,476, of which $10,476 is interest. This tabular format can be used to trace the capital recovery; or, when only the amount of unrecovered capital at a certain time is sought, it can be determined directly from the present worth of the remaining payments:

$$\text{Unrecovered capital(year 3)} = A(P/A, 10, 1)$$
$$= \$12,619(0.9091) = \$11,472$$
$$\text{Unrecovered capital(year 2)} = A(P/A, 10, 2)$$
$$= \$12,619(1.7355) = \$21,900$$

Then,

$$\text{Recovered capital(year 3)} = \$40,000 - \$11,472 = \$28,528$$
$$\text{Interest due(year 4)} = \$12,619 - \$11,472 = \$1147$$
$$\text{Recovered capital(year 2)} = \$40,000 - \$21,900 = \$18,100$$
$$\text{Interest due(years 3 \& 4)} = 2(\$12,619) - \$21,900$$
$$= \$3338$$

The equivalent annual payment equation can be modified to include a salvage value in two ways. If $S$ = salvage value, then

Equivalent annual cost = $(P - S)(A/P, i, N) + Si$

or $\qquad$ EAC = $P(A/P, i, N) - S(A/F, i, N)$

Both expressions yield the same EAC, but the first formula is used in this text because it is generally easier to manipulate. Consider an asset that costs $60,000 and has a $20,000 salvage value. The net amount that must be recovered from annuity payments is $P - S =$ $60,000 - $20,000 = $40,000; the remaining portion of the purchase price is returned by receipt of the salvage value, $20,000. However, the purchaser is deprived of the use of the $20,000 during the life of the asset, so interest is owed on this amount because it represents unrecovered capital. The $Si$ term in the formula accounts for this interest payment.

If the life of the $60,000 asset with a $20,000 salvage value is 4 years and the interest rate is 10 percent, then

EAC = ($60,000 − $20,000)($A/P$, 10, 4) + $20,000(0.10)
$\quad$ = $40,000(0.31547) + $2000 = $12,619 + $2000 = $14,619

The first term is the same capital-recovery expression depicted in Table 5.1. The amount of unrecovered capital can be calculated as described previously, except that the present worth of the salvage value must also be included:

Unrecovered capital(year 3) = EAC($P/A$, 10, 1) + S($P/F$, 10, 1)
$\qquad\qquad\qquad\qquad$ = $14,619(0.9091) + $20,000(0.9091)
$\qquad\qquad\qquad\qquad$ = $13,290 + $18,182
$\qquad\qquad\qquad\qquad$ = $31,472

and

Recovered capital(year 3) = $60,000 – $31,472 = $28,528

Note that the $20,000 salvage value is *not* added to the unrecovered capital as an outstanding sum; only the present worth is added because interest on the salvage value is already accounted for in the EAC computation.

The alternative formula for equivalent annual cost yields the same solution for the given data:

EAC = $P(A/P$, 10, 4) − $S(A/F$, 10, 4)
$\quad$ = $60,000(0.31547) − $20,000(0.21547)
$\quad$ = $18,928 − $4309 = $14,619

and

Unrecovered capital(year 3) = $18,928($P/A$, 10, 1) – $4309($P/A$, 10, 1) + $20,000($P/F$, 10, 1)
$\qquad\qquad\qquad\qquad$ = $18,928(0.9091) – $4309(0.9091) + $20,000(0.9091)
$\qquad\qquad\qquad\qquad$ = $17,204 – $3917 + 18,182 = 31,472

which reveals the portion of the salvage value's equivalent cash flow ($3917) attributed to year 4. However, the physical payment of $20,000 is still scheduled to occur at the end of year 4, just as the first cost was scheduled at time zero.

The equivalent annual cost, calculated by either formula, combines the first cost and salvage value into a single equivalent annuity, and the unrecovered capital at any time is therefore the present worth of the remaining installments of that annuity plus the present worth of the salvage value.

# SITUATIONS FOR EQUIVALENT ANNUAL-WORTH COMPARISONS

The term *annual worth* suggests a positive value, but the calculations can just as well produce a negative value. A negative annual worth indicates that the equivalent value of negative cash flow for disbursements is greater than the corresponding positive flow of receipts. Negative worths usually mean that an alternative is unacceptable. Exceptions occur when projects must be undertaken to satisfy certain requirements such as safety citations or building codes. Then the objective is to identify the alternative with the least equivalent cost (negative cash flow).

It is often very difficult, and not worth the required study time, to discover the income derived from one component in a complex system. For instance, the income produced by a copying machine is troublesome to derive exactly since its output is utilized by many people, often from different departments, working on many projects. In this type of situation, alternatives to satisfy the copying needs are evaluated on the basis of their relative costs, because each alternative capable of meeting the requirements of the system will produce the same income to the system. When it is apparent that *only* costs are involved in an evaluation, it is convenient to ignore the negative sign convention and let comparison figures represent the absolute value of costs.

Several situations for applying equivalent annual-worth calculations are described in the examples that follow.

## Consolidation of Cash Flows

"What's it worth?" is a deciding query in the appraisal of a proposal. It is difficult to ascertain what to expect from a proposal until the myriad receipts and disbursements associated with its conduct are collectively analyzed. Improvement programs are prime examples. Organizations regularly engage in programs to improve productivity, reduce accidents, raise quality, and the like. Each is a worthwhile goal, expected to have positive rewards, but each has costs too. Consolidating the various costs into a pattern that can be compared to potential rewards may take the form of a net annuity.

---

### Example 5.1   Equivalent Net Worth of Cash Flows

A consulting firm proposes to provide "self-inspection" training for clerks who work with insurance claims. The program lasts 1 year, costs $2000 per month, and professes to improve quality while reducing clerical time. A potential user of the program estimates that savings in the first month should amount to $800 and increase by $400 per month for the rest of the year. However, operation confusion and work interference are expected to boost clerical costs by $1200 the first month, but this amount should decline in equal increments to zero by the end of the training year. If the required return on money is 12 percent compounded monthly and there is a stipulation that the program must pay for itself within 1 year, should the consultants be hired?

### Solution 5.1

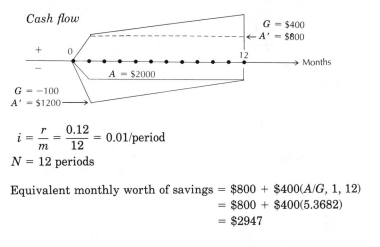

$$i = \frac{r}{m} = \frac{0.12}{12} = 0.01/\text{period}$$
$$N = 12 \text{ periods}$$

$$
\begin{aligned}
\text{Equivalent monthly worth of savings} &= \$800 + \$400(A/G, 1, 12) \\
&= \$800 + \$400(5.3682) \\
&= \$2947
\end{aligned}
$$

$$
\begin{aligned}
\text{Equivalent monthly worth of costs} &= -\$2000 - [\$1200 - \$100(A/G, 1, 12)] \\
&= -\$3200 + \$100(5.3682) \\
&= -\$2663
\end{aligned}
$$

$$
\text{Equivalent net monthly cash flow} = \$2947 - \$2663 = \$284
$$

*Equivalent cash flow*

The program looks very promising because the equivalent monthly worth is positive during the first year, and savings generated by the training should continue into the future.

Gradient factors are utilized in Example 5.1 to convert uniformly varying cash flows to their equivalent constant worths. Recovery of capital is not an issue, since no property ownership is involved. The comparison is made directly on the basis of expected income versus outgo.

## Recovery of Invested Capital

"Will it pay off?" is the question investors want answered. An adequate payoff recovers the invested capital plus the desired rate of return. Since returns are spread over the life of the investment, it is convenient to convert capital-recovery costs to the same annual pattern. The result of consequence from combining uniform cost and revenue flows is a positive, zero, or negative series of payments that respectively categorize the investment as gratifying, adequate, or insufficient.

### Example 5.2   Net Annual Worth of a Single Project

The purchase of a truck with an operator's platform on a telescoping hydraulic boom will reduce labor costs for sign installations by $10,000 per year. The price of the boom truck is $57,000, and its operating costs will exceed those of the present equipment by $100 per month. The resale value is expected to be $6000 in 12 years. Should the boom truck be purchased when the prevailing interest rate is 12 percent?

### Solution 5.2

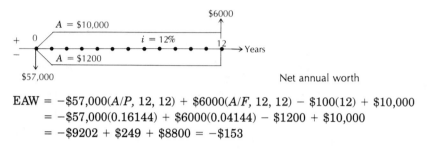

$$EAW = -\$57,000(A/P, 12, 12) + \$6000(A/F, 12, 12) - \$100(12) + \$10,000$$
$$= -\$57,000(0.16144) + \$6000(0.04144) - \$1200 + \$10,000$$
$$= -\$9202 + \$249 + \$8800 = -\$153$$

Equivalent annual-worth calculations indicate that the purchase and use of the boom truck will cause a loss equivalent to $153 per year for 12 years, compared with other investments that could earn a 12 percent return.

The solution to Example 5.2 was developed from the accompanying cash-flow diagram. The capital-recovery factor leads to the same solution when capital-recovery costs are registered negatively and the net annual savings are positive:

$$EAW = \text{annual savings} - \text{capital-recovery costs}$$
$$= \$10,000 - \$1200 - [(P - S)(A/P, 12, 12) + Si]$$
$$= \$8800 - [(\$57,000 - \$6000)(0.16144) + \$6000(0.12)]$$
$$= \$8800 - (\$8233 + \$720) = \$8800 - \$8953 = -\$153$$

## Net Cash Flow Comparison

"Which one is better?" may have conflicting answers. If the criterion is strictly economics, the alternative with the highest net worth is preferred, if worth is measured by revenues; but when worth is evaluated from costs, a low EAC is preferred.

### Example 5.3   Comparison of Net Annual Worths

A supplier of laboratory equipment estimates that profit from sales should increase by $23,000 per year if a mobile demonstration unit is built. A large unit with sleeping accommodations for the driver will cost $71,000, while a smaller unit without sleeping quarters will be $55,000. Salvage values for the large and small units after 5 years of use will be, respectively, $8000 and $3500. Lodging costs saved by the larger unit should amount to $3000 annually, but its yearly transportation costs will exceed those of the smaller unit by $1300. With money at 15 percent, should a mobile demonstration unit be built, and if so, which size is preferable?

**Solution 5.3**

*EAW of large mobile demonstration unit:*

| | |
|---|---:|
| Annual increase in profit | $23,000 |
| Savings in lodging costs over smaller unit per year | 3,000 |
| Extra transportation costs over smaller unit, per year | −1,300 |
| Capital-recovery cost: | |
| ($71,000 − $8000)($A/P$, 15, 5) + $8000$i$ | |
| $63,000 (0.29832)    $8000(0.15) | −19,994 |
| | Net AW = $4,706 |

*EAW of small mobile demonstration unit:*

| | |
|---|---:|
| Annual increase in profit | $23,000 |
| Capital-recovery cost: | |
| ($55,000 − $3500)($A/P$, 15, 5) + $3500$i$ | |
| $51,500 (0.29832) + $3500(0.15) | −15,888 |
| | Net AW = $7,112 |

The net annual worths indicate that both alternatives will produce positive cash flows while concurrently repaying investment costs. The small mobile demonstration unit is preferred because it promises a larger annual profit.

Since the profit increase expected from building either of the mobile labs is the same, the comparison could have been conducted by considering just the costs first:

| | Small Unit | Large Unit |
|---|---:|---:|
| Capital-recovery cost: | $15,888 | $19,994 |
| Net extra cost of smaller unit: $3000 − $1300 | 1,700 | |
| Total annual cost | $17,588 | $19,994 |

and then evaluating the best resulting alternative in terms of the expected income.

# CONSIDERATION OF ASSET LIFE

Translating cash flows to equivalent annuities is a mechanical process that becomes almost automatic with practice. Understanding the meaning of an economic comparison and being able to explain its significance to others are the critical skills. The discussion of economic asset life, as introduced in Chapter 4, is continued in this section to stress the importance of selecting an appropriate study period in equivalent annual-worth comparisons.

## Definitions of Asset Life

In time-value mechanics, $N$ is simply the number of compounding periods appropriate for the analysis of cash flows. $N$ takes on a special meaning when it represents the life of an asset that loses value as a function of use or time. The more frequently applied terms to describe the life of an asset are listed and defined as follows:

*Ownership life* or *service life* is the period of time an asset is kept in service by an owner or owners. Implied is a period of useful service from the time of purchase until disposal. Actually, under the vague expectation that it might somehow again prove useful, equipment is often retained beyond the point where it is capable of satisfying its intended function. A machine can have a *physical life* longer than its service life; the machine is still physically sound, but there is no useful function for it to perform.

*Accounting life* is a life expectancy based primarily on bookkeeping and tax considerations. It may or may not correspond to the period of usefulness and economic desirability. As will be seen in Chapter 11, the accounting records for the life and depreciation pattern of an asset affect taxes which in turn affect the net income derived from employing the asset.

*Economic life* is the time period that minimizes the asset's total equivalent annual cost or maximizes its equivalent net annual income. This period terminates when the asset is displaced by a more profitable replacement or the asset's service is no longer required. Economic life is also referred to as the *optimal replacement interval* and is the condition appropriate for most engineering economic studies.

Land is not subject to a specified life or to capital recovery because it historically appreciates in value rather than depreciating with age. The cost of land ownership is the interest not received on funds invested in the property.

## Comparisons of Assets with Equal and Unequal Lives

Examples 5.4 and 5.5 below are typical applications of EAC comparisons. The "lease or buy" question posed in Example 5.4 is raised with increasing regularity that corresponds to the rapid growth of leasing companies. It is now possible to lease almost any type of production equipment that is not custom designed for narrowly specialized service. Important tax considerations involved in the lease-buy choice are discussed in Chapter 12.

---

### Example 5.4   Alternatives with Equal Annual Costs

A machine needed for 3 years can be purchased for $77,662 and sold at the end of the period for about $25,000. A comparable machine can be leased for $30,000 per year. If a firm expects a return of 20 percent on investments, should it lease or buy the machine?

### Solution 5.4

$$\text{Equivalent annual cost to buy} = (\$77,662 - \$25,000)(A/P, 20, 3) + \$25,000(0.20)$$
$$= \$52,000(0.47473) + \$5000$$
$$= \$30,000$$

Annual cost to lease = $30,000

If the salvage value is considered reasonably accurate, the machine should be purchased because the funds invested in it will earn 20 percent (assuming 20 percent is an attractive rate of return for the firm).

The two alternatives in Example 5.4 are compared on the basis of their costs because the income resulting from their contribution is not available and, it is believed, both are capable of producing that contribution. The question is not whether to get a machine. It is known that the machine is necessary, so it is a choice between buying and leasing it. In selecting between the alternatives with equal equivalent annual worth, it should be recognized that they are equal only after ownership of the machine has earned 20 percent on the capital invested in it. Therefore, if the owners are satisfied with a 20 percent return on their money and no other considerations are involved, it is prudent to purchase.

### Example 5.5   Comparison of Assets with Unequal Lives

Two models of machines can be purchased to perform the same function. Type I has a low initial cost of $3300, high operating costs of $900 per year, and a short life of 4 years. The more expensive type II costs $9100, has annual operating expenses of $400, and can be kept in service economically for 8 years. The scrap value from either machine at the end of its life will just cover its removal cost. Which is preferred when the minimum attractive rate of return is 8 percent?

### Solution 5.5

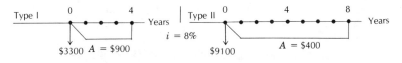

| *Type I Machine* | | *Type II Machine* | |
|---|---:|---|---:|
| Operating expenses | $ 900 | Operating expenses | $ 400 |
| Capital recovery: | | Capital recovery: | |
| $P(A/P, 8, 4) = \$3300(0.30192)$ | 996 | $P(A/P, 8, 8) = \$9100(0.17402)$ | 1584 |
| | EAC = $1896 | | EAC = $1984 |

The type I machine has a lower annual cost for service during the next 4 years and is therefore preferred.

The machines described in Example 5.5 exhibit the common feature that more expensive models, designed to serve the same function as less expensive versions, are expected to operate more economically and/or last longer. (If a costlier machine also produces better-quality products, the benefits from improved quality must be included in the analysis to make the outcomes comparable.) The difficulty in comparing alternatives with unequal lives is to account for the service provided during the period in which one outlasts the other.

The implied assumption in Solution 5.5 is that two machines of type I will be purchased consecutively to provide the same length of service as one type II machine. The equivalent annual cost for 8 years of service from two type I machines is, of course, the same as calculated in the solution above:

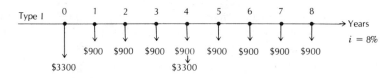

EAC = $3300($A/P$, 8, 8) + $3300($P/F$, 8, 4)($A/P$, 8, 8) + $900
    = $3300(0.17402) + $3300(0.73503)(0.17402) + $900
    = $574 + $422 + $900 = $1896 (as calculated previously)

The common-multiple assumption for evaluating assets with different lives is reasonable and widely used. Unless reliable forecasts can be made about future operating conditions and the probability of technical advances, the assumption that today's conditions will exist in the future is plausible. When future conditions can be estimated with confidence, these valuations are the data for equivalent annual-worth calculations. For instance, a confident prediction that current developmental work on the type I machine will produce refinements within 4 years to reduce operating costs by one-third while increasing the purchase price by one-half leads to a revised economic analysis:

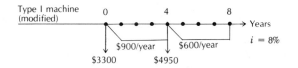

The annual worth is calculated by (1) translating the cash flow in the last 4 years to a present value at year 4 and discounting this value to year 0; (2) computing the present value of the first 4 years' cash flow; (3) adding the two present worths; and (4) converting the total to an 8-year annuity:

EAC(type I modified) = {[$600($P/A$, 8, 4) + $4950]($P/F$, 8, 4) + $900($P/A$, 8, 4) +
                        $3300}($A/P$, 8, 8)
    = {[$600(3.3121) + $4950](0.73503) + $900(3.3121) +
                        $3300}(0.17402)
    = [$6937(0.73503) + $2981 + $3300](0.17402)
    = ($5099 + $6281)(0.17402) = $1980

The modified type I machine now has nearly the same equivalent annual cost as the type II model. If a decision maker has confidence in the forecasted data, the choice between types could go either way, but it will more likely swing to type I because the lower purchase price and shorter life mean less capital is committed for a shorter period. This conservative philosophy provides some protection from unexpected developments. It was assumed in the comparison that the need for the machine would exist for 8 years. Many things can happen in 8 years to thwart the most carefully conceived plans—new designs, changing markets, successful competition, etc. The opportunity to reevaluate tactics in 4 years, as possible with the type I machine, is a subtle but valued attribute.

## Perpetual Life

Occasionally, an asset is treated as if it will last forever. The assumption of infinite life in terms of capital recovery is slightly more reasonable than the physical interpretation. Nothing made by humans, even Egyptian pyramids or the great wall of China, lasts forever, but the difference between infinity and 100 years in the numerical value of the capital-recovery factor is quite small:

$$(A/P, 10, \infty) = \frac{0.10(1.1)^{\infty}}{(1.10)^{\infty} - 1} = 0.10 \frac{\infty}{\infty} = 0.10$$

$(A/P, 10, 100) = 0.10001$

Therefore, in an economic comparison involving an asset with an infinite life, *such as land,* the interest rate replaces the capital-recovery factor. The manufactured assets most closely approaching perpetual life are dams, tunnels, canals, aqueducts, and monuments. The nature of very long-lived assets relegates them mostly to public projects, and there the trend has been to set a study period of 50 years or so in recognition of changing public needs and technological advances that generate new ways to fulfill the needs.

The similarity between the perpetual-life assumption for calculating equivalent annual worth and the capitalized cost method associated with present-worth models should be apparent. Both assume infinite life and, therefore, have very limited application.

## USE OF A SINKING FUND

The sinking-fund factor was discussed previously as an alternative means of calculating capital-recovery costs:

$$(P - S)(A/P, i, N) + Si = P(A/P, i, N) - S(A/F, i, N)$$

As is apparent in the equation, the sinking-fund factor is applied to compute the annuity required to accumulate a certain future amount. Organizations are sometimes obligated by legislated or contractual agreements to establish a fund, separate from their internal operations, to accumulate a specified amount by a specified time. This accumulation is called a *sinking fund.*

A provision for a sinking fund requires that an organization set aside a portion of its income each year in order to retire a bond issue (or, in some cases, an issue of preferred stock). Failure to meet the sinking-fund payments forces the bond issue to be thrown into default, causing serious credit and credibility problems. The payments are a direct cash drain on the organization. That is the purpose of the sinking fund – to protect investors by enforcing an orderly retirement of debt from current income.

A debt can be retired by regular payments from the sinking fund or by letting money accumulate in the sinking fund until the debt is due and then paying it in full (plus interest).

Periodic payments are associated with *sinking-fund bonds*. A call provision in such bonds gives the issuing organization the right to pay off a bond before its maturity date. Funds reserved from income are allocated each year to retire a portion of the bond issue. Sinking-fund payments thus utilized earn at the rate at which interest payments are avoided on the bonds retired.

When a sinking fund is established to accumulate sufficient money to meet the bond cost at maturity, annual payments are normally required to be invested in a savings institution. The interest rate for these "savings" typically is at a rate lower than the organization earns on its own capital, but the sinking fund is less an earning device than a way to assure that funds will not be diverted to other ventures.

For example, a firm borrows $1 million at 9 percent simple interest because it believes that the amount borrowed can be utilized within the firm to earn double the borrowing rate, 18 percent. If the $1 million is acquired by issuing 20-year bonds with the stipulation that a sinking fund be set up, the firm has to set aside a payment each year and put it in an external account. This account probably earns less than the 18 percent internally earned on investment funds, but it represents a very secure investment. Assuming the account pays 6 percent annual compound interest, the annual payments into the sinking fund would be

$$A = \$1,000,000(A/F, 6, 20)$$

$$= \$1,000,000(0.02719) = \$27,190$$

to make total annual debt repayment on the principal plus interest of $27,190 + $1,000,000(0.09) = $117,190.

## Review Exercises and Discussions

**Exercise 1**  An asset was purchased 5 years ago at a price of $52,000. It was expected to have an economic life of 8 years, at which time its salvage value would be $4000. If the function the asset was serving is no longer needed, what price must it be sold for now to recover the invested capital when $i = 12$ percent?

**Solution 1**  The expected annual cost of the asset over its 8-year life was

$$\text{EAC} = (P - S)(A/P, 12, 8) + S(0.12)$$
$$= (\$52,000 - \$4000)(0.20130) + \$4000(0.12)$$
$$= \$48,000(0.20130) + \$480 = \$10,142.40$$

The unrecovered capital at the end of the fifth year is the present worth of the last 3 years of the EAC annuity:

$$\text{Unrecovered capital(year 5)} = \$10,142.40(P/A, 12, 3)$$
$$= \$10,142.40(2.4018) = \$24,360$$

The same result could have been obtained using the alternative EAC formula:

$$\text{EAC} = P(A/P, 12, 8) - S(A/F, 12, 8)$$
$$= \$52,000(0.2013) - \$4000(0.0813) = \$10,142.40$$

**Exercise 2** Experience with a conventional mechanical log debarker suggests that its service life is 4 years. A newly designed hydraulic debarker costs one-third more than a mechanical debarker but makes much less noise. Both debarkers have about the same operating costs and no salvage value. What will the optimal replacement interval of the new hydraulic debarker have to be to make its cost comparable to the mechanical debarker at $i = 12$ percent?

**Solution 2**

AW(hydraulic debarker) = AW(mechanical debarker)
$$P(hd)(A/P, 12, N) = P(md)(A/P, 12, 4) \quad \text{and} \quad P(hd) = 1.33P(md)$$

$$(A/P, 12, N) = \frac{P(md)}{1.33P(md)}(0.32924) = 0.24693$$

$$N = 5 + 1\frac{0.27741 - 0.24693}{0.27741 - 0.24323} = 5 + 0.89 = 5.89 \text{ years}$$

The less tangible advantage of noise reduction associated with the hydraulic debarker should also be considered to make the alternatives' outcomes comparable.

---

**Exercise 3** A short concrete canal can be constructed as part of a flood-control project; the placement of a large galvanized culvert will serve the same function. The cost of the canal, which will last indefinitely, is $75,000, and maintenance costs will average $400 per year. A culvert, which will have to be replaced every 30 years, will cost $40,000 and have annual maintenance costs of $700. Salvage values are negligible for both alternatives, and the government interest rate is 6 percent. Which alternative has the lowest equivalent annual cost?

**Solution 3** Annual-cost comparison of a canal with perpetual life and a culvert with an economic life of 30 years:

*Canal*

| | |
|---|---:|
| Annual maintenance | $ 400 |
| Interest on investment: $75,000(0.06) | 4500 |
| Equivalent annual cost | $4900 |

*Culvert*

| | |
|---|---:|
| Annual maintenance | $ 700 |
| Capital recovery: $40,000(A/P, 6, 30) = $40,000(0.07265) | 2906 |
| Equivalent annual cost | $3606 |

The culvert has the advantage of a lower equivalent annual cost.

---

**Exercise 4** A grain elevator was built 15 years ago at a cost of $230,000. It was supposed to have a salvage value after 30 years of 10 percent of its first cost. Capital recovery is by a sinking fund held by a local bank that has paid interest during the period at 4 percent compounded annually. The owners now want to add a second grain elevator which will cost $400,000. How much additional capital will they need if they apply the capital-recovery reserves from the first elevator toward construction of the second?

**Solution 4** Annual payments made into the sinking fund for capital recovery of the first grain elevator were

$$A = (P - 0.1P)(A/F, 4, 30) = (\$230,000 - \$23,000)(0.01783)$$
$$= \$3691$$

The amount accumulated in the sinking fund after 15 payments is

$$F(15) = \$3691(F/A, 4, 15) = \$3691(20.023) = \$73,901$$

which can be deducted from the amount needed to finance a second grain elevator, $400,000. Then,

Additional capital needed = $400,000 − $73,901 = $326,099

# PROBLEMS

**5.1** Example 5.1 describes a training program which has uniformly increasing savings and uniformly decreasing costs.

 **5.1a** At what point during the year does the training program break even when $i = 0$? *(4.8 months)*

 **5.1b** At what point in time do savings just equal costs when the interest rate is 12 percent compounded monthly? *(10.8 months)*

 **5.1c** Explain why the breakeven point moved in the direction it did as the cash flow was discounted.

**5.2** A pilot plant has been constructed to convert garbage to oil, natural gas, and charcoal. The plant cost $4 million to build and will have a 20-year life with no salvage value. The cost of processing 1 tonne of garbage is $14. From each tonne are derived products which can be sold for $21. However, 20 percent of the end products are consumed as energy during the processing. The cost of delivery, sorting, and shredding a tonne of garbage is $2.50 after deducting the value of salvageable materials recovered. How many tonnes of garbage must be processed each year to recover the cost of the plant when the interest rate is 9 percent? *(1,460,667 tonnes/year)*

**5.3** A standby generator was purchased 6 years ago for $4200. Similar equipment had shown an economic life of 15 years with a salvage value of 15 percent of the first cost. The generator is no longer needed and is to be sold for $1800. The interest rate is 8 percent. What is the difference between the actual and anticipated equivalent annual capital-recovery costs? *($196/year)*

**5.4** Five years ago, a car owner bought an automobile for $5600. A trade-in of $600 was allowed on the purchase of the new car. The old one had been driven 112,651 km. If the owner's other investments earn 6 percent annually, what was the cost per km for capital recovery plus interest during the period of ownership? *($0.054 km)*

**5.5** Today is January 24, 1983. Suppose that 10 years ago you had started putting $100 per month in the bank. You made payments continually for 6 years and then stopped, but the accumulated deposit was left in the bank. On January 24, 1987, you plan to open a mousetrap factory. The money in the savings account will be used to advertise your new mousetrap. If you use $1000 per month in advertising, how many months can you continue before the fund is exhausted? The money is invested at 6 percent compounded monthly. *(14.5 months)*

**5.6** An investment in a cherry orchard is being considered. The asking price for the orchard is $120,000, half of which is accounted for by the land value. The cherry trees and harvesting equipment are past their prime and are expected to have no realizable value after 10 years. Income from the orchard, after deducting operating expenses and taxes, should be about $20,000 the first year, declining by $1000 each year. To obtain this net income, a working fund of $15,000 is required to maintain operations (the working fund is essentially invested capital because it is not available for other investments). Since the orchard is near a growing city, the land is expected to increase in value by 50 percent within 10 years. What is the annual worth of the orchard investment over 10 years when money is expected to earn 9 percent annually? *($2078)*

**5.7** Laser beams are to be used on a major construction project to assure the exact alignment of components. Two types of laser alignment systems, with the costs shown below, are suitable for the project.

|  | IC System | UC System |
| --- | --- | --- |
| First cost | $5000 | $3200 |
| Salvage value | 1000 | 0 |
| Annual operating cost | 600 | 950 |
| Additional taxes and insurance | 180 | 0 |

**5.7a** If both systems have a life of 4 years and the minimum rate of return is 15 percent, which offers the lowest equivalent annual cost? *(IC = $2331; UC = $2071)*
**5.7b** How much longer would the economic life of the IC system have to be in order to make the equivalent annual costs of the two systems equal? *(1.4 years)*

**5.8** In Problem 4.8, costs were given for a decision between a concrete and a galvanized warehouse building. Now another option is available. The manufacturer can lease a structure which is located about half a mile (0.805 kilometer) from the main plant and has approximately the same floor space as the warehouses being considered for construction. It can be leased for $50,000 per year. In addition to the lease expense, it will likely cost $2000 per month in extra material-handling expense to transport materials to and from the leased building.

How much can be saved by leasing when a 12 percent interest rate is applicable? *($3456 per year)*

**5.9** Compare the annual costs of the two alternatives described in Problem 4.27. *[EAC(both) = $554.82]*

**5.10** Two methods of supplying water and sewage treatment for a housing development outside the districts where water and sewage-disposal services are provided by the city are described by the accompanying cash flows for a 40-year study period:

| Years | Method 1 | Method 2 |
|-------|----------|----------|
| 0 | −$350,000 | −$735,000 |
| 1–10 | −11,000 | −8000 |
| 10 | −25,000 | +100,000 |
| 11–20 | −13,000 | −13,000 |
| 20 | −150,000 | +100,000 |
| 21–30 | −15,000 | −15,000 |
| 30 | −25,000 | −75,000 |
| 31–40 | −18,000 | −15,000 |

Both methods have the same absolute cash-flow amounts over the study period ($1,120,000), and both provide comparable quality of service. At an interest rate of 8 percent, which method has the lower equivalent annual cost?

**5.11** A family that enjoys outdoor activities can purchase a small, run-down cabin in a desirable mountain location for $6000. To make it livable they will have to repair the roof and construct a new outhouse at a cost of $1800 for materials and transportation. If the cabin is to be usable for skiing in the winter, they will have to add a fireplace or stove and insulation that will cost at least $2000. Other annual expenses for electricity, taxes, maintenance, etc., will average $550. They expect to own the cabin 5 years before a job transfer will force them to sell it. Assuming the repairs are done at once, heating arrangements are added by the end of the second year, and the cabin can be sold for $7000, how much could the family afford to spend each year for other outings in place of going to their cabin? Their savings earn 7 percent. What intangible factors might affect their decision to buy the cabin?

**5.12** A bond issue for $75,000 has been passed by voters to buy six minibuses for a senior citizens' transportation service. It is anticipated that the revenue from the bus service will yield a rate of return of 7 percent on the investment. A provision in the bond issue was that a sinking fund be established through a local bank to accumulate enough money to recover the $75,000 in 6 years. The bond issue is to pay 8 percent simple interest (due in a lump sum at maturity), and the local bank pays annual interest of 6 percent.
    **5.12a** What annual payment is required for the sinking fund at the bank?
    **5.12b** What annual return is required to recover the capital invested plus profit.

**5.13** A company borrows $100,000 under an agreement to set up a sinking fund to pay back the amount owed in 5 years. The interest earned on the sinking fund is 7 percent. Annual interest payments of $100,000 × 0.09 = $9000 are to be paid by the company to the lenders. The company expects internally invested funds to earn twice the interest rate paid on the external sinking fund. What is the annual cost to the company to repay the loan?

**5.14** A sheltered workshop requires a lift truck to handle pallets for a new contract. A lift truck can be purchased for $17,000. Annual insurance costs are 3 percent of the purchase price, payable at the first of each year. An equivalent truck can be rented for $667 per month, payable at the end of each month. Operating costs are the same for both alternatives. What minimum number of months must a purchased truck be used on the contract to make purchasing more attractive than leasing. Interest is 12 percent compounded monthly. (Assume the purchased truck has no salvage value at any time.)

**5.15** A clever investor purchased a piece of land 5 years ago for $175,000. Its appraised value now is twice the original cost. Year-end taxes have been 4 percent of the purchase price until now. A street assessment of $17,500 was paid 2 years ago. A land developer is willing to buy the land at the appraised price plus the investor's ownership costs on a 4-year contract at 9 percent compounded annually. How large should the developer's four annual payments be if the investor uses an annual interest rate of 15 percent in figuring the time value of ownership costs?

**5.16**  An asset is expected to depreciate in market value at a constant rate from its purchase price of $20,000 to a zero salvage value during its 8 years of physical life. Operating costs are expected to be $8000 the first year and to increase at a 10 percent compound rate as the asset gets older. What is the annual cost of ownership if the asset is replaced every 3 years? The required rate of return is 12 percent.

**5.17**  A sinking fund was set up to pay off a debt of $100,000 in 10 years. The payments earn 7 percent compound annual interest. How much of the debt has been accounted for after the seventh payment has been made?

**5.18**  The present wooden bridge over Deep Bay is in danger of collapse. The transportation department is currently considering two alternatives to alleviate the situation and provide for expected increases in future traffic. One plan is a conventional steel bridge, while the other is a tunnel under the bay. The department is familiar with bridge construction and mainte-nance, but has no experience with maintenance costs for tunnels. The following data have been developed for the bridge:

| | |
|---|---|
| First cost | $17,000,000 |
| Painting every 6 years | 1,000,000 |
| Deck resurfacing every 12 years | 3,000,000 |
| Structural overhaul at the end of 30 years | 4,000,000 |
| Annual maintenance | 300,000 |

The tunnel is expected to cost $24,000,000 and will require repaving every 12 years at a cost of $2,000,000. If both designs are expected to last 60 years with negligible salvage value, determine the maximum equivalent annual amount for maintenance that could be permitted for the tunnel while holding the total EAC to that of the bridge. Let $i = 6$ percent.

**5.19**  An earth compactor costs $18,000 and has an economic life of 9 years. However, the purchaser needs it only for one project that will be completed in 3 years. At the end of the project, it can be sold for half its purchase price. What is the annual cost to the owner if the required rate of return is 20 percent?

# EXTENSIONS

***5A  Amortization plus Interest***  Some government agencies and utility compa-nies use a method of capital recovery referred to as *amortization plus interest.* "Amortization" means money put aside at intervals for gradual payment of a debt. The agencies utilizing this method normally employ the sinking-fund factor to calculate depreciation on their assets; hence, amortization is associated with a sinking fund in this context. The "interest" part of the method occurs as a charge on the first cost of the asset.

The rationale for applying the "sinking fund plus interest on first cost" method runs somewhat as follows: "I pay out a certain sum $P$ for an asset, and this asset decreases in value to $S$ by the end of its economic life $N$. To account for this devaluation, I will make payments into a fund that earns interest at rate $i$ to accumulate $P - S$ dollars in $N$ years. However, during this period I am deprived of the use of amount $P$ because this amount is invested in the asset and unavailable to me. Therefore, I will charge interest at rate $i$ on $P$ for the entire period as compensation for not having the use of that money."

**QUESTIONS**

**5A.1**  For an asset described by $P = \$15{,}000$, $S = \$5000$, $i = 5$ percent, and $N = 20$ years, calculate its annual cost of ownership according to amortization plus interest: $AC = (P - S)(A/F, i, N) + Pi$.

**5A.2**  Apply the capital-recovery factor to obtain the annual cost for the asset in Question 5A.1. Use the formulas for the interest factors to prove that the two methods for recovering capital plus a return must produce the same annual cost.

**5A.3**  An advantage sometimes cited for the "amortization plus interest" method is that different interest rates can be used in the calculation. For instance, when the sinking fund for an asset earns interest at a rate of 5 percent, the asset's owner might want 10 percent compensation for the investment funds that are tied up in the asset. Consequently, $i = 5$ percent when used in the sinking fund, and $i = 10$ percent when applied to the first cost. With reference to Questions 5A.1 and 5A.2 and the discussion of the use of sinking funds in the chapter, comment on the use of two different interest rates in making an economic comparison.

**5B  *Equivalent Uniform Payments When Interest Rates Vary***  Interest rates have fluctuated widely in recent years as a response to different degrees of inflation. Rates also vary according to the type and size of investment; larger investments are often awarded higher interest rates, and riskier investments demand higher returns. Therefore, it is occasionally appropriate to assign different interest rates to specific periods of cash flow.

Present and future worths of cash flows with changing interest rates are calculated by translating each transaction backward or forward in time according to the prevailing interest rate in each period of the translation. For example, assume a deposit of $5000 was made 4 years ago, and a withdrawal of $2000 was made 2 years ago. The prevailing interest rate during the first year was 6 percent, and the rate increased by 1 percent each year. The amount in the account at the end of each year is shown in Table 5.2.

**TABLE 5.2**

| End of Year | Deposit or Withdrawal | $i$ during Year | Balance in the Account at End of Year |
|---|---|---|---|
| 0 | +$5000 | | |
| 1 | | 6% | $5000(F/P, 6, 1) = \$5300$ |
| 2 | −$2000 | 7% | $\$5300(F/P, 7, 1) - \$2000 = \$3671$ |
| 3 | | 8% | $\$3671(F/P, 8, 1) = \$3964.68$ |
| 4 | | 9% | $\$3964.68(F/P, 9, 1) = \$4321.50$ |

By the same approach, the present worth at time zero of the cash flow is

PW = $5000 − $2000(P/F, 6, 1)(P/F, 7, 1) = $3236.64

A uniform series of four payments equivalent to the given cash flow with changing interest rates is calculated as

$$P = A(P/F, 6, 1) + A(P/F, 6, 1)(P/F, 7, 1) + A(P/F, 6, 1)(P/F, 7, 1)(P/F, 8, 1)$$
$$+ A(P/F, 6, 1)(P/F, 7, 1)(P/F, 8, 1)(P/F, 9, 1)$$

$3236.64 = \;A[(0.94340) \;+\; (0.9340)(0.93458) \;+\; (0.94340)(0.93458)(0.92593)$
$$+ (0.94340)(0.93458)(0.92593)(0.91743)]$$

$$= A(3.3904)$$
$$A = \$3236.64/3.3904 = \$954.65$$

A corresponding calculation of a series of equal payments A from the future worth is carried out as

$$F = A + A(F/P, 9, 1) + A(F/P, 8, 1)(F/P, 9, 1) + A(F/F, 7, 1)(F/P, 8, 1)(F/P, 9, 1)$$

and

$$A = \frac{\$4321.50}{1 + 1.09 + \; 1.08\,(1.09) + \; 1.07\,(1.08)(1.09)}$$

$$= \frac{\$4321.50}{4.5268} = \$954.65$$

Thus, four year-end payments of $954.65 yield a future amount of $4321.50 when interest rates progress from 6 percent to 7 percent to 8 percent to 9 percent during the 4-year span, and the worth of this annuity is equivalent to a cash inflow of $5000 at time zero and an outflow of −$2000 at the end of year 2.

**5B.1** What series of equal annual payments is equivalent to the cash flow shown below?  *(A = $3158.58)*

| End of year | 0 | | 1 | | 2 | | 3 | | 4 | | 5 |
|---|---|---|---|---|---|---|---|---|---|---|---|
| Interest rate | | 7% | | 7% | | 10% | | 11% | | 9% | |
| Receipts | $10,000 | | | | $10,000 | | | | $10,000 | | |
| Disbursements | | | $3000 | | | | $5000 | | | | $10,000 |

# CHAPTER 6

# RATE-OF-RETURN COMPARISONS

OVERVIEW

Internal rate of return (IRR) is the last of the discounted cash flow comparison methods considered here. It is favored by some who claim it provides the most easily understood comparisons and that it produces percentage ranking figures that are very useful. IRR calculations may begin with either EAW or PW formulations, the latter being more prevalent. There is no way to avoid trial-and-error computations for complex formulations, but the structure offers clues as to where to begin.

Consistent results are obtained from EAW, PW, and IRR comparisons. A rate of return can be calculated for proposals that involve only costs, as well as income-producing proposals. PW and IRR calculations may appear to produce contradictory results when an alternative with heavy cash flows in early years is compared to an alternative having major flows in later years. The contradiction is resolved by basing selection on the minimum acceptable rate of return (MARR).

A cumulative cash flow pattern that reverses signs (from negative to positive or vice versa) more than once may have more than one internal rate of return. An applicable IRR is determined by applying an external rate of return to a portion of the cash flow that eliminates sign reversals. This external reinvestment rate is primarily a function of the MARR.

A minimum acceptable rate of return is the lowest level at which an alternative is still attractive. It varies among and within organizations. Although there are a wide variety of recommendations for determining this lowest level of acceptability, it is generally agreed that it should be no lower, and most likely considerably higher, than the cost of capital. How much higher depends on the circumstances, objectives, and policies of the

*118*

organization. The purpose of establishing a minimum acceptable rate of return is to ration capital to the most deserving proposals.

## PW, EAW, AND INTERNAL RATE OF RETURN

Rate of return is the most celebrated method of comparing investment alternatives. It is sometimes known as *true rate of return, discounted cash flow rate of return,* or *internal rate of return* (IRR). The IRR designation is adopted here because it emphasizes that the rate is indeed *internal* – the IRR is based solely on the investment's cash flow, and no external influences are recognized.

Under whatever name the rate-of-return concept is applied, it provides a percentage figure that indicates the relative yield on different uses of capital. Since interest rates are well understood throughout the world of commerce, there should be little danger of misinterpretation of IRR figures. Another minor advantage is that it avoids the necessity of knowing a required or minimum rate of interest before calculations can be conducted; the calculations produce a percentage figure that can be compared directly with other investment proposals. These features are achieved at the expense of more tedious calculations, a minor but frustrating drawback.

Annual-worth and present-worth formulations are the foundations for rate-of-return calculations. It was observed in the previous two chapters that EAW and PW are readily convertible at a common interest rate, and some problems are more easily formulated from one or the other approaches. Equivalently, the rate of return can be calculated by equating either the annual or present worths of cash flows to zero and solving for the interest rate (IRR) that allows the equality. Although both the EAW and PW approaches are legitimate, the rate of of return  is generally defined in terms of present worth:

> The rate of return over cost is that rate which, employed in computing the present worth of all costs and the present worth of all the returns, will make these two equal. Or, as a mathematician would prefer to put it, the rate which employed in computing the present worth of the whole series of differences between two income streams (some differences being positive and others negitive) will make the total zero.*

## UTILIZATION OF THE RATE-OF-RETURN METHOD

Because rate-of-return computations begin with a problem expressed in terms of present worth or annual worth, it is necessary to heed the guidelines for the EAW and PW methods. In particular, alternatives must be compared on the basis of equivalent outcomes. As in the previous discussions of discounted cash flow, we initially investigate the rate-of-return method without considering the effects of income taxes. Tax considerations are introduced in Chapter 12.

*I. Fisher, *The Theory of Interest*, Kelley and Millman, New York, 1930.

The rate of return for a single proposal is determined by setting the present worth (or EAW) of receipts equal to the present worth (or EAW) of disbursements. Then an interest rate is sought that makes the discounted flows conform to the equality:

Find $i$ so that   PW(receipts) = PW(disbursements)

The same relationship obviously occurs when the discounted flows are subtracted from each other to equal zero:

Find $i$ so that   PW(receipts) − PW(disbursements) = 0

When a single proposal is for a cost-reduction project, the receipts take the form of net savings from the method of operation used before the cost-reduction investment. For either PW formulation, the calculation of $i$ is usually a trial-and-error procedure.

---

### Example 6.1    Income-Producing Proposal

A parcel of land adjacent to a proposed highway exit is deemed likely to increase in value. It can be purchased now for $80,000 and is expected to be worth $150,000 within 5 years. During that period it can be rented for pasture at $1500 per year. Annual taxes are presently $850 and will likely remain constant. What rate of return will be earned on the investment if the estimates are accurate?

### Solution 6.1

The conditions of the proposal are depicted in a cash flow diagram. The income (positive cash flow) and disbursements (negative cash flow) can be equated according to their equivalent present worths as

$150,000(P/F, i, 5) + $1500(P/A, i, 5) = $80,000 + $850(P/A, i, 5)$

or the positive and negative cash flows can be subtracted as

$150,000(P/F, i, 5) − $80,000 + $1500(P/A, i, 5) − $850(P/A, i, 5) = 0$

which reduces to

$150,000(P/F, i, 5) − $80,000 + $650(P/A, i, 5) = 0$

The value of $i$ that conforms to the above equation is the rate of return on the $80,000 investment. Its value is determined by trial and error.

Now, a quick preliminary check to see if the relationship has a positive rate of return results from letting $i = 0$. At $i = 0$,

$150,000 − $80,000 + $650(5) = $70,000 + $3250 = $73,250$

The positive value indicates the investment will produce a positive rate of return because the total income is much greater than the outgo. The check also gives a very rough idea of how large the rate of return might be. For instance, the *72-rule* suggests that a sum doubles in value every $72/i$ years. Since the $80,000 almost doubles in value in 5 years, $i$ should be near $72/5 = 14.4$ percent.

Letting $i = 15$ percent as the first trial, we have

$$\$150,000(P/F, 15, 5) - \$80,000 + \$650(P/A, 15, 5) \overset{?}{=} 0$$
$$\$150,000(0.49718) - \$80,000 + \$650(3.3521) = -\$3244.14$$

The negative value indicates that the interest rate used was too large. Now it is known that $i$ lies between 0 and 15 percent.

Letting $i = 14$ percent gives

$$\$150,000(P/F, 14, 5) - \$80,000 + \$650(P/A, 14, 5) \overset{?}{=} 0$$
$$\$150,000(0.51937) - \$80,000 + \$650(3.4330) = \$136.95$$

which shows that 14 percent $< i <$ 15 percent. The approximate value of $i$ is determined by linear interpolation from

| $i$ | PW |
|-----|-----|
| 14% | $136.95 |
| ? | 0 |
| 15% | $-$3244.14 |

Range of $i = 15\% - 14\% = 1\%$

Range of PW $= \$136.95 - (-\$3244.14)$
$\qquad\qquad\quad = \$3381.09$

The amount by which $i$ is greater than 14 percent is equal to the proportion of the PW range to the point were PW $= 0$:

$$i = 14\% + 1\% \frac{\$136.95 - 0}{\$3381.09} = 14\% + 1\%(0.041)$$
$$\text{IRR} \doteq 14\%$$

---

A characteristic worth noting in the previous calculations is that whenever the present worth turns out to be positive, the next trial should employ a higher interest rate to approach the desired zero outcome. Conversely, lowering the interest rate in the present-worth formulation increases the resulting outcome.

A small degree of error is introduced by linear interpolation between interest-table values that are not linearly related. To keep the error as small as possible, interpolations should be conducted between adjacent interest tables. The error is naturally less between lower-interest-rate tables, separated by ½ percent, than at increments of 10 percent for the largest interest rates. For the purposes of this book, interpolated rates of return computed to the nearest tenth of a percent are adequate. The slight error that may be thus introduced will very seldom influence the choice among alternatives; this error is probably much less significant than actual deviations from the cash flows estimated in the comparisons.

## Example 6.2   Cost-Reduction Proposal

Subassemblies for a model IV scope are purchased for $71 apiece. The annual demand is 350 units, and it is expected to continue for 3 years, at which time the model V scope now under development should be ready for manufacturing. With equipment purchased and installed for $21,000, the production costs to internally produce the subassemblies should be $18,500 for the first year and $12,250 each of the last 2 years. The equipment will have no salvage value. Should the company make or buy the subassemblies?

## Solution 6.2

The savings expected in a cost-reduction proposal are treated as income. Assuming the transactions occur at the end of each year, the cash-flow diagram appears as shown below.

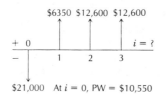

$21,000   At $i = 0$, PW = $10,550

Present annual cost = 350 × $71 = $24,850

Net savings (year 1) = $24,850 − $18,500 = $6350

Net savings (years 2, 3) = $24,850 − $12,250 = $12,600

PW = −$21,000 + $6350($P/F$, $i$, 1) + $12,600($P/F$, $i$, 2) + $12,600($P/F$, $i$, 3) = 0

Trying successively higher rates of return gives at $i$ = 10 percent,

PW = −$21,000 + $6350(0.90909) + $12,600(0.82645)
$$+ \$12,600(0.75132) = \$4652.62$$

at $i$ = 15 percent,

PW = −$21,000 + $6350(0.86957) + $12,600(0.75614)
$$+ \$12,600(0.65752) = \$2333.89$$

at $i$ = 20 percent,

PW = −$21,000 + $6350(0.83333) + $12,600(0.69445)
$$+ \$12,600(0.57870) = \$333.78$$

and at $i$ = 25 percent,

PW = −$21,000 + $6350(0.80000) + $12,600(0.64000)
$$+ \$12,600(0.51200) = -\$1404.80$$

By interpolation, the rate of return on the $21,000 investment is

$$\text{IRR} = 20\% + 5\% \frac{\$333.78 - 0}{\$333.78 - -\$1404.80} = 20\% + 0.96\% = 21\%$$

The answer to the make-or-buy question depends on how large a return the firm expects on its invested capital. Conditions for accepting the proposal to manufacture the subassemblies internally are displayed by the graph in Figure 6.1, where the present worth of the proposal is shown as a function of the required IRR. For any required rate of return lower than 21 percent, the firm should view the proposal favorably.

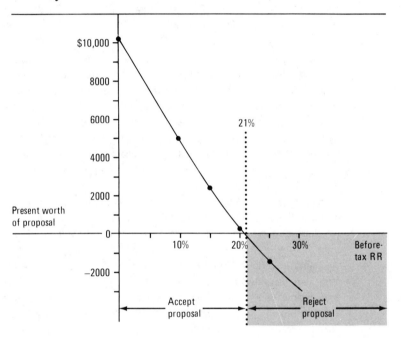

**FIGURE 6.1** Present worth of cash flow for the proposal in Example 6.2 at different interest rates. At any required IRR below 21 percent, the present worth of the proposal is positive and therefore acceptable. For a minimum acceptable IRR greater than 21 percent, the proposal exhibits a negative present worth and is thereby rejected.

## Interpretation

The cash flow patterns in Examples 6.1 and 6.2 illustrate the relationship between an investment and its recovery. There are two amounts or series of money, one positive and one negative, which are equivalent at a certain interest rate—the internal rate of return. At the IRR the present worth of net cash flow equals zero.

In Example 6.2, the initial investment of $21,000 will be returned in 3 years and additionally will earn 21 percent on the unrecovered balance of the investment. That is, during the first year, the interest earned on $21,000 will be $21,000 × 0.21 = $4410. After the first payment of $6350 is received, the remaining unrecovered capital ($21,000 − $6350 = $14,650) will earn $14,650 × 0.21 = $3076 during the second year. This pattern will continue throughout the life of the investment, as was demonstrated in Table 5.1. It is important to realize that the IRR is earned *only* on the capital originally invested; how the capital-recovery payments are reinvested has no bearing on the IRR. Stated another way, the $21,000 investment receives a return of 21 percent regardless of what is done with the three payments—they may be reinvested at different interest rates or not at all—because the analysis encompasses only the cash flow for the investment and its direct recovery payments.

## Clues for IRR Calculations

There is no way to avoid the trial-and-error search procedure for determining the IRR in problems with complex cash flows. But a little preplanning may narrow the area of search. An even neater tactic, if available, is to use a computer or calculator with a canned program.

The first maneuver to avoid unnecessary computations is to sum the cash flows. A negative total indicates the proposal being considered cannot meet even an $i = 0$ percent requirement, thereby eliminating it from further consideration whenever a positive IRR is required. The size of a positive net sum, with respect to amount and length of investment, gives a rough suggestion of the rate of return. For instance, the net cash flow at $i = 0$ percent is $10,550 in Example 6.2, and the initial investment is $21,000 for 3 years. This 50 percent return on investment over 3 years suggests a substantial IRR.

A quick proximity fix on the IRR is possible for problems that have their major cash flows at the beginning and end of the study period, or those consisting largely of constant cash-flow streams. When the salvage value is close to 100 percent of the first cost, the net annuity divided by the first cost gives a close approximation to $i$; that is, $A/P \doteq i$. As demonstrated in Example 6.1, when the total net income at $i = 0$ sums to about twice the initial outlay, $i \doteq 72/N$.

The more variation in cash flows, the more difficult the guessing game gets. Sometimes irregular cash flows can be rounded off to approximate an ordinary annuity, or individual transactions within short time intervals can be lumped together to allow gross preliminary calculations that suggest the vicinity of the IRR. For instance, in Example 6.2 the irregular receipts could be approximated by an average $A$ of, say, $10,000. Then, $A/P = \$10,000/\$21,000 = 0.4761$. With this figure as an entry to an interest table for a capital-recovery factor at $N = 3$, $(A/P, 20, 3) = 0.47473$ gives a good place to begin IRR trial computations.

## CONSISTENCY OF COMPARISON METHODS

In practically all situations, the acceptability of alternative courses of action will be identical whether evaluated according to their annual worths, present worths, or rates of return. (Some exceptions are noted in the next section.) The important aspect is to recognize the meaning of the measures of acceptability and the assumptions upon which they are based. Sample calculations applying all three comparison methods to the data in Table 6.1 reveal the consistency of results. They also illustrate how the rate of return is calculated to compare investments when only the disbursements are known and how to interpret the outcomes.

Suppose a certain function is currently being performed at an annual labor expense of $20,000. One alternative, plan *A*, is to leave the operation unchanged. In effect, this is the "do-nothing" alternative which is almost always present in a decision situation. A second alternative, plan *B*, is to invest $30,000 in layout modifications which will allow the function to be performed at a reduced labor cost of $15,000. The expense of the renovations must be recovered in 10 years according to operating policy. Plan *C* is a proposal to install a labor-saving device which will cut the labor cost to $12,000. The device will be worn out in 5 years and has no salvage value. Table 6.1 is a year-by-year tabulation of the cash flow for the three plans. If the company's minimum acceptable rate of return is 8 percent, which plan offers the greatest economic benefit?

| Year | Plan A | Plan B | Plan C |
|------|--------|--------|--------|
| 0 | | $30,000 | $25,000 |
| 1 | $20,000 | 15,000 | 12,000 |
| 2 | 20,000 | 15,000 | 12,000 |
| 3 | 20,000 | 15,000 | 12,000 |
| 4 | 20,000 | 15,000 | 12,000 |
| 5 | 20,000 | 15,000 | 37,000 |
| 6 | 20,000 | 15,000 | 12,000 |
| 7 | 20,000 | 15,000 | 12,000 |
| 8 | 20,000 | 15,000 | 12,000 |
| 9 | 20,000 | 15,000 | 12,000 |
| 10 | 20,000 | 15,000 | 12,000 |

**TABLE 6.1** Estimated cash flows for alternative operating plans.

## AW and PW Comparisons

Using the already familiar procedures for computing the equivalent annual worth (cost) of a cash-flow stream, the annual cost for the current operating method, plan *A*, is read directly from the table:

EAC(plan *A*) = labor expense = $20,000

In plan *B* the initial investment is spread over the 10-year study period and added to the annual labor expense to get

EAC(plan *B*) = $30,000(*A*/*P*, 8, 10) + $15,000
$$= \$30,000(0.14903) + \$15,000 = \$19,471$$

Since the study period comprises two cycles of the 5-year economic life of the labor-saving device in plan *C*, the annual cost will be the same over each 5-year period and is equal to

EAC(plan *C*) = $25,000(*A*/*P*, 8, 5) + $12,000
$$= \$25,000(0.25046) + \$12,000 = \$18,262$$

Thus, plan *C*, with the lowest annual cost, is preferred. Compared with the currently existing plan $A$, an investment of $25,000 in a labor-saving device will yield a return of 8 percent per year plus the equivalent receipt of $20,000 − $18,262 = $1738 each year from savings in labor expense for 5 years.

The equivalent present worth (cost) of the three plans is calculated by simply multiplying each EAC by the uniform-series present-worth factor, $(P/A, 8, 10) = 6.710$:

PW(plan $A$) = $20,000(6.710) = $134,200
PW(plan $B$) = $19,471(6.710) = $130,650
PW(plan $C$) = $18,262(6.710) = $122,538

Since a lower present cost is preferred, plan $C$ again gets the nod, as advertised. This means that over a 10-year period when money is worth 8 percent, plan $C$ is expected to cost $134,200 − $122,538 = $11,662 less in *today's dollars* to accomplish the same operation now being done under plan $A$. This total saving is, of course, the present worth of the annual gain beyond the 8 percent return calculated in the EAC comparison:

$1738(P/A, 8, 10) = $1738(6.710) = $11,662

## IRR Comparison

The given data provide examples of IRR comparisons that do not have natural cash flows which are positive. The positive cash flow stream is developed from the savings generated by each additional increment of investment. A more detailed discussion of incremental analysis is presented in the next chapter, but it is sufficient here to understand that *each increment of capital expended must be justified of itself*.

The smallest investment over the do-nothing alternative in plan $A$ is the $25,000 outlay for the labor-saving device in plan $C$. The "earnings" from this investment are the annual reductions in labor expense: $20,000 − $12,000 = $8000. Since the annual-worth formulation is more convenient for calculating the rate of return, the equivalent annual costs for plans $A$ and $C$ are equated as

EAC(plan $C$) = EAC(plan $A$)     at IRR

or,

First cost to initiate plan $C$ − present worth of annual savings using plan $C$ = 0 at IRR

$25,000 − $8000(P/A, i, 5) \gtrless 0$

$$(P/A, i, 5) = \frac{\$25,000}{\$8000} = 3.125$$

which, by interpolation between the 15 percent and 20 percent interest tables, furnishes

$$IRR = 15\% + 5\% \frac{3.352 - 3.125}{3.352 - 2.991} = 15\% + 5\% \frac{0.227}{0.361} = 18.1\%$$

proving plan $C$ is an acceptable alternative when the required rate of return is 8 percent.

Although it is already known from the EAC and PW comparisons that plan $C$ is preferred to plan $B$, it can be checked by determining the IRR for the $30,000 investment in plan $B$ over the do-nothing alternative, plan $A$:

$$PW(\text{plan } B) = PW(\text{plan } A) \quad \text{at IRR}$$
$$\$30,000 + \$15,000(P/A, i, 10) \stackrel{?}{=} \$20,000(P/A, i, 10)$$

$$(P/A, i, 10) = \frac{\$30,000}{\$20,000 - \$15,000} = 6.0$$

from which, by interpolation between 10 percent and 11 percent,

$$i = 10\% + 1\% \frac{6.1445 - 6.0000}{6.1445 - 5.8892} = 10.6\%$$

It is evident from comparing IRR(plan $C$) = 18.1 percent to IRR(plan $B$) = 10.6 percent that plan $C$ deserves its preference.

## IRR IRREGULARITIES

The consistency of AW and PW comparisons is above reproach, and both *generally* agree with IRR evaluations. However, there are two situations in which calculations obscure or contradict the preferences shown by the other two comparison methods. Both situations involve distinctive cash-flow patterns that provide a clue to possible confusion.

### Ranking Reversal

Let two projects have the cash flows indicated in Table 6.2. Both proposals require the same $1000 initial investment. The contrasting net annual returns are conspicuous; project $X$ starts low and increases, whereas project $Y$ has a high first-year flow followed by constant lower flows.

|  |  | END-OF-YEAR CASH FLOW | | | |
|---|---|---|---|---|---|
| Project | 0 | 1 | 2 | 3 | 4 |
| $X$ | −$1000 | $ 100 | $350 | $600 | $850 |
| $Y$ | −1000 | 1000 | 200 | 200 | 200 |

**TABLE 6.2** Cash flows for two projects with 4-year lives and no salvage value.

The two projects are first compared by their present worths when the minimum required rate of return is 10 percent:

$$PW(X) = -\$1000 + [\$100 + \$250(A/G, 10, 4)](P/A, 10, 4)$$
$$= -\$1000 + [\$100 + \$250(1.3810)](3.1698)$$
$$= \$411.56$$

$$PW(Y) = -\$1000 + [\$1000 + \$200(P/A, 10, 3)](P/F, 10, 1)$$
$$= -\$1000 + [\$1000 + \$200(2.4868)](0.90909)$$
$$= \$361.27$$

This *ranks project X higher than project Y.*

When an IRR comparison is made, the rankings switch, as shown by the following calculations: For project $X$,

$$PW = -\$1000 + [\$100 + \$250(A/G, i, 4)](P/A, i, 4) \stackrel{?}{=} 0$$

At $i = 20$ percent,

$$PW = -\$1000 + [\$100 + \$250(1.2742)](2.5887) = \$83.51$$

and at $i = 25$ percent,

$$PW = -\$1000 + [\$100 + \$250(1.2249)](2.3616) = -\$40.66$$

to give

$$IRR(X) = 20\% + 5\% \frac{\$83.51 - 0}{\$83.51 - -\$40.66} = 23.4\%$$

For project $Y$,

$$PW(Y) = -\$1000 + [\$1000 + \$200(P/A, i, 3)](P/F, i, 1) \stackrel{?}{=} 0$$

is solved by trial and error to obtain IRR($Y$) = 34.5 percent, which *ranks project Y ahead of project X.*

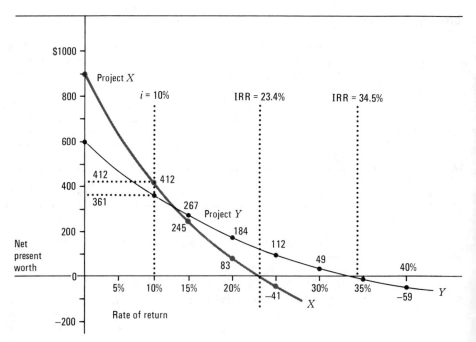

**FIGURE 6.2**
Relationship of net present worth and different discount rates, showing how the rankings for two projects can switch.

The net present-worth profiles for the two projects are shown in Figure 6.2. indicated from the previous calculations, the present worth of $X$ exceeds that of $Y$ at $i = 10$ percent, and the internal rate of return is higher for $Y$ than $X$ when PW = 0. The point of intersection of the two curves is the incremental rate of return as calculated in Table 6.3.

**TABLE 6.3**
Incremental rate of return that makes project $X$ equivalent to project $Y$. The $-\$900$ difference in year 1 leads to additional income the following 3 years, the rate of return being approximately 13 percent per year.

| Project | $X$ | $Y$ | $X - Y$ |
|---|---|---|---|
| Year 0 | $-\$1000$ | $-\$1000$ | $\$0$ |
| Year 1 | 100 | 1000 | $-900$ |
| Year 2 | 350 | 200 | 150 |
| Year 3 | 600 | 200 | 400 |
| Year 4 | 850 | 200 | 650 |

$$PW = -\$900 + \$150(P/F, 13, 1) + \$400(P/F, 13, 2) + \$650(P/F, 13, 3) \doteq 0$$

The intersection is the pivot point for selecting the superior alternative. Select $X$ when the required rate of return is less than 13 percent, and select $Y$ when the required rate is more than 13 percent but less than 35 percent. This selection rule abides by the PW comparison at $i = 10$ percent which indicated a preference for $X$. A similar PW comparison at $i = 14$ percent indicates a preference for $Y$:

$$PW(X) = -\$1000 + [\$100 + \$250(A/G, 14, 4)](P/A, 14, 4)$$
$$= \$265.20$$
$$PW(Y) = -\$1000 + [\$1000 + \$200(P/A, 14, 3)](P/F, 14, 1)$$
$$= \$284.49$$

As another example to support the selection procedure, assume an investment of $100 returns $200 at the end of 1 year; hence IRR($100) = 100 percent. Let another investment of $1000 return $1500 one year later; hence IRR($1000) = 50 percent. If the required rate of return is 10 percent, PW($100) = $81.82 and PW($1000) = $363.64, indicating a preference for the latter. The reason the $1000 investment is superior may be better understood by considering the IRR on the additional $900 increment of investment:

$$PW(\$900 \text{ increment}) = (-\$1000 - -\$100) + (\$1500 - \$200)(P/F, i, 1) = 0 \quad \text{at IRR}$$
$$= -\$900 + \$1300(P/A, 45, 1) \doteq 0$$

Thus, the additional $900 investment has an internal rate of return of 45 percent, which well exceeds the minimum required rate of 10 percent, making it acceptable and confirming the preference shown by the previous present-worth comparison.

## Multiple Rates of Return

When the *cumulative* cash flow of a project switches from negative to positive (or the reverse) *more than once*, the project may have more than one internal rate of return. In such situations, relatively rare in practice, no single percentage is immediately available to rank the alternative; two or more IRR figures are equally correct, as demonstrated in Example 6.3.

---

### Example 6.3   Two Solutions for an IRR Evaluation

One of the alternatives for improving an operation is to do nothing to it for 2 years and then spend $10,000 on improvements. If this course of action is followed, the immediate gain is $3000 followed by two years of breakeven operations. Thereafter, annual income should be $2000 per year for 4 years. What rate of return can be expected from following this course of delayed action?

### Solution 6.3

The cash-flow diagram suggests that there might be a sign reversal in the flow pattern. This is confirmed by tabulating the cumulative cash flow, where it is clear that total transactions reverse from positive to negative at year 2 and again reverse

| End of Year | Cumulative Cash Flow |
|---|---|
| 0 | +$3000 |
| 1 | +3000 |
| 2 | −7000 |
| 3 | −5000 |
| 4 | −3000 |
| 5 | −1000 |
| 6 | +1000 |

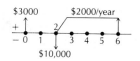

signs at year 6. Since a double sign reversal is not always accompanied by dual rates of return, trials can be conducted at arbitrarily selected interest rates to determine the general PW profile. Based on

$$PW = \$3000 - \$10{,}000(P/F, i, 2) + \$2000(P/A, i, 4)(P/F, i, 2) \gtrless 0$$

at $i = 0$,

$$PW = \$3000 - \$10{,}000 + \$2000(4) = \$1000$$

(also indicated by the cumulative cash-flow pattern shown above); at $i = 10$ percent,

$$PW = \$3000 - \$10{,}000(0.82645) + \$2000(3.1698)(0.82645) = -\$25$$

(which indicates by the sign reversal from PW at $i = 0$ that one IRR is slightly less than 10 percent); at $i = 51$ percent,

$$PW = \$3000 - \$10{,}000(0.43906) + \$2000(1.5856)(0.43906) = \$2$$

(where the second sign reversal confirms there is a second IRR).

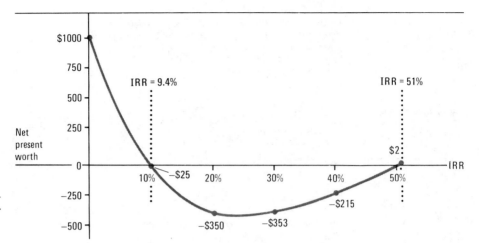

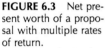

**FIGURE 6.3** Net present worth of a proposal with multiple rates of return.

The profile of present worths over the discounting range of 0 to 51 percent is shown in Figure 6.3. The equivocal answer for the proposal's IRR is that it is either 9.4 percent or 51 percent when returns can be assumed to be reinvested at either rate.

A more specific answer to the IRR question in Example 6.3 is developed by applying an *external rate of return* to a limited portion of the cash flow that will disturb the total cash-flow pattern as little as possible while eliminating one of the sign reversals. The external reinvestment rate may be the minimum attractive rate of return employed by the organization or a rate suggested by the PW profile. The significance of the choice is apparent from comparisons in Table 6.4, where the $3000 receipt is assumed to be invested at an explicit interest rate for 2 years. Under this assumption, one sign reversal is avoided and the present worth of the modified cash flow is

$$PW = \$3000(F/P, i\%, 2) - \$10,000 + \$2000(P/A, i, 4) \doteq 0$$

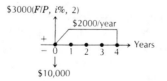

where $i$ is the external interest rate.

From Table 6.4 it is apparent that the proposal is attractive only when the external rate of return is below 9.4 percent and above 51 percent. When funds can be invested externally at, say, 15 percent, there is no incentive to invest in a proposal that returns just 12.4 percent, as does the described alternative when the first $3000 payment is invested at 15

| External Reinvestment Rate Applied to the $3000 Payment for 2 Years, % | IRR on Net Investment When an External Reinvestment Rate Is Utilized, % | |
|---|---|---|
| 0 | 5.5 | |
| 5 | 7.5 | |
| 9.4 | 9.4 | |
| 15 | 12.4 | Range where the project's |
| 20 | 18.9 | IRR is lower than the |
| 30 | 22.7 | external rate of return |
| 40 | 33.4 | |
| 51 | 51 | |
| 60 | 82 | |

**TABLE 6.4**  Different IRR percentages resulting from external reinvestment rates used on a limited portion of the cash flow to convert a dual rate of return to a single IRR.

percent. However, if only a 5 percent return can be confidently obtained on external investments, then the $3000 invested at that rate for 2 years would amount to

$$FW(\text{year } 2) = \$3000(F/P, 5, 2) = \$3000(1.1025) = \$3307$$

which is subtracted from the $10,000 disbursement at that date to produce the cash flow, shown below, which has one sign change.

| Year | 0 | 1 | 2 | 3 | 4 | 5 | 6 |
|---|---|---|---|---|---|---|---|
| Cash flow | 0 | 0 | −$6693 | $2000 | $2000 | $2000 | $2000 |

Now the IRR for the modified cash-flow pattern is just the interest rate that makes an initial investment of $6693 equivalent to a $2000 annual annuity for 4 years:

$$PW = -\$6693 + \$2000(P/A, i, 4) = 0 \quad \text{at IRR}$$

$$(P/A, i, 4) = \frac{\$6693}{\$2000} = 3.3465$$

and

$$IRR = 7\% + 1\% \frac{3.3871 - 3.3465}{3.3871 - 3.3121} = 7.5\%$$

The use of an external interest rate may seem to be an artificial device to alleviate a mathematical difficulty, but it is both realistic and reasonable. Funds received from an ongoing project are indeed reinvested in new projects that have passed the minimum-acceptable-rate-of-return test. These funds then earn at least the required rate, but it would be unrealistic to expect them to earn an enormously higher rate, such as the 51 percent suggested by the sample problem. However, if 51 percent were the actual external reinvestment rate, then the given cash flow pattern would also meet that criterion.

## MINIMUM ACCEPTABLE RATE OF RETURN

The *minimum acceptable* rate of return (MARR) is a lower limit for investment acceptability set by organizations or individuals. It is a device designed to make the best possible use of a limited resource, money. Rates vary widely according to the type of organization, and even within the organization. Historically, government agencies and regulated public utilities have utilized lower required rates of return than competitive industrial enterprises. Within a given enterprise, the required rate may be different for various divisions or activities. These variations usually reflect the risk involved. For instance, the rate of return required for cost-reduction proposals may be lower than that required for research and development projects in which there is less certainty about prospective cash flows.

There is a wealth of literature on the subject, but a poverty of agreement. It is generally accepted that the lower bound for a minimum required rate of return should be the *cost of capital*. The constitution of this cost is also subject to controversy. As discussed in Chapter 9, the cost of capital for competitive industries must reflect the expense of acquiring funds from various sources; and, as discussed in Chapter 10, the cost of safe government bonds is a basis for the lower bound of interest rates used to evaluate public investments.

How much above the cost of capital to set the minimum required rate of return depends on an organization's circumstances and aspirations. A small company strapped for cash and burdened by a low credit rating must have a very, very attractive proposal before it can consider investing. Larger established companies tend to view the rate as a realistic expectation of how much their capital can earn when invested. This MARR is a typical figure promised (and later substantiated) for a large number of high-quality investment proposals available to the firm; it is assumed that the proceeds earned from current projects can be reinvested at comparable rates in future proposals. The rate so derived is sometimes called the *opportunity cost of capital* because any proposal funded to earn a lower rate precludes the opportunity to earn the minimum attractive rate of return.

The effect of establishing a minimum required rate of return is to allocate capital. It is allocated to divisions of an organization and to the whole organization as a function of time. The purpose is to avoid unproductive investments in marginal activities, perhaps favored for political reasons, and to conserve capital during periods when fewer "attractive" proposals are submitted. Capital allocation is implemented by adhering to the MARR unless powerful intangible factors are boldly involved, or, as an engineering economics function, allocating is accomplished by selecting the most advantageous alternative, when one of the alternatives is to do nothing.

## Review Exercises and Discussions

**Exercise 1** A $1000 utility bond with 4 years remaining before maturity can now be purchased for $640. It pays interest of $20 each 6-month period. What rate of return is earned by purchasing the bond at the current market price plus a brokerage charge of $20?

**Solution 1** This is a variation of the bond problem in Example 4.8. In the original version the question was how much could be paid for the described bond in order to earn a rate of return of 18 percent compounded semiannually. The solution revealed that the PW of the bond at $i = 9$ percent per period was $612.56. So we know the actual rate of return must be smaller than 18 percent compounded semiannually.

Trying $i = 10$ percent compounded semiannually, or 5 percent per period for 8 periods, gives

$$PW = \$1000(P/F, 5, 8) + \$20(P/A, 5, 8) - (\$640 + \$20) \overset{?}{=} 0$$
$$= \$1000(0.67684) + \$20(6.4631) - \$660 = \$146.10$$

which indicates $i$ should be greater than 5 percent per period. At $i = 14$ percent compounded semiannually, again for 8 periods.

$$PW = \$1000(P/F, 7, 8) + \$20(P/A, 7, 8) - \$660 \overset{?}{=} 0$$
$$= \$1000(0.58201) + \$20(5.9712) - \$660 = \$41.43$$

which is closer, but $i$ is still too low. The present worth of the bond at $i = 8$ percent per period is \$655.20; the difference between this PW and the selling price is \$655.20 − \$660 = −\$4.80. By interpolation between the PWs at 7 percent and 8 percent,

$$i = 7\% + 1\% \frac{\$41.43 - 0}{\$41.43 - (-\$4.80)} = 7\% + 0.9\% = 7.9\%$$

which means the bond purchased for \$660 will earn 15.8 percent compounded semiannually.

---

**Exercise 2**  An old hotel was recently damaged by a fire. Since it has a desirable location in the old part of the city that is currently being rejuvenated by an urban-renewal project, it will be rebuilt and renovated as either a showroom and office building or a modern apartment building. Estimated receipts and disbursements for the 30-year life of the refurbished structure are shown.

|  | *Offices* | *Apartments* |
|---|---|---|
| First cost of renovation | \$340,000 | \$490,000 |
| Increase in salvage value from renovation | 120,000 | 190,000 |
| Annual receipts | 212,000 | 251,200 |
| Annual disbursements | 59,100 | 88,000 |
| Present value of fire-damaged building | 485,000 | 485,000 |
| Expected salvage value of the fire-damaged building after 30 years | 266,000 | 266,000 |

If the required rate of return is 12 percent, which renovation plan is preferable?

**Solution 2**  Investigating first the lowest-cost alternative, we check to see if an office building will be profitable at $i = 0$.

$$PW = \underbrace{-(\$485,000 + \$340,000)}_{P = -\$825,000} + \underbrace{(\$120,000 + \$266,000)(1)}_{S = \$386,000} +$$

$$\underbrace{(\$212,000 - \$59,100)(30) = \$4,148,000}_{A = \$152,900}$$

Knowing a positive cash flow exists, a rough estimate of the IRR is determined from the more significant flows of $P$ and $A$:

$$(A/P,\ i,\ 30) \doteq \frac{A}{P} \doteq \frac{\$152{,}900}{\$825{,}000} \doteq 0.1853$$

which falls bewteen the 15 percent and 20 percent interest tables. Then, by trial and error,

$$PW = -\$825{,}000 + \$386{,}000(P/F,\ i,\ 30) + \$152{,}900(P/A,\ i,\ 30) \stackrel{?}{=} 0$$

At IRR = 18 percent,

$$\begin{aligned} PW &= -\$825{,}000 + \$386{,}000(0.00698) + \$152{,}900(5.5168) \\ &= \$21{,}213 \end{aligned}$$

At IRR = 19 percent,

$$\begin{aligned} PW &= -\$825{,}000 + \$386{,}000(0.00560) + \$152{,}900(5.2478) \\ &= -\$20{,}450 \end{aligned}$$

From these, by interpolation, IRR = 18.5 percent.

The conversion of the fire-damaged hotel into a showroom and office building is thus an acceptable alternative; the 18.5 percent IRR is greater than the required 12 percent.

The alternative plan to convert to an apartment has incremental additional values of

*First cost:*   $490,000 − $340,000 = $150,000
*Salvage value:*   $190,000 − $120,000 = $70,000
*Net annual returns:*   $251,200 − $88,000 − $152,900 = $10,300

The incremental rate of return is calculated as

$$PW = -\$150{,}000 + \$70{,}000\ (P/F,\ i,\ 30) + \$10{,}300(P/A,\ i,\ 30) \stackrel{?}{=} 0$$

At IRR = 6 percent,
$$\begin{aligned} PW &= -\$150{,}000 + \$70{,}000(0.17412) + \$10{,}300(13.764) \\ &= \$3958 \end{aligned}$$

At IRR = 7 percent,
$$\begin{aligned} PW &= -\$150{,}000 + \$70{,}000(0.13137) + \$10{,}300(12.409) \\ &= -\$12{,}991 \end{aligned}$$

By interpolation,

$$IRR = 6\% + 1\%\ \frac{\$3958 - 0}{\$3958 - (-\$12{,}991)} = 6.2\%$$

The IRR lower than the required 12 percent rate disqualifies the additional investment needed to proceed from the office plan to the apartment plan. It should be noted that the apartment plan still has a total IRR greater than the minimum required 12 percent:

$$PW = -\$975{,}000 + \$456{,}000(P/F,\ i,\ 30) + \$163{,}200(P/A,\ i,\ 30) \stackrel{?}{=} 0$$

At IRR = 16.7 percent,*
$$\begin{aligned} PW &= -\$975{,}000 + \$456{,}000(0.0097) + \$163{,}200(5.9298) \\ &= -\$2834 \end{aligned}$$

At IRR = 16.6 percent,

*$(P/F,\ i,\ 30)$ and $(P/A,\ i,\ 30)$ for 16.7 and 16.6 percent are obtained from a calculator.

$$PW = -\$975,000 + \$456,000(0.00998) + \$163,200(5.96399)$$
$$= \$3178$$

Even with a 17 percent rate of return, the apartment plan is not an acceptable alternative because the additional investment required for its implementation does not meet the minimum rate of return standard. The results are summarized in the table.

| | *Office Plan* $\longrightarrow$ | *Increment* $\longrightarrow$ | *Apartment Plan* |
|---|---|---|---|
| First cost | $825,000 | $150,000 | $975,000 |
| Salvage value | $386,000 | $70,000 | $456,000 |
| Annual returns | $152,900 | $10,300 | $163,200 |
| Rate of return | 18.5% $\longrightarrow$ | 6.2% $\longrightarrow$ | 16.7% |

**Exercise 3**  Expected cash flows for a strip-mining project are estimated as shown in the cash-flow diagram below.

A start-up cost is incurred immediately. Then income exceeds outlays for the next 7 years. During the eighth year the major cost is for landscape improvement. Does the strip-mining project appear to be a profitable investment?

**Solution 3**  The − to + to − cash-flow pattern suggests dual rates of return. The suspicion is verified by trial-and-error calculations based on

$$PW = \$100,000 + \$20,000(P/F, i, 1) + \$100,000(P/F, i, 2) + \$100,000(P/F, i, 3) +$$
$$\$50,000(P/A, i, 4)(P/F, i, 3) - \$350,000(P/F, i, 8) \doteq 0$$

to identify the IRRs shown below.

| | | PW AT 2.9% | | PW AT 44.5% | |
|---|---|---|---|---|---|
| *End of Year* | *Cash Flow* | *Factor* | *Amount* | *Factor* | *Amount* |
| 0 | −$100,000 | 1.00 | −$100,000 | 1.00 | −$100,000 |
| 1 | 20,000 | 0.97 | 19,000 | 0.69 | 14,000 |
| 2 | 100,000 | 0.94 | 94,000 | 0.47 | 47,000 |
| 3 | 100,000 | 0.92 | 92,000 | 0.33 | 33,000 |
| 4 | 50,000 | 0.89 | 45,000 | 0.22 | 11,000 |
| 5 | 50,000 | 0.86 | 43,000 | 0.15 | 7,500 |
| 6 | 50,000 | 0.83 | 42,000 | 0.10 | 5,000 |
| 7 | 50,000 | 0.81 | 40,000 | 0.07 | 3,500 |
| 8 | −350,000 | 0.78 | −275,000 | 0.06 | −21,000 |
| *Net PW* | | | 0 | | 0 |

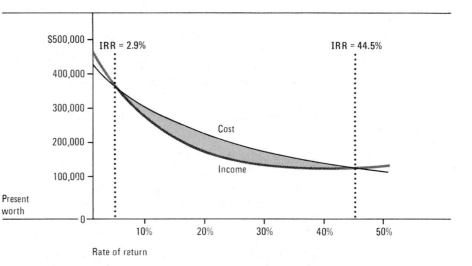

A more comprehensive picture of the proposed strip-mining venture is provided by the discounted income and cost curves shown in Figure 6.4. It is apparent that the project can be considered profitable only when the interest rate used in the present-worth calculations is below 3 percent or above 45 percent. This means that the strip-mining project will be attractive only when the organization is satisfied with a modest 3 percent rate of return or is optimistic enough to accept the premise of a reinvestment rate of 45 percent or greater. Between the points where the curves intersect in Figure 6.4, the PW is negative. Thus, a minimum attractive rate of return of 10 percent rejects the project when it is used as an external reinvestment rate to remove the sign reversal in the cash flow, as demonstrated below.

Let $i$ = 10 percent to compound the values of the first two transactions (−$100,000 and $20,000); the cash-flow diagram is revised as*

When

$$\text{FW(year 0)} = \$100,000 + \$20,000(F/P, 10, 1) - \$100,000(F/P, 10, 2)$$
$$= \$900$$

then, at year 0,

$$\$900 = \$100,000 + \$20,000(F/P, 10\%, 1) + -\$100,000(F/P, 10\%, 2)$$
$$= \$100,000 + \$22,000 - \$121,000$$

to reveal that the net PW is negative even when $i$ = 0 percent:

$$\text{PW} = \$900 + \$100,000(P/F, 0,1) + \$50,000(P/A, 0, 4)(P/F, 0, 1)$$
$$- \$350,000(P/F, 0, 6)$$
$$= \$900 + \$100,000 + \$200,000 - \$350,000 = -\$49,100$$

---

*To eliminate the sign reversal, an external rate must be applied to the first and second cash flows in this example. This contrasts with Example 6.3, where an external rate was needed for the first flow only.

## PROBLEMS

**6.1** Sometimes *objets d'art* are respectable investments. In 1975 a marble bust of Benjamin Franklin, from which the engraving was made for U.S. $100 bills, was auctioned for U.S. $310,000. It was sculpted in France in 1778 by Jean-Antoine Houden. In 1939 the same bust sold for U.S. $30,000. What internal rate of return was earned by the collector who owned the statue from 1939 to 1975?

**6.2** Assume *Hotstuff* magazine offers two types of subscriptions, payable in advance, as follows:

1-year subscription     $10
2-year subscription     $16

**6.2a** In comparing the economy of a 1-year subscription with that of a 2-year subscription, what is the internal rate of return on the extra investment in the 2-year subscription? *(66.7%)*

**6.2b** As an added bonus, a nature-lover's calendar is included with each subscription to *Hotstuff*. However, only one calendar is included, even with a 2-year subscription. If you figure your money is worth 10 percent, how much could you afford to pay for next year's calendar so that both subscription plans can be considered equal in value? *($3.40)*

**6.3** A $5000 bond matures in 10 years and pays 3 percent interest twice a year. If the bond sold for $5050, what is the actual investment rate?

*(5.9% compounded semiannually)*

**6.4** A construction firm can lease a crane required on a project for 3 years for $180,000 payable now, with maintenance included. The alternative is to buy a crane for $240,000 and sell it at the end of 3 years for $100,000. Annual maintenance costs are expected to be $5000 the first 2 years, and $10,000 the third year (payable at the end of each year). At what interest rate would the two alternatives be equivalent? *(9.4%)*

**6.5** Compare the flume and ditch-and-tunnel alternatives to provide power and water for the mill described in Problem 8.21. Base the IRR calculation on a 60-year economic life for both alternatives.    *(IRR on extra investment increment = 4.6%)*

**6.6** Additional parking space for a factory can be either rented for $6000 per year on a 10-year lease or purchased for $90,000. The rental fees are payable in advance at the beginning of each year. Taxes and maintenance fees will be paid by the lessee. The land should be worth at least $60,000 after 10 years. What rate of return will be earned from the purchase of the lot? *(IRR = 4.2%)*

**6.7** Proposal 1 has an initial cost of $1500 and a positive cash flow that returns $200 the first year and increases by $200 each of the following years until the end of the 5-year study period. Proposal 2 also has a 5-year life and an initial cost of $1500. Its positive cash flow is constant at $200 for the last 4 years. It also has another receipt in year 1. All receipts occur at the end of the year.

**6.7a** What is the rate of return on proposal 1? *(IRR = 22%)*

**6.7b** If the two proposals are equally attractive at $i = 14$ percent annually, how large is the first payment in proposal 2? *($1562)*

**6.8** Two types of productivity programs are being considered for funding. Both have an initial cost of $10,000 for training equipment and consulting contracts. Program *A* promises to produce constant net revenues of $4000 per year for 5 years. Net revenues from program $B$ are expected to be $10,000 the first year and $2000 per year for the next 4 years. All revenues are considered end-of-year receipts.

**6.8a** Which program is preferable at IRR = 10 percent? *(Program A, PW = $5163)*

**6.8b** Which program is preferable at IRR = 20 percent? *(Program B, PW = $2647)*

**6.8c** Draw a graph of PW versus IRR for the two proposals, and state a decision rule for selecting between the two proposals.

**6.9** You have loaned $1000 to a friend, whom you consider a good credit risk, at a nominal interest rate of 12 percent compounded monthly. The loan period is 1 year. You plan to take each monthly installment received from your friend and invest it on the day received in a savings account that pays you interest at the nominal rate of 6 percent compounded monthly. What nominal interest rate are you receiving on the total return from the loan plus the reinvestment of the monthly repayment installments? All installment transactions occur at the end of each period. *(9.23% compounded monthly)*

**6.10** Two mutually exclusive projects are being considered: Project $X$ requires $500 and results in a return amounting to a one-time-only profit of $1000 five years from now. Project $Y$ also requires $500, but will return $170 per year for each of the next 5 years. Determine at what IRR the two projects are equivalent, and explain the significance of the intersection point of the two PW profiles for the selection of the preferred alternative.

**6.11** A 5-year subscription can be purchased today for $48. One-year subscriptions, payable in advance year by year, could be purchased to provide the same number of issues. The current price of a 1-year subscription is $10, but it will probably increase in price at the rate of $2 per year. What IRR is earned by the 5-year subscription?

**6.12** The cash flow for a project is shown in the table below.

| Year | 0 | 1 | 2 | 3 | 4 | 5 |
|---|---|---|---|---|---|---|
| Cash flow | $3000 | $1000 | −$5000 | −$5000 | $2000 | $5000 |

The first two payments (in thousands of dollars) represent advance payments for distribution rights on a motion picture. The next 2 years show a negative cash flow from production costs, and the last 2 years are net receipts from the finished picture. If advance payments can be invested at an external interest rate of 7 percent, what rate of return can be expected from the project?

**6.13** Owing to perennial complaints by students and faculty about the lack of parking spaces on campus, a parking garage on university-owned property is being considered. Since there are no university funds available for the project, it will have to pay for itself from parking fees over a 15-year period. A 10 percent minimum rate of return is deemed reasonable in deciding how large the structure should be. Based on the income and cost data shown below, how many levels should be built?

| Number of Levels | Cumulative Construction Costs | Annual Operating Cost | Income per Year |
|---|---|---|---|
| 1 | $ 600,000 | $35,000 | $100,000 |
| 2 | 2,200,000 | 60,000 | 350,000 |
| 3 | 3,600,000 | 80,000 | 570,000 |
| 4 | 4,800,000 | 95,000 | 810,000 |

**6.14**    A business property can be purchased today for $90,000; the expected resale value after 20 years is $60,000. If annual rental income is $11,800 and expenses are $4700, what before-tax rate of return would be earned by purchasing the property?

**6.15**    A cash-flow pattern shows an income of $250 at the end of year 1 between expenditures of $100 now and $156 at the end of year 2.

   **6.15a**    Calculate the dual rates of return by trial and error.

   **6.15b**    Use the quadratic formula to solve for the two rates. As a reminder, the quadratic formula is $(-b \pm \sqrt{b^2 - 4ac})/2a$, and the coefficients in this case are $a = -100$, $b = 250$, and $c = -156$.

**6.16**    The owner of a truck-weighing and lumber-scaling station has agreed to lease the facility for 15 years at $10,000 per year under an agreement that the scales and other equipment will be overhauled and repaired by the owner at the end of the eighth year at a cost not to exceed $150,000.

   **6.16a**    What rate(s) of return will the owner receive for the station lease with the equipment-repair agreement?

   **6.16b**    After negotiations on the above lease, caused by concern that the equipment needed overhauling before 8 years, it was agreed that the owner would pay up to $105,000 for repairs at the end of year 4 instead of making the repairs at the end of year 8. What rate(s) of return will the owner receive under the revised agreement?

   **6.16c**    Check the revised agreement to see if it is acceptable at an IRR of 20 percent. Use the 20 percent as an external reinvestment rate to determine a single IRR for the lease and repair agreement in Problem 6.16*b*. How would you explain the expected IRR to the owner?

# SECTION TWO

# ECONOMIC ANALYSES Economics is reputed to be an academic, not a vocational, subject,* whereas engineering is a practical subject that applies science to workaday problems. Combining economics with engineering blends theory with practice. It leads to the application of economic principles to the practical problems of efficiently allocating and utilizing scarce resources. It is the foundation for deciding which engineering proposals are financially worthy of support. Economic principles ignored in decision making are wasted, but unprincipled economic decisions are criminal.

An engineering economic analysis can be likened to food for the decision maker. It nourishes healthy decision making. A recipe for its preparation could be

- Gather facts and sift well to eliminate extraneous data.
- Blend facts with financial practices.
- Carefully stir according to established methodologies.
- Season with creativity to recognize unusual relationships.
- Garnish with graphics, and serve with confidence.

The menu in this section includes the structural analysis of alternatives, replacement analysis, financial analysis, and benefit-cost analysis. Each form of analysis is associated with a particular class of problems likely to confront an engineering economist.

*Campbell R. McConnell and W.H. Pope, *Economics: Principles, Problems and Policies*, 2nd Canadian Ed., McGraw-Hill Ryerson, Toronto, 1981.

# CHAPTER 7

## STRUCTURAL ANALYSIS OF ALTERNATIVES

OVERVIEW

From previous chapters we know that alternatives can be compared according to their present worths, equivalent annual worths, and internal rates of return. The selection of a preferred proposal from a set of alternatives depends on the structure of the set.

Given proposals $A$ and $B$ and unlimited capital, the alternatives are to select any, all, or none, when the alternatives are *independent* – i.e., when acceptance of one has no effect on the acceptance of any other alternative in the set.

When selection is narrowed to the do-nothing alternative, or $A$, or $B$, the alternatives are *mutually exclusive*. The alternative with the highest present worth based on the MARR is preferred. An identical choice results from applying an incremental IRR comparison; the preferred alternative is the largest total investment in which each additional increment of capital above the last acceptable investment level has an incremental IRR greater than the MARR.

When alternatives are related to each other in any way that influences the selection process, they are said to be *dependent*. For instance, proposal $B$ would be dependent if it could be selected only *after* proposal $A$ was accepted; then the choice would be limited to doing nothing, selecting $A$, or accepting $A$ and $B$. The case of mutually exclusive reinvestment-dependent alternatives is discussed in Extension 7A.

*143*

# DEVELOPMENT OF ALTERNATIVES

An *alternative* in engineering economics is an investment possibility. It is a single undertaking with a distinguishable cash flow. Alternatives vary from doing nothing—leaving the existing cash flow intact—to very elaborate and lengthy projects. It is necessary to understand both the composition of an alternative and its structural relationship to other investment options.

## Identifying Alternatives

Many people besides engineers develop and evaluate investment alternatives. However, few other professions are so intimately and regularly involved with selecting the best device or way to do a particular operation. And the operation usually has long-term consequences. That is why it is important for engineers, and others engaged in similar decision situations, to be competent economic analysts.

Analysis starts with the identification of alternatives. A need to do something originates from asking, "What needs to be done?" "What can be done?" "What should be done?" A general idea for an undertaking evolves into a family of alternatives through further questioning of the feasibility of alternative solutions, how to do them, and when. Answers to such probes may suggest several ways and means to accomplish the same mission, or other missions that deserve attention.

Perhaps the most bothersome question in the search for alternatives is: "How many is enough?" Decision making can be paralyzed by a continuing search for a still better option. At the other extreme, acting on the first option that comes to mind assures a fast decision, but seldom a wise one. A clue to a compromise was given in Example 1.2, where the opportunity cost of a less than ideal solution was related to the cost of making the decision. The governing objective is to develop a set of alternatives large enough to include the best possible option.

## Defining Alternatives

From previous discussions of comparison methods we know the basic data required for an economic analysis are the timing and amount of cash flows. These come from an understanding of the present situation and comprehension of future situations. Besides the current MARR and today's cost commitments, knowledge is needed about future objectives, resources, and operational constraints.

Proposals for investments typically exceed available funding. Some proposals can be sliced from the list of alternatives owing to their excessive size. Others may be suspect from their assumptions about future resources, especially when their attraction stems from unproven technology or "iffy" cost estimates. Part of this uncertainty can be handled by techniques presented in Chapters 17 and 18, but for now all the data will be considered reliable. Therefore, cash flows are treated as certain to occur as estimated, and financial relationships among alternatives are assumed to be known.

Alternatives can be classified as *independent, mutually exclusive,* or *dependent.* The classification establishes how a proposal is evaluated in the selection process.

# CLASSIFICATION OF ALTERNATIVES

On the first pages of this text the role of engineering economists was defined to include the identification of alternatives and analysis of their worth. Since then, alternatives have been evaluated for many different situations. Alternatives that share certain features can be categorized together to facilitate analysis. The alternatives in Table 7.1 will be utilized to illustrate the classifications; for computational convenience all proposals have the same life and no salvage value.

**TABLE 7.1**  Cash flows for proposals having the same life and no salvage value.

| Proposal | Investment | Life | Net Annual Cash Flow | Net PW at $i = 5\%$ |
|---|---|---|---|---|
| N | −$1000 | 5 | +$300 | +$299 |
| E | −2000 | 5 | +400 | −268 |
| W | −3000 | 5 | +900 | +896 |
| S | −4000 | 5 | +1000 | +329 |

An *independent alternative* is not affected by the selection of another alternative. Each proposal is evaluated on its merit and will be accepted if it meets the criteria of acceptability. Comparisons of independent investment proposals are designed to determine which proposals satisfy a minimum level of economic value. All those that surpass the minimum level may be implemented so long as sufficient capital is available. For example, if the proposals in Table 7.1 were independent and the criterion of acceptability were a return of 5 percent on any investment, proposals N, W, and S would be satisfactory investments because they possess positive net PW at the required interest rate.

Alternatives are *mutually exclusive* when the selection of one eliminates the opportunity to accept any of the others. Most of the comparisons made in previous chapters were among mutually exclusive alternatives. Operational problems normally fit into this category, because a single course of action is sought to solve a particular, often urgent, problem. When the best solution is determined, the problem is theoretically resolved by implementing the indicated course of action.

Multiple alternatives are often associated with levels of development for the same asset or activity. Each level is an alternative, and the purpose of analysis is to select the most promising level. For instance, the proposals in Table 7.1 would be considered mutually exclusive if they represented different sizes of the same design (e.g., diameters of pipes or thicknesses of insulation) or incremental levels of resource application (e.g., number of crews assigned or number of units ordered).

Let the proposals in Table 7.1 represent investments in insulation to reduce heat loss (equivalently, to conserve energy), and the cash flows the savings from various thicknesses compared with the cost of heating without insulation. The net present worth of proposal W,

$$PW(W) = -\$3000 + \$900(P/A, 5, 5)$$
$$= -\$3000 + \$900(4.3294) = -\$3000 + \$3896 = \$896$$

is greater than that of any of the other proposals and indicates that the thickness of insulation it represents is the one to use.

It is often instructive to observe the incremental returns for mutually exclusive alternatives. Savings resulting from each additional $1000 of investment are indicated in Table 7.2.

| Levels of Investment Proposals | Increment of Investment, $\Delta I$ | Incremental Savings per Year, $\Delta S$ | $\Delta S/\Delta I$ |
|---|---|---|---|
| No investment to $N$ | $ \$\ \ 0–\$1000$ | $ \$\ \ 0–\$\ 300$ | $300/\$1000$ |
| Investment $N$ to $E$ | $1000–\ 2000$ | $300–\ \ \ 400$ | $100/\ 1000$ |
| Investment $E$ to $W$ | $2000–\ 3000$ | $400–\ \ \ 900$ | $500/\ 1000$ |
| Investment $W$ to $S$ | $3000–\ 4000$ | $900–\ 1000$ | $100/\ 1000$ |

**TABLE 7.2**  Incremental annual savings in relation to increments of investment.

It appears that proposal $W$ is again far superior. However, the increment of investment from $N$ ($I = \$1000$) to $W$($I = \$3000$), from one acceptable level of investment to the next *acceptable* level, increases the savings from $300 to $900 per year to produce a ratio of

$$\frac{\Delta S}{\Delta I} = \frac{\$900 - \$300}{\$3000 - \$1000} = \frac{\$600}{\$2000} = \$300/\$1000$$

which is identical to the return earned on $N$. This means that money invested in alternative $N$ earns at the same rate as an investment in $W$. The only reason $W$ would be preferred to $N$ is that a larger investment at a given rate of return earns a larger total amount, ignoring other influencing factors such as the future availability of energy. The actual percentage rate of return earned on incremental investments will be discussed in the next section.

Occasionally, individual investment opportunities are linked to other alternatives through legal, administrative, political, or physical requirements. Then the acceptance of one alternative depends on the simultaneous acceptance of one or more related alternatives. Cash flows are also affected by relational factors, as in a flood-control proposal where the benefits of a levee of a given height depend on the acceptance of proposed dams on the headwaters of the river. These are *dependent alternatives*.

Returning again to Table 7.1, assume proposal $W$ could be implemented only if $E$ were also funded. This linkage simply consolidates two investments into one alternative with an initial cost of $2000 + $3000 = $5000 which is expected to earn $400 + $900 = $1300 annually. The evaluation then proceeds with $E + W$ treated as an individual alternative. The end effect of relational considerations is a listing of grouped, internally dependent alternatives which are collectively unrelated. An impetus for investigating relational connections is to avoid the selection of a course of action that cannot be implemented without additional commitment of resources. A situation in which alternatives are evaluated according to the rate of return at which capital may be reinvested is presented in Extension 7A.

## IRR ANALYSIS OF SEVERAL MUTUALLY EXCLUSIVE ALTERNATIVES

The aim of a cash-flow analysis is to put all competing alternatives into a comparable investment perspective. It acts as a screen. The alternative with the most promising future from one evaluation is then pitted against winners of other evaluations where intangible and financial considerations become critical. No organization has sufficient capital to fund all conceivable worthwhile proposals. Care must be taken in all evaluations to assure correct and consistent selections. Two logical-sounding selection criteria that sometimes lead to inaccurate conclusions are

1　Selecting the alternative that offers the highest internal rate of return on total investment
2　Selecting the alternative with the largest investment that meets the minimum required rate of return.

The first criterion may bypass alternatives that earn lower rates of return which are still higher than other alternatives available. The second criterion could lead to a larger investment than desirable, which prevents a portion of the funds from earning higher returns available through substitute investments. A decision procedure to avoid inaccurate selections is shown by the flowchart in Figure 7.1. The procedure implicitly assumes that

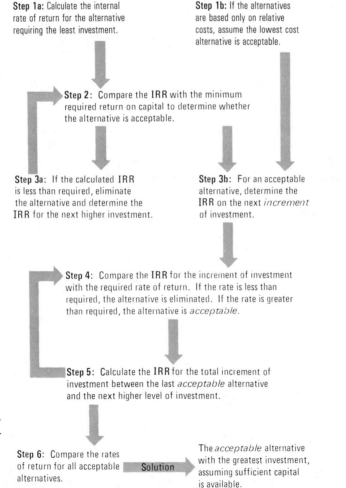

**Step 1a:** Calculate the internal rate of return for the alternative requiring the least investment.

**Step 1b:** If the alternatives are based only on relative costs, assume the lowest cost alternative is acceptable.

**Step 2:** Compare the IRR with the minimum required return on capital to determine whether the alternative is acceptable.

**Step 3a:** If the calculated IRR is less than required, eliminate the alternative and determine the IRR for the next higher investment.

**Step 3b:** For an acceptable alternative, determine the IRR on the next *increment* of investment.

**Step 4:** Compare the IRR for the increment of investment with the required rate of return. If the rate is less than required, the alternative is eliminated. If the rate is greater than required, the alternative is *acceptable.*

**Step 5:** Calculate the IRR for the total increment of investment between the last *acceptable* alternative and the next higher level of investment.

**Step 6:** Compare the rates of return for all acceptable alternatives.

Solution

The *acceptable* alternative with the greatest investment, assuming sufficient capital is available.

**FIGURE 7.1** Flowchart for a selection among several mutually exclusive investment alternatives when a minimum rate of return is required and capital is assumed to be unlimited.

any size investment is possible. Whether the selected proposal is actually funded is a financial decision that relates available capital to all types of investment proposals and their effect on the funding organization. The IRR comparison rates the alternatives as inputs to the final decision process.

---

## Example 7.1 Comparison of Several Mutually Exclusive Alternatives

Four designs for a product with their associated revenue and cost estimates have been presented to top management for a decision. A 10-year study period was used. A minimum rate of return of 10 percent before taxes, a rate expected from other investments with similar risk, is required. Based on the following projected cash flows, which of the four alternative designs appears the most attractive?

|  | DESIGN | | | |
|---|---|---|---|---|
|  | A | B | C | D |
| Initial investment | $170,000 | $260,000 | $300,000 | $330,000 |
| Annual receipts | 114,000 | 120,000 | 130,000 | 147,000 |
| Annual disbursements | 70,000 | 71,000 | 64,000 | 79,000 |

**TABLE 7.3** Ten-year cash flows.

### Solution 7.1

The alternatives are arranged in order of increasing investment requirements in Table 7.3. A supplementary table of incremental values is given below. The annual net returns are calculated by subtracting the annual disbursements from the annual receipts for each alternative and then obtaining the differences between alternatives. For example,

Annual net return of increment $A{\rightarrow}B$ = ($120,000 − $71,000) −

($114,000 − $70,000) = $5000

|  | INCREMENT | | |
|---|---|---|---|
|  | $A{\rightarrow}B$ | $B{\rightarrow}C$ | $C{\rightarrow}D$ |
| Additional investment | $90,000 | $40,000 | $30,000 |
| Annual net return | 5,000 | 17,000 | 2,000 |

Using the steps in Figure 7.1, the IRR of design $A$ is calculated from

$-\$170,000 + (\$114,000 - \$70,000)(P/A, i, 10) \stackrel{?}{=} 0$

and

$(P/A, i, 10) = \dfrac{\$170,000}{\$44,000} = 3.8636$

which, by interpolation, gives a rate of return of 22.5 percent. It is thereby an acceptable alternative because IRR = 22.5 percent > 10 percent required.

The increment of investment from design $A$ to design $B$ is $260,000 − $170,000 = $90,000, and the net annual returns are $5000. These annual returns will obviously not pay back the investment in 10 years: $5000 × 10 < $90,000. Therefore, design $B$ is eliminated from contention because its incremental IRR is lower than the required 10 percent.

Design $C$ *is evaluated by comparing it with the last acceptable alternative,* which in this case is design $A$. Then the incremental comparison $A{\rightarrow}C$ progresses as

$$-\$300,000 - (-\$170,000) + (\$130,000 - \$64,000 - \$44,000)(P/A, i, 10) \overset{?}{=} 0$$

$$(P/A, i, 10) = \frac{\$130,000}{\$22,000} = 5.9090$$

to obtain

$$IRR = 10\% + 1\% \frac{6.1445 - 5.9090}{6.1445 - 5.8892} = 10.9\%$$

With its rate of return greater than 10 percent on the indicated extra increment of investment, design $C$ becomes an acceptable alternative.

The next additional increment of investment to afford design $D$ shows

$$(P/A, i, 10) = \frac{\$30,000}{\$2000} = 15$$

which is unacceptable by inspection. Therefore, assuming that sufficient capital is available, design $C$ is preferred. Its rate of return on total capital invested is calculated from

$$(P/A, i, 10) = \frac{\$300,000}{\$130,000 - \$64,000} = 4.5454$$

which leads to an IRR of 18.9 percent.

The results of the evaluation of alternative designs in Example 7.1 are supplemented and summarized in Table 7.4.

**TABLE 7.4** IRR relationships for Example 7.1.

| Design | Total Investment | Annual Return | IRR on Total Investment,% | | Incremental IRR |
|---|---|---|---|---|---|
| A | $170,000 | $44,000 | 22.5 | ------------ | $A{\rightarrow}B$: (−) |
| B | 260,000 | 49,000 | 13.5 | ------------ | $A{\rightarrow}C$: 10.9% |
| C | 300,000 | 66,000 | 18.9 | ------------ | $C{\rightarrow}D$: (−) |
| D | 330,000 | 68,000 | 15.9 | | |

One type of mistake would have been to select design $A$, which has the greatest rate of return on total investment, as the preferred alternative. This choice would prevent the additional investment of $300,000 − $170,000 = $130,000 in design $C$, which returns 10.9 percent. Since 10.9 percent is higher than the 10 percent expected from other investments with similar risks, a loss of about 1 percent on $130,000 would occur. However, it is prudent to keep in mind the high returns possible through an investment in design $A$ in case there is insufficient capital to fund design $C$ or if there is another independent opportunity for investing $130,000 at an IRR greater than 10.9 percent.

Another type of error would be to select the largest investment that still meets the 10 percent rate-of-return requirement. The unsatisfactory IRR for the extra investment in design $D$ over design $C$ was apparent in the incremental analysis. Therefore, putting $330,000 − $300,000 = $30,000 into design $D$ forces this amount of capital to earn less than the 10 percent it could receive if invested elsewhere.

---

### Example 7.2  Compatibility of PW and IRR Incremental Analysis

Given the same data for a selection between mutually exclusive alternatives, PW and EAW methods agree with the choice indicated by the rate-of-return method, *as long as the IRR is applied to increments instead of the whole investment.* Computing the present worths of the four projects described in Example 7.1 provides the values shown in Table 7.5.

| | INVESTMENT | | ANNUAL RETURN | | PW AT 10% | |
|---|---|---|---|---|---|---|
| *Design* | *Total* | *Increment* | *Total* | *Increment* | *Total* | *Increment* |
| A | $170,000 | | $44,000 | | $100,358 | |
| | | $90,000 | | $5,000 | | −$59,278 |
| B | $260,000 | | $49,000 | | $41,080 | |
| | | $40,000 | | $17,000 | | $64,457 |
| C | $300,000 | | $66,000 | | $105,573 | |
| | | $30,000 | | $2,000 | | −$17,711 |
| D | $330,000 | | $68,000 | | $87,826 | |

**TABLE 7.5** Present worths of designs from Example 7.1 when the MARR is 10 percent.

Comparing Table 7.5 with Table 7.4 confirms that PW calculations based on *total* investment point to the same selection as IRR calculations for *incremental* investments. Both indicate a preference for design $C$. The supplementary calculation of the present worths of incremental investments also agrees with IRR results. Note that

$$PW(C) = PW(A) + PW(A \rightarrow B) + PW(A \rightarrow C)$$
$$\$105,537 = \$100,358 - \$59,278 + \$64,457$$

The incremental $PW(A \rightarrow B)$ is negative, confirming its unacceptableness. Combining $PW(A \rightarrow B)$ with $PW(B \rightarrow C)$ produces a net positive gain that corresponds to $IRR(A \rightarrow C) >$ MARR, indicating the acceptability of design $C$. Thus the $90,000 + $40,000 = $130,000 investment increment that affords design $C$ over design $A$ earns 10 percent plus a present sum of $105,537 − $100,358 = $5179, or, equivalently, it earns an internal rate of return greater than the required 10 percent—10.9 percent. This increment is preferable to investing the $130,000 in another investment that will earn just the minimum acceptable rate of return—10 percent.

Comparing the IRR of a single investment to the MARR to determine its acceptability may appear to be in violation of the incremental IRR criterion. It is a legitimate comparison because the increment between a do-nothing alternative and a do-something proposal is the same as the total investment. Therefore, the incremental IRR equals the IRR on the total investment, satisfying the incremental analysis procedure.

## ANALYSIS OF INDEPENDENT ALTERNATIVES

The demarcation between dependent and independent alternatives gets fuzzy at times. Consider the plans for different product designs in Example 7.1. When only one new product design is sought, the four product proposals are certainly mutually exclusive. Similarly, four plans for remodeling an office are surely mutually exclusive. The best product proposal and the best office plan appear to be completely independent of each other. Yet both contribute to the profit status of the organization.

The product proposal is for a new product that will bring in revenue in excess of costs in order to increase profit, and the office plan is designed to produce improved working conditions that will lower costs to increase profit. At least tangentially, both plans are related through their contribution to the firm's financial standing and by their reliance for initial funding on the firm's capital. In effect, they may be mutually exclusive.

It is seldom worthwhile to trace tenuous links that may relate various investment proposals, particularly so during initial comparison screenings. Diligent detective work could probably uncover links between any and all alternatives, but their effect on early economic comparisons would be negligible. Most mutually exclusive alternatives are clearly evident via coinciding functions; and conditional dependencies are conspicuous by physical relationships, such as the condition for adding a second floor to a building is the construction of the first floor. Such obvious relationships are natural and necessary recognitions for most economic evaluations. The question of how to finance the alternatives may or may not enter the initial comparisons.

Independent proposals can be collected in various combinations and evaluated as grouped to determine how well each combination meets the investment objectives. The groupings selected depend on the conditions set for the evaluation. For instance, one division of a firm might be allowed to fund two proposals while other divisions are allowed only one. Then each combination would include two proposals from the favored division with one from each of the other divisions.

Several programming techniques, such as linear programming, are adaptable to systematic selections among numerous combinations.* A direct search method is used to illustrate

**TABLE 7.6** Three-year cash flows for four independent proposals, all of which have passed a screening based on a minimum required rate of return of 10 percent.

| Proposal | First Cost | END-OF-YEAR CASH FLOW | | |
| --- | --- | --- | --- | --- |
| | | Year 1 | Year 2 | Year 3 |
| I | −$1000 | $ 550 | $ 550 | $ 550 |
| II | −2000 | 875 | 875 | 875 |
| III | −3000 | 1400 | 1400 | 1400 |
| IV | −4000 | 1665 | 1665 | 1665 |

*The classic work in applying linear programming to capital budgeting decisions is H. Martin Weingartner, *Mathematical Programming and the Analysis of Capital Budgeting Problems*, Prentice-Hall, Englewood Cliffs, N.J., 1963.

the conversion of independent proposals to mutually exclusive combinations because it is conceptually simple and adequate for most routine situations. Consider the four independent proposals listed in Table 7.6, from which any combination with first costs totaling $5000 or less can be selected. After appropriate groupings that satisfy the specified capital limitation are identified, each combination is evaluated by one of the discounted cash-flow comparison methods. Since only one combination can be selected, the decision is between mutually exclusive alternatives.

A check-off procedure for identifying appropriate combinations of proposals is shown in Table 7.7. The leftmost columns indicate by a 1 when a proposal is included in a combination, and by a 0 when it is not. The first combination is the do-nothing alternative; the four zeros in the first row indicate no proposals are included. Altogether there are nine combinations that have total first costs of $5000 or less.

**TABLE 7.7** Binary numbers 0 and 1 represent the proposals included in a combination. An IRR is calculated for each combination to rank the alternatives. Note that the extra $1000 investment required for alternative 9 over alternative 7 earns less than 0 percent rate of return.

| PROPOSALS | | | | | END-OF-YEAR CASH FLOW | | | | |
|---|---|---|---|---|---|---|---|---|---|
| I | II | III | IV | Alternative | 0 | 1 | 2 | 3 | IRR,% |
| 0 | 0 | 0 | 0 | 1 | 0 | 0 | 0 | 0 | 0 |
| 1 | 0 | 0 | 0 | 2 | −$1000 | $ 550 | $ 550 | $ 550 | 30 |
| 0 | 1 | 0 | 0 | 3 | −2000 | 875 | 875 | 875 | 15 |
| 0 | 0 | 1 | 0 | 4 | −3000 | 1400 | 1400 | 1400 | 18.8 |
| 1 | 1 | 0 | 0 | 5 | −3000 | 1425 | 1425 | 1425 | 20 |
| 0 | 0 | 0 | 1 | 6 | −4000 | 1665 | 1665 | 1665 | 12 |
| 1 | 0 | 1 | 0 | 7 | −4000 | 1950 | 1950 | 1950 | 21.7 |
| 1 | 0 | 0 | 1 | 8 | −5000 | 2215 | 2215 | 2215 | 15.7 |
| 0 | 1 | 1 | 0 | 9 | −5000 | 2275 | 2275 | 2275 | 17.3 |

Tangible ratings for a managerial decision on the allocation of capital are clearly presented in the table. The highest IRR is earned by allocating just $1000 to fund proposal I. The next highest IRR results from an investment of $4000 in proposals I and III. If the full $5000 is to be allocated, 17.3 percent is the best IRR that can be expected. The final allocation is a management prerogative relying on economic and political objectives.

Much more complex comparisons can be conveniently accomplished by the iterative approach represented by Table 7.7. However, without constraints such as a limit on investment capital, the number of combinations grows rapidly as more proposals are included, and computations grow correspondingly cumbersome. Computerized and programmed assistance then becomes a near necessity.

# REVIEW EXERCISES AND DISCUSSIONS

**Exercise 1**   Data for three alternative investment plans are listed below.

| Alternative | Investment | Salvage Value | Life, Years | Annual Net Cash Flow |
|---|---|---|---|---|
| X | $ 6,000 | $ 0 | 3 | $2600 |
| Y | 12,000 | 3000 | 6 | 2500 |
| Z | 18,000 | 0 | 6 | 4000 |

When the minimum attractive rate of return is 10 percent, which alternative(s) should be selected under each of the following decision conditions?

**a** Individual alternatives are mutually exclusive.
**b** Individual alternatives are independent.

**Solution 1** The present worths of the three alternatives displayed in the table could be calculated as

$$PW(X) = -\$6000 + \$2600(P/A, 10, 3) = -\$6000 + \$2600(2.4868)$$
$$= \$465$$

$$PW(Y) = -\$12,000 + \$2500(P/A, 10, 6) + \$3000(P/F, 10, 6)$$
$$= -\$12,000 + \$2500(4.3552) + \$3000(0.56448)$$
$$= \$582$$

$$PW(Z) = -\$18,000 + \$4000(P/A, 10, 6) = -\$18,000 + \$4000(4.3552)$$
$$= -\$579$$

**a** The deception that alternative $Y$ is more attractive than alternative $X$ occurs because the present worths are not based on equal time durations. When both investments are compared over a 6-year study period, implicitly assuming that a second investment in $X$ can be made at the end of 3 years at the original cost, the present worth of repeated investments in $X$ ($X_1X_2$) is

$$PW(X_1X_2) = -\$6000 - \$6000(P/F, 10, 3) + \$2600(P/A, 10, 6)$$
$$= -\$6000 - \$6000(0.75132) + \$2600(4.3552) = \$816$$

Therefore, when the individual alternatives are mutually exclusive, $X$ is preferred.

**b** Under the assumption that funds are available for all alternatives that meet the minimum attractive rate of return, investments in $X$ and $Y$ are indicated by their positive present worths. Both satisfy the 10 percent return criterion.

---

**Exercise 2** The five investment proposals shown below have been investigated carefully and are deemed to be equally safe. An investor will be satisfied if a minimum before-tax return of 9 percent is realized.

| Proposal | Investment P | Life N, years | Salvage Value S | Net Annual Cash Flow |
|----------|-------------|---------------|-----------------|----------------------|
| Alpha    | $30,000     | 5             | $    0          | $ 7,500              |
| Beta     | 60,000      | 5             | 10,000          | 13,755               |
| Gamma    | 20,000      | 5             | 0               | 5,000                |
| Delta    | 40,000      | 5             | 10,000          | 10,000               |
| Epsilon  | 30,000      | 5             | 5,000           | 7,500                |

Using EAW calculations, determine:

**a** Which proposal is preferred if only one can be selected?
**b** How much should be invested if the proposals are independent and unlimited capital is available?
**c** Which proposals should be utilized if an investor wishes to allocate exactly $60,000 of

investment capital, and any funds not put into one or more of the proposals will be used to purchase bonds that pay annual interest of 7½ percent on the amount invested?

**Solution 2**  The annual worth of each proposal is calculated as follows:

$$\text{EAW (Alpha)} = \$7500 - \$30,000(A/P, 9, 5) = \$7500 - \$30,000(0.25709)$$
$$= \$7500 - \$7713 = -\$213$$

$$\text{EAW (Beta)} = \$13,755 + (-\$60,000 + \$10,000)(A/P, 9, 5) + (-\$10,000)(0.09)$$
$$= \$13,755 - \$50,000(0.25709) - \$900$$
$$= \$13,755 - \$13,755 = 0$$

$$\text{EAW (Gamma)} = \$5000 - \$20,000(A/P, 9, 5) = \$5000 - \$20,000(0.25709)$$
$$= \$5000 - \$5142 = -\$142$$

$$\text{EAW (Delta)} = \$10,000 - (\$40,000 - \$10,000)(A/P, 9, 5) - \$10,000(0.09)$$
$$= \$10,000 - \$30,000(0.25709) - \$900$$
$$= \$10,000 - \$8613 = \$1387$$

$$\text{EAW (Epsilon)} = \$7500 - (\$30,000 - \$5000)(A/P, 9, 5) - \$5000(0.09)$$
$$= \$7500 - \$25,000(0.25709) - \$450$$
$$= \$7500 - \$6875 = \$625$$

**a**  If only one proposal can be accepted, Delta is preferred because it has the largest net annual worth on the capital invested.

**b**  With unlimited capital, Delta and Epsilon are obvious selections, owing to their positive net annual worths. Beta should also be accepted, even with its zero annual worth, because the $60,000 invested will still earn 9 percent; any positive AW indicates a return *beyond* the minimum attractive rate, 9 percent. Therefore, $60,000 + $40,000 + $30,000 = $130,000 should be invested from the unlimited treasury.

**c**  An investment capital limitation of $60,000 allows three logical choices:

  **(1)**  Invest the full amount in Beta where it will earn exactly 9 percent.

  **(2)**  Invest in Delta ($40,000) plus Gamma ($20,000) to earn 9 percent plus $1387 − $142 = $1245.

  **(3)**  Invest in Delta plus a $20,000 bond. This combination is obviously superior to the similar combination of Epsilon plus a $30,000 bond. The annual worth of Delta plus the bond is calculated from the cash flow diagram below, where annual returns from the bond are 0.075 × $20,000 = $1500.

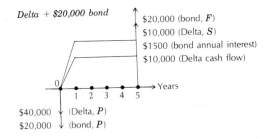

*Delta + $20,000 bond*

$20,000 (bond, **F**)
$10,000 (Delta, **S**)
$1500 (bond annual interest)
$10,000 (Delta cash flow)

$40,000 (Delta, **P**)
$20,000 (bond, **P**)

$$\text{EAW} = \$10,000 + \$1500 - (\$40,000 + \$20,000)(A/P, 9, 5) +$$
$$(\$20,000 + \$10,000)(A/F, 9, 5)$$
$$= \$11,500 - \$60,000(0.25709) + \$30,000(0.16709)$$
$$= \$11,500 - \$15,425 + \$5013 = \$1088$$

Thus the EAW of the $60,000 investment in Delta plus the bond is better than the $60,000 Beta investment proposal, but less rewarding than investing in Delta and Gamma.

---

**Exercise 3** The four independent proposals in Table 7.6 are still under consideration, and new conditions have been added. Proposal I is so attractive that it must be included in any accepted combination. Another proposal with the following cash flow has been added to the list:

| | END-OF-YEAR CASH FLOW | | | |
|---|---|---|---|---|
| *Proposal* | *0* | *1* | *2* | *3* |
| IIA | − $2500 | $1150 | $1150 | $1150 |

In addition to proposal I, either proposal II or IIA must be in any acceptable combination. If the management decision is to fund the combination possessing the highest IRR regardless of the amount of capital required, which proposals will be funded?

**Solution 3** All possible combinations that satisfy the investment criteria are delineated in Table 7.8.

| | ALTERNATIVES | | | | | | | | | | | |
|---|---|---|---|---|---|---|---|---|---|---|---|---|
| *Proposal* | *1* | *2* | *3* | *4* | *5* | *6* | *7* | *8* | *9* | *10* | *11* | *12* |
| I | 1 | 1 | 1 | 1 | 1 | 1 | 1 | 1 | 1 | 1 | 1 | 1 |
| II | 1 | 1 | 1 | 1 | 0 | 0 | 0 | 0 | 1 | 1 | 1 | 1 |
| IIA | 0 | 0 | 0 | 0 | 1 | 1 | 1 | 1 | 1 | 1 | 1 | 1 |
| III | 0 | 1 | 0 | 1 | 0 | 1 | 0 | 1 | 0 | 1 | 0 | 1 |
| IV | 0 | 0 | 1 | 1 | 0 | 0 | 1 | 1 | 0 | 0 | 1 | 1 |

**TABLE 7.8**

From knowing the IRRs for individual proposals already listed in Table 7.7, and by calculating IRR(IIA) = 18 percent, all combinations which include proposal II can be eliminated because IRR(II) = 15 percent; compared to proposal IIA, the inclusion of proposal II has to lower any combination's IRR below 18 percent. This narrows the choice to alternatives 5, 6, 7, and 8 in Table 7.8.

Again noting from Table 7.7 that the IRR of proposal III is above 18 percent while that of proposal IV is below, the best combination must be alternative 6. This combination has a first cost of $1000 + $2500 + $3000 = $6500 and annual returns of $550 + $1150 + $1400 = $3100, which lead to an IRR of 20.3 percent. Utilizing dominating relationships can bypass a lot of computations.

# PROBLEMS

**7.1** A spare-parts service department for a construction-equipment supplier must be established in the Yukon to meet contractual commitments. The firm has eliminated the option of building a new field office because it expects to conduct business in the Yukon for just the next 10 years, during the construction boom. At best, the field office will meet expenses and make a small profit contribution. Only three structures that are available for purchase meet the space needs and have the desired location. A major portion of the investment will likely be recovered by appreciation in land values. A minimum acceptable rate of return of 15 percent before taxes is expected on such investments. What rate of return will be earned by each increment of investment from the anticipated cash flows shown?

|                | Site 1     | Site 2     | Site 3     |
|----------------|-----------|-----------|-----------|
| Purchase price | $140,000  | $190,000  | $220,000  |
| Resale value   | 125,000   | 155,000   | $175,000  |
| Net revenue    | 24,000    | 31,000    | 41,000    |

$[IRR(1) = 16.9\%; IRR(1\rightarrow2) = 11.7\%; IRR(1\rightarrow3) = 19.8\%]$

**7.2** Compare the rates of return for the following plans, and select the preferable alternative. The minimum acceptable rate of return is 6 percent.

|                      | Plan 1    | Plan 2    | Plan 3    |
|----------------------|-----------|-----------|-----------|
| First cost           | $40,000   | $32,000   | $70,000   |
| Salvage value        | $10,000   | $6,000    | $20,000   |
| Economic life        | 7 years   | 7 years   | 7 years   |
| Annual receipts      | $18,000   | $18,000   | $24,500   |
| Annual disbursements | $11,000   | $14,500   | $14,500   |

*(Plan 1, IRR = 9.5%)*

**7.3** A temporary water line is required to supplement the water supply at a plant until city water becomes available in a new industrial area. Three alternative pipe sizes with associated pumping facilities will satisfy the water requirements:

|                     | PIPE SIZE | | |
|---------------------|-----------|-----------|-----------|
|                     | 35.6 cm   | 40.6 cm   | 45.7 cm   |
| First cost          | $18,000   | $25,000   | $34,000   |
| Annual pumping cost | 6,400     | 4,400     | 2,800     |

The pipeline and pumping stations will be in the same locations for all three alternatives. The planning period is 5 years, and pipe can be recovered at the end of the period. It is expected to yield 40 percent of its first cost when recovered, and the cost of recovery will be $2000 regardless of pipe size. Compare the rates of return for the alternatives when a 9 percent return before taxes is desired.     $[IRR(14\rightarrow16) = 20\%; IRR(16\rightarrow18) = 7.4\%]$

**7.4** Three alternative investments to be compared by the rate-of-return method are described below. The MARR is 9 percent.

| Alternatives   | X         | Y         | Z         |
|----------------|-----------|-----------|-----------|
| First cost     | $20,000   | $16,000   | $10,000   |
| Annual expense | $5,000    | $3,000    | $4,000    |
| Annual income  | $11,500   | $11,500   | $7,000    |
| Economic life  | 4 years   | 2 years   | 4 years   |

**7.4a** Which alternative has the highest overall IRR, and what is it?*[IRR(X) = 11.4%]*
**7.4b** Which incremental investment has the greatest rate of return, and what is it? *[IRR(Z→X) = 15%]*

**7.5** Four requests for expenditures are listed below.

| Proposal | First Cost | Net Annual Savings |
|---|---|---|
| (1) Hot Shot | $50,000 | $20,000 |
| (2) Serendipity | 60,000 | 26,100 |
| (3) Slam Bang | 75,000 | 32,400 |
| (4) Big Bucks | 100,000 | 41,700 |

All proposals have a life of 3 years, and the minimum acceptable rate of return is 12 percent.

**7.5a** Which proposal(s) should be accepted if they are independent? *(2, 3, 4)*
**7.5b** Which proposal should be accepted if they are mutually exclusive?*(Proposal 3)*

**7.6** An estimating service for contractors plans to provide an additional service for its customers. Besides the normal routine for making estimates, an additional follow-up service will be offered to review the records of each project and analyze actual costs versus estimated costs. Based on the expected workload for the next 3 years, the proposal could be conducted by:

**1** One secretary and a clerk with total direct and indirect wages of $14,000 per year, using hand-operated equipment with an initial cost of $1400
**2** One secretary with total annual wages of $7500, using computerized equipment which is priced at $8000 and has maintenance costs of $150 per month
**3** Subcontracting part of the work at a monthly cost of $700 and hiring a part-time secretary for $5000 per year

Any investment must be written off in 3 years with no salvage value, and an 8 percent rate of return is required. Assuming all three alternatives provide work of equal quality, which one should be selected? Use an EAC comparison, and check the incremental IRR.

$[EAC(1) = \$14,543; EAC(2) = \$12,404; EAC(3) = \$13,400; IRR(3→2) = 25\%]$

**7.7** Based on the data in Exercise 2 and the investment conditions in part c (where the investment capital is limited to $60,000), explain the following characteristics of the solution given on page 160:

**7.7a** The reasoning that eliminated the Epsilon proposal without recourse to calculations when it is compared to the Delta proposal as part of the $60,000 investment in a proposal plus a bond
**7.7b** The reason why the annual worth of Delta plus a $20,000 bond paying 7½ percent interest is less than the AW of the Delta proposal alone

**7.8** A firm finds that it will be necessary to air-condition a rather large area for its computers and data-processing equipment. An engineering study revealed that the more money spent on insulating the walls and ceiling area, the less money is required for the air-conditioning unit. The engineer's estimates are as follows:

| | 1 | 2 | 3 | 4 |
|---|---|---|---|---|
| First cost of insulation | $35,000 | $45,000 | $60,000 | $80,000 |
| First cost of air-conditioning equipment | 52,000 | 45,000 | 38,000 | 32,000 |
| Annual power cost | 6,500 | 5,100 | 4,100 | 3,500 |

The study also estimated that the insulating material would have a life of 20 years with zero salvage value, and the air-conditioning equipment would have a life of 10 years with no salvage value. Taxes and insurance are expected to be 2 percent of the first cost per year. Which alternative should be selected if the firm requires a 15 percent rate of return before taxes? Use a PW comparison, and check the incremental IRR.

**7.9**   An asset can be purchased for $105,000 if payment is in cash. It can also be purchased by a payment of $45,000 now plus a payment of $75,000 in 3 years *or* it can be purchased with 10 yearly payments of $15,000 each with the first payment made now. Calculate the incremental rates of return for the alternatives, and state which one is preferred if MARR = 9 percent.

**7.10**   The Advanced Product Engineering Group has developed a list of potential, mutually exclusive project proposals as possible new investments. All have a 10-year life and no salvage value. Using IRR calculations and the data shown below, determine which project, if any, should be accepted. Use MARR = 10%.

| Project | First Cost | Annual Cash Flow |
|---------|-----------|------------------|
| A | $100,000 | $16,980 |
| B | 65,000 | 13,000 |
| C | 20,000 | 2,710 |
| D | 40,000 | 6,232 |
| E | 85,000 | 16,320 |
| F | 10,000 | 1,770 |

**7.11**   The four alternative investment proposals described below are being evaluated.

| Proposal | Initial Investment | IRR for Proposal | INCREMENTAL IRR COMPARED WITH PROPOSAL | | |
|----------|-------------------|------------------|-----|-----|-----|
| | | | A | B | C |
| A | $100,000 | 19% | | | |
| B | 175,000 | 15% | 9% | | |
| C | 200,000 | 18% | 17% | 23% | |
| D | 250,000 | 16% | 12% | 17% | 13% |

**7.11a**   If the proposals are mutually exclusive, which one should be selected if the MARR is 15 percent?                                                                *(Proposal C)*
**7.11b**   If the proposals are independent, which should be selected if the MARR is 15 percent?                                                                                      *(All)*
**7.11c**   If the proposals are independent, what is the highest rate of return that can be gained when investment capital is limited to $275,000 and any funds not allocated to the given proposals can be invested at 15 percent?                                        *(17.2%)*

**7.12**   The think-tank group at Imagineering Inc. has recently come up with six proposals for consideration. Each of the alternative projects has an estimated life of 10 years with no salvage value. Their potential impacts are given below.

| Project | A | B | C | D | E | F |
|---------|------|------|------|------|------|------|
| Required capital | $8000 | $4000 | $1000 | $3000 | $1500 | $9000 |
| Annual cash flow | $1100 | $800 | $200 | $715 | $250 | $1400 |

**7.12a**  Assuming Imagineering Inc. has unlimited capital and the projects are independent, which should be accepted? The MARR is 12 percent.
**7.12b**  Given that Imagineering has only $9000 of investment capital available, determine which of the independent alternatives should be selected to maximize the overall rate of return. Assuming that any capital not used for project funding can be invested elsewhere at 15 percent, what is the best return obtainable on the $9000?
**7.12c**  Assuming the projects are mutually exclusive and the MARR is still 12 percent, which, if any, of the proposals should be accepted?

**7.13**  Cash flows from five investment proposals are itemized below.

| Proposal | Investment | ANNUAL NET CASH FLOWS EACH YEAR | | | | |
|---|---|---|---|---|---|---|
| | | 1 | 2 | 3 | 4 | 5 |
| A | −$15,000 | $ 4,500 | $ 4,500 | $ 4,500 | $ 4,500 | $ 4,500 |
| B | −25,000 | 12,000 | 10,000 | 8,000 | 6,000 | 4,000 |
| C | −20,000 | 2,000 | 4,000 | 6,000 | 8,000 | 10,000 |
| D | −30,000 | 0 | 0 | 15,000 | 15,000 | 15,000 |
| E | −10,000 | 4,500 | 4,500 | −2,500 | 4,500 | 7,500 |

All investment opportunities are evaluated using a 15 percent rate of return and are based on a 5-year study period.
**7.13a**  If the proposals are mutually exclusive, which one is the best investment based on its present worth?
**7.13b**  If investment capital is limited to $30,000, which proposals should be accepted?

**7.14**  A half dozen cost-reduction proposals have been forwarded by the industrial engineering department. A 20 percent rate of return is expected, and all equipment investments are to be written off in 5 years with no salvage value.

| Proposal | Equipment Cost | Net Annual Savings |
|---|---|---|
| Combine | $25,000 | $ 9,500 |
| Rearrange | 60,000 | 21,500 |
| Modify | 20,000 | 7,000 |
| Eliminate | 20,000 | 9,000 |
| Up quality | 40,000 | 17,000 |
| Make safer | 30,000 | 10,000 |

**7.14a**  Which proposal should be selected if only one can be accepted? *(Up quality)*
**7.14b**  Which proposals should be selected if all proposals are independent and there is effectively unlimited capital available for cost-reduction projects?  *(All proposals)*
**7.14c**  What is the highest IRR that can be earned from any combination of independent alternatives that has a total investment cost of at least $50,000 but less than $100,000?  *(32.8%)*
**7.14d**  What combination of alternatives would produce the greatest total savings on an investment of not over $100,000?  *(Up quality plus Rearrange)*
**7.14e**  Would you recommend the combination identified in Problem 7.14c or 7.14d? Why?  *(Proposals in neither 7.14c nor 7.14d are best)*

**7.15**  Six mutually exclusive alternatives are being considered. They are listed in order of increasing first costs in the following table, where the rate of return for the overall investment in each and the incremental IRR for every increment are given. All the alternatives have the same lives and comparable intangible values.

| Alternative | IRR on Overall Investment | IRR ON INCREMENTS OF INVESTMENT COMPARED WITH ALTERNATIVE: | | | | |
|---|---|---|---|---|---|---|
| | | *I* | *II* | *III* | *IV* | *V* |
| I | 1% | | | | | |
| II | 8% | 21% | | | | |
| III | 11% | 15% | 12% | | | |
| IV | 15% | 22% | 19% | 17% | | |
| V | 13% | 19% | 16% | 15% | 9% | |
| VI | 14% | 21% | 18% | 16% | 14% | 21% |

**7.15a** If one of the alternatives *must* be implemented but there are insufficient funds available to afford any of the last three alternatives, which one should be selected? Why? *(III)*

**7.15b** What would you recommend if none of the alternatives is mandatory (do nothing is an acceptable alternative); there are still insufficient funds for alternatives IV, V, and VI; and the minimum attractive rate of return is 12 percent? Why?*(Do nothing)*

**7.15c** If the selection of one of the alternatives is mandatory, at what range of MARR is alternative I the proper choice? *(MARR>15 percent)*

**7.15d** At what minimum required rate of return is alternative IV the correct choice? *(15%)*

**7.15e** If funds are almost unlimited and no minimum rate of return is required (although the cost of capital is 9 percent), which alternative would you select? Why?*(VI)*

**7.15f** If the minimum attractive rate of return is 12 percent, what would be the opportunity cost, expressed as a rate-of-return percentage, when a shortage of funds causes alternative III to be selected? *(1%)*

**7.16** Three independent proposals have passed a preliminary screening to confirm that all are acceptable at a minimum IRR of 15 percent. Each one has an economic life of 4 years. The cash flows are given in the table, with the salvage values included in the final year's income.

| Proposal | First Cost | END-OF-YEAR CASH FLOWS | | | |
|---|---|---|---|---|---|
| | | *1* | *2* | *3* | *4* |
| A | $17,000 | $10,000 | $ 8,000 | $ 6,000 | $ 4,000 |
| B | 22,200 | 4,000 | 7,000 | 10,000 | 13,000 |
| C | 20,700 | 8,000 | 8,000 | 8,000 | 8,000 |

**7.16a** Which combination of proposals should be selected if sufficient capital is available to fund any choice, so long as the rate of return is 20 percent or greater? Why?

**7.16b** Which combination of proposals should be selected when the minimum must be 15 percent, but an income of at least $14,000 per year is necessary?

# EXTENSION

## 7A  Analysis of Mutually Exclusive, Reinvestment-Dependent Alternatives

An investment made today could allow special investment opportunities in the future that would not otherwise be available. Such an investment is *reinvestment-dependent*. If one or more alternatives in a set of mutually exclusive proposals is reinvestment-dependent, the special reinvestment opportunities must be included in the analysis.

The PW and incremental-IRR methods described in this chapter are sufficient when future investments are independent of current investments. In this case, *current* proposals are accepted or rejected on the basis of the cash flows they generate, and *future* investments are evaluated according to their cash flows. Reinvestment-dependency can also be ignored when future investments are expected to earn less than the MARR, because such future investments would be rejected owing to their negative PW.

Reinvestment-dependency typically results from a current investment that permits a higher rate of return to be earned on reinvested receipts or allows the investment of new capital at a higher rate than would otherwise be possible. For instance, the purchase of a computer might yield an IRR of 30 percent *and* provide the opportunity for future purchases of peripheral equipment that would return 40 percent on subsequent investments; the latter investments would not be possible without the former.

Analysis of reinvestment-dependent alternatives is conducted by (1) estimating the rate of return applicable to future cash flows from reinvestments and additional capital investments; (2) determining the amount, timing, and future worth of the dependent cash flows; and (3) discounting the FW back to the present at the MARR. The study period during which funds can be reinvested must be the same for all alternatives *and* no less than the longest life of any proposal in the mutually exclusive set. The preferred alternative is the investment plan with the maximum net present value.

To illustrate a comparison involving reinvestment-dependency, assume that the three investments in Table 7.9 are mutually exclusive. Investment *A* provides no special reinvestment opportunities. Investment *B* allows its annual receipts to be reinvested each year at IRR = 20 percent. Proposal *C* recaptures its original investment plus interest in 1 year and permits another investment at year 2 equal to twice the original investment, to earn a 30 percent rate of return. Reinvestment opportunities are continued over a 4-year study period. The MARR is 10 percent.

Since receipts from proposal *A* are assumed to be invested at the MARR,

$$PW(A) = -\$1000 + \$400(P/A, 10, 4) = \$268$$

Of course, the same PW(*A*) results from FW(*A*) discounted back to time zero:

$$PW(A) = [-\$1000(F/P, 10, 4) + \$400(F/A, 10, 4)](P/F, 10, 4)$$
$$= \$392(P/F, 10, 4) = \$268$$

The two $600 receipts in proposal *B* can be reinvested at 20 percent as soon as they are received, and therefore have a future worth in 4 years of

FW(reinvestments) = $600(F/P, 20, 3) + $600(F/P, 20, 2) = $1901

Then, discounting the future worth back to time zero at MARR = 10 percent makes the cash flows of the alternatives comparable:

PW(B) = −$1000 + $1901(F/P, 10, 4) = $298

In proposal C the $1100 capital-recovery payment is assumed to earn just the MARR of 10 percent when reinvested, but the original investment allows a new $2000 investment to earn 30 percent for 2 years. The terminal value of the two investments is

FW(reinvestments) = $1100(F/P, 10, 3) + $2000(F/P, 30, 2) = $4844

The present worth of proposal C is calculated by discounting the future worth at 10 percent for 4 years and subtracting the present worths of the $1000 and $2000 outlays:

PW(C) = −$1000 − $2000(P/F, 10, 2) + $4844(P/F, 10, 4) = $665

Outcomes of PW comparisons with and without reinvestment are shown in Table 7.9. The change in preference between alternatives resulting from opportunities for reinvestment amply demonstrate the importance of recognizing the existence of reinvestment-dependent options and accommodating dependent cash flows in the analysis.

**TABLE 7.9**
Comparison of proposals B and C that permit future investments at a rate of return greater than the MARR = 10 percent with proposal A that allows no special reinvestment opportunities. Proposal C is superior for the 4-year study period.

| End of Year | Alternative A | Alternative B | Alternative C |
|---|---|---|---|
| 0 | −$1000 | −$1000 | −$1000 |
| 1 | 400 | 600* | 1100 |
| 2 | 400 | 600* | −2000† |
| 3 | 400 | 0 | 0 |
| 4 | 400 | 0 | 0 |
| Reinvestment rate | MARR | 20% | 30% |
| PW at IRR = 10% (ignoring reinvestments) | $268 | $41 | 0‡ |
| FW(reinvested receipts) | 0 | $1901 | $4844 |
| PW at IRR = 10% (including reinvestments) | $268 | $298 | $665 |

*Receipts reinvested at 20 percent.
†New capital invested at 30 percent.
‡Based only on original $1000 investment.

Two mutually exclusive proposals have the cash flows shown on page 169. All receipts from proposal J and K can be reinvested at 20 percent and 25 percent, respectively. The reinvestment rates are expected to continue throughout the 5-year comparison period. The minimum acceptable rate of return for all investments is 15 percent.

| Year | Proposal J | Proposal K |
|------|-----------|-----------|
| 0 | −$100,000 | −$100,000 |
| 1 | 60,000 | 60,000 |
| 2 | 50,000 | 15,000 |
| 3 | 40,000 | 60,000 |
| 4 | 30,000 | 0 |
| 5 | 0 | 0 |

**QUESTIONS**

**7A.1** What is the PW of each proposal when reinvestment opportunities are ignored?

**7A.2** What are the PWs when receipts are reinvested at the given rates?

**7A.3** Proposal $L$ also requires an initial investment of $100,000, but it permits no special reinvestment possibilities. What uniform annual cash flow would make independent proposal $L$ as attractive as the preferred reinvestment-dependent alternative?

**7A.4** Under what conditions would it be sufficient to base the choice among mutually exclusive, reinvestment-dependent alternatives on FWs alone?

# CHAPTER 8

# REPLACEMENT ANALYSIS

OVERVIEW

A replacement analysis is conducted to determine if and when an asset currently in service (the *defender*) should be replaced by a more economical alternative (a *challenger*). The suggested analysis procedure is to calculate the equivalent annual cost of each alternative. The current value of the defender is considered to be the capital cost for the alternative of keeping the existing equipment in service.

The analysis is based on a *study period* when there is a known limit on the time a defender's service is required. A *least common multiple analysis* may be used when the asset's services are needed indefinitely. Then a replacement should be made when the EAC of the challenger is lower than the defender's cost for the coming year *and* its EAC for its remaining service life.

Existing assets may be replaced because of deteriorating performance, obsolescence, or inadequate capacity. The current value of a defender is its market value, and the first cost of the challenger should include all expenses required to make it operational. Salvage value is an estimate of the future worth of an alternative at the time its services are no longer needed and should incorporate all disposal expenses. Cyclic replacement by identical assets should take place at the interval which minimizes equivalent annual cost, as explained in Extension 8A.

*164*

## REPLACEMENT STUDIES

*Replacement* refers to a broad concept embracing the selection of similar but new assets to replace existing assets, and evaluation of entirely different ways to perform an asset's function. For instance, old trucks could be replaced with new models that operate similarly but have advanced features that improve their performance. The trucks could also be replaced with a conveyor system, an overhead crane, a subcontract for hauling, or even manual labor, if any of these methods serves the needed function at a lower total cost.

Replacement decisions are critically important to a firm. A hasty decision to "get rid of that junk" because a machine is temporarily malfunctioning, or a decision to faddishly buy the latest model because "we take pride in being very modern," can be a serious drain on operating capital. A firm hard pressed for operating funds may go to the other extreme by adopting a policy that postpones replacements until there is no other way to continue production. A policy of postponement places a firm in the dangerous position of becoming noncompetitive. Reliance on inefficient equipment and processes that lead to higher long-run operating costs or low quality, while competitors enjoy declining costs and better quality gained from modern machinery, is a delaying action that eventually must be paid for, perhaps in bankruptcy. Engineers bear responsibility to recognize when an asset is no longer employed efficiently, what replacements should be considered, and when replacement is economically feasible.

A replacement decision is a choice between the present asset, sometimes called the *defender,* and currently available replacement alternatives, sometimes called *challengers.* The defender may or may not be at the end of its economic life. An asset is *retired* when its owner disposes of it, but it may still serve other owners as second-hand equipment before it is scrapped. Unsatisfactory performance and inability to meet current capacity needs are the main causes of retirement. The challenger may or may not perform the function of the defender in the same way.

Replacement studies are usually made as equivalent annual-cost calculations to take advantage of data traditionally collected as annual charges: depreciation, maintenance costs, operating expenses, salaries, taxes, etc. In this chapter the comparisons are made on a before-tax basis, and the book values of assets as derived from depreciation accounting are not considered. These and other considerations, such as the effect of price escalations, are developed in subsequent chapters.

## REPLACEMENT ASSUMPTIONS AND ANALYSIS

An entire chapter is devoted to replacement analysis because replacement questions occur so regularly, and because there is a lack of agreement on how to best analyze replacement problems.* Differences occur mainly in the handling of a defender's worth at the time of the study and in the treatment of different lives for the defender and challengers.

*For example, Norman N. Barish and Seymour Kaplan, *Economic Analysis: For Engineering and Managerial Decision Making,* 2nd ed., pp. 147-166, McGraw-Hill, New York, 1978, and American Telephone and Telegraph Company, *Engineering Economy,* 3d ed., pp. 323-339, McGraw-Hill, New York, 1977.

## Current Salvage Value of the Defender

The procedure we shall follow in determining the defender's worth is to consider the salvage value of the old asset to be the cost of keeping the defender in service. That is, the best estimate of the defender's worth when replacement is being considered (usually its market value) is the capital cost for the no-change alternative. This approach is followed because tax effects become simpler to evaluate and comparisons are easier between the defender and several challengers.

The alternative procedure is to consider the defender's salvage value as a receipt (positive cash flow) that offsets part of the purchase price (negative cash flow) of each challenger. Then the net differences between the cash flows of the defender and each challenger are compared. To illustrate the two approaches, consider the choice between a defender that has a current market value of $5000 and a challenger that can be purchased for $7500. Both have a service life of 3 years with no salvage value expected at the end of that time. Their operating costs are shown in Table 8.1.

| Year | Defender (D) | Challenger (C) | Difference (D − C) |
|------|------|------|------|
| 0 | P = $5000 | P = $7500 | −$2500 |
| 1 | 1700 | 500 | 1200 |
| 2 | 2000 | 1100 | 900 |
| 3 | 2500 | 1300 | 1200 |

**TABLE 8.1** Costs for replacement alternatives $D$ and $C$.

Operating costs typically increase as an asset gets older. Since the defender has already provided prior service, its annual costs are usually higher than the challenger's. Also, the first-year operating cost for a challenger may be very low when a warranty is issued by the seller.

If the market value of the defender is considered to be the capital cost of its continued service with the MARR at 12 percent, then

$$\begin{aligned} EAC(D) &= [\$5000 + \$1700(P/F, 12, 1) + \$2000(P/F, 12, 2) \\ &\quad + \$2500(P/F, 12, 3)](A/P, 12, 3) \\ &= (\$5000 + \$4892)(0.41635) = \$4119 \end{aligned}$$

The equivalent annual cost of the $7500 challenger that reduces the yearly operating costs is

$$\begin{aligned} EAC(C) &= [\$7500 + \$500(P/F, 12, 1) + \$1100(P/F, 12, 2) \\ &\quad + \$1300(P/F, 12, 3)](A/P, 12, 3) \\ &= (\$7500 + \$2249)(0.41635) = \$4059 \end{aligned}$$

which indicates that it should replace the defender. A PW comparison would show the same preference, of course, by indicating a lower present worth of costs over the 3-year period for the challenger:

$$PW(D) = -\$9892 \quad \text{and} \quad PW(C) = -\$9749$$

The other way to make the comparison is to subtract the market value of the defender from the first cost of the challenger ($7500 − $5000 = $2500) to establish the net purchase price. Then the differences in annual operating costs are determined as the savings (positive cash flow) associated with the replacement. Using these differences $(D - C)$ from Table 8.1 gives

$$EAW(D - C) = [-\$2500 + \$1200(P/F, 12, 1) + \$900(P/F, 12, 2)$$
$$+ \$1200(P/F, 12, 3)](A/P, 12, 3)$$
$$= (-\$2500 + \$2643)(0.41635) = \$60$$

Since identical cost estimates were used and the asset lives were the same, the equivalent annual worth of replacing the defender equals the difference between the previously calculated EACs:

$$EAC(D) - EAC(C) = \$4119 - \$4059 = \$60$$

It is important to remember that in the recommended procedure of calculating an EAC for *each* alternative the defender's salvage value at replacement time cannot be both a capital cost for the defender *and* a reduction in the challenger's purchase price; it is the former, not the latter.

---

### Example 8.1  Inflated Salvage Value of a Defender

A second challenger competes with the defender described in Table 8.1. This challenger $(CX)$ has a purchase price of $9000, but $6000 is offered for the defender as a trade-in and the seller guarantees that operating costs will be no more than $800 per year. Should the offer be accepted when the required rate of return is 12 percent and no salvage value is expected at the end of challenger $CX$'s 3-year life?

### Solution 8.1

It is not unusual for a vendor to offer more than the market value for a used asset, to make the sale; the seller hopes to obtain a steady buyer and likely has accounted for the discount with an inflated selling price. Therefore, *the difference between a known market value and a seller's higher offer is treated as a reduction in the challenger's purchase price.* The discount of $6000 - $5000 = $1000 is applied to the $9000 first cost of challenger $CX$, reducing its effective purchase price to $8000. Then, with the yearly $800 operating cost,

$$EAC(CX) = (\$9000 - \$1000)(A/P, 12, 3) + \$800$$
$$= \$8000(0.41635) + \$800 = \$4131$$

This value is compared with $EAC(D)$ based on the defender's real market value ($5000) and $EAC(C)$ of the first challenger's actual purchase price; the new challenger is rejected because its $EAC(CX)$ is higher, even with the purchase-price discount included.

---

## Defender and Challengers with Different Lives

Ways to make comparisons of assets having different lives were introduced in Chapters 4 and 5. There are two basic methods: study period and least common multiple. The former is applicable when an asset is required for only a specified period, and the latter is appropriate when the asset is needed indefinitely. In both cases the most economical time for the replacement to occur should be checked.

The duration of a study period is set by the period of known need for an asset's service. When this time period is less than or equal to the remaining service life of the defender, and the challengers have longer lives, the salvage values at the time of service termination must be estimated. These salvage values are then inserted for $S$ in the equivalent annual capital-cost formula, EAC $= (P - S)(A/P, i, N) + Si$, where $N$ is the number of years in the study period. It may be necessary to check several termination points to secure the lowest total EAC (sum of equivalent capital and operating costs) because the replacement can take place during any year of the study period, or not at all.

When a known service need extends beyond the defender's remaining service life, it is usually assumed that the defender will be replaced by the best challenger. This policy applies to both the original defender and a replacement of the original challenger, if the study period is longer than the challenger's life. In some studies it may be feasible to anticipate that a better challenger will become available later in the study period; then future replacement plans will include this best-possible challenger. The cash flow of each alternative during a study period thus includes the original capital cost, net purchase price of repeated (or best available) replacements, salvage value at the termination of the study period, and annual operating costs.

A common-multiple analysis is based on assumptions that an asset is replaced with an identical asset and that there is a continuing requirement for its services. Identical replacement is a reasonable assumption for a challenger, but unrealistic for the defender. A defender is typically an older piece of equipment exhibiting decreasing efficiency, and it is doubtful that an identical piece could be found, even if it were wanted. However, a common-multiple comparison is still appropriate for the continuous-service case because it indicates whether a challenger promises a lower EAC than the existing asset. If so, the next question is when to make the replacement.

Consider the defender described in Table 8.1 and a challenger with a first cost of $12,000, salvage value of $2000 at the end of its 5-year economic life, and annual operating costs of $700. Services provided by the equipment will be needed indefinitely. When MARR = 12 percent, repeated identical replacements of the challenger lead to

$$\text{EAC(challenger)} = (\$12,000 - \$2000)(A/P, 12, 5) + \$2000(0.12) + \$700$$
$$= \$2774 + \$240 + \$700 = \$3714$$

Since this equivalent annual cost is significantly lower than the previously calculated EAC(defender) = $4119, replacement is advisable. The rationale for this decision is that keeping the defender for 3 years costs the equivalent of $4119 per year, *after which it will be replaced by the minimum-cost replacement;* the best current challenger will be that minimum-cost replacement unless there is reason to believe that an even better challenger will become available in 3 years.

Given a challenger with a lower EAC than the defender, and no expectation of a better challenger in the foreseeable future, the remaining question is when to make the replacement. The replacement normally takes place when the cost of one more year's service by the defender exceeds the equivalent annual cost of the challenger. An exception occurs in the rare instance when a defender's market value does not progressively decline with age or its operating costs do not progressively increase.

As an example of the normal capital and operating cost pattern, assume the defender in Table 8.1 loses $2000 in value from one more year of service. Then its salvage value at the end of the year is $3000, making its EAC for next year

$$EAC(D_{one\,yr}) = (\$5000 - \$3000)(A/P, 12, 1) + \$3000(0.12) + \$1700$$
$$= \$2000(1.12) + \$360 + \$1700 = \$4300$$

which exceeds EAC(challenger) = $3714. The replacement should be made immediately.

Additional examples of replacement analysis are provided in the following sections, where comparison procedures are related to the causes of replacement: deterioration, obsolescence, and inadequacy.

# REPLACEMENT DUE TO DETERIORATION

Deterioration is manifested through excessive operating costs, increased maintenance cost, higher reject rates, or a combination of added equipment costs. As costs climb, it soon becomes apparent that a replacement study is warranted. Successive studies may be required to determine when the costs for operating another period without change become greater than the annual cost expected from the replacement. The assumption is that the challenger, when acquired, will be kept its full economic life, but it will not be acquired until its equivalent annual cost is lower than next year's cost for the defender. Before final acceptance, the challenger must also pass the test that its equivalent annual cost is smaller than the equivalent annual cost of the defender, based on the defender's remaining years of service.

---

**Example 8.2   Annual Costs for Next Year and Remaining Years of Ownership of an Existing Asset Compared to the Equivalent Annual Cost of a Proposed Replacement**

An existing machine is worth $2500 today and will lose $1000 in value by next year plus $500 per year thereafter. Its $8000 operating cost for this year is predicted to increase by $1000 annually, owing to deterioration. It will be retired in 4 years, when its salvage value will be zero.

A new, improved machine that satisfactorily performs the same function as the existing machine can be purchased for $16,000 and is expected to have relatively constant annual operating costs of $6000 to the end of its 7-year economic life, at which time the salvage value will be $1500. No major improvements are expected in designs for machines of this type within 7 years.

If the minimum attractive rate of return is 12 percent, should the existing machine be replaced? If so, when?

## Solution 8.2

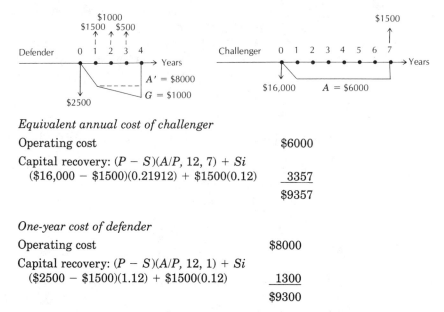

*Equivalent annual cost of challenger*

| | |
|---|---|
| Operating cost | $6000 |
| Capital recovery: $(P - S)(A/P, 12, 7) + Si$ | |
| ($16,000 − $1500)(0.21912) + $1500(0.12) | 3357 |
| | $9357 |

*One-year cost of defender*

| | |
|---|---|
| Operating cost | $8000 |
| Capital recovery: $(P - S)(A/P, 12, 1) + Si$ | |
| ($2500 − $1500)(1.12) + $1500(0.12) | 1300 |
| | $9300 |

Since the defender has a lower annual cost for next year, it should be retained. To anticipate the future replacement budget, conditions for service during year 2 should also be checked. At the beginning of year 2 the existing asset has a value of $1500, which declines to $1000 at the end of the year. Operating costs for the year are $8000 + $1000 = $9000.

*Equivalent annual cost of defender during year 2*

| | |
|---|---|
| Operating cost | $9000 |
| Capital recovery: ($1500 − $1000)(1.12) + $1000(0.12) | 680 |
| | $9680 |

If the cost estimations are deemed reasonable, purchase of the challenger should be anticipated 1 year from now.

It would be a mistake to base the decision on comparison of the equivalent annual cost of the existing machine for its four remaining years before retirement, as follows:

*Equivalent annual cost of defender based on a 4-year life*

| | |
|---|---|
| Operating cost: $A' + G(A/G, 12, 4)$ | |
| $8000 + $1000(1.3588) | $ 9,359 |
| Capital recovery: $(P - S)(A/P, 12, 4) + Si = $2500(0.32924)$ | 823 |
| | $10,182 |

The challenger would then have been purchased while the defender's cost of one more year of ownership was lower than the replacement's equivalent annual cost. A comparable calculation for the conditions expected 1 year from now confirm the decision to make the replacement then:

*Equivalent annual cost of defender based on the last 3 years before retirement*

| | |
|---|---|
| Operating cost: $A' + G(A/G, 12, 3)$ | |
| $9000 + $1000(0.9246) | $ 9,925 |
| Capital recovery: $P(A/P, 12, 3) = $1500(0.41635)$ | 625 |
| | $10,550 |

# REPLACEMENT DUE TO OBSOLESCENCE

Each new development or refinement of an older asset makes the previous way of accomplishing an objective less appealing. Improved methods and machines affect replacement studies in two opposing ways. Improvements usually result in higher first costs for a challenger and reduce the salvage value of a defender; together these two capital costs tend to favor retention of the existing asset. However, dramatic operating-cost reductions or impressive quality gains provided by technologically advanced challengers are the typical causes of obsolescence, and these annual savings tend to exceed the capital-cost advantage of a defender.

Progressive design enrichments can outdate an existing asset well before its economic life has expired. When this happens, the owned asset probably retains considerable resale value, unless the new design is revolutionary. The replacement study should be based on the current *market* value of the defender, *not* on the accounting records or original estimates of resale value because these figures rely on data acquired before the existence of the improved challenger became known. The remaining years of service life for an obsolete asset usually conform to the original estimate of $N$.

---

### Example 8.3   Selection of a Salvage Value for an Obsolete Asset

A low-volume office copying machine was purchased 2 years ago for $700. At the time of purchase it was believed that the machine would have an economic life of 5 years and a salvage value of $100. Operating costs over the first 2 years for material, labor, and maintenance have averaged $4200 annually and are expected to continue at the same level. Some type of copier will be needed for the next several years.

The same company that manufactured the presently used copying machine has a new model which costs $1000 but will perform the current workload with operating costs of $3500 per year. They are offering $500 for the old model as a trade-in on the new machine. The expected salvage value for the new model is $200 at the end of 10 years.

Another company has a different type of copier which is available only on a lease basis. The company claims that leasing their copier at $750 per year will reduce the operating expense for the present amount of work to $2750. Since they do not accept trade-ins, the machine now in use would have to be sold in the open market, where it is expected to bring only $250.

If the minimum acceptable rate of return is 10 percent before taxes, should the defending copier be replaced by one of the challengers?

### Solution 8.3

The market value of the present copier seems to depend on the alternative to which it is being compared, but in either case the remaining period of expected service is 3 years and the salvage value is $100. Trade-in values are often placed unrealistically high to enthuse a buyer. What the bloated trade-in really amounts to is a discount from the selling price. For the given data, it appears that the true market value is $250 rather than $500. The difference is a discount of $500 − $250 = $250 which makes the effective purchase price = $1000 − $250 = $750. In order to compare both challengers to the defender under equitable conditions, the apparent market value ($250) is used, and the price for purchasing a copier is discounted accordingly.

*Equivalent annual cost of defender*

| | |
|---|---|
| Operating costs | $4200 |
| Capital recovery: $(P − S)(A/P, 10, 3) + S(0.10)$ | |
| ($250 − $100)(0.40212) + $100(0.1) | 70 |
| | $4270 |

*Equivalent annual cost of the challenger from the same vendor*

| | |
|---|---|
| Operating costs | $3500 |
| Capital recovery: $(P − S)(A/P, 10, 10) + S(0.10)$ | |
| [($1000 − $250) − $200](0.16275) + $200(0.1) | 110 |
| | $3610 |

*Equivalent annual cost of the leased challenger*

| | |
|---|---|
| Operating costs | $2750 |
| Annual lease contract | 750 |
| | $3500 |

The annual-cost calculations indicate both challengers are preferred to the defender. Leasing is more attractive than buying, if it can be assumed that lease charges will not increase. Another consideration is the possibility that future improvements will make the current $1000 challenger obsolete in the near future. A lease is less expensive, for next year at least, and provides flexibility to take advantage of future cost-reduction developments if they occur.

Using the trade-in value for the existing asset in Example 8.3 does not alter the solution appreciably:

*Equivalent annual cost of defender when P = trade-in value = $500*

| | |
|---|---|
| Operating costs | $4200 |
| Capital recovery: ($500 − $100)(0.40212) + $100(0.1) | 171 |
| | $4371 |

*Equivalent annual cost of purchased challenger when P = $1000*

| | |
|---|---|
| Operating costs | $3500 |
| Capital recovery: ($1000 − $200)(0.16275) + $200(0.1) | 150 |
| | $3650 |

The disparity between annual worths using the trade-in value ($4371 − $3650 = $721) and the market value for the defender ($4270 − $3610 = $660) is $721 − $660 = $61. It is due to the difference in the capital-recovery periods of the defender and challenger. Equal reductions in the present values of the challenger and defender favor the defender in a comparison because it almost always has a shorter life. Thus the use of effective value is a more conservative approach.

Viewing a replacement decision from a stranger's outlook may clarify the situation and provide impartiality. A stranger viewing the choice of a copier described in Example 8.3 could place the decision in the following context: "I need a copying machine. From one manufacturer I can buy a new machine for $1000 which will have a $200 salvage value at the end of 10 years. The annual operating costs for this machine will be $3500. From the same manufacturer I can also get a used copier for $500 which will last 3 years. It will have a $100 salvage value and annual operating expenses of $4200. On the other hand, I can lease a machine for $750 a year, with expected operating costs of $2750, or buy a used machine for $250 which will last 3 years and have annual operating costs of $4200. I will select the alternative which provides the lowest equivalent annual cost."

# REPLACEMENT DUE TO INADEQUACY

When current operating conditions change, an older asset occasionally lacks the capacity to meet new requirements. Sometimes a similar asset can be purchased to supplement the old asset, as in the case of placing a new generator alongside an old one to meet new power demands. New layouts, building additions, and design changes are examples of possible modifications to increase capacity.

Alternatives or supplements to an existing asset are usually compared with a challenging new asset which may perform an equivalent function in an entirely different manner. Replacing a wood stove with an oil furnace, for example, provides an entirely different way to heat a home. Even though a challenger is deemed a desirable replacement, the defender may still have value as usable equipment. In such cases it can be sold or retained for standby purposes. It is also possible that secondary uses can be found for assets replaced from their primary function; the wood stove replaced by an oil furnace might be used as an incinerator.

## Example 8.4 Upgrading versus Demolition and Replacement

A small bridge leading to a proposed industrial park has a load limit of 4536 kg. A manufacturing firm will lease a building site in the park if the capacity of the bridge is raised to 27,216 kg. The developers of the land have two alternatives. They can reinforce the old bridge, or they can tear it out and fill in the low area, leaving a culvert to carry away surface water.

The present bridge has no realizable salvage value. Reinforcement would cost $30,000 and should provide adequate access for 10 years without any major additional work. The salvage value from added materials would be $8000 in 10 years.

A culvert-and-fill approach to the park would cost $60,000 and should meet all requirements for the next 50 years. There would be no salvage value. In addition, it will cost $2000 to remove the old bridge. Maintenance costs are expected to be $2200 per year less than upkeep for a bridge.

Annual property taxes and insurance on the improvements will be 1 percent of the first cost. The required return on investments is 8 percent before taxes. If the developer feels that a new approach to the park is required, which alternative should be selected?

## Solution 8.4

Since a replacement for the old bridge is definitely necessary, there is no distinct defender-challenger relationship. The lower-initial-cost alternative, reinforcement, would best fit the role of defender. It's equivalent annual cost is the sum of capital recovery, extra maintenance costs, and taxes plus insurance.

*Equivalent annual cost of reinforcing the bridge*

| | |
|---|---:|
| Additional maintenance costs | $2200 |
| Capital recovery: $(P - S)(A/P, 8, 10) + S(0.08)$ | |
| ($30,000 − $8000)(0.14903) + $8000(0.08) | 3919 |
| Taxes and insurance: $30,000(0.01) | 300 |
| | $6419 |

*Equivalent annual cost of the culvert and fill*

| | | |
|---|---:|---:|
| Capital recovery: $P(A/P, 8, 50)$ | | |
| ($60,000 + $2000)(0.08174) | $5068 | |
| Taxes and insurance: $60,000(0.01) | 600 | |
| | $5668 | |

From strictly a cost viewpoint, the culvert and fill has a clear advantage of $6419 − $5668 = $751 per year. Other management considerations could influence the final choice. For instance, the developers might be willing to forgo the annual $751 benefit in order to be allowed an opportunity to change plans in 10 years when the reinforced bridge will again need a replacement study. They might be short of capital at the present time or have other possible investments with a greater potential rate of return than that earned on the extra increment of investment ($62,000 − $30,000 = $32,000) required for the culvert and fill. (Note that the extra increment earns 8 percent *plus* $751 a year.)

# PRECAUTIONS FOR REPLACEMENT STUDIES

The value of a replacement study, like other economic evaluations, is directly proportional to the validity of the data. Some costs have more effect in a comparison than others. Replacement decisions are very sensitive to recurring cash flows, especially operating costs. Unfortunately, operating expenses are more difficult to extrapolate into the future than other periodic cash flows such as taxes and insurance.

A conservative approach when estimates are highly uncertain is to give every advantage to the defender. This is accomplished by assuming that the present differential between the operating costs of the defender and challenger will remain constant during the study period, and that there are no capital-recovery costs for the defender. If a challenger still looks good under these handicaps, it is truly a valid contender.

Salvage values are necessarily subject to question because they occur at the most distant point in a replacement study. The basic principle is to use the best *current* estimate of the future, regardless of previous estimates. Appraisals may change from one study to the next, owing to price fluctuations, availability, and needs. An often-neglected cost associated with salvage is the expense of getting an old asset ready for the new purchaser. These expenses could include dismantling, overhaul, painting, crating, cartage, and repairs to the area vacated by the disposed asset. When such costs exceed the disposal price, the salvage value is a loss and is treated as a minus quantity ($S$ is negative) in capital-recovery calculations.

Another commonly ignored cost is the expense associated with putting a new asset in operating order. Special wiring, piping, guard rails, foundations, and other facilities may be needed before new equipment can operate. Radically different or complex equipment often requires more "debugging" than is provided by the supplier. In a replacement study these once-only, operational-type costs should be treated as capital costs.

The bridge-replacement example demonstrated a case in which there was no choice about making a replacement study. More commonly an asset performs its intended function without obvious financial loss. If an acceptable challenger goes unnoticed, the accumulated yearly losses from failing to recognize the need for a replacement can be substantial. One clue to the replaceability of an asset is its economic life. As an asset nears the end of its original life estimation, it becomes a more likely candidate for a replacement study. Other clues include an awareness of new developments which could lead to asset obsolescence and the deterioration of performance, as indicated by reject rates or frequent repairs. Since machines age less obviously than humans and cannot complain about their frailties, it is an engineering function to diagnose infirmities and prepare remedies.

# Review Exercises and Discussions

**Exercise 1**   A grinder was purchased 3 years ago for $40,000. It has provided adequate service, but an improved version is now available for $35,000 which will reduce operating costs and cut inspection expenses. Costs and salvage values for the two machines are shown below. Should a replacement be made if the required rate of return is 15 percent and the services of a grinder will be needed for only 4 more years?

| Year | Defender ($D$) | | Challenger ($C$) | |
|---|---|---|---|---|
| | *Operating cost* | *Salvage value* | *Operating cost* | *Salvage value* |
| 0 | | $12,000 | | $35,000 |
| 1 | $3400 | 7,000 | $ 200 | 30,000 |
| 2 | 3900 | 4,000 | 1000 | 27,000 |
| 3 | 4600 | 2,500 | 1200 | 24,000 |
| 4 | 5600 | 1,000 | 1500 | 20,000 |
| 5 | | | 2000 | 17,000 |
| 6 | | | 2600 | 15,000 |

**Solution 1**   The first calculation determines the EAC when replacement is made immediately. This allows consideration of only the first 4 years of the challenger's 6-year economic life. Its salvage value after 4 years is $20,000. The defender's current salvage value, $12,000, is its market worth now; the original purchase price of $40,000 has no bearing on the replacement decision.

$$\text{EAC}(D) = [\$12,000 + \$3400(P/F, 15, 1) + \$3900(P/F, 15, 2)$$
$$+ \$4600(P/F, 15, 3) + \$5600(P/F, 15, 4) - \$1000(P/F, 15, 4)](A/P, 15, 4)$$
$$= \$23,560(0.35027) = \$8252$$

$$\text{EAC}(C) = (\$35,000 - \$20,000)(A/P, 15, 4) + \$20,000(0.15)$$
$$+ [\$200(P/F, 15, 1) + \$1000(P/F, 15, 2)$$
$$+ \$1200(P/F, 15, 3) + \$1500(P/F, 15, 4)](A/P, 15, 4)$$
$$= (\$15,000 + \$2577)(A/P, 15, 4) + \$20,000(0.15)$$
$$= \$17,577(0.35027) + \$3000 = \$9157$$

A replacement should not be made now, nor should one be made anytime during the remaining period of needed service, as indicated below by the EACs for the other three periods of possible ownership.

| *Periods of Service* | *Defender* | *Challenger* |
|---|---|---|
| EAC(if used in years 2–4) | $7399 | $9,170 |
| EAC(if used in years 3 and 4) | 7061 | 9,543 |
| EAC(if used only in year 4) | 7475 | 10,450 |

**Exercise 2** The headquarters building owned by a rapidly growing company is not large enough for current needs. A search for enlarged quarters revealed only two alternatives that provide sufficient room, enough parking, and the desired appearance and location. One can be leased for $144,000 per year, and the other can be purchased for $800,000, including a $150,000 cost for land.

The study period for the comparison is 30 years, and the desired rate of return on investments before income taxes is 12 percent. It is believed that land values will not decrease over the ownership period, but the value of a structure will decline to 10 percent of the present worth in 30 years. Property taxes are 4 percent and rising. For comparison purposes, annual tax payments should be uniformly close to 5 percent of the purchase price.

The present headquarters building is already paid for and is now valued at $300,000. The land it is on is appraised at $60,000. An engineer suggested that consideration be given to remodeling the present structure. The engineer estimates that an expenditure of $300,000 will provide the necessary room and improve the appearance to make it comparable to the other alternatives. However, the remodeling will occupy part of the existing parking lot. An adjacent privately owned parking lot can be leased for 30 years under an agreement that the first year's rent of $9000 will increase by $500 each year. If upkeep costs are the same for all three alternatives, which one is preferable?

**Solution 2** The cash flows are summarized in the following three diagrams:

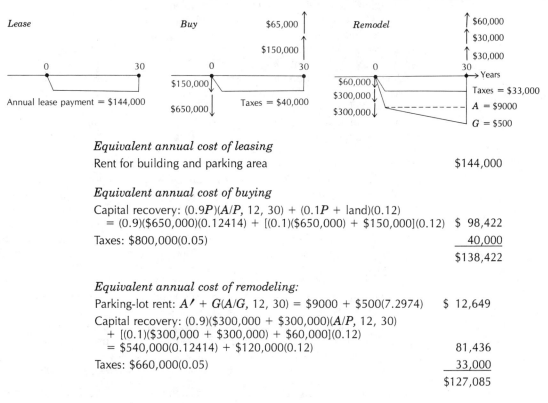

*Equivalent annual cost of leasing*

Rent for building and parking area                                               $144,000

*Equivalent annual cost of buying*

Capital recovery: $(0.9P)(A/P, 12, 30) + (0.1P + \text{land})(0.12)$
  $= (0.9)(\$650,000)(0.12414) + [(0.1)(\$650,000) + \$150,000](0.12)$  $\$\ 98,422$

Taxes: $\$800,000(0.05)$                                                                                 40,000

                                                                                                              $138,422

*Equivalent annual cost of remodeling:*

Parking-lot rent: $A' + G(A/G, 12, 30) = \$9000 + \$500(7.2974)$   $\$\ 12,649$

Capital recovery: $(0.9)(\$300,000 + \$300,000)(A/P, 12, 30)$
  $+ [(0.1)(\$300,000 + \$300,000) + \$60,000](0.12)$
  $= \$540,000(0.12414) + \$120,000(0.12)$                                       81,436

Taxes: $\$660,000(0.05)$                                                                          33,000

                                                                                                              $127,085

Remodeling the presently occupied building is the preferred course of action. Note that the only capital recovery on land value is for interest on the amount invested in land, and that the already-paid-for value of the present headquarters building is included in the capital-recovery charge.

## PROBLEMS

**8.1** At the end of half its expected economic life, a 4-year-old machine has a book value of $5800 from its original cost of $9200. Estimated operating costs for the next year will amount to $6000. An equipment dealer will allow $3600 if the machine is traded in now, and $2800 if it is traded in a year later. The dealer proposes the purchase of a new machine to perform the same function; it will cost $14,000 installed. This machine will have an estimated operating cost of $4500 per year, and at the end of 4 years will have a salvage value of $3000. Is it profitable to replace the existing machine now if the minimum return on investments is 15 percent before taxes?

[*Next year's cost for defender* = *$7340; C (challenger)* = *$8803*]

**8.2** Machine *A* was installed 6 years ago at a total cost of $8400. At that time it was estimated to have a life of 12 years and a salvage value of $1200. Annual operating costs, excluding depreciation and interest charges, have held relatively constant at $2100. The successful marketing of a new product has doubled the demand for parts made by machine *A*. The new demand can be met by purchasing an identical machine which now costs $9600 installed. The economic life and operating costs for the two machines will be the same. The salvage value for the second *A*-type machine will be $1600.

Machine *B*, a different type, costs $17,000 installed but has twice the capacity of machine *A*. Its annual operating costs will be about $3100, which should be relatively constant throughout its 10-year economic life. Salvage is expected to be $4000. The present machine can be used as a trade-in on the new machine *B*. It is worth $3000.

Compare the two alternatives on the basis of equivalent annual cost when the interest rate is 10 percent. [*EAC(A + A)* = *$6067; EAC(B)* = *$5616*]

**8.3** Compare the alternatives of replacing two type-*A* machines with one type-*B* machine, as described in Problem 8.2 by the IRR method. Does the resulting IRR have any advantage over the results obtained from an annual-worth comparison when it is necessary to explain the evaluation to someone not familiar with discounted cash-flow comparisons? Explain.

**8.4** A firm purchased a pump and motor for $1925 installed. It was later discovered that the pump had been improperly selected for the required head and discharge. As a result, the power bill for operating the pump was $900 for a year.

A new pump, suited to the requirements, is available for $2450 installed, with a guarantee that power costs will not exceed $500 annually. The original pump and motor can be sold for $375.

Assume a 10-year study period with zero salvage value for both pumps at the end of the period. The firm uses a minimum attractive rate of return of 10 percent before taxes. Based on present-worth calculations, should the pump be replaced?

[*Yes, as PW(old)* = *$5904.60; PW(new)* = *$5522*]

**8.5** Machine 1 will do a required operation adequately; it can be delivered immediately at a price of $11,250. Its operating costs are $9500 annually, and it will have no realizable salvage value at the end of its 5-year economic life. This machine is being compared with another presently available machine; machine 2 has a first cost of $30,000, annual operating costs of $6500, and a salvage value of $3000 in 10 years.

The much improved machine 3 performs the same function as the other two contenders; it has a first cost of $14,500 with an expected salvage value of $4250 after 5 years. Its major advantage is a lower operating cost of $5000 per year. The only drawback is that the machine is so much in demand that there is a 2-year wait for delivery. Since the firm cannot delay acquiring one of the machines, it must choose between the currently available alternatives 1 and 2. It uses a 15 percent rate of return before taxes for economic comparisons.

**8.5a** Compare the alternatives using the common-multiple method of analysis.
$$[EAC(1) = \$12,856; EAC(2) = \$12,331]$$
**8.5b** Compare the alternatives using a 10-year study period.
**8.5c** Compare the alternatives using the best-possible-replacement approach.
$$[EAC(1 + 3) = \$11,474; EAC(2) = \$12,331]$$

**8.6** Assume your present car is a clunker that could be sold to a used-car dealer for $500. It will probably keep running for two more years, at which time it will have a scrap value of $100. Operating costs next year are expected to be $2400 and will likely be $2950 the following year. Its resale value will decrease by $250 during the coming year.

The lowest priced new car you can find costs $6500. If you buy it, you plan to keep it for 7 years, at which time it will have a market value of $500. The car dealer has offered you $750 for your clunker as a trade-in on the new one, and claims your operating costs should drop to $1200 the first year and should increase by about $250 in each of the following years. Your annual interest rate is 11 percent.

**8.6a** What is the equivalent annual cost of the challenger?
$$[EAC(new\ car) = \$3122]$$
**8.6b** What are the equivalent annual costs for your old car?
$$[EAC(keep\ 1\ year) = \$2705; EAC(keep\ 2\ years) = \$3128]$$

**8.7** Assume a friend of yours is thinking about buying a new car. Her presently owned car can be sold for $1600, or it can provide adequate service for two more years at an operating cost of $1500 next year and $1700 the year afterward. She has been offered $2000 for her car as a trade-in on a demonstrator that has a purchase price of $6000. The demonstrator is expected to have an economic life of 6 years, with operating costs of $800 the first year and increasing by $150 per year thereafter. The value of her car in 2 years will be the same as the new car in 6 years: $600. An 8 percent interest charge is appropriate. Assuming she will need a car indefinitely, what advice can you offer based on equivalent annual costs?

**8.8** Using a 12 percent minimum acceptable rate of return, calculate the present worth of the costs for the two alternatives described below, based on a best-possible-replacement policy, when the need for the equipment is expected to continue indefinitely.

The present equipment could be sold now for $5000, but in 3 years it will have no salvage value owing to radically improved equipment expected to be available then; it will cost $1000 to remove the old equipment in 3 years. This alternative (A) has annual expenses of $3900.

A greatly improved version of the equipment which is to be introduced in 3 years will have annual operating costs of $1900, a first cost of $10,000, and a salvage value of $2000 at the end of its 3-year life.

A presently available replacement has a price of $13,500 and a salvage value of $500 at the end of its 6-year economic life. This alternative (B) has operating costs of $3000 per year.                                                                  [PW(A) = $24,431; PW(B) = $25,581]

**8.9**  Tip Top Testers Inc. is considering the purchase of a new testing machine. The following cost estimates have been obtained:

Purchase price of equipment   = $90,000
Installation cost for equipment = $10,000

| End of year | 1 | 2 | 3 | 4 | 5 | 6 |
|---|---|---|---|---|---|---|
| Market value | $70,000 | $50,000 | $40,000 | $30,000 | $10,000 | $5000 |

The expected service life is 6 years. Operating expenses will be $10,000 the first year, increasing by $2000 per year each following year.

**8.9a**  When MARR = 10 percent, determine the EAC of owning and operating the equipment over the expected service life.

**8.9b**  Assume TTT Inc. has purchased the tester described above and used it for 3 years. A new model is now available at a cost of $90,000 which includes installation charges. This unit is expected to have negligible salvage value after an 8-year life, and operating expenses are expected to be a constant $15,000 per year. Should the new equipment be purchased now if the old machine can be sold at its market value, the need for a tester will continue indefinitely, and the MARR is still 10 percent?

**8.10**  A question has arisen whether it is more economical to replace a forklift truck or to rebore the engine and completely rebuild the present one. The original cost of the present truck 10 years ago was $9000. To rebore the engine and completely rebuild the truck will extend its life another 5 years and will cost $7200. A new forklift truck of the same capacity will have a first cost of $12,300 and will have an estimated life of 10 years. Fuel and lubricants for the rebuilt truck will be about $4000 per year. Similar costs for the new truck will be about 15 percent less. Repairs for the new truck are expected to be about $300 per year less than for the rebuilt truck. Neither unit will have any realizable value when retired. State your assumptions, and determine the equivalent present worths of the two alternatives using an interest rate of 8 percent.

**8.11**  A necessary function can be performed by any of the assets described by the accompanying data:

| Alternative | P | N | S | Annual Cost |
|---|---|---|---|---|
| I | $6000 | 6 | $2000 | $ 800 |
| II | 3000 | 3 | 1000 | 1000 |
| III | 2000 | 3 | 0 | 1200 |

When investment funds are expected to earn 12 percent annually, what is the equivalent annual cost of the alternatives according to each of the following comparison procedures?

**8.11a**  Common-multiple method.

**8.11b**  Best possible replacement as determined in a 9-year evaluation period.

**8.12**  A new delivery truck has a sticker price of $6895, but the dealer will sell it for $6300 cash. A 3-year-old van can be traded for $2700 on the new truck purchased at the sticker price, or it can be sold to a used-car dealer for $2500. The resale value of the van is expected to decrease annually by 40 percent of the previous year's value each year.

Operating costs for the van will be $1020 next year and will increase each following year by $400.

A new truck is expected to have operating costs of $700 per year for the next 2 years; these costs will then increase by $300 each year. After 6 years a truck can likely be sold for 10 percent of its sticker price. It is the policy to retire trucks and vans after 6 years of service and to earn 8 percent annually on invested funds.

Assuming the price of a new truck will not increase in the next few years, when should the van be replaced?

# EXTENSION

**8A  Economic Life for Cyclic Replacements**  Many mechanical items used in service agencies and manufacturing are replaced by essentially the same machine when the original wears out. Informal rules may be used to establish cyclic replacement times. One government department replaces a car whenever it exceeds total kilometrage of 104,605 km or 5 years of service, or the cumulative maintenance cost equals the purchase price. Such rules recognize that automobiles, trucks, typewriters, and similar machines become less efficient and accumulate higher and higher repair bills as they age. Conversely, the longer they are kept in operation, the lower will be their average annual capital cost because the purchase price is spread over more years. The sum of these two types of cost  is the total cost of providing the machines' services. As shown in Figure 8.1, total lifetime cost continues to increase with age, but average annual cost passes through a minimum.

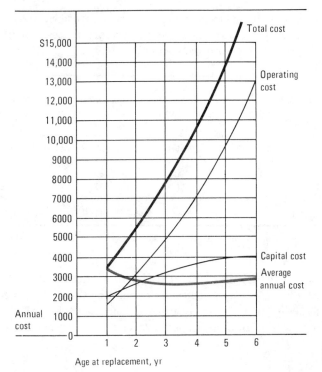

**FIGURE 8.1**   Cost pattern for increasing age of an asset.

## CYCLIC REPLACEMENT ANALYSIS WHEN MARR = 0 PERCENT

The objective of a cyclic replacement study is to determine the pattern of replacement that will minimize the average annual cost. Data for future costs must be estimated, but cost figures for most assets that are used enough to warrant a cyclic replacement study are available from internal or suppliers' records. Simplifying assumptions made to introduce the calculation procedure include a replacement price that remains constant and no interest charges for the use of capital. However, relaxing these assumptions does not affect the optimum cycle time very much unless there are dramatic changes in price or exceptionally high interest rates.

Calculations to determine the minimum-cost age follow an iterative routine in which the capital cost (decrease in salvage value to a certain age) is added to the accumulated operating cost (maintenance plus use expenses) for that same period. Each sum is divided by the relevant age to give an average cost for that replacement interval. This routine is illustrated in Table 8.2 for a city delivery service that owns a fleet of small trucks for store-to-home deliveries. The purchase price per truck is $5000, and the anticipated schedule of future operating costs and salvage values is

|  | YEAR | | | | | |
|---|---|---|---|---|---|---|
|  | *1* | *2* | *3* | *4* | *5* | *6* |
| Operating cost | $1500 | $1600 | $1900 | $2300 | $2800 | $3400 |
| Resale value | 3000 | 2300 | 1700 | 1300 | 1100 | 900 |

These costs are inputs to the tabular solution method which reveals that trading the trucks in every 4 years for new ones is the minimum-cost replacement cycle. The cost data from Table 8.2 were graphed in Figure 8.1.

| *Age of Truck at Replacement, Years* (1) | *Cumulative Operating Costs* (2) | *Cumulative Capital Cost** (3) | *Total Cost* [(2) + (3)] (4) | *Average Annual Cost* [(4) ÷ (1)] (5) |
|---|---|---|---|---|
| 1 | $ 1500 | $2000 | $ 3500 | $3500 |
| 2 | 3100 | 2700 | 5800 | 2900 |
| 3 | 5000 | 3300 | 8300 | 2767 |
| 4 | 7300 | 3700 | 11,000 | 2750 |
| 5 | 10,100 | 3900 | 14,000 | 2800 |
| 6 | 13,500 | 4100 | 17,600 | 2933 |

**TABLE 8.2** Average-annual-cost calculations for replacing an asset when the purchase price is constant and no interest is charged on capital.

*Cumulative capital cost equals $5000 less resale value.

## CYCLIC REPLACEMENT ANALYSIS WHEN MARR = 10 PERCENT

Essentially the same procedure for calculating the minimum-cost replacement age can be used when interest charges are included. This calculation determines the *economic life* of an asset subject to cyclic replacement—its *least-cost replacement interval.*

Data from Table 8.2 are again utilized to illustrate the discounted cash flow approach. Setting the MARR at 10 percent and assuming each year is the economic life $N$ of the asset, the equivalent annual cost of owning the asset $N$ years is calculated from

EAC = capital recovery + equivalent annual operating cost
$$= (P - S)(A/P, i, N) + Si + FW(\text{operating costs for } N \text{ years})(A/F, i, N)$$

The annual cost for 1 year of ownership when $i = 10$ percent is

$$EAC_{N=1} = (\$5000 - \$3000)(A/P, 10, 1) + \$3000(0.10) + \$1500(P/F, 10, 1)$$
$$= \$2000(1.10) + \$300 + \$1500(0.90909) = \$3864$$

For successive years,

$$EAC_{N=2} = (\$5000 - \$2300)(A/P, 10, 2) + \$2300(0.10)$$
$$+ [\$1500(F/P, 10, 1) + \$1600](A/F, 10, 2)$$
$$= \$2700(0.57619) + \$230 + [\$1500(1.10) + \$1600](0.47619)$$
$$= \$1786 + \$1548 = \$3334$$

$$EAC_{N=3} = (\$5000 - \$1700)(A/P, 10, 3) + \$1700(0.10)$$
$$+ [\$1500(F/P, 10, 2) + \$1600(F/P, 10, 1) + \$1900](A/F, 10, 3)$$
$$= \$3300(0.40212) + \$170 + [\$1500(1.21) + \$1600(1.10) +$$
$$\$1900](0.30212)$$
$$= \$1497 + \$1654 = \$3151$$

$$EAC_{N=4} = (\$5000 - \$1300)(A/P, 10, 4) + \$1300(0.10)$$
$$+ [\$1500(F/P, 10, 3) + \$1600(F/P, 10, 2)$$
$$+ \$1900(F/P, 10, 1) + \$2300](A/F, 10, 4)$$
$$= \$3700(0.31547) + \$130$$
$$+ [\$1500(1.331) + \$1600(1.21) + \$1900(1.10) + \$2300](0.21547)$$
$$= \$1297 + \$1793 = \$3090$$

$$EAC_{N=5} = (\$5000 - \$1100)(A/P, 10, 5) + \$1100(0.10) + [\$1500(A/P, 10, 4)$$
$$+ \$1600(F/P, 10, 3) + \$1900(F/P, 10, 2) + \$2300(F/P, 10, 1)$$
$$+ \$2800](A/F, 10, 5)$$
$$= \$3900(0.26380) + \$110 + [\$1500(1.4641) + \$1600(1.331)$$
$$+ \$1900(1.21) + \$2300(1.10) + \$2800](0.16380)$$
$$= \$1139 + \$1958 = \$3097$$

which indicates that the economic life of the truck and the minimum-cost replacement period is 4 years. This is the same replacement interval indicated in Table 8.2, where the analysis was conducted at $i = 0$. Note that equivalent annual capital costs decline as the ownership period increases, while the equivalent annual operating costs increase owing to deteriorating performance. The pattern of changes in capital and operating costs should be checked periodically, when like-for-like replacements are in effect, to confirm that the economic life remains the same. The effects of inflation on replacement prices and operating costs are examined in Chapter 13.

## QUESTIONS

**8A.1** A mechanical testing machine with an initial cost of $8000 closely follows the cost pattern shown below.

| Year | Operating Cost | Salvage Value |
|------|----------------|---------------|
| 1 | $3500 | $6000 |
| 2 | 3800 | 5000 |
| 3 | 4200 | 4300 |
| 4 | 4600 | 3900 |
| 5 | 5100 | 3500 |
| 6 | 5800 | 3200 |
| 7 | 6700 | 3000 |

Using 0 percent interest and assuming that replacement equipment will follow the same cost pattern, determine the economic life.

*(4 years; average annual cost = $5050)*

**8A.2** A new type of testing machine to perform the same function as that depicted in Question 8A.1 is now available at a purchase price of $14,000. The new machines cost more, but they have twice the capacity of the older models. A company plans to replace four of the older type with the new design. The four candidates for replacement are now 2 years old. They will be replaced when the expected cost of keeping them in service one more year is greater than the average annual cost for new machines of comparable capacity. The expected cost pattern for the new type of testing machine is:

| Year | Operating Cost | Salvage Value |
|------|----------------|---------------|
| 1 | $ 7200 | $10,800 |
| 2 | 7600 | 8600 |
| 3 | 8400 | 7500 |
| 4 | 9500 | 5500 |
| 5 | 11,000 | 4000 |

When should the replacement occur if no interest is charged?       *(at 3 years)*

**8A.3** A truck with a first cost of $8000 has the depreciation and service pattern shown below:

| | END OF YEAR | | | | | |
|---|---|---|---|---|---|---|
| | 1 | 2 | 3 | 4 | 5 | 6 |
| Depreciation during year | $2800 | $2000 | $1400 | $ 500 | $ 400 | $ 400 |
| Annual service cost | 1800 | 2100 | 2500 | 2900 | 3400 | 4000 |

**8A.3a** Assuming no interest charges are necessary for the evaluation, how many years should the truck be kept in service before replacement?

**8A.3b**   Assume the truck presently owned is 2 years old. It is known that a truck will be needed for only 6 more years. When should another truck having the same cost pattern be purchased in order to minimize ownership and operating costs during the 6 years?

**8A.4**   A production machine has an initial cost of $3750 and has no salvage value at any time. The costs of inferior performance and maintenance are $300 the first year and increase by $300 each successive year the machine is used. Develop a total-cost formula, that does not include interest charges, for the special case in which operating expenses increase each year by the amount of the first year's cost. Then use the formula to solve for the minimum-cost ownership period.       *(n = 5 years)*

**8A.5**   A factory uses 11 machines of identical design. Each one costs $5000. In operation, maintenance costs are $1000 the first year and increase by 20 percent each year (for example, the third-year maintenance cost is $1000 × 1.2 × 1.2). Since the machines are of special design, they have no salvage value at any time. The MARR is 10 percent. What is the economic life for cyclic replacement of the machines?

**8A.6**   The Shortcircuit Co. is considering the purchase of a newly developed Sparksalot chip tester. The following data have been provided by the manufacturing engineering group for a cost evaluation: The purchase price of the equipment is $45,000 + $5000 for installation. The installation cost for each replacement is $5000. The maximum life is 6 years, with the following intermediate salvage values: year 1, $30,000; year 2, $20,000; year 3, $15,000; year 4, $11,000; year 5, $8000; and year 6, $6000. Operating expenses will be $20,000 for year 1, with an annual increase of $4000 in future years.

   Based on a required rate of return of 20 percent and an assumption of cyclic replacement, determine the economic life of the tester.

# CHAPTER 9

# FINANCIAL ANALYSIS

OVERVIEW

Economic comparison methodologies developed in previous chapters implied financial considerations, but our concern was directed mainly toward the equivalency of cash flow streams from competing alternatives. We skirted the question of financing the proposals. In this chapter the cost of capital is examined, a comparison method is introduced that does not rely on discounting, and capital budgeting is discussed as a procedure for selecting proposals when investment capital is limited.

The *weighted cost of capital* is a composite rate which represents the cost of all acquired funding for an organization. It can be calculated from the cost of debt and equity capital weighted according to the proportion of funds from each source. The resulting figure sets a lower bound for the minimum acceptable rate of return by which proposals are evaluated.

The *payback method* (first cost divided by annual net cash flow) indicates how much time will elapse before the amount invested is recovered from the net cash flow it generates. In its simplest form, the recovery period is based on actual dollar flows; in more sophisticated applications the flow is discounted. The payback method is popular because it is simple to apply and stresses the turnover of capital, but it may show a preference for an alternative that is inferior by a discounted cash-flow comparison.

Proposals to be funded are selected by a *capital-budgeting* process. The *capital-inventory* approach matches the rates of return from different investments against the cost of acquiring capital; all proposals with returns greater than capital costs are acceptable. In *capital rationing* a limit is set on the amount of investment capital, and the best proposals are funded until the supply of capital is exhausted. Objective capital budgeting is difficult, owing to the need to consider numerous combinations of proposals affecting all parts of the organization, dependencies among requests for expenditures, various degrees of riskiness, intangible aspects, mandatory or "urgency" ratings for certain investments, and politic factors.

# FINANCIAL FOCUS

Financial management has traditionally been concerned with obtaining funds and how to use them. Although sources of funding are explored in Chapter 15, the primary focus of this text is on the effective use of funds. Engineers and managers of operating units have responsibilities for proposing and evaluating investments that support the productivity of operations, be they highway construction, steel production, office services, mail delivery, or any other input→output functions.

*Financial analysis* couples the availability of capital with evaluation of ways to invest capital. The size of a pool of investment funds available at a given time is a function of many financial decisions. The pool is fed by streams of funds originating from the sale of stock, borrowing, retained earnings from previous operations, and money from a firm's owners (equity funds). The sources and extent of the capital pool result from top-level, strategic decisions that are guided by financial managers. Engineering economic decisions are more closely aligned with operating-level, tactical considerations than with the financial structure of the firm, but financial policies warrant attention because they inevitably affect the *where, when,* and *how* of capital allocation.

# COST-OF-CAPITAL CONCEPTS

The cost of capital is derived from the composition of the capital pool. The term "pool" is appropriately suggestive of capital from many sources, pooled for funding purposes. The proportion of capital from different sources obtained at different costs to a firm is represented by a *weighted cost of capital.* This weighted cost sets the lower bound for the minimum acceptable rate of return (MARR), as discussed in Chapter 6.

The actual rate of return expected from new investments is normally greater than the cost of capital. How much greater depends on the risk involved. Riskier proposals are subject to higher discount rates to compensate for the chance that they will not meet net-return expectations. But even a minimum-risk investment, such as the purchase of government bonds, must yield a return greater than the interest rate a firm is charged on its debts; otherwise, it would be sensible to direct currently available funds toward debt retirement in anticipation of future, more rewarding investment opportunities.

# CALCULATION OF THE WEIGHTED COST OF CAPITAL

The appealing proposition that all proposals can be funded if they exceed the cost of borrowing is a fallacy. Consider the case where a firm has an 8 percent cost of debt and a

12 percent cost of equity (owners naturally expect to earn more on their equity than the lending rate, or they would not have their money invested in the firm; they would be lending it). If the firm borrows heavily to fund current proposals that promise to return just 9 percent, it may use up its debt capacity (every firm has a limit on the total amount of debt it can accumulate, just as individuals do, depending on resources and reputation). When that capacity is reached, any future funding for proposals must be at the 12 percent rate because the investment funds have to come from equity capital. Then a new proposal with an IRR of 11 percent could not be funded, although it would be more attractive than the previously funded proposals promising 9 percent. This situation is avoided by a cutoff rate based on capital weighted to represent all its sources.

The weighted cost of capital $k_w$ may be calculated from the formula

$$k_w = p_1 k_1 + p_2 k_2 + \cdots + p_n k_n$$

where there are $n$ types of financing sources in proportions $p$ of total capital, each source with its own cost $k$. For instance, if a firm is financed from bonds, preferred stock, and common stock with costs of 7, 9, and 12 percent and in proportions 20, 30, and 50 percent, respectively, then

$$\begin{aligned} \text{Weighted cost of capital} = k_w &= 7\%(0.2) + 9\%(0.3) + 12\%(0.5) \\ &= 1.4\% + 2.7\% + 6\% \\ &= 10.1\% \end{aligned}$$

The cost of capital is troublesome to estimate, despite the apparent precision of its formula. There are differences in opinions about both costs and proportions and, naturally, a number of variations to the general formula have been proposed. Our intent is not to define one optimal formula, but to explore the underlying logic. Therefore, we shall not delve into all the potential sources of financing nor consider the effects of leverage and taxes, but we shall examine the nature of the calculations required to identify proportions and determine rates for a firm's investment capital.*

The financial structure of a firm is comprised of debt and equity, usually in the form of bonds, promissory notes, preferred stock, common stock, and retained earnings. Each carries an obligation for monetary returns. From the discussion of valuation methods for preferred and common stocks in Chapter 4,

$$k_{\text{preferred stock}} = \frac{\text{dividend}}{\text{price}}$$

and

$$k_{\text{common stock}} = \frac{\text{dividend next year}}{\text{price}} + \text{growth rate}$$

Although these formulas are simplistic compared to sophisticated formulations that account for special considerations, they provide a reasonable approximation of return rates. Debt issues are still easier to accommodate because the interest rates are stated in the contractual agreements.

*For an excellent discussion of these topics see Eugene F. Brigham, Alfred L. Kahl, and William F. Rentz, *Canadian Financial Management: Theory and Practice,* Holt, Rinehart and Winston of Canada, Ltd., Toronto, 1983.

The proportions of debt and equity financing can be determined from the existing proportions stated in the firm's balance sheet (see Chapter 11), expected future proportions, or current market values for the firm's securities. *Current market value* is widely recommended because it avoids the uncertainties of forecasting and reflects investors' current assessments of the financial state of the firm.

### Example 9.1 Capital Cost as a Weighted Average of the Cost of Debt, Equity, and Retained Earnings

One way to measure the cost of capital is to assume that the return on any project funded at the weighted average rate will not change the market price of the firm's stock. That is, if the yield from a project equals the composite cost of funds from other sources, the money generated will neither raise nor lower the stock price. Since changes in the price of stock act as a rough index of a firm's economic health, and managers do not care to see the index dip, the cost of capital effectively sets a bottom limit for the rate of return required from future investments.

With $k$ representing the discount rate that aligns future cash flows with the present value of debt and equity funding, the cost of capital from each source can be calculated according to the valuation procedures for stocks and bonds. If 20 percent of a firm's capital comes from $1000 bonds, now selling for $926, which mature in 10 years and pay annual dividends of $50, then

$$\$926 = \$50(P/A, k, 10) + \$1000(P/F, k, 10)$$

from which $k$ is computed by trial and error to be 6 percent.

Next, if 50 percent of the firm's capital is represented by common stock which now sells for $65 per share, pays no dividends, but is expected to continue to increase in price by $7 per year for the next 5 years,

$$\$65 = [\$65 + \$7(5)](P/F, k, 5)$$

from which $k$ is found to be 9 percent.

With the remaining 30 percent of total capital derived from retained earnings which, at a minimum, should be valued the same as common stock because stockholders are being denied dividends from retained earnings, the weighted cost of capital can be determined as shown in Table 9.1.

| Source of Capital | Percentage of Total (1) | Cost, % (2) | Weighted Cost, % [(1) × (2)] |
|---|---|---|---|
| Debt (bonds) | 20 | 6 | 1.2 |
| Equity (stock) | 50 | 9 | 4.5 |
| Retained earnings | 30 | 9 | 2.7 |
| *Cost of capital* | | | 8.4 |

**TABLE 9.1** Calculation of the cost of capital as a weighted average of the funding from debt, equity, and retained earnings.

## PAYBACK COMPARISON METHOD

The *payback* method (sometimes called the *payout* method) avoids the need to calculate the cost of capital and still recognizes financial concern for limited resources. It guards against unexpected price (cost) increases and utilizes a cutoff criterion by requiring proposals to return their original investment from the savings they generate in a specified period of time, usually of short duration. It is typically applied to relatively small investment proposals that originate from operating departments. A department manager often has the authority to accept proposals up to a given ceiling without subjecting them to outside review.

The formula for obtaining a rough measure of the time an investment takes to pay for itself is simple to use and understand:

$$\text{Payback period} = \frac{\text{required investment}}{\text{annual receipts} - \text{annual disbursements}}$$

$$= \frac{\text{first cost}}{\text{annual net cash flow}}$$

Data utilized in applying the formula are usually direct, *not discounted*, cash-flow amounts, and no salvage values are included. The resulting figure tells how long before the amount invested is recovered in actual dollars.

Claims such as "This investment will pay for itself in 18 months" are commonly heard in industry, and they indicate anxiety about the elapsed time before a proposed investment begins to show a profit. The payback period was an extremely popular investment criterion in this country and throughout the world. Lately, however, discounted-cash-flow methods are becoming more popular.*

In actual practice the simple payback formula is sometimes modified to recognize capital recovery through depreciation charges and to include some discounted values. Still, the simple payback formula is widely used without elaborations, though it yields ratings that may lead to incorrect conclusions unless carefully interpreted. Its deficiencies arise from failing to give recognition to cash flows that occur after the payback period has passed and ignoring the time value of money.

For instance, as an extreme illustration of payback-period deception, an investment of $1000 in an asset with a life of 1 year and an associated net return of $1000 would yield a

$$\text{Payback period} = \frac{\$1000}{\$1000/\text{year}} = 1 \text{ year}$$

Another investment of $1000 promises to return $250 per year during its economic life of 5 years and yields

$$\text{Payback period} = \frac{\$1000}{\$250/\text{year}} = 4 \text{ years}$$

Favoring the alternative with the shortest payback period would rate the first alternative best, yet this alternative actually earns nothing: $1000 − $1000 = 0. Meanwhile, the

---

*Helen Baumgartner and V. Bruce Irvine, "A Survey of Capital Budgeting Techniques Used in Canadian Companies," *Cost and Management*, pp. 51-54, Jan. – Feb. 1977.

spurned second alternative would have provided an annual return of 8 percent: $P/A = $1000/$250 = 4 = (P/A, 8, 5)$.

If the results of payback calculations are questionable, why are they used? There are at least two apparent reasons. One is simplicity. Calculations are quick and simple, and the results are intuitively logical. The other reason stems from a preoccupation with the flexibility of capital. If the money spent on an improvement is recovered rapidly, the funds can be allocated again to other desired projects. This concept tends to engender a false sense of security with reasoning such as, "If the project can quickly pay for itself, it must be good" or, "Only the best projects can meet our short-payback-period requirement."

While the payback-period criterion is not always appropriate, it does address the problem of working-capital management by attempting to protect a firm's liquidity position. During times of constricted income, when a firm may have trouble meeting operating expenses and have very limited capacity for funding new investments, an extremely short (as low as 6 months) payback period assures that only quick-profit projects will be endorsed. In such exceptional situations, cash-availability considerations may be equal to or more important than total earnings. As an auxiliary criterion, requiring a short payback period guards against the chance of losses due to new technological developments.

---

### Example 9.2   Payback-Period Comparisons for Alternatives with Different Lives

The supervisor of a small machine shop has received three suggestions for reducing production costs. Suggestion $A$ is for new jigs and fixtures; $B$ is to rebuild an existing machine to improve its performance; and $C$ is a new machine to replace some manual labor. The following estimates have been made for the three alternative investments:

|                        | $A$    | $B$    | $C$    |
|------------------------|--------|--------|--------|
| First cost             | $1800  | $2350  | $4200  |
| Economic life, years   | 3      | 4      | 8      |
| Net annual cash flow   | $645   | $840   | $1100  |
| Payback period, years  | 2.8    | 2.8    | 3.8    |

The supervisor selects alternative $B$, explaining that, because of limited capital for investments, shorter payback periods are preferable. With alternatives $A$ and $B$ having the same payback period, $B$ is favored because the annual savings are greater than for $A$. What are the fallacies in this reasoning?

### Solution 9.2

Based on just the payback-period criterion, consistent attention to the condition of limited capital would dictate a preference for alternative $A$ over $B$ because $A$ requires less investment capital. Based on the rate of return on each investment, $C$ is the most attractive, as attested to by

IRR($A$): $(P/A, i, 3) = 2.8$    or    $i = 3.5\%$
IRR($B$): $(P/A, i, 4) = 2.8$    or    $i = 15\%$
IRR($C$): $(P/A, i, 8) = 3.8$    or    $i = 20\%$

The flaws in the reasoning stem from a strict reliance on the payback criterion. Too short a period can obviously block acceptance of some high-return alternatives. If successive investments in shorter-lived alternatives produce a smaller rate of return than investment in one longer-lived alternative, flexibility is purchased by the losses in total earnings. In the example, successive utilization of alternatives $A$ and $B$ limits the maximum investment level to \$2350 during 7 years, but it also limits the rate of return to less than half that achievable by accepting alternative $C$.

# CAPITAL BUDGETING

It could be said that the central theme of this book is *capital budgeting—the process of analyzing and determining optimum capital expenditures.* Successful capital budgeting is vital for the long-run prosperity of any industrial organization. Funding decisions affect all departments within a firm, and mistakes in forecasting or fulfilling asset requirements for any type of operation can damage the others. Both immediate and long-term needs have to be considered. And these needs have to be evaluated in conjunction with questionable future developments in unique markets and in the economy as a whole. The combined effects of internal pressures and external uncertainties make the capital-budgeting decision at once the most important and difficult kind of decision in financial management.

The basic role of an engineering economist in capital budgeting is to uncover, examine, and prepare analyses of profitable ways to invest capital. The prepared analyses are acted upon by screening groups that vary in size and composition for different organizations; successive screenings by departmental groups may be forwarded to a board of top-level managers, all proposals may be put through a committee-type screening mechanism before a final allocation by select executives, or some other management device may be designed to guarantee a *careful, objective scrutiny* of requested expenditures. Major outlays for strategic objectives usually await approval of the board of directors or top management.

## Capital Inventory

It is almost certain that in any ambitious firm there will be more requests for expenditures than there is capital to satisfy them. An abundance of proposals is a healthy sign that operating personnel, engineers, and managers are actively pursuing improvements. A firm might increase the amount of capital available in a budget period by external financing or by retaining a larger than normal share of earnings, but considerations of debt obligations and stockholders' interests limit the amount procurable. Unless unusually attractive investment opportunities become apparent, the amount of capital available is essentially set by the long-term financial policies of the firm. Asset expansion is necessarily related to future sales, because a decision to invest in a fixed asset is made in anticipation of future returns from sales, and future sales are the basis of capital formulation.

The *capital-inventory* approach for selecting which proposals to fund matches the cost of capital to the returns expected from investments. As portrayed in Figure 9.1, the shaded blocks form a ladder of investment proposals promising various rates of return; $IRR_1$ is a smooth curve representing the blocks. Curves $IRR_2$ and $IRR_3$ represent other configurations of investment opportunities that might become available during a budgeting period. The cost of each additional dollar acquired for purposes of making capital expenditures is given by the bold MCC (*marginal cost of capital*) curve. This curve is relatively flat up to an amount which exhausts the normal sources of capital; beyond this point, it rises sharply as more expensive sources are tapped.

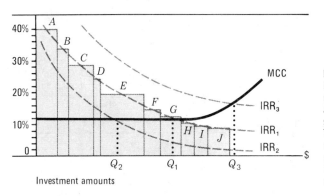

**FIGURE 9.1** Capital-inventory graph showing the marginal cost of capital (MCC) and three investment-proposal schedules ($IRR_1$, $IRR_2$, $IRR_3$). The smooth-curve schedules represent discrete investment projects, as indicated by the lettered ladder of proposals represented by $IRR_1$.

If all proposals that promise a rate of return greater than the marginal cost of capital are funded in schedule $IRR_1$, capital allocations would be made to proposals *A* through *G*. These investments total $Q_1$. The same criterion would indicate investments in the amount $Q_2$ for the $IRR_2$ schedule; $Q_2$ is smaller than $Q_1$ because the investment opportunities of schedule $IRR_2$ are not so lucrative as those of $IRR_1$. A wealth of proposals with high rates of return might induce the firm to secure additional capital to allow the $Q_3$ level of investment for the $IRR_3$ schedule. Any proposals that have a rate of return smaller than the marginal cost of capital are rejected by the investment-inventory criterion.

## Capital Rationing

The practice of placing a fixed limit, or limited range, on total investments rations capital to the best proposals that can be funded within the budget limits. The floor for capital rationing is the cost of capital; that is, if the available investment capital exceeds the requested expenditures, no request would be granted that yields a rate of return smaller than the cost of capital. Such requests should not even be made if economic evaluations are conducted properly, because the minimum rate of return for an acceptable alternative is always equal at least to the cost of capital.

Figure 9.2 shows a *cutoff rate* that conforms to a ceiling on capital. The point on the *cutoff index* is set by the intersection of a line from the amount of capital available for investments $Q_1$ and the $IRR_1$ curve which represents proposals laddered according to the cutoff index. For the condition shown, the cutoff point limits acceptable proposals to a number less than would be admissible using a capital inventory. Rationing capital to amount $Q_1$ rather than allowing all investments $Q_2$ which exceed the marginal cost of capital (MCC) increases the *average* rate of return on accepted investments. However, the firm may be missing an opportunity to increase its *total* profit by not funding all proposals that earn more than the cost of acquiring the capital for funding.

**FIGURE 9.2** Cutoff rate established by the point where the investment-opportunity schedule ($IRR_1$) crosses a projection of the amount of capital available $Q_1$. Capital rationing limits acceptable proposals to a higher cutoff index than allowed by $Q_2$.

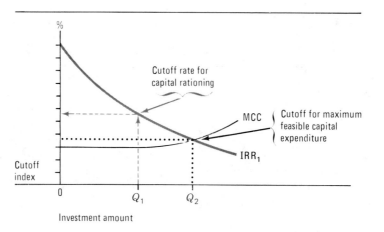

The cutoff rate for a budget ceiling becomes the *minimum acceptable rate of return* for the budgeting period when the cutoff index is expressed as a percentage. The laddering of proposals could also be accomplished by rating proposals according to

$$\text{Present-worth index} = \frac{\text{PW(receipts} - \text{disbursements)}}{\text{PW(investments)}}$$

$$= \frac{\text{PW(net cash flows)}}{\text{first cost}}$$

when the entire investment occurs at time zero. Ranking proposals and accepting only the best ones until all the available capital is allocated works reasonably well, but care should be exercised to apply the concept adroitly and without bias.

---

### Example 9.3  Capital Rationing Using a Cutoff Rate of Return and a Present-Worth Cutoff Index

Six independent alternatives are listed in Table 9.2. None of the proposals is expected to have any realizable salvage value. If the marginal cost of capital is 12 percent and the amount of investment capital is limited to $100,000, which requests for expenditure should be granted?

| Proposal | Request for Expenditure | Investment | Net Savings | Useful Life, Years |
|----------|-------------------------|-----------|-------------|---------------------|
| A | Remodel loading dock | $30,000 | $12,600 | 9 |
| B | Modernize office | 35,000 | 12,250 | 4 |
| C | Purchase shredder | 10,000 | 4,450 | 4 |
| D | Install conveyor | 25,000 | 10,025 | 4 |
| E | Purchase press | 30,000 | 9,700 | 4 |
| F | Construct storage shed | 45,000 | 11,150 | 9 |

**TABLE 9.2**

## Solution 9.3

The rate of return for proposal $A$ is calculated as

$$PW(A) = -\$30,000 + \$12,600(P/A, i, 9) \overset{?}{=} 0$$

At IRR = 40 percent,

$$PW(A) = -\$30,000 + \$12,600(2.3790) = -\$25$$

or IRR $\doteq$ 40 percent. Rates of return for the other proposals are shown below.

| Proposal | A | B | C | D | E | F |
|----------|-----|-----|-----|-----|------|-----|
| IRR | 40% | 15% | 28% | 22% | 11%* | 20% |

*Unacceptable because the rate of return is smaller than the cost of capital.

Since present-worth calculations are based on a given interest rate, the minimum cost of capital, 12 percent, is assumed reasonable for budgeting and is used to determine the present-worth index of proposal $A$ as

$$\text{Present-worth index}(A) = \frac{PW(\text{net savings})}{\text{investment}}$$

$$= \frac{\$12,600(P/A, 12, 9)}{\$30,000} = \frac{\$12,600(5.3282)}{\$30,000}$$

$$= 2.24$$

The remaining present-worth indexes are given below.

| Proposal | A | B | C | D | E | F |
|----------|------|------|------|------|-------|------|
| PW index | 2.24 | 1.06 | 1.35 | 1.22 | 0.98* | 1.32 |

*Unacceptable because the index is smaller than 1.0.

The proposals, ranked according to their index values and cumulative investment totals, are tabulated to determine the cutoff level as shown on page 203.

| | Ranked Pro- posals | Rate of Re- turn, % | Invest- ment | Cumula- tive In- vestment | Ranked Pro- posals | PW Index | Invest- ment | Cumula- tive In- vestment |
|---|---|---|---|---|---|---|---|---|
| | A | 40 | $30,000 | $ 30,000 | A | 2.24 | $30,000 | $ 30,000 |
| | C | 28 | 10,000 | 40,000 | C | 1.35 | 10,000 | 40,000 |
| Cutoff | D | 22 | 25,000 | 65,000 | F | 1.32 | 45,000 | 85,000 |
| level | F | 20 | 45,000 | 110,000 | D | 1.22 | 25,000 | 110,000 |
| | B | 15 | 35,000 | 145,000 | B | 1.06 | 35,000 | 145,000 |
| | E | 11 | 30,000 | Not acceptable | E | 0.98 | 30,000 | Not acceptable |

The rankings produced by the internal-rate-of-return and present-worth calculations are different. The reasons for the difference are assumptions embodied in the two methods. The internal-rate-of-return method assumes that intermediate cash flows are reinvested at the calculated IRR. The PW Index assumes that those cash flows are reinvested at the MARR. Unlike the proposals in Example 9.3, the two methods frequently lead to the same selections in other capital-budgeting situations.

The combination of proposals $A$, $C$, and $D$ uses only $65,000 of the available capital. Assuming the remaining $35,000 is invested in proposal $B$, which still has a return greater than the marginal cost of capital, the combination $(A + C + D + B)$ has the following net present worth:

$$PW(A + C + D + B) = -\$100,000 + \$12,600(P/A, 12, 9)$$
$$+ (\$4450 + \$10,025 + \$12,250)(P/A, 12, 4)$$
$$= \$48,302$$

A different and better combination is to fund proposals $A$, $F$, and $D$. This combination gives

$$PW(A + F + D) = -\$100,000 + (\$12,600 + \$11,150)(P/A, 12, 9)$$
$$+ \$10,025(P/A, 12, 4)$$
$$= \$56,993$$

## Qualifications for Capital Budgeting

The discussion of capital inventory and rationing was simplified by ignoring several considerations that frustrate actual applications:

1 Determining a cutoff rate, or an index cutoff point, does not automatically identify the best combination of proposals to take advantage of the limited capital, as evidenced in Example 9.3. *Linear-programming* models have been developed to assist the rationing exercise, but each model has its own assumptions that limit general applicability.

2 *Independent* projects are not always *completely* independent. Sometimes a proposal from one department is made on the assumption that a proposal from another department will be funded. A proposal with a very high rate of return might be made for an addition to an activity that is only marginally profitable; the highly profitable addition could be voided if the marginal activity is modified or eliminated. An *interdependency* could exist as an informal policy of the capital budgeters to try to spread investments along geographical or organizational lines.

3 All the proposals in Example 9.3 were treated as if they had identical *risk*. Rarely do different courses of action have the same probability of success. Riskier ventures typically are expected to yield a higher rate of return. Adding a percentage of the required rate of return to compensate for risk is a reasonable practice, but its conservative flavor thwarts the objective laddering implicit in an investment-opportunity schedule. Ways to analyze risk and to select preferred alternatives subject to risk are presented in Chapters 17 and 18.

4 The capital-budgeting process normally includes no formal provisions for evaluating the effects of *intangibles*, mainly because there is no completely satisfactory way to analyze and include intangible factors in decision making. Still, since intangibles do influence decisions, and rightfully so, they should be exposed and examined. The methods given in Chapter 19 for quantifying intangibles and including them in the decision process encourage careful examinations, at a minimum, and certainly add objectivity to the analysis.

5 Mandatory projects are effectively exempt from capital rationing when failure to fund them can shut down operations. Government regulations, such as required pollution controls, are the cause of many *mandatory investments*. These investments may have a negative rate of return, but they still top the list of requests for expenditure. Other projects that are not compulsory but are rated urgent may be ranked by management edict above proposals with higher rates of return.

One large corporation divides its investment-opportunity schedule into distinct categories: New projects must have a rate of return greater than 25 percent to be even considered for funding; improvements or modifications to existing projects have a floor at 17 percent; and investments that increase labor utilization are accepted if they produce a 10 percent return. These minimum required percentages reflect the risk involved and management views about the most effective use of capital. An amount of capital is allocated for each category and is rationed to proposals within the category according to the rankings. Projects considered mandatory, such as safety improvements, are funded from the top of the capital pool, irrespective of their return on investment.

6 Subtle forms of persuasion may intimidate or prejudice the workings of the decision-making process. *Politic* considerations surround most decisions, and capital-allocation

evaluations are not exempt. Perhaps it is important to reward the originator of an idea by accepting the most recent proposal, after several rejections. Even if the proposal has a modest IRR; such encouragement may spur more activities of the type desired. Successful proposal sponsors gain stature, and the types of proposals currently accepted tend to guide the submission of future proposals. Susceptibility to the "squeaky wheel" principle that directs oil to the noisiest wheel may bias judgment, yet the aggressiveness exhibited in seeking attention (and change) may be in the best interest of the firm. A manager's relationship to peers and subordinates can be affected by success in pushing proposals through, but should personal relationships be a factor in determining the merits of proposals? Though the questions are many and the answers are not easy, competent capital budgeting is at stake.

## Review Exercises and Discussions

**Exercise 1**   Go-Go was incorporated 3 years ago. The following data have been collected to determine its current cost of capital:

| Outstanding Debt, Preferred Stock, and Common Stock (in millions of dollars) | | |
| --- | --- | --- |
| | *Market Value* | *Cost %* |
| Bonds (9½% due in year 2000) | 16 | 9.1 |
| Other debt | 24 | 9.6 |
| Preferred stock ($36 per share) | 17 | 7.4 |
| Common stock ($40 per share) | 159 | |

| Common Stock Record for 3 Years | | | | |
| --- | --- | --- | --- | --- |
| | *Year 1* | *Year 2* | *Year 3* | *Average Growth Rate, %* |
| Dividend per share | $1.55 | $1.60 | $1.67 | 3.8 |
| Earnings per share | $2.49 | $2.70 | $2.98 | 9.5 |

What weighted cost of capital best represents Go-Go's financial status?

**Solution 1**   The total debt of $16 + $24 = $40 (million) has a weighted average interest rate of 9.3 percent. This rate can be adjusted to an after-tax rate through the use of Go-Go's tax rate of 48 percent (interest payments are deductible from profits, so the actual outlay for interest is effectively 52 percent of the amount paid when the corporate tax rate is 48 percent):

After tax interest rate on debt = 9.3%(1 − 0.48) = 4.8%

Assuming a common stock dividend for next year of $1.76,

$$k_{\text{common stock}} = \frac{\$1.76}{\$40} + 0.038 = 0.082 \quad \text{or} \quad 8.2\%$$

This rate appears to be somewhat low for shareholders' expectations with respect to the yield on Go-Go bonds. Since the dividend rate is low because the company is reinvesting its earnings to support future growth, the growth rate for earnings per share (9.5 percent) reasonably seems to be a more representative figure for investors' expected return. Accepting this reasoning gives

$$k'_{\text{common stock}} = \frac{\$1.76}{\$40} + 0.095 = 0.139 \quad \text{or} \quad 13.9\%$$

A weighted cost of capital of 11.9 percent results from the calculations shown in Table 9.3.

|  | Amount | Proportion | Rate, % | Weighted Rate, % |
|---|---|---|---|---|
| Debt | $ 40 | 0.194 | 4.8 | 0.94 |
| Preferred stock | 7 | 0.034 | 7.4 | 0.25 |
| Common stock | 159 | 0.772 | 13.9 | 10.73 |
| Totals | 206 | 1.000 |  | 11.92 |

**TABLE 9.3**

**Exercise 2**  Another possible cutoff index is the net difference between the present worths of income (or savings) and expenditures. Apply this index to obtain a ranking for the six proposals in Example 9.3.

**a**  Which proposals should be funded when capital is limited to $100,000?
**b**  Which proposals should be funded when the capital budget is only $75,000? Compare the combinations indicated by the net-present-worth method and the internal rate-of-return methods for this budget level.

**Solution 2**  The net present worth of proposal $A$ at the minimum discount rate of 12 percent is

PW($A$) = −$30,000 + $12,600($P/A$, 12, 9) = $37,135

The remaining PWs are calculated similarly to yield the amounts by which the proposals are ranked.

| Ranked Proposals | Net PW | Net Savings | Investment | Cumulative Investment |
|---|---|---|---|---|
| A | $37,135 | $12,600 | $30,000 | $30,000 |
| F | 14,409 | 11,150 | 45,000 | 75,000 |
| D | 5,449 | 10,025 | 25,000 | 100,000 |
| C | 3,516 | 4,450 | 10,000 | 110,000 |
| B | 2,207 | 12,250 | 35,000 | 145,000 |
| E | −538 | 9,700 | 30,000 | Not acceptable |

**a**  The ranked proposals suggest the same combinations of investments as identified in Example 9.3: Fund proposals $A$, $F$, and $D$.
**b**  When available capital is limited to $75,000, the rankings by net present worth suggest allocations of proposals $A$ and $F$. The internal-rate-of-return method suggests $A$, $C$, $D$.

Rating by the net present worth emphasizes the discounted amount of total benefits. Unless corrected for unequal lives among proposals, the higher ratings naturally go to the proposals which yield returns for a longer period of time, even when these returns are at a lower rate than is obtainable with shorter-lived projects. Most analysts feel the total return from long-lived assets is a legitimate comparison criterion, especially for public projects (discussed in the next chapter).

# PROBLEMS

**9.1** Given the following data, calculate the weighted cost of capital.

| Source | Market value |
|---|---|
| Bonds: Value now = $95 per $100 maturity value in 7 years; coupon rate = 8% compounded quarterly | $9.5 million |
| Preferred stock: Value now = $100 per $100 par value; 7% annual dividend | $2.0 million |
| Common stock: $21 per share, having increased from $13 five years ago; next year's dividend = $1.80; 5-year growth rate = 5.8% | $20.0 million |
| Retained earnings: Expected to earn at the same rate as stock price growth | $1.5 million |

**9.2** A troubled firm is assessing its cost of capital. Its proportion of debt to equity is 1:2. The debt is in the form of long-term securities for which the interest rates average 5.9 percent. Until the past year the firm's common stock had increased in value at an 11 percent compound rate, and dividends grew at a 13 percent rate. A recent report by an investment advisory service, critical of the company's management, contributed to a drop in its stock value from $65 per share to $45. The report predicted that the company would grow at a 6 percent rate for the next several years. The dividend payable next year ($5) conforms to the historical growth rate. What weighted cost of capital seems most reasonable. Why? *(13.3%)*

**9.3** A company's current capitalization structure is 35 percent equity and 65 percent debt. The estimated weighted average of all debt financing over an extended future period is 4.2 percent. The corresponding cost of all outstanding equity financing is 10.77 percent.

**9.3a** What is the cost of capital? *(6.5%)*

**9.3b** Using the firm's cost of capital as its required rate of return, how much could it afford to pay for an investment that promised to return $10,000 for three consecutive years starting 2 years from now? *($24,870)*

**9.3c** Should the firm make the investment (in Problem 9.3*b*) if the risk is considered quite small? Why?

**9.4** Four basic forms of debt and equity financing are described in Table 9.4.

| Name of Security | Type | Market Value | Life | Obligation to Pay Return | Return | Vote |
|---|---|---|---|---|---|---|
| First-mortgage bond | Mortgage on physical assets | | 30–35 years | First | | None |
| Debenture bond | Unsecured obligation of the company | | 10–50 years | Second | | None |
| Preferred stock | Part owner of company | | Usually perpetual | Third | | Usually None |
| Common stock | Part owner of company | | Perpetual | Last | | Yes |

**TABLE 9.4**

**9.4a** Complete Table 9.4 for Market Value and Return.

**9.4b** Discuss the relative merits of investing in each security from the viewpoint of a private investor.

**9.4c** Discuss the relative merits of each source of funds from the viewpoint of a small company that recently went public (owners sold stock to the public), is in desperate need of cash, has not been able to sell all the initial stock offering, and has mortgages on 10 percent of its physical assets.

**9.5** A company expects a new machine to save $15,000 per year for 8 years and to have a salvage value of $2000 at the end of its economic life. Eighty percent of the firm's capital is represented by common stock which sells for $30 per share, pays annual dividends of $2.70, but has not increased in selling price over the last 4 years. The other 20 percent of its capital comes from long-term debt on which the annual interest rate averages 12 percent. How much can the company pay for the new machine if the investment is to earn twice the cost of capital? *($59,612)*

**9.6** Machine *A* saves $2000 each year of its 3-year economic life and has a simple payback period of 2 years when calculated without using discounted cash flow. Machine *B* has an economic life of 4 years, earns the same rate of return, and has the same annual savings as machine *A*. What is its simple, nondiscounted payback period? *(2.43 years)*

**9.7** Use the payback criterion to select a preferred investment proposal from the five cash-flow patterns given in Problem 7.13. *(B at 2.4 years)*

**9.8** Eight investment proposals having identical economic lives are given below.

| Proposal Number | Investment | IRR, % | Proposal Number | Investment | IRR, % |
|---|---|---|---|---|---|
| 1A | 10 | 12 | 3A | 15 | 2 |
| 1B | 15 | 14 | 3B | 20 | 9 |
| 2A | 5 | 11 | 4A | 10 | 8 |
| 2B | 15 | 10 | 4B | 20 | 15 |

**9.8a** If all the proposals are independent and the capital rationing cutoff rate is 10 percent, which ones should be accepted? *(1A, 1B, 2A, 2B, 4B)*

**9.8b** If the two levels of each numbered proposal are mutually exclusive, and the cutoff rate is still 10 percent, which ones should be accepted? *(1B, 2A, 4B)*

**9.9** Six independent investment proposals have the same payback period based on the after-tax cash flows shown below.

| Proposal | 0 | 1 | 2 | 3 | 4 | 5 |
|---|---|---|---|---|---|---|
| | | | YEAR | | | |
| 1 | −$1000 | $200 | $300 | $500 | $300 | $200 |
| 2 | −900 | 300 | 300 | 300 | 300 | 300 |
| 3 | −800 | 0 | 400 | 400 | 800 | 0 |
| 4 | −700 | 0 | 0 | 700 | 400 | 400 |
| 5 | −600 | 300 | 200 | 100 | 300 | 500 |
| 6 | −500 | 300 | 100 | 100 | 200 | 0 |

**9.9a** Which alternative would be preferred when the cash flows are discounted to their present worths at a discount rate of 8 percent?

**9.9b** Comment on the cash-flow patterns that are most likely to cause the payback criterion to disagree with a preference indicated by the discounted cash-flow criterion.

**9.9c** What cash-flow pattern is most likely to make the payback and discounted cash-flow comparisons agree?

**9.9d** Which alternatives would be selected by a capital-inventory approach when the cost of capital is 10 percent?

**9.9e** If the available capital is limited to $2000 and any unused funds can be invested at 10 percent, what combination of investments should be selected?

**9.10** Ten requests for expenditure have been received. All are for investments to reduce operating costs, and all have about the same risk. The assets involved have a useful life of 4 years and no salvage value. Investment amounts and the uniform cash flows are shown in Table 9.6.

**9.10a** If the alternatives are independent and the cost of capital is 13 percent, how much should be invested?

**9.10b** If the alternatives are independent and capital is limited to $100,000, which proposals should be accepted? What is the cutoff rate?

**9.10c** Answer the questions in Problem 9.10*b* when the only change is that proposal 4*A* is mandatory.

| Proposal | Investment | After-Tax Cash Flow |
|---|---|---|
| 1*A* | $10,000 | $ 3,087 |
| 1*B* | 20,000 | 7,434 |
| 1*C* | 30,000 | 10,722 |
| 1*D* | 40,000 | 14,012 |
| 2*A* | 10,000 | 4,159 |
| 2*B* | 20,000 | 8,020 |
| 2*C* | 30,000 | 11,151 |
| 3*A* | 10,000 | 3,863 |
| 3*B* | 20,000 | 6,864 |
| 4*A* | 30,000 | 9,877 |

**TABLE 9.6** After-tax cash flows expected to result from capital expenditures for the listed proposals. All alternatives have the same useful life and risk.

**9.10d**  Use the present-worth index to answer Problem 9.10*a*.

**9.10e**  Let the numbers in the proposal identifications represent four different departments in the organization. Determine the answers to the questions in Problem 9.10*b* if it is company policy to accept at least one proposal from every department.

**9.10f**  Assume the policy in Problem 9.10*e* is changed to the capital-inventory approach in which departments 1 and 3 have a 15 percent limit on cost of capital and the other two departments have a 20 percent minimum.

**9.10g**  Let the numbers in the proposal identifications represent four categories in which the lettered alternatives (*A, B, C,* and *D*) are mutually exclusive. Which proposal should be selected from which categories if capital is limited to $70,000?

# EXTENSIONS

**9A  Life Cycle Costing**  A study that gives special attention to both direct and indirect cash flows over the *complete* life of a project is called *life cycle analysis*. The intent of life cycle analysis is to direct attention to factors that might be overlooked —especially inputs that occur during the inception stage, to get a project underway, and activities associated with the termination phase. The aspect of life cycle analysis introduced in this extension is life cycle *costing*.

Life cycle costing (LCC) has been a strength of engineering economics for over 50 years. LCC is used for product development studies and project evaluations.*

LCC is expected to reduce total cost by selecting the correct designs and components to minimize the *total* cost of service, not just the first cost. For instance, additional expenditures for the preliminary design might lower operating costs and thereby reduce total costs.

Expenditures during the life of most projects roughly follow the pattern shown in Figure 9.3 (next page). The first stage, design, accounts for research, engineering design, administration, and financing costs. The development stage takes the basic plan and converts it to hardware or services through charges for fabrication, installation, delivery, training, trial runs, and material purchases. After the process is established, operating costs required to keep it going include personnel, consumable supplies, overhead, maintenance, and services.

*Design to cost* is a variation of LCC that sets a limit on the total lifetime cost and forces designers to work backward from the disposal phase, to the operating expenses, through production costs, and finally to initial design charges. For example, a government request for proposals for training services might specify a limit on the funds available. Starting from this upper limit, submitted proposals would be expected to designate costs for course development, set-up arrangements for the instruction, educational services and supplies per student, follow-up training, and evaluation procedures for determining the value of training provided. Proposals so structured provide costs by phases, which makes monitoring easier.

*For applications of LCC see W.J. Kolarik, "Life Cycle Costing and Associated Models." *1980 Conference Proceedings* of the American Institute of Industrial Engineers.

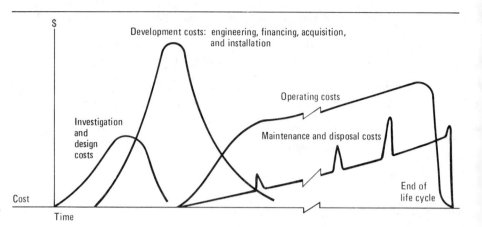

$

Development costs: engineering, financing, acquisition,
and installation

Operating costs

Investigation
and
design
costs

Maintenance and disposal costs

End of
life cycle

Cost

Time

**FIGURE 9.3** Typical
stages of life-cycle costs
for a product or ser-
vice.

## QUESTION

**9A.1**  Discuss how a closer focus on all the costs associated with a product or service
could lead to a more valuable economic analysis. Consider LCC with respect to
resource shortages and environmental concerns that might affect "twilight" costs late
in a life cycle.

**9B  A World of Investment Criteria**  Industrial organizations in every nation
face similar problems in screening out the most advantageous investments to
improve production. Discounted cash-flow analysis is the most celebrated screening
device in this country and is widely used elsewhere. The payback period also has
international acceptance, apparently more so than the theoretically sounder discounting methods. In developing countries where capital is severely limited, the
emphasis on capital turnover in the payback-period criterion is more appreciated. In
centralized socialist societies, the payback criterion in various versions is broadly
applied because it conforms nicely to ideological beliefs concerning the social harm
of interest charges.

Samuelson and Scott observe that:

> Recent studies show that the social engineers of the Soviet Union are anxious not to
> be denounced as capitalistic apologists; yet they need some form of interest rate (or
> "discount factor," or "payoff period") for making efficient investment calculations.
> As a result, about a dozen different accounting methods are in vogue there for
> introducing a thinly disguised interest-rate concept into Soviet planning proce-
> dures.†

This observation is supported by Dr. Kljusev in his writings:

> The methods for estimating the efficiency of the investment which are characteris-
> tic of the circumstances of capitalist production cannot automatically be used in a
> socialist economy because the stimulus and interests of the investment are
> different.*

†P. Samuelson & A. Scott, *Economics*, 5th Canadian Edition, McGraw-Hill Ryerson, Toronto, 1980, p. 66.
*N. Kljusev, *About Criteria and Methods of Valuation of Economic Effectiveness of Investment*, Ekonomisk
Institut of Skopje, Yugoslavia.

Dr. Kljusev also notes that the efficiency criterion (known too as the "lucrativity index")

$$E = \frac{\text{difference in annual cost between two alternatives}}{\text{difference in investment between two alternatives}}$$

or its reciprocal (the "period of return") is the most widely used economic evaluation method in the USSR and other socialist countries. But it still is considered inadequate because it is viable only for the relative economic efficiencies of alternative ways to produce the same article; it does not account for the apportionment of new revenue between continued investment to broaden production and amounts made available for personal and social expenditures.

Several extensions of basic economic comparison models have been forwarded by writers from different countries. The suggestions generally reflect particular communal concerns for strategic or tactical effects of capital expenditures, as indicated by the samples below.

1  Special attention should be given to investments involving convertible currency: Encourage projects that conserve or build foreign-exchange credits.
2  A weighting method should be used to evaluate the territorial impact of investments: Direct industrial development toward underdeveloped areas.
3  The time between appropriation and realization should be considered in comparing investments: Proposals that promise quick results should be rewarded.
4  Consider the total returns expected from a completely developed program rather than piecemeal returns in deciding which alternatives are most beneficial: Variations due to budgetary constraints and general economic conditions may mask the total effect of a program.
5  Develop ways to quantitatively include the social effects as well as the economic effects: Supplement economic models with a quantitative mechanism to express societal worth.
6  Stress considerations such as maintainability of equipment, flexibility of use, and variability of inputs when evaluating tactical investments: Detailed anticipation of future supply and demand conditions should influence present choices among long-lived assets, possibly causing a sacrifice of immediate profits in expectation of higher later benefits.

**QUESTIONS**
**9B.1**  Discuss the suggested extensions in terms of their applicability to engineering economic studies. What current trends in this country (e.g., consumerism, recycling, environmental protection) are likely to affect future investment decisions, and how might their influence be shown quantitatively in economic analyses?
**9B.2**  Comment on the quote below by Raymond Mayer. Do you agree with the statements? Why? Does this perspective account for the popularity of the payback-period criterion?

Theoretical methods of capital investment analysis, although sound and well established, have proven to be unacceptable to many industrial managers. The typical business man agrees that the relevant factors in the evaluation of an investment proposal are: the dollar investment, the cost of money, the alternative's life and salvage value, and its operating costs and revenues. But he also knows that accurate estimates of their values are not usually possible. Given this risk of error, it follows that he cannot appreciate the need for tedious calculations involving obscure compound interest factors. Even more important, he feels that the use of these interest factors gives the calculated results an aura of precision which simply is not there due to the approximate nature of the estimates.*

*R. Mayer, "Capital Investment Analysis Another Way," *Industrial Engineering*, July 1970.

# CHAPTER 10

# ANALYSIS OF PUBLIC PROJECTS

OVERVIEW

*Benefit-cost analysis* is a well-rooted method of evaluating public projects. The basic measure of acceptability is a benefit-to-cost ratio greater than 1.0 or, equivalently, a positive net difference between benefit and cost. Incremental B/C ratios should also exceed unity for added increments of investment. B/C > 1 is a standard of minimum approval but is not an effective ranking criterion. Discounting procedures, computational practices, and capital-rationing considerations are essentially the same in the private and public sectors.

The appropriate interest rate for the evaluation of public projects is a much-discussed issue. Social projects are particularly sensitive to the rate of discount applied, because most major expenditures occur early while the benefits extend many periods into the future; thus, a high discount rate tends to reduce the relative proportion of benefit to cost. Low discount rates are recommended by those who feel it is government's social responsibility to undertake projects that do not necessarily provide immediate returns comparable with those earned in the private sector. Counterarguments claim that resources are wasted when transferred from private uses, where returns are high, to low-yield public investments. One measure of the *social discount rate* results from computing the total cost of government borrowing.

Social projects often provide *public goods*—facilities or services available to all if available to one. The actual amount paid for a public good may not be a true measure of its worth. A *consumers' surplus* exists when a good is worth more to the user than the price paid for it. *Spillover benefit* or *cost* occurs when an activity affects third parties not directly involved in a project or program. These special properties of social involvement complicate the evaluation of benefits and costs and are discussed in Extension 10A.

Many project benefits and most project costs can be determined directly, as in industrial studies, and are subject to the same cautions for economic completeness. Owing to the nature of some benefits, monetary values must be derived from a combination of contributing factors. It is then the responsibility of policymakers to decide which projects to fund of those that pass the B/C hurdle.

# THE PUBLIC SECTOR

The public and industrial sectors of our economy interact as mutually supportive, but occasionally contradictory, forces. Government functions to facilitate the operation of a free-enterprise system may thwart or make difficult certain actions deemed advantageous by certain industrial subsystems. Despite claims of "government is best which governs least," the private sector simply does not have the means to provide all the necessary social goods and services. Government activities regulate and support the legal framework of the marketplace, establish and collect taxes for the redistribution of income, and allocate resources to programs and projects believed beneficial to society. Ideally, these activities will mirror the disposition of the citizenry with reasonable accuracy, while not completely satisfying the loudly vocal minorities calling either for no governing or for governmental solutions to all the perceived ills of society. The diversity of public-sector activities designed to serve so many interests complicates the evaluation of their effectiveness.

Comparison methods discussed in previous chapters are suitable for the evaluation of government activities. Some considerations, such as taxes and payoff periods, are less significant in the public sector, and other considerations such as the secondary effects of benefits are more prominent. In this chapter, attention is directed toward the evaluation of specific projects rather than the general economic functions of government. Thus, the role of government to provide national defense, education, and dams is not questioned; subjects of evaluation are explicit investment proposals to implement these government functions.

Evaluations take the form of *benefit-cost* (sometimes called *cost-benefit*) analyses. Operationally, the technique is similar to the present-worth index. Conceptually, an analysis considers the worthiness of shifting resources from the private sector to the public sector, and to what extent a public project should be pursued when its benefits exceed its costs. Many factors besides a benefit-cost analysis influence the final decision about funding public projects, and weaknesses of benefit-cost analyses as traditionally conducted have cast doubts on the resulting ratings, but the analytical procedures still invite credibility and objectivity in appraisals of public expenditures.

# BENEFIT-COST ANALYSIS

Benefit-cost analysis has been defined as:

An analytical approach to solving problems of choice. It requires the definition of objectives, identification of alternative ways of achieving each objective, the identification, for each objective, of that alternative which yields the required level of benefits at the lowest cost. This same analytical process is often referred to as cost-effectiveness analysis when the benefits or outputs of the alternatives cannot be quantified in terms of dollars.

## Benefit-to-Cost Criteria

In comparing benefit (B) to cost (C), several different perspectives are reasonable. Consider the simplified data in Table 10.1 that describe the alternatives for a small flood-control project. The current average annual damage from flooding is $200,000. Three feasible options are available to reduce the damages; each larger investment of public funds provides greater protection.

| Alternative | Equivalent Annual Cost of Project | Average Annual Flood Damage | Annual Benefit |
|---|---|---|---|
| A : No flood control | $         0 | $200,000 | $         0 |
| B : Construct levees | 40,000 | 130,000 | 70,000 |
| C : Small reservoir | 120,000 | 40,000 | 160,000 |
| D : Large reservoir | 160,000 | 10,000 | 190,000 |

**TABLE 10.1** Annual costs and benefits from different levels of investment in a small flood-control project.

The three projects and the do-nothing alternative are mutually exclusive. Data for selecting the most attractive alternative are shown below, where the figures are in thousands of dollars.

| Alternative | Annual Benefit, B | Annual Cost, C | TOTAL B/C | TOTAL B − C | INCREMENTAL $\Delta B$ | INCREMENTAL $\Delta C$ | INCREMENTAL $\Delta B/\Delta C$ | INCREMENTAL $\Delta B - \Delta C$ |
|---|---|---|---|---|---|---|---|---|
| A | $   0 | $   0 | 0 | $ 0 | | | | |
| B | 70 | 40 | 1.75 | 30 | $70 | $40 | 1.75 | $30 |
| C | 160 | 120 | 1.33 | 40 | 90 | 80 | 1.125 | 10 |
| D | 190 | 160 | 1.19 | 30 | 30 | 40 | 0.75 | −10 |

The following criteria indicate different plausible preferences among the alternatives:

1   Minimum investment: Choose **alternative A**. If funds are severely limited, this may be the only possible choice.
2   Maximum benefit: Choose **alternative D**. Flooding would occur only during extremely wet seasons.
3   Aspiration level: Depends on the threshold set for cost or benefit. If, for instance, the aspiration level is to reduce flood damage by 75 percent, **alternative C** should be chosen because it meets the aspiration with a lower cost than alternative D. Similarly, an annual-cost threshold of $100,000 indicates a preference for **alternative B**.
4   Maximum advantage of benefits over cost (B − C): Choose **alternative C**.

5   Highest benefit-to-cost ratio (B/C): Choose *alternative B.*
6   Largest investment that has a benefit-to-cost ratio greater than 1.0: Choose *alternative D.*
7   Maximum incremental advantage of benefit over cost ($\Delta B - \Delta C$): Choose *alternative B.*
8   Maximum incremental benefit-to-cost ratio ($\Delta B/\Delta C$): Choose *alternative B.*
9   Largest investment that has an incremental B/C ratio greater than 1.0: Choose *alternative C.*

A benefit-cost comparison directly rejects a project when the extra benefits are less than the costs and, by implication, when the extra benefits from a project are less than the extra benefits obtainable for alternative uses of the funds in the private sector of the economy. It is questionable whether society as a whole, present and future members included, is rewarded by public projects that have markedly lower returns than are currently earned in private commerce.

Reallocation of resources from the private sector, comprised mostly of tax collections, to a public project usually affects the distribution of wealth. Suppose the taxes collected to finance the flood-control project were drawn disproportionately from low-income taxpayers, and the land to be protected by the levee or dams were owned by wealthy farmers. If equality of income distribution is a government policy, the project would receive a low recommendation regardless of its B/C ratio. Similarly, the project could be questioned if the flood plain were inhabited by homeowners who knew the risk of flooding when they bought the building lots at lower prices than flood-free land prices, but are now pushing for flood protection at the expense of the general public.

## Benefit-to-Cost Comparisons

The mechanics of benefit-cost comparisons are straightforward and simple—deceptively so. The basic comparison formulas are

$$B/C = \frac{\text{present worth of benefits}}{\text{present worth of costs}}$$

$$= \frac{\text{equivalent annual benefits}}{\text{equivalent annual costs}}$$

and

Present value of net benefit $(B - C) = PW(\text{benefits}) - PW(\text{costs})$

where the present worth of benefits is the discounted, *constant* dollar value of goods and services expected to result from a project or program for each of the years it is in effect. Estimates may reflect changes in the *relative* prices, when there is a reasonable basis for estimating such changes, but should not include any forecast change in the general price level during the planning period.

The present worth of costs is the discounted annual value in *constant* dollars of resources, goods, and services required to establish and carry out a project or program. All economic costs, including acquisition, possession, and operating costs, must be included whether or not actually paid by the government. Such costs, *not* generally involving a direct payment by the government, include imputed market values of public property and provincial and local property taxes forgone.

It is apparent from the B/C and B − C formulas that benefit-to-cost comparisons are simply reformulated PW comparisons. Consequently, the precautions applicable to PW calculations also pertain to benefit-to-cost calculations. For instance, a preference for $X2$ is indicated by a comparison of the two present-worth levels given below for project $X$ according to the incremental differences for benefits and costs:

| Alternative | B | C | B/C | B − C | ΔB | ΔC | ΔB/ΔC | ΔB − ΔC |
|---|---|---|---|---|---|---|---|---|
| $X1$ | 4 | 2 | 2 | 2 | 3 | 2 | 1.5 | 1 |
| $X2$ | 7 | 4 | 1.75 | 3 | | | | |

Although $X1$ has a higher B/C than $X2$, the incremental ratio for the extra benefit and cost exceeds 1.0, making $X2$ an acceptable alternative. If it can be assumed that sufficient capital is available to fund either alternative, $X2$ is selected because it provides greater benefits. However, when the total costs for projects exceed the resources allocated to the proposing agency, capital-budgeting procedures are required and intangible effects may influence the selection.

## Example 10.1   Incremental Benefit-to-Cost Evaluation

A number of small earthen dams are contemplated for the headwaters of a drainage system. Four tributaries originate in a national park and flow together to form a river which passes through private lands. Each year there is some flooding, and every few years a major inundation occurs. Construction of one or more dams will ease the threat of high water. Dams on all the tributaries would largely eliminate the chance of a major flood.

In addition to the damage to private lands, floods also ruin fire and logging roads in the park. Other benefits from the dams include the value of the impounded water for fire protection and recreational use. The following benefit and cost estimates have been developed for the only topologically feasible combinations of dams:

| Dam Sites | Construction Costs | Annual Maintenance and Operation | Annual Flood Benefits | Annual Fire Benefits | Annual Recreation Benefits |
|---|---|---|---|---|---|
| 1 | $1,200,000 | $20,000 | $200,000 | $20,000 | $30,000 |
| 1 and 2 | 1,500,000 | 35,000 | 190,000 | 40,000 | 30,000 |
| 1, 2, and 3 | 2,700,000 | 50,000 | 280,000 | 60,000 | 60,000 |
| 1, 2, 3, and 4 | 3,500,000 | 60,000 | 300,000 | 70,000 | 70,000 |

A 40-year life and no salvage value is assumed for earthwork dams. An interest rate of 4 percent is deemed appropriate for the investment. This rate reflects the low risk involved and is in line with the historical interest rate for bonds issued by the federal government to finance public projects.

Based on B/C ratios, which of the four alternatives should be selected?

### Solution 10.1

A B/C ratio based on equivalent annual values for each alternative is calculated from

$$\text{B/C ratio} = \frac{\text{annual flood and fire savings} + \text{recreation benefits}}{\text{equivalent annual construction costs} + \text{maintenance}}$$

where

Equivalent annual construction cost = initial construction cost $\times (A/P, 4, 40)$

The incremental B/C ratio is determined from the additional benefits returned by an increment of cost above the last acceptable alternative (B/C ratio > 1.0).

| | | | INCREMENTS OF | | | |
|---|---|---|---|---|---|---|
| Dam Sites | Annual Benefits | Annual Cost | Benefit | Cost | Total B/C Ratio | Incremental B/C Ratio |
| 1 | $250,000 | $ 80,630 | $ 10,000 | $30,140 | 3.10 | 0.32 |
| 1 and 2 | 260,000 | 110,770 | 140,000 | 75,630 | 2.34 | 1.42 |
| 1, 2, and 3 | 400,000 | 186,400 | 40,000 | 50,420 | 2.14 | 0.79 |
| 1, 2, 3, and 4 | 440,000 | 236,820 | | | 1.85 | |

For an accurate evaluation, the requirement that annual benefits must equal annual costs should be applied to each separable increment of project costs. Site 1 is compared to the alternative "no action" and yields a total B/C ratio = incremental B/C ratio = 3.10, which qualifies it as an acceptable alternative. The next increment that meets the B/C-ratio standard is the location of dams at sites 1, 2, and 3 compared with a dam at site 1:

$$\text{B/C}(3) = \frac{\$10,000 + \$140,000}{\$30,140 + \$75,630} = 1.42$$

Adding another dam site fails to produce an acceptable B/C ratio:

$$\text{B/C}(4) = \frac{\$40,000}{\$50,420} = 0.79$$

Therefore, preference is indicated for the third alternative, dams at sites 1, 2, and 3.

Without an incremental analysis, the last alternative (four dams) might have been selected, because it does possess a B/C ratio greater than 1.0 and offers the greatest total benefits. Another mistake would be to eliminate all other alternatives because the dam at site 1 has a larger benefit-to-cost ratio than the rest of the options. The reasoning errors behind such conclusions are the same as those examined for incremental rates of return (Chapter 7). The conclusion to accept the three-dam alternative based on the given data would also result from a rate-of-return or present-worth evaluation.

It is interesting to note the *sensitivity* of the selection to changes in the data. Using a required interest rate of 7 percent instead of 4 percent would change the choice to the first alternative (one dam) because all the added benefit and cost increments would produce B/C ratios smaller than unity. Including only the flood-control benefits would also make site 1 the only alternative with an acceptable B/C ratio. The number of spillover benefits to include in an analysis and the monetary rating given to less tangible benefits can significantly influence decisions.

## Irregularities in B/C Comparisons

No investment criterion seems to be able to escape all theoretical objections. The benefit-cost criterion has been subjected to considerable criticism based on its oversimplification of complex inputs, susceptibility to misinterpretation, and potential for misuse. Some of the more prominent objections are discussed below.

## 1 INSENSITIVITY TO PRIORITIES

A B/C ratio includes the cost and benefit of a particular project but no indication of how valuable the benefit is, as compared with other projects, or the relative amount of resources involved.* As an extreme example, two projects could have the same B/C ratio and have costs of $1 million and $1 billion. The billion-dollar project might have long-range consequences for improvement of the environment in a sparsely populated region while the million-dollar project would serve a critical inner-city need. Eventually both projects might serve the same number of people, but the smaller project would have far greater immediate benefits for the taxpayers who are funding it. A third $100,000 project, with the same B/C as the other two, could be to preserve a site that will be destroyed if not subsidized immediately. Assuming there are not enough resources available to undertake all three projects, the B/C ratios are of little help in setting priorities.

A related objection is that the B/C standard assumes benefits are equally valuable to the rich and poor. Thus, a project to push a new highway through a densely populated low-cost-housing neighbourhood would use money partially drawn from the poor to force them to relocate to make room for a highway that would mainly benefit wealthier suburban commuters.

The argument against the above criticisms is that the B/C criterion was not designed to rank projects; it sets only a minimum level of acceptability and does not pretend to identify the source of investment funds. Analysis can provide an important and helpful tool for making decisions, but it is no more than a tool. Problems involving social policy and value judgments must be considered and weighed in conjunction with the results of benefit-cost analysis and the final decision made by the human policymaker.

---

*Discussed in A. Maass, "Benefit-Cost Analysis: Its Relevance to Public Decisions," *Quarterly Journal of Economics*, vol. LXXX, May 1966.

## 2 VARIATIONS DUE TO FORMULA INPUTS

The numerator of the B/C ratio is usually taken to mean the net benefit—the sum of all benefits minus all disbenefits. If the disbenefits were treated as costs in the denominator, the ratio would obviously change. For instance, if the present worth of benefit is 10, disbenefit is 3, and cost is 5, then

$$B/C = \frac{10 - 3}{5} = 1.40$$

But if the disbenefit is counted as a cost, then

$$B/C = \frac{10}{5 + 3} = 1.25$$

This variation presents no difficulty when it is remembered that the purpose of the B/C > 1 criterion is simply to distinguish between acceptable and unacceptable alternatives. There is no way in which shifting of disbenefits from the numerator to the denominator can cause a B/C ratio to change from greater than 1.0 to less than 1.0. Equivalently, the new present value (benefit minus disbenefit minus cost) must be the same regardless of the order of subtractions. Nor will an incremental analysis indicate any difference in the absolute acceptability of alternatives owing to the location of disbenefits in the B/C ratio.

Two alternatives are evaluated below, first by subtracting disbenefits from benefits and then by adding them to costs. In both cases, though the value of the ratios differ, the extra increment of investment is found to be acceptable according to the $\Delta B/\Delta C > 1$ standard.

| Alter-native | PRESENT WORTH OF BENEFIT, DISBENE-FIT, AND COST | | | | DISBENEFITS SUBTRACTED FROM BENEFITS | | | | DISBENEFITS ADDED TO COSTS | | | |
|---|---|---|---|---|---|---|---|---|---|---|---|---|
| | *B* | *D* | *C* | *B−D−C* | *B/C* | $\Delta B$ | $\Delta C$ | $\Delta B/\Delta C$ | *B/C* | $\Delta B$ | $\Delta C$ | $\Delta B/\Delta C$ |
| *X* | 10 | 3 | 5 | 10−3−5=2 | 7/5=1.4 | 9−7=2 | 6−5=1 | 2/1=2 | 10/8=1.25 | 13−10=3 | 10−8=2 | 3/2=1.5 |
| *Y* | 13 | 4 | 6 | ·13−4−6=3 | 9/6=1.5 | | | | 13/10=1.3 | | | |

The relative sizes of B/C ratios provide an indication of investment productivity that may be misleading. Consider a project $P1$, in which an investment of 10 and annual costs of 95 produce yearly benefits of 100 for 20 years: At $i = 10$ percent,

$$B/C(P1) = \frac{100(P/A, 10, 20)}{10 + 95(P/A, 10, 20)} = \frac{100(8.5135)}{10 + 95(8.5135)}$$

$$= \frac{851}{10 + 809} = 1.04$$

Compare this project to $P2$, which also has an initial investment of 10, no annual costs, and a yearly benefit of 1.25 for 20 years: At $i = 10$ percent,

$$B/C(P2) = \frac{1.25(8.5135)}{10} = \frac{10.6}{10} = 1.06$$

Both projects are barely acceptable, and $P2$ has a slightly higher B/C ratio, but $P1$ will "pay back" the initial investment in $10/(100 - 95) = 2$ years, while $P2$ requires $10/1.25 = 8$ years before the sum of annual benefits equals the investment. Stated another way,

IRR($P1$):    $(100 - 95)(P/A, i, 20) - 10 = 0$      at $i = 50\%$
IRR($P2$):            $1.25(P/A, i, 20) - 10 = 0$      at $i = 10.9\%$

The rate of return of $P1$ far exceeds that of $P2$, although their B/C ratios were nearly the same.

This apparent conflict is caused by the inability of the B/C formula to distinguish between cash-flow patterns; it tends to underrate the quality of a project with high annual costs. This same characteristic was discussed in Chapter 9, where ranking reversals were noted for alternatives evaluated by PW and IRR comparisons when the discount rate was raised to a certain level. In the example above, a discount rate of 11 percent would make $P2$ an unacceptable alternative:

$$\text{B/C}(P2) = \frac{1.25(P/A, 11, 20)}{10} = \frac{1.25(7.9633)}{10} = \frac{9.95}{10} = 0.995$$

whereas $P1$ remains acceptable at the 11 percent rate:

$$\text{B/C}(P1) = \frac{100(P/A, 11, 20)}{10 + 95(P/A, 11, 20)} = \frac{796}{10 + 757} = 1.038$$

# THE DISCOUNT-RATE QUESTION

The appropriate interest rate to use in evaluating public investments is a voluminously debated issue. Although numerous suggestions have been forwarded, none has been awarded complete acceptance. About the only near consensus is that discount rates established for early benefit-cost analyses in the depressed 1930s (around $2\frac{1}{2}$ to $3\frac{1}{4}$ percent) are not valid today. The effect of the discounting rate of benefit-cost ratios for projects with different lives is shown in Figure 10.1. The five curves represent B/C ratios at different discount rates for an initial investment of $1 that returns a total of $2 in equal installments over $N$ years. Therefore, at a 0 percent discount rate and $N = 10$,

$$\text{B/C} = \frac{(2/10)(P/A, 0, 10)}{1} = \frac{0.2(10)}{1} = 2$$

but at $i = 10$ percent for 10 years,

$$\text{B/C} = \frac{(2/10)(P/A, 10, 10)}{1} = \frac{0.2(6.1445)}{1} = \frac{1.23}{1} = 1.23$$

## Range of Discount Rates

The government borrowing rate is an obvious measure of financing costs for public projects. It is akin to the *cost-of-capital* concept by which a minimum attractive rate of return is determined for investments in the private sector. The cost of capital to the government can

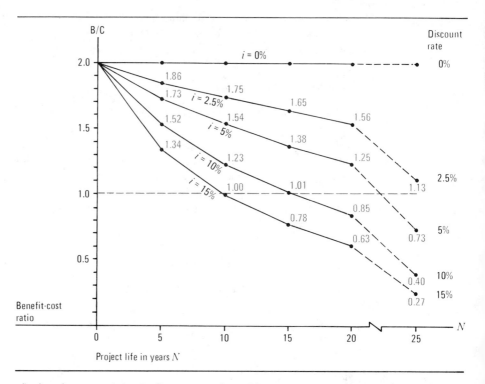

**FIGURE 10.1** Graph of benefit-cost ratios at five discount rates for different project lives of a proposal to invest $1 in order to receive $2 in equal installments prorated over the project's life.

also be taken as a minimum discount rate for public projects. In recent years the interest rate for government borrowing has varied between 7 percent and 19.5 percent, depending on the level (federal, provincial, or local), special privileges offered, current economic conditions, and length of the loan. Since government bonds are generally considered to be riskfree, any public project should promise a minimum return at least equal to the bond rate. Otherwise, the resources that could be used to fund projects should instead be applied to debt repayment.

The rates of return expected in the private sector are higher than the interest rates on government bonds. This is a reasonable condition because a firm would invest in riskfree government bonds if it did not expect larger returns from industrial investments. According to E.J. Mishan,*"It is commonly assumed that the correct rate of interest is that which reflects society's rate of time preference." His view recognizes the opportunity cost to general welfare that occurs when resources are used to produce benefits smaller than could have been obtained if the resources were applied elsewhere. Specifically, a public project that barely exceeds B/C = 1 when evaluated at a low discount rate would produce fewer benefits than could have been obtained by leaving the amount invested in the private sector.

An argument for charging lower rates for public projects is that certain socially desirable programs would never meet higher evaluation standards but are nonetheless worthwhile. This line of reasoning emphasizes the responsibility of the present population to assure

---

*E.J. Mishan, *Cost-Benefit Analysis*, Praeger, 1976, p. 176.

adequate living conditions for future generations. Since most people are more concerned with satisfying their current needs and wants than with saving for the future, proponents of low discount rates say only government action can enforce investments for future benefits. This transfer of resources necessarily yields a lower return than resources used for current consumption.

Counterarguments question the legitimacy of allowing a few policymakers to decide what is best for general welfare, especially when their allocations appear to contradict public preferences shown in a free market. It is generally agreed that no generation has the right to completely consume resources that cannot be replaced by its successors (for example, erosion of soil, extinction of a wildlife species, destruction of natural phenomena). The dispute is with subsidizing future generations by resource expenditures acceptable only if evaluations are based on artificially low discount rates. Such special assistance is not warranted, critics say, because the future is also served by public and private investments that earn returns comparable to current resource commitments. From a historical perspective that indicates each generation has been wealthier than its predecessor, it appears imprudent to justify "wasteful" resource allocations on the basis of protecting future beneficiaries.

## Social Discount Rate

The rate of interest used in evaluating public projects is often referred to as the *social discount rate*. It reflects the cost of capital obtained from the private sector and the opportunity cost of resources applied to public projects rather than private investments. The methodology frequently employed by the Treasury Board and crown corporations is simple to calculate. It is the ten year average of quarterly Treasury Bill rates. This was 9.92% in the first quarter of 1982. For higher risk projects the current rate on long term government bonds is sometimes used. This was 15.11% in the first quarter of 1982. The Treasury Board usually communicates these rates to interested agencies once a year.

It is well known in the financial market that government bonds are perceived to have low risk which is rewarded by the lower interest rate needed to attract capital. The inference for public projects is that the government is in a better position than a private entrepreneur to cope with risk; governments undertake so many projects that their operations are essentially immune to risk, on the average. However, critics point out that there have been some obvious and major failures in government-funded projects and proposals. Therefore, like investments in the private sector, the social discount rate should include a risk factor. A surcharge of ½ to 1 percent has been suggested, but this cross-the-board addition fails to account for differences in the nature of risk for various classes of projects.

# BENEFIT-COST APPLICATIONS

The methodology of benefit-cost analysis is applied to government projects in many nations. Its applicability as a public-investment criterion in most sociopolitical environments is discussed in *Guidelines for Project Evaluation,** a publication of the United Nations Industrial Development Organization:

> The main reason for doing social benefit-cost analysis in project choice is to subject project choice to a consistent set of general objectives of national policy . . . . When one project is chosen rather than another, the choice has consequences for employment, output, consumption, savings, foreign exchange earning, income distribution and other things of relevance to national objectives. The purpose of social benefit-cost analysis is to see whether these consequences taken together are desirable in the light of objectives of national planning. . . .
>
> It is worth remembering that social benefit-cost analysis is not a technique but an approach. It provides a rational framework for project choice using national objectives and values. Projects are judged in terms of their precise impact on the economy, and this impact is evaluated by using parameters reflecting national goals, social objectives and global facts. This is relevant not merely for evaluation of given projects but also for formulating new ones and implementing the chosen projects. There are always a very large number of elements one can vary in formulating new projects. Which of these are important and worth pursuing will depend on the guidance provided by social benefit-cost analysis. Similarly, in implementation there are always small choices between variants that are not fully specified in the plan and are left to the implementors, and it helps to have a clear picture of the social benefits and costs of these choices.

## Criticisms

Many of the charges of misuse of benefit-cost analyses are the result of specific projects that have gone awry. The well-publicized cases of dams that failed to stop flooding as promised and project overruns that boosted costs well above anticipated benefits could be considered as evidence of the need for more exacting benefit-cost analysis, rather than of deficiencies in the B/C criterion.

In addition to the theoretical critiques of the applicable discount rate and the fairness of benefit measurements, criticism has been leveled at the way the analyses are conducted. It is claimed that unrealistically high values have been assigned to intangibles to compensate for low monetary benefits in projects that would be unacceptable when evaluated only on quantifiable data. Indirect or intangible costs seldom seem to get the same recognition as nonmonetary benefits. Costs have been underestimated, say critics, because the local impact of major federal projects was not anticipated; labor and material prices went up because of increased local demand caused by the project to the detriment of both project expenses and consumers in the community.

Projects are sometimes undertaken without the support of the residents in the area. Planners are thus forced into the position of telling residents what is good for them, which requires a selling campaign that may create costly delays or added community-relations costs. Part of the problem could be alleviated by exposing a project to a public vote. However, difficulties of informing the voters about the issues involved and the remoteness

---

*P. Dasgupta, A. Sen, and S. Marglin, *Guidelines for Project Evaluation*, United Nations, 1972.

of many projects from their base of funding (the taxpayers) limit the workability of decisions by vote. A choice between a football stadium and an art museum in a city would probably arouse enough interest by those affected to assure a careful appraisal and representative turnout of voters. Yet an equal expenditure to develop a wildlife refuge might inspire less interest, even if all the affected voters could be given a chance to vote. On all questions of national objectives, there will likely be a few opponents, and many of these will be in the geographical locality where a project is to be carried out. Local protests can naturally be expected from people whose lives are disrupted by a project designed to serve the general welfare. It is the duty of policymakers to give consideration and adequate compensation to the local interests while supporting regional and national social interests.

## Examples

Three benefit-cost analyses are described in the following pages. The applications are digested to point out certain highlights; the actual studies and techniques employed were much more exhaustive. Example 10.2 illustrates a feasibility study that disqualified public expenditures in solving a local problem. The sensitivity of inputs to B/C calculations is demonstrated in Example 10.3. A postaudit to determine the actual benefit and cost of a program is featured in Example 10.4.

### Example 10.2   Feasibility Investigation of a Water-Resource Project

The purpose of this study was to determine what could be done to reduce flood damages and to conserve, use, or develop the St. John River Basin's water resource.

Six alternatives were investigated: (1) floodproofing of individual structures, (2) building levees, (3) improving river channels, (4) instituting a system of land-owner-constructed dams, (5) implementing a system of small tributary reservoirs, and (6) erecting multipurpose reservoirs. The costs of floodproofing, levees, and channel improvements were found to be much greater than the benefits, mainly because of the lack of secondary benefits. Landowner-constructed dams built with government financial support would have some localized benefits, but would require an unreasonable amount of land for the storage obtained, and problems of balancing outflows made the alternative impractical.

The last two alternatives also proved to be economically infeasible, as shown in Figure 10.2. Flood-control benefits were based on historical flood damages updated to 1974 prices, estimates of flood-stage reductions by operation of the projects investigated, and projections of economic growth in the area. Recreation benefits were based on user-day projections. The cost of the cheapest alternative water supply was used in the analysis as a measure of the water-supply benefits that could reasonably be expected. Data provided by the Canadian Wildlife Service showed that wildlife benefits resulting from any of the project alternatives would be negligible. Costs included construction and, as appropriate, land; relocation of roads, railroads, and utilities; fish-passage facilities; wildlife-migration features; recreation developments; design costs; and construction supervision costs.

| | Noon Dam | Wren Dam | Tumtum Dam | Tributary Dam System |
|---|---|---|---|---|
| *Costs, total* | | | | |
| Construction | $51,352,000 | $52,944,000 | $37,024,000 | $19,090,000 |
| Investment† | 57,386,000 | 59,165,000 | 41,374,000 | 21,333,000 |
| *Costs, annual* | | | | |
| Interest and amortization‡ | 3,380,000 | 3,485,000 | 2,437,000 | 1,257,000 |
| Operation, maintenance, and replacement | 210,000 | 180,000 | 170,000 | 135,000 |
| *Total average annual cost* | $ 3,590,000 | $ 3,665,000 | $ 2,607,000 | $ 1,392,000 |
| *Benefits, average annual* | | | | |
| Flood control | $ 945,400 | $483,100 | $258,500 | $126,300 |
| Recreation | 573,000 | 345,000 | 401,000 | 163,000 |
| Irrigation water supply | 85,000 | 85,000 | 85,000 | 85,000 |
| Municipal and industrial water supply | 90,600 | 63,400 | 8,800 | 0 |
| Fish and wildlife enhancement | 0 | 0 | 0 | 0 |
| *Total average annual benefits* | $1,694,000 | $976,500 | $753,300 | $374,300 |
| *Benefit-cost ratio* | 0.47:1 | 0.27:1 | 0.29:1 | 0.27:1 |

†Construction cost plus interest during construction.
‡The annual cost equivalent to the total cost spread over a 100-year period computed at 5 7/8 percent interest rate.

**FIGURE 10.2** Benefit-cost analyses for alternative reservoir projects.

## Example 10.3 Critical Examination of a B/C Analysis

The Crooked Creek project consists of land-treatment measures and channel improvement. In 1971 an original proposal for the project was reevaluated to include additional expenditures for wildlife mitigation, modification and addition of laterals, inclusion of sediment-control features, and the updating of installation costs. The original study in 1965 had a benefit-cost ratio of 2.1 and included the following annual benefits:

| | |
|---|---|
| Flood-damage reduction | $46,666 |
| More intensive use | 7,044 |
| Improved efficiency | 21,100 |
| *Total benefit cited in the 1965 study* | $74,810 |

The interest rate used for discounting costs in the original study was 3 1/8 percent. The current rate is 5 3/8 percent. The revised costs in 1971 evaluated at the two discount rates and the corresponding B/C ratios are shown below.

| | ANNUAL COSTS | | | |
| --- | --- | --- | --- | --- |
| *Discount rate, %* | *Structural* | *O and M* | *Total* | *B/C* |
| 3 1/8 | $38,655 | $19,100 | $57,765 | 1.30 |
| 5 3/8 | 55,040 | 19,100 | 74,140 | 1.01 |

While the project does not fail the benefit-cost test, at the revised interest rate it clearly becomes marginal. A more realistic cost for the land acquired would make the project uneconomic. An appropriate rate of interest for the land adjustment cost is determined as

| | |
| --- | --- |
| Ratio of annual income to market value | 5.6% |
| Plus rate of capital appreciation | 5.0% |
| Less rate of inflation | 1.6% |
| Discount rate | 9.0% |

which changes the project cost to

| | *Annual cost* |
| --- | --- |
| Structural costs (less land) at 5 3/8% | $45,152 |
| Land cost at 9% | 15,559 |
| Operation and maintenance | 19,100 |
| Total cost | $79,100 |

and leads to

$$B/C = \frac{\$74,810}{\$79,100} = 0.95$$

"The project fails the benefit-cost analysis even before environmental costs and excessive agricultural benefits are deducted."

### Example 10.4   Follow-up Study to Evaluate Benefit versus Cost for a Human-Resource Program

An Employment Training Centre was established in 1967 under contract with the Department of Indian and Northern Affairs. The Centre was designed as a residential employment training program for Indian families, solo parents, and single adults. Emphasis is placed on training and counseling intended to aid trainees in adjusting to typical work situations and to living off the reservation.

Using earnings differentials to measure benefits from human-resource investment programs is a standard method of evaluation. The major resource costs are staff services, where salaries are taken as the measure of their value in an alternative use; other direct costs such as supplies; and the opportunity costs of training – the earnings forgone as a result of undertaking training.

In June 1970, a follow-up study was conducted by mail of all trainees who had entered the Centre between March 1968 and February 1970. The calculation of a benefit-cost ratio using the data from this survey is shown below. Of the group of 170 returning adequate survey forms, 70 were currently employed at an average hourly wage of $2.25 after training, whereas 82 members of the same group were employed before training was given. Because the average wage rate after training was significantly higher than the average wage before training, there was still a positive earnings differential associated with training, equal to $573 per year per trainee:

$$\text{Additional annual earnings/trainee} = \frac{(\$4680 \times 70) - (\$2808 \times 82)}{170} = \$573$$

*Benefit of program*   PW of extra annual earnings over 41 years (the number of remaining years in the labor force for trainees whose average age was 24) at a 6% discount rate                    $8674

*Cost of program*   Contracted cost for an average length of training of 8 months at $658 per month per trainee = $5264. Forgone earnings (number of trainees working before training times their monthly earnings times the months of training, divided by the total number of trainees) = $[(82)(\$2808/12)(8)]/170 = \$902$. Then, PW of total cost = $5264 + $902        $6166

$$\text{B/C} = \frac{\$8674}{\$6166} = 1.41$$

The benefit-cost analysis described above is about the simplest possible for a human resource investment program. Earnings before and after training are compared, differentials projected, at a constant amount, over the years ex-trainees can be expected to remain in the labor force. The present value of these amounts are then compared to direct program costs plus the opportunity costs of trainees to estimate benefit-cost ratios. Every step of the analysis can be challenged on theoretical and empirical grounds. Pretraining earnings may be understated; perhaps earnings differentials should be projected at growing, rather than constant, amounts in future years; the lack of complete followup data may bias the estimated earnings differentials; a control group should really be established; maybe 6 percent is not the "right" discount to use; an estimate of the value of the physical facilities in an alternative should really be included as a cost—all this and probably more could be charged. To focus on these niceties of analysis would be to miss an important aspect of program analysis. Analysis should not only ask the question, "Is this a good program?" or "Has the benefit-cost ratio been appropriately and accurately estimated and is it greater than unity?" but should provide program managers with the information they need to change particular aspects of their program in an effort to improve performance.

## Review Exercises and Discussions

**Exercise 1**   A proposal has been made to modify certain navigational aids that will decrease the cost of operation by $10,000 per year for the next 30 years. A loss in benefit during the same period amounts to $1000 per year. Conduct a benefit-cost evaluation with a discount rate of 10 percent, assuming the modifications will be completed with little extra cost as part of the routine maintenance.

**Solution 1**
$$B/C = \frac{-\$1000(P/A,\ 10,\ 30)}{-\$10,000(P/A,\ 10,\ 30)} = 0.1$$

The criterion of B/C > 1.0 for acceptability is not applicable when both the benefit and cost of a project are negative. The ratio of savings to costs is obviously 10:1 in favor of the proposal. Thus, when both the numerator and denominator of a B/C ratio are negative, a ratio of less than 1.0 indicates acceptability. Further, a project with a positive B and a negative C is automatically accepted.

**Exercise 2**   The present worth of benefits and costs for two mutually exclusive "base" proposals are shown below, along with data for three supplementary projects which can be combined with either base to yield additional benefits. The supplementary projects are not mutually exclusive. Which combination of projects is preferred when resources are limited to $400,000?

| BASIC-PROJECT PROPOSALS | | | | SUPPLEMENTARY PROJECTS | | |
|---|---|---|---|---|---|---|
| *Project* | *B* | *C* | *B/C* | *Project* | *B* | *C* |
| $P1$ | $300,000 | $150,000 | 2.0 | $S1$ | $75,000 | $50,000 |
| $P2$ | 450,000 | 250,000 | 1.8 | $S2$ | 140,000 | 100,000 |
| | | | | $S3$ | 300,000 | 150,000 |

**Solution 2**   Since $P1$ has a higher benefit-cost ratio than $P2$, it is a logical base for combinations. Only those combinations that approach but do not exceed the $400,000 limit are considered because the objective is to maximize benefits with the resources available.

| *Combination* | *Benefit* | *Cost* | *B − C* | *B/C* |
|---|---|---|---|---|
| $P1 + S1 + S2$ | $515,000 | $300,000 | $215,000 | 1.72 |
| $P1 + S3$ | 600,000 | 300,000 | 300,000 | 2.0 |
| $P1 + S1 + S3$ | 675,000 | 350,000 | 325,000 | 1.93 |
| $P1 + S2 + S3$ | 740,000 | 400,000 | 340,000 | 1.85 |

Of these combinations, the one that spends all the available resources, $P1 + S2 + S3$, provides the greatest benefits ($740,000), yields the highest net benefits ($340,000), has a B/C ratio (1.85) greater than 1.0, and gives an incremental benefit-cost ratio exceeding unity,

$$\Delta B / \Delta C = \frac{\$740,000 - \$675,000}{\$400,000 - \$350,000} = \frac{\$65,000}{\$50,000} = 1.3$$

is the most satisfying.

However, the best possible combination is one that utilizes the other base, $P2$. The combination of $P2 + S3$ has a total benefit of $\$450,000 + \$300,000 = \$750,000$ and a total cost of $\$250,000 + \$150,000 = \$400,000$ to yield

$$(B - C)(P2 + S3) = \$750,000 - \$400,000 = \$350,000$$

and

$$(B/C)(P2 + S3) = \frac{\$750,000}{\$400,000} = 1.875$$

This combination might be overlooked by the preselection error of eliminating $P2$ from consideration because its benefit-cost ratio is less than the B/C for $P1$. It is also interesting to note that in this case the B/C ratio provides an accurate ranking of top contenders because both have the same total cost.

---

**Exercise 3**    Benefit-cost ratios for two mutually exclusive alternatives have been calculated with disbenefits assigned to both numerator and denominator  as shown:

| Alter-native | PRESENT WORTH | | | | |
|---|---|---|---|---|---|
| | $B$ | $D$ | $C$ | $B/C = (B - D)/C$ | $B/C = B/(C + D)$ |
| $A\,1$ | 150 | 0 | 100 | $(150 - 0\ )/100 = 1.5$ | $150/(100 + 0) = 1.5$ |
| $A\,2$ | 200 | 20 | 120 | $(200 - 20)/120 = 1.5$ | $200/(120 + 20) = 1.43$ |

What reply would you make to a claim that $A1$ is economically superior because its B/C ratio is equal to or better than that obtained from $A2$, regardless of the way disbenefits are handled?

**Solution 3**    The net benefit of $A2$ is $200 - 20 - 120 = 60$, versus $150 - 100 = 50$ for $A1$. Thus, if any preference is shown by the benefit-cost criterion, it is bestowed on $A2$. An incremental analysis conducted either way,

| | DISBENEFIT IN NUMERATOR | | | | DISBENEFIT IN DENOMINATOR | | |
|---|---|---|---|---|---|---|---|
| | $B$ | $C$ | $B/C$ | | $B$ | $C$ | $B/C$ |
| $A\,1$ | 150 | 100 | | $A\,1$ | 150 | 100 | |
| $A\,2$ | 180 | 120 | $30/20 = 1.5$ | $A\,2$ | 200 | 140 | $50/40 = 1.25$ |

confirms that $A2$ is an acceptable project because its incremental B/C ratio is consistently greater than 1.0.

---

**Exercise 4**    Consider a project that proposes a new four-lane highway leading from the downtown core of a city to a major arterial bypass in the suburbs. What factors besides the construction requirements could be considered in the total project cost?

**Solution 4**    Benefit-cost analyses for some major highway-construction projects consume hundreds of pages. A few of the considerations include:

1   Air pollution from traffic flow
2   Expenditures for traffic control
3   Accident frequency and severity, past and forecast
4   Parking expectations in affected areas
5   Time and cost consequences of congestion, before and after
6   Shift of business competition
7   Accessibility of outlying jobs to central-city poor
8   Changes in property values due to accessibility
9   Relocation of dwellings in the highway path; associated disruption of neighborhoods
10   Visual and auditory impact
11   Temporary effects of construction: wages, price of materials, living costs, employment, etc.

# PROBLEMS

**10.1** A 3.54 km stretch of highway is known locally as "Fog Hollow." In an attempt to reduce accidents, the shoulders along Fog Hollow could be widened at a cost of $64,000 per km, and large electric warning signs could be installed at both ends of the dangerous stretch. The signs would be controlled by a computer hooked to sensing devices to display recommended speeds for various fog conditions. The fog-warning signs could be installed for $165,000 and would have annual maintenance costs of $7000 during their 10-year life.

If the average accident cost in Fog Hollow amounts to $2385, how many accidents per year would have to be avoided by the project to make it acceptable for a 20-year study period? The discount rate used for such projects is 6 percent.    *(21)*

**10.2** Two projects, HERE-2 and THERE-4, are mutually exclusive. Using the B/C criterion, which should be selected? The numbers below indicate the present worth of benefits and costs; the two projects have equal lives.

| Project | Benefit | Cost |
|---------|---------|------|
| HERE-2  | 5       | 3    |
| THERE-4 | 6       | 5    |

*(Select HERE-2; $\Delta B/\Delta C = 0.5$)*

**10.3** Two projects from each of four departments have been submitted for evaluation. The projects from each department are mutually exclusive.

| Department | Project | Benefit | Cost |
|------------|---------|---------|------|
| A          | A 1     | $100,000 | $ 70,000 |
|            | A 2     | 112,000 | 80,000 |
| B          | B 1     | 70,000  | 55,000 |
|            | B 2     | 76,000  | 60,000 |
| C          | C 1     | 160,000 | 100,000 |
|            | C 2     | 184,000 | 120,000 |
| D          | D 1     | 110,000 | 75,000 |
|            | D 2     | 122,000 | 85,000 |

**10.3a**   Which projects should be funded according to the B/C criterion if one project must be selected from each department?                                    *(A2, B2, C2, and D2)*

**10.3b**   Which projects should be funded if only $300,000 is available?

*(A1, B1, C1, and D1)*

**10.4**   A provincially sponsored "forest protective association" is evaluating alternative routes for a new road into a formerly inaccessible region. Different routes for the road provide different benefits, as indicated in the following table:

| Route | Construc-tion Cost | Annual Saving in Fire Damage | Recrea-tional Benefits | Timber Access | Annual Mainte-nance Cost |
|-------|-------|-------|-------|-------|-------|
| A | $185,000 | $5000 | $3000 | $ 500 | $1500 |
| B | 220,000 | 5000 | 6500 | 500 | 2500 |
| C | 310,000 | 7000 | 6000 | 2800 | 3000 |

The roads are assumed to have an economic life of 50 years, and the interest rate normally required is 3 percent per year.

**10.4a**   According to a B/C comparison, which route should be selected?

*[B/C(B) = 1.09; ΔB/C(B) = 1.48]*

**10.4b**   Would the choice be changed if the interest rate were doubled?

*(None acceptable)*

**10.4c**   Would the choice be changed if annual maintenance costs were not included?                                       *[B/C(C) = 1.31; ΔB/C(C) = 1.09]*

**10.5**   The Dry Springs Flood Control District has applied for a federal grant to eliminate a persistent flooding problem. Two alternative projects are being considered, and the following data have been collected.

| | Plan 1 | Plan 2 |
|---|---|---|
| First cost | $25,000,000 | $50,000,000 |
| Average annual reduction in flood damage | 1,300,000 | 2,800,000 |
| Annual irrigation benefits | 350,000 | 600,000 |
| Annual recreation benefits | 100,000 | 300,000 |
| Annual operating and mainten-ance costs | 210,000 | 400,000 |

A social discount rate of 6 percent is recommended. The life of both plans is estimated at 50 years, and no salvage value is expected.

**10.5a**   Calculate the benefit-cost ratio using disbenefits in the numerator, and compare it with B/C when disbenefits are added to costs in the denominator.

*[Both ratios are about the same: B/C(1) = 0.97, B/C(2) = 1.04]*

**10.5b**   Determine the incremental benefit-cost ratio of plan 1 to that of plan 2 using both methods from Problem 10.5a.     *[Δ(B − D)/ΔC = 1.10; ΔB/Δ(C + D) = 1.11]*

**10.6** Three proposals have been submitted for developing a recreational facility along a scenic highway. The proposals are:

**1** Build a picnic ground with 25 picnic sites, each including a table, parking space, and charcoal grill.
**2** Build a picnic/camping facility with 20 picnic sites and 10 camp sites.
**3** Build a picnic/camping/cabin facility with 15 picnic sites, 10 camp sites, and 5 cabins.

The expected demand per site, first cost, and annual maintenance cost for each type of site are given below. In addition, the estimated value to the public per visit (above charges) is given for each type of facility.

| Type of Unit | Expected Visits/ Year/Unit | First Cost/ Unit | Annual Mainten- ance Cost/Unit | Perceived Value/Visit |
|---|---|---|---|---|
| Picnic site | 800 | $1000 | $200 | $0.50 |
| Camping site | 200 | 2000 | 250 | 2.50 |
| Cabin site | 200 | 5500 | 400 | 7.00 |

Based on a 10-year study with no residual value anticipated after 10 years, and a discount rate of 5 percent, determine which proposal, if any, should be accepted.

*(Accept cabin proposal: $\Delta B/\Delta C = 1.09$)*

**10.7** The Provincial Transportation Department has collected data for a proposal to construct an overpass and extra lanes at a busy, dangerous highway intersection. Estimated land-acquisition, demolition, and construction costs are:

| | |
|---|---|
| Land and demolition | $410,000 |
| Additional lanes (0.966 km at $621,118/km) | $600,000 |
| Overpass construction | $2,740,000 |

and annual maintenance is expected to average $105,000 per year during the 30-year life of the project.

Improved safety is the primary benefit expected from the project. A road count revealed that 12,000 vehicles per day pass through the intersection. An average of 2.4 fatalities per year have occurred at the present usage rate. Usage is expected to rise to 15,000 vehicles per day by the time improvements are completed, and accidents would be expected to rise commensurately. For every fatal accident there are 19 nonfatal accidents and 160 property-damage accidents. Settlements for fatal, nonfatal, and property accidents are calculated, respectively, at $65,000, $5000, and $1000. The improved intersection is expected to reduce all accidents by 90 percent.

Expenses associated with patrolling, maintaining the traffic signals, and directing traffic at the intersection are currently $31,000 per year; these would be eliminated by the project. Twenty-one percent of the vehicles using the intersection now must stop, with an average wait of 0.8 minute. The average cost of a stop for a vehicle's operation is estimated at 6 cents, and waiting time is assumed to be worth $2.40 per hour. When the overpass is in operation, all stops will be avoided, but 40 percent of the vehicles will have an added travel distance of 0.322 km. A vehicle operating cost of 11.2 cents per km is assigned as an average value.

The overpass will reduce pollution. This reduction is valued at $50,000 per year. Annual taxes forgone from property condemned for the expansion amount to $8000. The discount rate for the study is 8 percent.

**10.7a** What is the benefit-cost ratio based only on the primary benefit of improved safety and just the building costs?

**10.7b** What is the B/C based on secondary benefits and the building cost?

**10.7c** What is the total B/C? What other factors might be considered in the project?

**10.8** A dam on Roily River is being evaluated. A 50-year life and a 9 percent discount rate are to be used. Estimates have been obtained for the following benefits and costs:

| | |
|---|---|
| Flood losses prevented in the Roily River area | $ 900,000/year |
| Flood losses reduced in downstream rivers | 800,000/year |
| Increases in property values along the Roily River (present worth of values) | 1,000,000 |
| Income from electric power produced | 3,200,000/year |
| Construction of dam and access roads | 25,000,000 |
| Cost of powerhouse and transmission facilities | 10,000,000 |
| Interest costs during construction | 2,000,000 |
| Operating and maintenance costs | 100,000/year |

Assume construction costs occur at time zero but the benefits do not begin until the start of the fifth year and interest charges during production are prorated evenly over the 4-year period.

**10.8a** What is the benefit-cost ratio?

**10.8b** Assume opponents of the dam are questioning the study on the basis that no costs were included for the destruction of a popular recreation area that would be inundated by the dam's reservoir. The land is all federally owned, but a very popular park that features mineral-water springs will be inundated. What value would have to be placed on this park and associated recreational areas to make the project unacceptable? Could a reasonable case be developed to abandon the project? What other benefits and disbenefits might be considered?

**10.9** Two alternative routes for a new expressway are being evaluated. One follows the valley along a river, and the other takes a short cut through a range of hills.

The river route has a length of 48.28 km and a first cost of $14,250,000. Its annual cost of maintenance will be $3106 per km and a major overhaul will be required every 10 years at a cost of $1,500,000.

The hilly route will be 11.27 km shorter than the river route, but it will cost $19 million. Annual maintenance costs will be $4972 per km and the major overhaul and surfacing every 10 years will cost $1,150,000.

Traffic on either expressway is predicted to average 6000 vehicles per day, one-fourth of which will be commercial traffic. Anticipated average speed on either route is 80.5 km per hour. Time is valued at $14.00 per hour for commercial traffic and $5.00 per hour for other vehicles. The average operating costs for commercial and noncommercial traffic are, respectively, 43.6 cents and 12.4 cents per km for the river route and 49.8 cents and 13.6 cents per km on the steeper hilly route.

Compare the alternative routes according to an incremental benefit-cost ratio based on a 30-year life and a discount rate of 7 percent.

**10.10** When the owner of an old mansion in a residential neighborhood died, she left a will deeding 2 hectares to the city if the city agreed to use it for a park and maintain the ornate gardens of the site for 40 years. If the city chooses not to accept the offer, the land will be sold to a developer at a price of $260,000. The city uses its municipal-bond rate of 7 percent for evaluating recreational projects.

Modifying the garden to make it into a suitable park would require an investment of $110,000. Annual maintenance, service, and policing would cost $21,000. Forty adjacent homes would increase in value by $2000 each if the land were used as a park. Property taxes in the area are 2.4 percent of the assessed value.

The park would be used mostly for passive recreation such as walking, picknicking, and resting. No team sports would be allowed, and playground equipment for children would be minimal. It is estimated that 30,000 visitors per year would spend an average of 1 hour in the park.

**10.10a** What value per hour would visitors to the park have to place on their visits to have the benefit equal cost?

**10.10b** Is the value per visit calculated in Problem 10.10a a reasonable figure? Compare it with the cost of roughly equivalent experiences which people pay for.

**10.10c** What action would you recommend that the city take?

**10.11** A proposal to develop a new type of mine-shaft borer is being evaluated by a government agency. The project, if approved, will be carried out as a joint venture with a private company which will share the research-and-development investment with the government. The new borer is an adaptation of a tunnel-boring machine made by the cooperating company to perform as a coal-mining machine. Benefits and costs are described below.

*Direct benefits* (Advantage over conventional shaft-sinking techniques)  The conventional cost for sinking a 300 m shaft, which takes an average of 18 months, is $1.7 million per shaft. The cost for the new borer to sink a 300 m shaft is:

First cost prorated over a life of 15 shafts = $137,000/shaft

Operation (cutter and maintenance costs) = $152,000/shaft

Labor (crew × wages × 6 months to sink shaft) = $420,000/shaft

*Time benefits*  Because a borer will complete a shaft in 6 months instead of the conventional 18 months, production profits are available 1 year sooner. Assuming a typical shaft produces 250,000 t of coal, average profit is $2.80 per t, and financing costs are 10 percent for the coal-mining companies, a company will benefit both from obtaining profits sooner and from reduced financing charges because the investment in a mine is recovered 1 year sooner when a new borer is used.

*Spillover benefits*  Savings expected from other mining operations besides coal mining which can utilize the advanced technology available from the borer are $3.9 million per year.

*Derived benefits*  Additional benefits from improved safety are likely but are not included in the analysis.

*Costs*  The government share of the 3-year development costs are, respectively, $100,000, $500,000, and $500,000 for years 1, 2, and 3. An equal amount will come from the private sector for deployment and demonstration activities.

Twenty-seven new borers are expected to be built and sold. Five will be in operation in year 4, 14 in year 5, 24 in year 6, and 27 thereafter. Each borer is expected to sink two shafts per year. Using a 10-year study period and a discount rate of 10 percent, what is the B/C ratio for the borer project? State all assumptions required in your analysis.

# EXTENSION

**10A   Benefit and Cost Data for Public Projects**   According to the theorems of economics, a person is indifferent to the.choice between having an additional unit of any commodity and paying the equilibrium price of that commodity. Many benefits and costs applicable to public projects can be determined from the going market price of commodities. However, there is a class of *public goods* that are available to all if they are available to a single individual. Public parks, drinking water, and clean air are examples of public goods. The value an individual attaches to such goods is elusive because the benefits may be taken for granted and the individual feels that they will be available whether or not he or she contributes an amount equal to the value received. Also, in many cases there is no marketplace in which to measure the value of a public good, even if it could be assumed everyone enjoys a public good in the same amount and would willingly pay for it.

### CONSUMERS' SURPLUS

The concept of *consumers' surplus* has been utilized to explain the difference between what consumers actually pay for a public good and what they might be willing to pay. As shown in Figure 10.3 the demand curve indicates the value (expressed in dollars) placed by consumers on various quantities of a public good: The willingness to pay is a function of quantity. The shaded area is the *consumers' surplus,* representing the surplus value a consumer receives over the amount paid for at price $P$. This surplus is difficult to measure because demand curves are difficult to develop, but some measure of the value of goods above price $P$ is desirable in determining the worth of certain kinds of benefits derived from public projects.

Assume electricity is to be supplied to a region where it was never before available. A hydroelectric project produces power priced at $\$P$ per kilowatthour to residents of the region. Benefits from the project might be based on the market value of the power sold, $P \times Q$, when the residents buy $Q$ kilowatthours. Then, true benefits are understated, because the market value is based on the price of the *last* unit of power purchased. In general, a consumer would willingly pay an amount significantly greater than the market price for the first kilowatthour furnished, a little less for the second kilowatthour, and so on. This bonus to the consumer represents an extra lump sum the consumer would theoretically be willing to pay for the opportunity to buy electric power at price $P$. The correct measure of the benefit provided by the project should include the surplus in addition to the actual dollar value of power sold.

A consumers'-surplus analysis should take into account several conceptual questions concerning appropriateness to a given project. Exact quantitative measures may be difficult to justify. However, one frequently encountered case is easily handled. When a project provides a quantity of public good at a lower price than

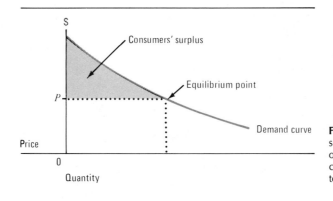

**FIGURE 10.3** Consumers' surplus as the extra amount over the market price $P$ that consumers would be willing to pay for quantity $Q$.

previously possible, the increase in usage is the difference between the previous and present quantities consumed. In Figure 10.4, usage has increased from $Q_1$ to $Q_2$ as a function of a price decrease from $P_1$ to $P_2$ realized from a new public project. The new dollar amount of consumption is $P_2Q_2$, and the increase from the previous level is $P_2Q_2 - P_1Q_1$. But the benefit from the new price should also include the incremental change in the consumers' surplus. If the demand curve can be assumed linear over the range of $Q_1$ to $Q_2$, then the change in consumers' surplus is calculated as

$$\Delta(\text{consumers' surplus}) = \frac{(P_1 - P_2)(Q_1 + Q_2)}{2}$$

which is added to the dollar value of increased consumption to provide a measure of total benefit.

### Example 10.5   Questionable Quantity of Consumers' Benefits

Let the conditions in Figure 10.4 represent a road-construction project. The original unimproved road provided benefits to users that are shown in Figure 10.4 by the enclosed area $xyE_1Q_1$. Paving, grading, and straightening can improve the value of the road until its benefits are represented in the figure by the area $xyE_2Q_2$. Because the new road completely replaced the existing one, the total benefit claimed is the entire area $xyE_2Q_2$. Is this the correct benefit for the road-improvement project?

### Solution 10.5

The claimed benefit overstates the value added by the road-improvement project. The original benefit $xyE_1Q_1$ produced by the old road exists regardless of improvements. The new benefit from the project that can be counted is represented by the area $Q_1E_1E_2Q_2$, which can be calculated as

$$\text{Added benefit} = P_2Q_2 - P_1Q_1 + \frac{(P_1 - P_2)(Q_1 + Q_2)}{2}$$

$$= P_2Q_2 - P_1Q_1 + \frac{1}{2}(P_1Q_1 + P_1Q_2 - P_2Q_1 - P_2Q_2)$$

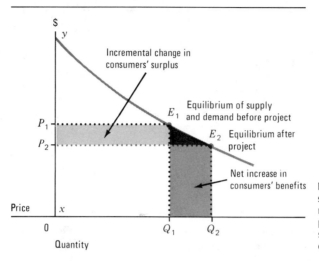

FIGURE 10.4  Change in consumers' surplus caused by a new project that decreases the price from $P_1$ to $P_2$ with a resulting increase in quantity consumed from $Q_1$ to $Q_2$.

$$= \frac{1}{2}(P_2 Q_2 - P_2 Q_1 + P_1 Q_2 - P_1 Q_1)$$

$$= \frac{1}{2}(P_2 + P_1)(Q_2 - Q_1)$$

## SPILLOVER BENEFITS AND COSTS

Spillovers (or externalities) exist when there is a divergence between private and social benefit or between private and social cost. An example of spillover benefits is the increase in land values brought about by the construction of a new highway or park. Spillovers are easily overlooked and are sometimes tricky to quantify, owing to filtering effects, but engineering economists should be conscious of spillover considerations for public projects because they constitute a significant source of benefits and costs. Cognizance is necessary to avoid B/C ratios bloated by exaggerated spillover benefits. Similarly, spillover costs deserve close inspection since their magnitude may be exaggerated by damage reports from injured parties. It is reasonable to view any spillover claim with some suspicion, if only to trace its logic.

Enumeration of spillovers may suggest the most effective direction for public expenditures. For example, in the case of production plants that are dumping pollutants, a tax on the effluent which is a measure of the external costs of pollution can make private costs identical with social costs. Or a subsidy could be granted to the offending plants to assist them in reducing the undesirable discharges. Both courses of action are probably better alternatives than public ownership of the production facilities. In other cases the spillovers may be so extensive that public ownership is preferable, as in a multipurpose river-basin project. It would be more practical for the government to plan, undertake, and operate the entire river-basin development than it would be to create a system of market incentives capable of directing the combined resources of private investors toward the desired social objectives.

## PROJECT COSTS

Costs for all resources required to achieve the stated objectives of a project should be included in the analysis. Each alternative in multilevel proposals should be self-contained in terms of cost, to avoid double counting or overlapping expenses. A few cost considerations of particular significance to benefit-cost analyses are:

1 Imputed costs of existing assets employed on a project should be included when there are alternative uses for the assets. For instance, land or facilities desired for use in another project besides the one being analyzed would be treated in both projects as costs based on fair market values. Neglecting such costs would be similar to a contractor building houses on inherited land and then basing the selling price of the homes on just the construction costs because the land was free.
2 Preliminary costs of investigation and technical services required to get a project started are part of the project's budget. Once the project is under way, interest charges during the construction period before earnings begin are applicable expenditures. Management costs, whether incurred by the sponsoring agency or contributed by the beneficiaries, are part of the total project cost.
3 Spillover costs comprise all significant adverse effects caused by the construction and operation of a project and are expressed in terms of market prices whether or not actual outlays for compensation are made. For instance, an irrigation project could reduce the quality of water downstream from the area to be serviced; the additional treatment facilities necessary to restore the quality of the water or provisions for water from another source would be costs to the irrigation project.

## PROJECT BENEFITS

Public projects are typically conceived to provide a certain benefit or family of benefits. Many of the difficulties of quantifying these benefits have already been discussed. The nature of some social benefits often precludes their measurement by direct market pricing, because there is no market in the private sector which offers the benefits.

To illustrate the valuation of benefits directly attributable to gains that are valued by marketplace statistics, consider a proposal to provide irrigation to 5000 hectares of farmland. Water supplied by irrigation is an input to the production of food and fiber. Beneficial effects from irrigation are based upon their total value to agricultural producers and are measured as the increase in net farm income with and without a plan for providing irrigation water. Changes in net farm income may be estimated by analyzing changes in gross farm income and expenses for each separate enterprise or by using representative farm budgets. A sample compilation is shown in Table 10.2.

Data used to estimate farm investment, receipts, and expenses are drawn from representative practices, prices, and budgets experienced during comparable situa-

| Component | Without Project | With Project | Difference Due to Project |
|---|---|---|---|
| Area in hectares | 5000 | 5000 | |
| Number of farms | 20 | 50 | 30 |
| Farm investment | $1,500,000 | $5,000,000 | $3,500,000 |
| Farm receipts | $490,000 | $2,500,000 | $2,010,000 |
| Farm interest expense | ($67,500) | ($225,000) | ($1,560,000) |
| Other farm expenses | ($372,500) | ($1,775,000) | |
| *Net farm income* | $50,000 | $500,000 | $450,000 |
| Disbenefit for alternative earnings forgone by new farmers: 30 new farms × $2000 | | | $60,000 |
| *Irrigation benefit* | | | $390,000 |

**TABLE 10.2**  Summary of components contributing to benefits from an irrigation project.

tions. The disbenefit for the opportunity cost of wages that farm workers would receive if they did not operate their own farms is based on census data for farm-work earnings compiled by Agriculture Canada.

Statistics for estimating many types of benefits are not as directly applicable as in the irrigation project. It is then necessary to derive a benefit value by research that combines data from several sources. Recreational benefits are a good example of derived values. Factors affecting recreational values include the number and distribution of the population in the project area; socioeconomic characteristics including disposable income, occupation, education, age, and mobility of the relevant population; and the population's leisure time and recreational habits as indicated by trends in hunting and fishing license sales, sales of recreational equipment, and total demand. Such factors suggest the potential participation rate but do not put dollar amounts on the value of the participation.

To facilitate valuation, two types of recreation days are recognized, a *recreation day* being defined as a unit of use consisting of a visit of one individual to a recreation development during a reasonable portion of a 24-hour period:

| Type of Recreation Day | Value of 1 Day's Use |
|---|---|
| *General*  Type of activity attracting the majority of outdoor recreationists—requires the development of convenient access and maintenance of adequate facilities (for example, swimming, picnicking, nature studies, tent and trailer camping, canoeing) | $2.25–$6.75 |
| *Specialized*  Type of outdoor activity for which opportunities are limited, intensity of use is low, and which often involve a large personal expense by the user (for example, cold-water fishing, big-game hunting, wilderness pack trips) | $9.00–$27.00 |

Indications of the values that users put on such experiences can be obtained from charges for similar activities in the private sector, time and cost of travel required to partake in an activity, cost of alternative uses of the facilities, and questionnaires about how much a user would be willing to pay for various experiences. A suggested composite value for a visitor day to any area is simply the gross national product per day divided by the total population.

Some attributes of a public project are *intangible*. In the 1940s, aesthetic values were considered of immeasurable worth, so any cost that made them available to the public was acceptable. This line of reasoning meant every project that promised aesthetic values automatically had a B/C ratio of at least 1.0. An equivalent conclusion results from placing an infinite value on irreplaceable assets such as wilderness areas.

A more systematic approach to the evaluation of intangible characteristics defines categories of attributes and employs a subjective rating system to rank the quality of different projects. Formal environmental quality-evaluation procedures have been developed to compare intangible benefits and disbenefits for alternative water- and land-use plans. (Rating concepts for intangibles are discussed in Chapter 19.) The procedure starts with the identification of the environmental resources involved in a proposed project. Resources include open spaces, stream systems, beaches, wilderness areas, historical and cultural features, and ecological systems. These resources are then evaluated according to the following criteria:

1 *Quantity* Specific environmental features are enumerated and measured in units such as acres of wilderness; miles of white water; area of lakes; and number of waterfalls, animals, scenic attractions, and significant sites.

2 *Quality* The desirability of an environmental feature is rated by assigning a number from 1 to 10 after comparing the features with known or projected conditions at other locations.

3 *Human influence* Subjective 1-to-10 ratings are made to indicate the degree to which people would use the resource identified; the degree to which it is protected for continued use; and the degree that it contributes to education, scientific knowledge, and human enjoyment.

4 *Uniqueness* A 1-to-10 rating measures the frequency of occurrence of a specific resource in the project relative to its occurrence elsewhere.

5 *Significance* Irreversible damage to a resource is rated on a 1-to-10 scale that indicates the magnitude of adverse effects on the environment. The rating reflects the scarcity of supply of a resource and the capability of its returning to its original or natural state after the proposed project is implemented.

The ratings for intangible benefits are typically reported as an appendix to the monetary comparisons. A narrative may accompany the presentation of intangible considerations to explain how the ratings were developed, to discuss opposing views, and to provide supplementary information.

It is doubtful that any B/C analysis is immune from all criticism. There are too many facets involved. However, a thorough analysis will at least expose all the issues and quantify as many of them as possible. Then pros and cons are channeled toward more definitive and objective assessments—and reassessments.

## QUESTIONS

**10A.1** A public good is represented by a linear demand schedule ranging from equilibrium at $1 for the first unit available to zero when 1 million units are available. The current level of availability and consumption is 300,000 units.

**10A.1a**   What is the dollar volume of current consumption?                    *($210,000)*

**10A.1b**   What is the dollar volume of the current consumers' surplus? *($45,000)*

**10A.1c**   If a public project can decrease the cost to 40 cents per unit, what additional total benefit does it produce?                              *($165,000)*

**10A.1d**   What would the consumers' surplus be if the project were carried out?                                                                        *($180,000)*

**10A.1e**   What is the dollar volume of consumption after the project is completed?                                                                *($240,000)*

**10A.1f**   Calculate by formula the increase in consumers' surplus resulting from the project. Check the figure obtained with respect to the answers to the previous problems.                                                           *($135,000)*

**10A.1g**   Would it be possible for a demand schedule to be such that total consumption would decrease from a previous level after implementation of a project that allowed the quantity consumed to increase as a function of a decreased price? Illustrate your answer. Comment on the change in consumers' surplus.

**10A.2**   A public good has a linear demand function such that the first unit available is valued at $100,000, but when 50,000 units are available, the per unit value drops to $2.

**10A.2a**   What is the consumers' surplus when the demand is 30,000 units?

**10A.2b**   What would be the change in the consumers' surplus if a project increased demand from 30,000 to 50,000 units?

**10A.3**   There are public schools and private schools. From consideration of spillover benefits, why is the public investment in education logical?

**10A.4**   In recent years many cities have constructed large municipal stadiums. The sales pitch to get voters' approval for funding often appealed to civic pride and implied that the stadium would be self-supporting as well as an attraction for visitors whose purchases would increase revenues for many merchants. After completion, some stadium projects failed to meet advertised expectations and caused difficulties that the voters had not anticipated.

Disregarding misjudgments of construction costs, which far exceeded original estimates in many cases, and inaccuracies which overestimated the income that would be received from promotions booked into a stadium, what disbenefits and spillover costs could have been logically anticipated and accounted for in a thorough benefit-cost analysis? List 10 considerations, and discuss how values could be obtained for the factors involved.

**10A.5**   Assume that a modest-size city park with which you are familiar is the end product of a public project. That is, a project produced the present park based on an accepted benefit-cost analysis. Further assume that the land became available for the park because a school on the site burned down, and since there was sufficient classroom space available in nearby schools, the city decided not to rebuild the facility. Instead, it decided the land would be used for other city purposes or sold to add money to the city treasury. One of the proposals for the land was to build the park that now exists.

**10A.5a**   Based on the above scenario, list the benefit and cost categories that should have been included in the evaluation of the park project.

**10A.5b**   Insofar as possible, quantify the benefit and cost categories in terms of current values to complete the benefit-cost analysis. Use a 30-year life and a discount rate of 7 percent. Discuss the intangible benefits involved.

# SECTION THREE

# MANAGEMENT OF MONEY

"The name of the game is business, and the score is kept with money" is a catchy old saying that contains a lot of truth. Perhaps business is too serious to be called a game and money is too restrictive a measure, but there are plenty of players and they are surely interested in finances. Even nonprofit organizations and governments are subject to economic yardsticks. Very few individuals or organizations are immune to the economic evaluation criteria.

Professor Han of the University of Novi Sad in Yugoslavia observed an intriguing semantic quality associated with the quest for money. In English we say that we "make money" in the notion of manufacturing it, or "earn money" as just compensation for labor. Oriental languages roughly translate as "seeking" money. In German one "serves" for money, and in Russian one "works" for it. Hungarians "search" for money. The French and Italian versions are inspired by the notion of "winning" money. An appropriate but apparently unused phrase would be to "manage" money. Engineering economists manage money by directing and controlling its movement.

Only the very brash or very naïve would enter a chess competition without

237

knowing the rules and practices of the game. Similar inadequacies may fail to bar the unprepared and the unsuspecting from economic competition. Many are lulled into complacency by an honest but often erroneous belief that they possess an innate money sense that will carry them through. In the last section we dealt with some of the mechanics of economic competition. In this section we shall investigate the special rules that govern the business game (depreciation and taxes) and the way it is played by experienced competitors (industrial practices, consideration of inflation, and sensitivity analysis).

# CHAPTER 11

# ACCOUNTING AND DEPRECIATION

OVERVIEW

If, indeed, "the name of the game is business and you keep score with money," then the rules are set by government, the scorekeepers are accountants, and the referee is the tax collector. An engineering economist acts as a playmaker.

Engineering economists do not have to become accountants to carry out economic evaluations, but they should be aware of the accounting function and how it can contribute to better analyses. An accounting system records financial data. These records indicate the financial condition of an organization, record data from which estimates for future activities can be obtained, and reveal how closely implemented proposals met expectations. An *income statement* shows the revenue and expenses over a period of time. Retained earnings from the income statement are an input to the *balance sheet*, where accounts are tabulated for a given date to give values for the basic accounting equation; *assets minus liabilities equal net worth.*

Accounting records are also scorecards that show what actually happened to a proposal after it was accepted and augmented. The use of financial ratios to evaluate the strength of a business is examined in Extension 11A.

Provisions for recovering capital invested in income-producing assets are made by charging depreciation against current income. These depreciation charges and the regular operating expenses are deductible from gross income in determining taxable income. *The depreciation method required for tax purposes affects the timing and amount of tax payments, which in turn affect the after-tax worth of proposals.*

*Depreciation charges* are made in accounting records to recover capital spent for production assets and to substantiate deductions from current income for tax calculations. The two most commonly used depreciation methods are *straight line* and *declining balance*. The latter is an accelerated method which allows higher depreciation charges earlier in the write-off period. Accelerated charges decrease the time value of taxes. Rigid rules for depreciation accounting for tax purposes are set by Revenue Canada, according to laws passed by Parliament.

# ACCOUNTING

An accountant and an engineering economist may work with the same financial data, but they do so for different purposes. The engineering economist deals with the future to evaluate proposed courses of action. Each proposal is analyzed with respect to its future cash flow and potential for earning a certain rate of return.

The accountant deals with transactions that have already occurred to determine what *was* the return on capital. The accountant does not have an entry for the cost of capital, unless there is an actual disbursement to be made, such as interest due on a loan. The views of the accountant and engineering economist coincide when a postaudit is conducted to see how closely actual figures came to figures estimated during the evaluation of a proposal. Then, both are looking at what happened and how it affected the economic health of the organization.

## Balance Sheet

The fundamental accounting equation is

*Assets − liabilities = net worth*

Periodically, a *balance sheet* is prepared to show the monetary values of the elements in the accounting equation. This statement is accurate only for the date given on the balance sheet, because specific amounts vary from day to day. It is a measure of financial health in the same way a report of an annual medical checkup is a measure of an individual's health. Both statements might be different if prepared on a different day, because both are summaries of all contributing factors to the day of preparation. These summary effects make the statements analytically valuable as readings on current conditions, and, when compared to previous statements, as an indicator of what to expect in the future. (Extension 11.A illustrates the potential of analyzing financial ratios.)

An abbreviated balance sheet is shown in Figure 11.1. The left side tabulates the assets that total to an amount equal to the sum of the liabilities and net worth on the right side. The *assets* fall into three categories that represent the resources of the organization:

*Current assets*    Those that will become cash within 1 year (inventory, accounts receivable, etc.)

*Fixed assets*    Those that cannot be readily converted to cash (land, buildings, etc.)

*Other assets*    Intangible or difficult to classify (prepaid insurance, patents, etc.)

*Liabilities* are obligations of known amounts owed to creditors. They are usually listed in order of due dates; *current liabilities* are payable within 1 year, and *long-term liabilities* are not due for over a year. The *net worth* (shareholders' equity) represents the book value of the owners' investments in the organization. *Retained earnings* are profits from past operations which belong to the shareholders and have been retained within the organization for reinvestment.

FIGURE 11.1 Balance sheet showing an organization's major accounts as of a specific date.

Democo Ltd.
Balance Sheet
June 30, 19xx

| ASSETS | | LIABILITIES | |
|---|---|---|---|
| *Current assets* | | *Current liabilities* | |
| Cash | $ 5,400 | Accounts payable | $35,200 |
| Accounts receivable | 9,000 | Bank loans | 9,000 |
| Raw-material inventory | 11,000 | Accrued taxes | 4,800 |
| Work in progress inventory | 10,000 | *Long-term liabilities* | |
| Finished products | | Bonds (due in 12 years). | 15,000 |
| inventory | 16,600 | | $64,000 |
| Land | 37,000 | NET WORTH | |
| Buildings and equipment. | 83,000 | Capital stock | $100,000 |
| *Other assets* | | Retained earnings | 24,000 |
| Prepaid services | 16,000 | | $124,000 |
| | $188,000 | | $188,000 |

Fixed assets are usually shown at their book value as determined by the difference between what was paid for the assets minus accumulated depreciation. If the buildings and equipment in Figure 11.1 had originally cost $100,000 and had since been depreciated by $17,000, the entry in the balance sheet could have taken the form:

*Fixed assets*

Land .................................... $37,000
    Buildings and equipment ....... $100,000
    Less: Accumulated depreciation ...... 17,000
                                        $83,000

There are many other variations and different headings for accounts in balance sheets. Since all the accounts are summaries, supplementary accounting records are necessary to observe the cash flow.

## Example 11.1   The Balance of a Business

Sam Sales is an engineering sales representative for an air-conditioning manufacturer. He is paid a commission on the amount of commercial air-conditioning equipment he sells. As he traveled within his assigned territory (Great White North) calling on prospective customers, he became fascinated by the variety of novelties displayed near the cash registers at restaurants and stores.

One day Sam saw a person filling up one of the novelty displays and started talking to him. Before they were done talking, Sam agreed to purchase the novelty distributorship. The seller wanted to go to a different climate, and Sam figured he could combine the novelty business with his other travels.

The distributorship was priced at $23,000 and included an exclusive franchise for Hoser postcards, $14,200 in inventory stored in a warehouse where rent was prepaid for 12 months at $100 per month, and accounts receivable of $3100 from ongoing sales. Sam agreed to take over the accounts payable of $1900 and accrued taxes of $300 from the seller.

Sam met the $23,000 selling price by putting up $5000 from his savings, borrowing $8000 on a 2-year bank loan, and getting the former owner to take an unsecured note promising to pay the remainder over 3 years. Then Sam withdrew $10,000 more from his savings for *working capital* to handle day-to-day cash transactions for his venture, now called "Sales' Gimmicks." Construct a balance sheet for the new company as of the current date, December 31, 19x0.

### Solution 11.1

Sam Sales' beginning balance sheet is shown in Figure 11.2.

**SALES' GIMMICKS**
**Balance Sheet**
**December 31, 19x0**

| ASSETS | | LIABILITIES | |
|---|---|---|---|
| Cash ................. | $10,000 | Accounts payable .......... | $ 1,900 |
| Accounts receivable ..... | 3,100 | Accrued taxes .............. | 300 |
| Inventory .............. | 14,200 | Bank loan .................. | 8,000 |
| Prepaid rent ........... | 1,200 | Note due seller ............. | 10,000 |
| Franchise ............. | 4,500* | | |
| | | NET WORTH | |
| Total assets .......... | $33,000 | Sam Sales' equity ........... | $12,800† |
| | | Total liability and equity ... | $33,000 |

**FIGURE 11.2**

*The value of the franchise is the amount included in the purchase price for existing customer goodwill and the exclusive territorial rights to distribute Hoser postcards.

†Sam's equity is derived from the $15,000 withdrawn from savings minus the amount of taxes and accounts payable ($300 + $1900).

## Income Statement

A statement of the earnings of an organization over a stated period of time is call an *income statement* or a *profit-and-loss statement*. The net profit or loss it discloses represents the difference between revenue from the sale of goods or services and the sum of all the operating expenses plus taxes. The net profit may be held as retained earnings or distributed to the owners. An abbreviated income statement is shown in Figure 11.3. Its development precedes the balance sheet because the bottom-line figure, net income after tax, is an entry in the balance sheet under net worth. Both the income statement and the balance sheet are needed to understand an organization's financial position, and then only the more prominent features are revealed.

|  | Democo Ltd.<br>Income Statement<br>Year Ended June 30, 19xx |  |
|---|---|---|
| *Income* |  |  |
| Product sales | $247,500 |  |
| Fees for services | 16,500 | $264,000 |
| *Expenses* |  |  |
| Cost of goods sold | $119,000 |  |
| Administrative | 82,000 |  |
| Depreciation | 9,200 |  |
| Utilities | 6,000 |  |
| Other (insurance, rent, etc.) | 7,800 | $224,000 |
| Income before income tax | | $40,000 |
| Income tax at (40%) | | 16,000 |
| *Net income after tax* (to retained earnings) | | $24,000 |

**FIGURE 11.3** Income statement for the same organization during the same time period represented by the balance sheet in Figure 11.1.

## Cost Accounting

The major accounts displayed in the balance sheet and income statement are composed of many smaller accounts, each of which is, in turn, composed of more detailed items. For instance, the cost of goods sold in the income statement includes direct labor, direct material, and factory overhead. More detailing breaks down the costs of direct labor by craft and work assignment, and the cost of material by type, use, and timing. This type of information is in the accounting system and recorded because the summarizing balance sheets and income statements are built up from the elemental cost data. The collection of these costs for producing a product or service is called *cost accounting.*

The cost of goods sold category is particularly useful to an engineering economist because it contains data that can be extracted and interpreted to estimate costs for proposals that alter the production process. The cost data about the current process are applicable to the do-nothing or defending alternative, and *predictive cost accounting* estimates the cost of future operations of the same nature from past performance.

---

### Example 11.2 A Summary Statement of Profit or Loss

After Sam Sales bought the novelty business, he laid out a year-long operating plan in the form of a monthly budget. He knew that his postcards and other novelties would enjoy their highest sales during the summer. He also realized that he would not have time to service all his outlets during the busy season while continuing his primary job in engineering sales, and he was not nearly confident enough in his Gimmicks Company to rely on it alone for a living.

He could hire helpers part time in the summer as route servicers, but he was worried about his cash-flow position. With only $10,000 for working capital, he could not afford to build up his inventory levels too high or he would run out of cash to pay the bills. The results of juggling amounts between cost categories and the time periods are shown in the monthly budget accounts in Table 11.1. The plan anticipates a decline in the postcard inventory during the winter to stock up on novelties. During the summer the monthly receipts would pay for the additional help, and the cash balance should not drop below $4000.

SALES' GIMMICKS MONTHLY CASH BUDGET

|  | Jan. | Feb. | Mar. | Apr. | May | June |
|---|---|---|---|---|---|---|
| *Starting Cash* | $10,000 | $ 9,670 | $11,840 | $13,510 | $12,790 | $13,070 |
| *Sales* | | | | | | |
| Cards | 6,000 | 5,000 | 6,000 | 6,000 | 8,000 | 9,000 |
| Other | | 500 | 1,000 | 1,500 | 2,000 | 3,000 |
| Cash Income | $ 6,000 | $ 5,500 | $ 7,000 | $ 7,500 | $10,000 | $12,000 |
| *Disbursements* | | | | | | |
| Cards | 1,000 | | 2,000 | 4,000 | 6,000 | 12,000 |
| Other | 3,000 | 1,000 | 1,000 | 500 | 500 | 1,000 |
| Salaries | 600 | 600 | 600 | 600 | 1,400 | 2,100 |
| Travel | 1,000 | 1,000 | 1,000 | 1,000 | 1,000 | 1,300 |
| Office Salaries | 450 | 450 | 450 | 450 | 450 | 700 |
| Office Expenses | 100 | 100 | 100 | 150 | 150 | 200 |
| Other Expenses | 180 | 180 | 180 | 220 | 220 | 280 |
| Loan Payments | | | | | | |
| Interest | | | | 1,000 | | |
| Taxes | | | | 300 | | |
| *Cash outflow* | $ 6,330 | $ 3,330 | $ 5,330 | $ 8,220 | $ 9,720 | $17,580 |
| Gain/Loss | −330 | 2,170 | 1,670 | −720 | 280 | −5,580 |
| Ending Cash* | $9,670 | $11,840 | $13,510 | $12,790 | $13,070 | $ 7,490 |

|  | July | Aug. | Sep. | Oct. | Nov. | Dec. |
|---|---|---|---|---|---|---|
| *Starting Cash* | $ 7,490 | $ 3,850 | $12,710 | $20,980 | $23,860 | $26,920 |
| *Sales* | | | | | | |
| Cards | 10,000 | 13,000 | 11,000 | 7,000 | 5,000 | 6,000 |
| Other | 4,000 | 5,500 | 4,500 | 2,000 | 2,000 | 4,000 |
| Cash Income | $14,000 | $18,500 | $15,500 | $ 9,000 | $ 7,000 | $10,000 |
| *Disbursements* | | | | | | |
| Cards | 6,000 | 4,000 | 2,000 | 2,000 | | 1,000 |
| Other | 2,000 | 1,000 | 1,000 | 1,000 | 1,000 | 200 |
| Salaries | 2,100 | 2,100 | 1,950 | 650 | 650 | 650 |
| Travel | 1,300 | 1,300 | 1,100 | 600 | 600 | 800 |
| Office Salaries | 700 | 700 | 700 | 450 | 450 | 1,050 |
| Office Expenses | 200 | 200 | 200 | 200 | 200 | 300 |
| Other Expenses | 640 | 340 | 280 | 220 | 1,040 | 220 |
| Loan Payments | 4,500 | | | | | 4,500 |
| Interest | 200 | | | 1,000 | | |
| Taxes | | | | | | |
| *Cash outflow* | $17,640 | $ 9,640 | $ 7,230 | $ 6,120 | $ 3,940 | $ 8,720 |
| Gain/Loss | −3,640 | 8,860 | 8,270 | 2,880 | 3,060 | 1,280 |
| Ending Cash* | $ 3,850 | $12,710 | $20,980 | $23,860 | $26,920 | $28,200 |

*Ending Cash = Starting Cash + Cash Income − Cash Outflow

**TABLE 11.1** Monthly budget for cash receipts and disbursements for Sales'Gimmicks Company. Loan expense includes $2200 in interest and $9000 toward repayment.

Develop an income statement for the year by assuming that the actual receipts and disbursements came out exactly as budgeted in Table 11.1 for the first year's operation of Sales' Gimmicks. The tax rate is 20 percent on the $26,300 income, and the after-tax total is held as retained earnings.

Assume that accounts payable, accounts receivable , and inventory are the same on December 31, 19x1 as they were on December 31, 19x0. The $300 of taxes for 19x0 are a cash outflow in 19x1 but do not affect the 19x1 income statement. (Only taxes for 19x1, which are paid in 19x2, affect the 19x1 income statement.) The $1,200 of prepaid rent, however, must be included in the 19x1 income statement.*

### Solution 11.2

The income statement for the first year's operation of Sales' Gimmicks Company, based on the budget shown in Table 11.1, is in Figure 11.4. The income and expense categories summarize the expected effects of operations during the 1-year period analyzed. Sam did pretty well; the return on his initial investment was about 100 percent in 1 year.

| SALES' GIMMICKS COMPANY | | |
|---|---|---|
| Year Ending December 31, 19x1 | | |
| *Income* | | |
| Net Sales: Postcards ..................... | $92,000 | |
| Other gimmicks ............... | 30,000 | |
| Total net sales ........................ | | $122,000 |
| Cost of goods sold: Postcards .............. | 40,000 | |
| Other gimmicks ........ | 13,200 | |
| Total cost of goods sold ................ | | 53,200 |
| Gross profit on sales ....................... | | $68,800 |
| *Expenses* | | |
| Route servicers' salaries ............... | $14,000 | |
| Travel expenses ..................... | 12,000 | |
| Office salaries and expenses ........... | 9,100 | |
| Other expenses (storage, pilferage, etc.) ... | 4,000 | |
| Loan interest ...................... | 2,200 | |
| Rent............................ | 1,200 | |
| Total expenses .................... | | $42,500 |
| Net operating profit ................... | | $26,300 |
| Income tax ....................... | | 5,260 |
| Net profit (to retained earnings) .......... | | $21,040 |

**FIGURE 11.4**

# DEPRECIATION

Depreciation means a decrease in worth. Most assets are worth less as they get older. Newly purchased production assets have the advantage of latest technical improvements

*For further details of accounting, see L.S. Rosen and M.H. Granof, *Canadian Financial Accounting: Principles and Issues*, Prentice-Hall of Canada, Scarborough, Ont., 1980.

and operate with less chance of breakdown or need for repairs. Except for possible antique value, production equipment gradually becomes less valuable through wear. This lessening in value is recognized in accounting practices as an expense of operating. Instead of charging the full purchase price of a new asset as a one-time expense, the outlay is spread over the life of the asset in the accounting records. This concept of amortization may seem to disagree with the actual cash flow for a particular transaction, but for all transactions taken collectively it provides a realistic representation of capital consumption in profit-and-loss statements.

## Reasons for Depreciation Accounting

The costs of production can be divided into *direct* money costs—wages, salaries, raw materials, etc.—and *imputed* costs—payments not contractually required for production during a short accounting period. In financial accounting, depreciation is an imputed cost. The principal objectives for charging a depreciation cost can be summarized as (1) to recover capital invested in production assets, (2) to accurately determine imputed costs of production for cost records, and (3) to include the cost of depreciation in operating expenses for tax purposes.

To emphasize the importance of depreciation, consider the plight of an individual who used $25,500 in savings and borrowed $30,000 to buy a used tractor, truck, and hauling rig to start a landscaping service. Business was good. A gross income of $60,000 per year allowed annual operating and loan-repayment expenses of $27,000 to be met. After 5 years of comfortable living with good wages, the loan was repaid but the equipment was worn out. Its salvage value after the 5 years of use was only $500. When it was time to purchase replacement equipment, the original $25,500 was no longer available to use as a down payment. The investment had not been recovered from the earnings it afforded.

From the vantage point of hindsight, it is obvious that the landscaper should have made provisions to set aside $25,500 − $500 = $25,000 during the life of the equipment. This would have shown the actual earnings during the period, and allowed capital consumption to be shown as an expense.

## Depreciation Accounts

In making depreciation studies it is convenient to visualize a charge for depreciation as being a series of payments made to a specific fund for the replacement of the asset being studied. While this notion is quite reasonable in concept, it is seldom followed in industrial practice. A bookkeeping account shows the annual charge for depreciation.

An exception to the practice of keeping accounts of depreciation funds by book entries is the occasionally used external sinking fund. In this depreciation method a separate fund is established by payments invested outside the company. The interest earned by the fund is the interest paid by the organization that holds the investments. The annual payments are determined by the sinking-fund formula $(A/F, i, N)$, where $F$ is the amount needed to replace the asset, $N$ is the economic life, and $i$ is the interest received on the invested funds. A firm that is having financial troubles may be required to set up a sinking fund. Otherwise, a sinking-fund depreciation schedule is seldom used in private industry.

The original cost of the asset minus the accumulated depreciation is called the *book value*. Land is one of the few assets which is not depreciated because land values normally remain constant or appreciate. Therefore, any portion of an investment representing land is deducted from the original cost when making depreciation calculations.

## Causes of Declining Value

Being aware of the potential causes of decreasing worth may assist in determining the most appropriate depreciation schedule for an asset.

1 *Physical depreciation*  The everyday wear and tear of operation gradually lessens the physical ability of an asset to perform its intended function. A good maintenance program retards the rate of decline, but it seldom maintains the precision expected from a new machine. In addition to normal wear, accidental physical damage can also impair ability.

2 *Functional depreciation*  Demands made on an asset may increase beyond its capacity to produce. A central heating plant unable to meet the increased heat demands of a new building addition no longer serves its intended function. At the other extreme, the demand for services may cease to exist, as with a machine which produces a product no longer in demand.

3 *Technological depreciation*  Newly developed means of accomplishing a function may make the present means uneconomical. Steam locomotives lost value rapidly as railroads turned to diesel power. Current product styling, new materials, improved safety, and better quality at lower cost from new developments make old designs obsolete.

4 *Depletion*  Consumption of an exhaustible natural resource to produce products or services is termed *depletion*. Removal of oil, timber, rock, or minerals from a site decreases the value of the holding. This decrease is compensated for by a proportionate reduction in earnings derived from the resource. Theoretically, the depletion charge per unit of the resources removed is

$$\frac{\text{Present value of resource}}{\text{Remaining units of resource}} = \text{depletion rate (\$/unit)}$$

Allowances for depletion vary with the type of resource and with the most recent legislation. Highest allowances are theoretically allowed for the resources which require the greatest expenditures for discovery and development. (See Review Exercise 1.)

5 *Monetary depreciation*  A change in price levels is a subtle but troublesome cause of problems. Customary accounting practices relate depreciation to the original price of an asset, not to its replacement. If prices rise during the life of an asset, as in the case of recent high inflation rates, a comparable replacement becomes more expensive. This means that the capital recovered will be insufficient to provide an adequate substitute for the worn-out asset. It also suggests that the selling price of the product being produced by the asset does not accurately reflect the cost of production. Because the depreciation is actually happening to the invested capital representing the asset instead of to the asset itself, monetary depreciation is very difficult to accommodate. It cannot be charged as an operating expense for tax purposes. The "nonresponsive" nature of depreciation and its affect on a proposal's rate of return during periods of high inflation are discussed in Chapter 13.

# DEPRECIATION METHODS

Of the many depreciation methods available, two will be examined in the following pages: *straight line* and *declining balance*. These methods are based strictly on time. That is, an asset used every day has the same depreciation charge as one used only once per year. Some advocate that depreciation should be based on the amount of use as well as the economic life. It is possible to combine a usage factor with a time-based method such as straight-line depreciation to reflect the rate of decreasing value with use.

Each depreciation method has unique features which appeal to different management philosophies. A method by which the bulk of the money invested is recovered early in the life of an asset is a popular conservative view. An early write-off guards against sudden changes which could make the equipment less valuable and shifts some taxes toward later years. Methods in which the annual charge is constant simplify the accounting procedure. In general, the desirable features of a depreciation method are that it (1) recovers the capital invested in an asset, (2) maintains a book value close to the actual value of the asset throughout its life, (3) is easy to apply, and (4) is acceptable to Revenue Canada. Both methods will be illustrated by reference to the problem information shown in Table 11.2.

The symbols used in the development of the formulae are

$P$ = purchase price (present worth at time zero) of asset
$S$ = salvage value or future value at end of asset's useful life
$N$ = useful life of asset
$n$ = number of years of depreciation or use from time of purchase
DC = annual charge for depreciation
BV = book value shown on accounting records

## Straight-Line Method

Straight-line depreciation is the simplest to apply and the most widely used of the depreciation methods. The annual depreciation is constant. The book value is the difference between the purchase price and the product of the number of years of use times the annual depreciation charge:

$$DC = \frac{P - S}{N}$$

$$BV(\text{end of year } n) = P - \frac{n}{N}(P - S)$$

**TABLE 11.2** Data and problem statement for Examples 11.3 and 11.4

Trucks purchased by a delivery company cost $7000 each. Past records indicate the trucks should have a useful life of 5 years. They can be sold for an average of $1000 each after 5 years of use. The company currently receives 7 percent interest on invested funds. Determine:

a   The depreciation charge during year 1
b   The depreciation charge during year 2
c   The accumulated depreciation by the end of year 3
d   The book value at the end of year 3

### Example 11.3  Straight-Line Depreciation Applied to the Basic Data

### Solution 11.3

**a and b**  Since the annual depreciation cost is constant, the charges for both the first and second year are

$$DC = \frac{P - S}{N} = \frac{\$7000 - \$1000}{5} = \$1200/\text{year}$$

**c**  The depreciation reserve at the end of the third year is the sum of the annual depreciation charges for the first 3 years and is equal to $3 \times \$1200 = \$3600$.

**d**  $BV(3) = \$7000 - \dfrac{3}{5}(\$7000 - \$1000)$

$= \$7000 - 0.6(\$6000) = \$3400$

or, with the book value considered as the difference between the purchase price and the amount accumulated in the depreciation reserve,

$BV(3) = \$7000 - 3(\$1200) = \$3400$

## Declining-Balance Method

The declining-balance method is a means of amortizing an asset at an accelerated rate early in its life, with corresponding lower annual charges near the end of service. A constant depreciation rate is applied to the book value for each depreciation period. Since the undepreciated balance decreases each year, the depreciation charge also decreases, and

$BV(n) = P(1 - \text{depreciation rate})^n$

$DC(n) = BV(n - 1) \text{ (depreciation rate)}$

### Example 11.4  Declining-Balance Depreciation Applied to the Basic Data, given a depreciation rate = 40% or 0.4.

### Solution 11.4

**a**  $DC(1) = P(0.4) = \$7000(0.4) = \$2800$

**b**  $DC(2) = BV(1)(0.4) = (\$7000 - \$2800)(0.4)$
$= \$4200(0.4) = \$1680$

**c**  The accumulated depreciation at the end of year 3 is the sum

$DC(1) + DC(2) + BV(2)(0.4) = \$2800 + \$1680 + \$2520(0.4)$
$= \$4480 + \$1008 = \$5488$

**d**  $BV(3) = P - \text{accumulated depreciation} = \$7000 - \$5488 = \$1512$

A difficulty may arise with the use of declining-balance depreciation because the salvage value is not included in the calculation of depreciation charges. Continuing Example 11.4 to determine the book value at the end of year 5, we find

$$BV(5) = \$7000(0.6)^5 = \$544$$

which is well below the anticipated salvage value of $1000. However, it is not uncommon for the book value calculated by declining-balance depreciation to exceed the asset's value at the end of its life. This situation *always* occurs when S = 0.

# DEPRECIATION AND TAXES

Depreciation is treated for tax purposes as a deductible expense of doing business. The taxation rules governing the deductions are elaborate and complex. Only very general observations are included here.

## Depreciable Property

The property on which depreciation may be claimed must contribute to income produced in a trade or business and have a useful life of more than 1 year. Tangible property may be depreciated to the extent that it is subject to wear and tear, to decay or decline from natural causes, to exhaustion, and to obsolescence. Buildings may be depreciated; land may not.

Intangible assets with a limited period of usefulness can be depreciated. These include patents, copyrights, franchises, and trademarks. The burden of proving the value of the intangibles for tax purposes rests with the owner. Straight-line depreciation is the only method allowed for intangible property.

## Useful Life and Salvage Value

The useful life of an asset for depreciation purposes is not necessarily the economic life, but is the period over which the asset may reasonably be expected to be useful in the production of income. The useful life depends on an asset's use, age when acquired, repair policy, and other factors. It may be modified as a result of obsolescence and other causes, apart from physical wear and tear, that actually diminish the value of the property or shorten its life.

## Capital Cost Allowance (CCA)

The Canadian capital cost allowance system is considered to be rather unique. For both individuals and corporations, the only allowable tax deductible depreciation expense is the capital cost allowance (CCA). The CCA applies to classes of assets. Every asset must be included in an asset class and each class has a specified CCA rate. Usually, the CCA rate is applied by the declining balance method to the undepreciated capital cost (UCC) of the asset class. (The capital cost generally means the full cost to the taxpayer and includes legal, accounting, engineering and other costs of acquiring the property.)

Each asset class must be accounted for separately, as follows:

**Step 1** Start with the undepreciated capital cost (UCC) at the beginning of the year.

**Step 2** Subtract the proceeds from assets disposed of during the year. If these proceeds exceed the original capital cost of the asset, the excess is a capital gain, and only the capital cost of the item can be included here.

**Step 3** Add the total allowable cost of asset additions during the year. This is 50% of the actual cost, according to the November 12, 1981 budget, for assets acquired on November 13, 1981 and later. The other 50% is added next year.

**Step 4** Subtract any government assistance payments and/or Investment Tax Credits. This gives the UCC used in tax calculations for the taxation year.

**Step 5** The appropriate CCA rate is then applied to the UCC (from step 4) to calculate the Capital Cost Allowance for the taxation year. This CCA amount is the maximum that can be used on the tax return for depreciation. (Most Canadian firms use the straight line depreciation method for their annual and quarterly reports to shareholders.) The UCC is then reduced by the annual CCA amount to become the UCC at the beginning of the next taxation year.

**TABLE 11-3** provides some information about the CCA rates. It is important to check the Income Tax Regulations for the latest CCA rates, or even better to consult with a tax specialist.

**CAPITAL COST ALLOWANCE RATES**

*Class 3, CCA rate 5%* – buildings made of brick, cement or stone, including component parts.

*Class 6, CCA rate 10%* – other buildings.

*Class 7, CCA rate 15%* – ships, scows, etc., and their equipment.

*Class 8, CCA rate 20%* – machinery and equipment not included in any other class.

*Class 10, CCA rate 30%* – autos, trucks, etc.

Source: Revenue Canada, Taxation; *1981 T2 Corporation Income Tax Guide.*

Note that the CCA for a few types of assets is computed by the straight line method:

*Classes 13 and 14, CCA over the life of the asset* – Leasehold improvements; patents, franchises, licenses, etc.

*Classes 24 and 29, CCA rate 50%* – Water pollution control equipment; certain machinery used in the manufacture or processing of goods.

These straight line classes are also affected by the November 12, 1981 budget. For example, suppose a Class 29 asset was purchased for $10,000 in 1982. Under the new CCA rules, the firm may deduct $2,500 in 1982, $5,000 in 1984, and $2,500 in 1985.

## Review Exercises and Discussions

**Exercise 1** A tract of timber was purchased for $500,000. Cruise data placed a value of $420,000 on 4718 m³ of standing timber. Land value was appraised at $80,000. What is the income statement depletion allowance for the first year if 1036 m³ of timber are removed from the parcel? What is the depletion allowance for tax purposes?

**Solution 1**   The depletion allowance which appears on the income statement of a company's annual report is generally calculated according to the following formula:

$$\text{Depletion allowance} = \frac{\text{cost of property} \times \text{units sold during year}}{\text{total number of recoverable units}}$$

Deducting the value of the land from the total investment ($500,000 − $80,000 = $420,000) sets the property cost for the 4718 m³ of recoverable timber. When 1036 m³ are removed in one year,

$$\text{Depletion allowance (year 1)} = \frac{\$420,000 \times 1036 \text{ m}^3}{4718 \text{ m}^3} = \$92,226$$

For tax purposes, the depletion method is to apply an allowable depletion percentage to the book value of the property. The percentage is based on the type of exhaustible resource and is applicable to profits derived from the Canadian resource property. Percentage rates are subject to change, but in general the amount deducted cannot exceed 25 percent of the taxable income derived from the property. Since profits were not given, the depletion allowance for tax purposes can not be calculated.

---

**Exercise 2**   Compare the pattern of book values as a function of asset age resulting from the application of the straight-line and declining-balance depreciation methods to an asset that has a life of 6 years, initial cost of $22,000, and salvage value of $1000. Assume the asset is in Class 8 and was purchased before November 1981.

**Solution 2**   The annual charge by straight-line depreciation is ($22,000 − $1000)/6 = $3500, the amount by which the book value decreases each year.

By the declining-balance method the depreciation charge is 1/5 of the book value each year. In year 1 it is $22,000/5 = $4,400. By year 6 the book value would be BV(6) = $22,000(1 − 1/5)⁶ = $5767, which is well above the expected salvage value.

---

# PROBLEMS

**11.1**   What use can be made of general-accounting and cost-accounting records by an engineering economist? What precautions should be exercised in this usage?

**11.2**   Compare the features that are desirable in a depreciation method with the causes of declining value of an asset. What does this comparison suggest about the accounting concept of depreciation versus the considerations involved in an economic analysis?

The basic data in Table 11.4, about the In-Out Universal Corporation, are to be utilized in Problems 11.3 to 11.5 and Extension 11A. They show the condition of I-O-U on December 31 and the transactions that occurred during the prior 6 months.

| State of Accounts for In-Out Universal on December 31, 19xx | |
|---|---|
| *Account* | *Balance* |
| Accounts payable ....................... | $ 50,000 |
| Accounts receivable .................... | 80,000 |
| Accrued taxes ......................... | 20,000 |
| Buildings (net value) .................... | 205,000 |
| Cash on hand.......................... | 40,000 |
| Dividends payable ..................... | 20,000 |
| Equipment (net value).................... | 180,000 |
| Finished goods......................... | 30,000 |
| Land value ........................... | 115,000 |
| Long-term mortgages ................... | 390,000 |
| Material inventory ..................... | 40,000 |
| Notes payable ........................ | 60,000 |
| Shareholders' equity ................... | 150,000 |

| Transactions for In-Out Universal during the 6 Months prior to December 31, 19xx | |
|---|---|
| *Category* | *Amount* |
| Administration expenses ................ | $ 30,000 |
| Depreciation charged .................. | 30,000 |
| Direct labor costs .................... | 70,000 |
| Factory overhead charged .............. | 35,000 |
| Finished goods (July 1, 19xx) ........... | 75,000 |
| Interest payments .................... | 40,000 |
| Inventory, materials (July 1, 19xx) ......... | 15,000 |
| Materials purchased (July 1 to December 31) . | 115,000 |
| Sales: Cash .......................... | 200,000 |
| Credit ........................ | 200,000 |

**TABLE 11.4**

**11.3** Construct a balance sheet from the accounts given in Table 11.4. What are the dollar values of the terms in the basic accounting equation? *($690,000 − $540,000 = $150,000)*

**11.4** Prepare a cost-of-goods-sold schedule from the amounts given in Table 11.4. Include materials, labor, and factory overhead. What was the cost of goods sold in the period from July 1 to December 31? *($240,000)*

**11.5** Prepare an income statement for the 6-month period from the data in Table 11.4. What is the net profit if the accrued-taxes account represents the taxes owed for the period? *($40,000)*

**11.6** How does a court order requiring a company in financial difficulties to set up a sinking-fund protect the shareholders of the company?

**11.7** An asset cost $400 when purchased 4 years ago. A scrap value of $50 was expected at the end of its 7-year useful life. The asset is in Class 7. Determine the depreciation charge during the coming year and the asset's current book value by:

**11.7a** Straight-line depreciation               *[DC(5) = $50; BV(4) = $200]*
**11.7b** Declining-balance depreciation

**11.8**   A production machine with a first cost of $2000 is expected to last 4 years, when it will be worth $200. Tabulate the book value at the end of each year by the declining-balance method of depreciation, if the machine is in class 8.

**11.9**   An asset has an initial cost of $65,000 and an estimated salvage value of $5000 after 12 years.

**11.9a**   What depreciation rate for the declining-balance method would produce a book value at the end of year 12 that comes closest to equaling the estimated salvage value?
*(Maximum allowable = 0.1667)*

**11.9b**   What is the amount of accumulated depreciation after 5 years if straight-line depreciation is used?
*($25,000)*

**11.9c**   If the declining-balance depreciation rate is 10 percent, what would the book value be after 3 years?
*($47,385)*

**11.10**   An asset with a life of 7 years was purchased 4 years ago at a cost of $10,000. It now has a book value of $5,200 based on straight-line depreciation. What is its expected salvage value?

# EXTENSIONS

**11A   *Analysis of Financial Statements***   A sound financial position is the bedrock upon which successful enterprises are built. Accounting practices measure the financial conditions. Accounting statements are the reports of the measurement. Interpretation of the reported figures is the responsibility of the analyst. Engineering economists may become involved in financial-statement analyses through their professional responsibilities to evaluate dealings with other companies, such as a subcontractor's capacity to meet contractual commitments or a supplier's ability to continue follow-up services, and in personal investing to evaluate the operating performance of a company.

The relationship of accounts to the return on investment is broached in Figure 11.5. The left leg of the progression shows the accounts that comprise *total investment,* where *permanent investment* represents land, buildings, equipment, etc. *Sales* divided by total investment is the *turnover,* or number of times per year the capital is used. It suggests how hard the investment is being worked. This turnover times the earnings as a percent of sales gives the *return on investment.* For earnings on sales of 3 percent (determined by subtracting the value of sales from the cost of sales and then dividing this amount by total sales) and for a turnover of 4 times per year, the annual return on investment is 12 percent.

Certain figures from accounting records have been found to be good barometric readings of a firm's future performance. A half dozen of the more prominent ratios employed to analyze financial conditions are described below and are applied to the Democo data in Figures 11.1 and 11.3.

1   The *current ratio* gives an indication of a company's liquidity—its ability to meet current financial obligations. The current ratio applied to the balance-sheet data given in Figure 11.1 is

$$\text{Current ratio} = \frac{\text{current assets}}{\text{current liabilities}} = \frac{\$52,000}{\$49,000} = 1.06$$

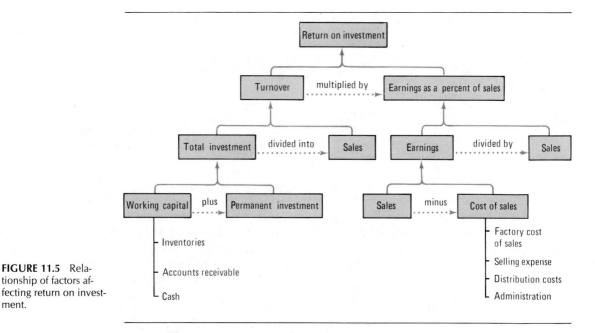

**FIGURE 11.5** Relationship of factors affecting return on investment.

which is below the level of 2:1 that is generally considered satisfactory. A lower ratio suggests the company may have a cash-flow problem in meeting current obligations.

2   The *acid-test ratio* is a more rigorous evaluation of liquidity made by subtracting inventories and other prepaid expenses from current assets to obtain *quick assets*—assets readily convertible into dollars. With a 1:1 ratio deemed reasonable, the firm represented in Figure 11.1 appears to have a fairly serious liquidity problem:

$$\text{Acid-test ratio} = \frac{\text{current assets} - \text{inventories}}{\text{current liabilities}}$$

$$= \frac{\$52,000 - \$37,600}{\$49,000} = 0.29$$

3   The *equity ratio* indicates the dependency of a company upon its creditors for working capital:

$$\text{Equity ratio} = \frac{\text{total equity}}{\text{total liabilities and equity}}$$

Based on the data from Figure 11.1 and assuming retained earnings are actually owned by the shareholders rather than the corporation,

$$\text{Equity ratio} = \frac{\$124,000}{\$188,000} = \frac{\$100,000 + \$24,000}{\$64,000 + \$124,000} = 0.66$$

which is below the generally preferred lower limit of 0.75.

4   The *operating ratio* shows the percentage of every dollar received from net sales which is needed to meet the cost of production and operations:

$$\text{Operating ratio} = \frac{\text{total expenses}}{\text{net sales}} = \frac{\$224,000}{\$247,500} = 0.905$$

A lower ratio is preferred by management for obvious reasons. The relatively high ratio for the firm represented in the income statement of Figure 11.3 suggests cost-reduction or sales-promotion efforts should be considered.

5   *Inventory turnover* is a ratio used to evaluate the passage of goods through a firm's operations:

$$\text{Inventory turnover ratio} = \frac{\text{net sales}}{\text{inventory}} = \frac{\$247,500}{\$37,600} = 6.6$$

where the total inventory given in the balance sheet is assumed to be the average level for the year. With typical turnover ratios of 5 to 10, the given firm appears to have a reasonable balance of inventory on hand. Desirable ratios vary widely for industries with different operating requirements.

6   A *net-profit ratio* compares the profit after taxes with sales, total assets, or shareholders' equity and is usually expressed as a percentage:

$$\text{Net-profit ratio} = \frac{\text{profit after taxes}}{\text{sales}} = \frac{\$16,000}{\$247,000} = 6.5\%$$

$$\text{or} \quad \frac{\text{profit after taxes}}{\text{total assets}} = \frac{\$16,000}{\$188,000} = 8.5\%$$

$$\text{or} \quad \frac{\text{profit after taxes}}{\text{shareholders' equity}} = \frac{\$16,000}{\$124,000} = 12.9\%$$

With sales in the denominator, the ratio indicates the volume of business needed to earn a certain profit. When the denominator is total assets or equity, the ratio is indicative of the return on investment. The sample company appears to be providing adequate but not handsome returns.

Financial ratios are much more meaningful when they are compared with industrial averages and past ratios. Industrial averages are published by several sources to indicate norms for specific industries. A graph that plots changes in ratios with respect to time is an indicator of management effectiveness, especially when compared with an equivalent graph of industry norms. However, the ratios offer only general guidelines. A deeper investigation is needed if it is important to fully understand a company's operations. For instance, a major research effort could absorb funds that would otherwise be displayed as profit. The resulting low net-profit ratio would make the firm appear weak, while in reality it might have developed a strong position for future profits. *

*For a deeper discussion of financial ratios, see Eugene F. Brigham, Alfred L. Kahl, and William F. Rentz, *Canadian Financial Management: Theory and Practice*, Holt, Rinehart and Winston of Canada, Toronto, 1983.

### Income Statement
### Year Ended December 31, 19xx

| | Salt Co. | Pepper Co. |
|---|---|---|
| Net sales .................... | $220,000 | $126,800 |
| Cost of goods sold ........... | 108,000 | 55,000 |
| Gross profit on sales ....... | $112,000 | $ 71,800 |
| *Operating expenses* | | |
| Maintenance and repairs ..... | $ 6,000 | $ 4,000 |
| Depreciation ............... | 15,200 | 12,000 |
| Bad-debt expense ........... | 3,600 | 3,200 |
| Selling expense ............. | 37,000 | 32,000 |
| Administrative and general ... | 12,600 | 11,000 |
| Total operating expense .... | $74,000 | $62,200 |
| Net operating profit.......... | $37,600 | $9,600 |
| Other income............... | 3,000 | 1,600 |
| Other expense .............. | 17,000 | 8,000 |
| Net income .............. | $23,600 | $3,200 |

**FIGURE 11.6** Income statements for Salt and Pepper Companies.

### Balance Sheet
### December 31, 19xx

| | Salt Co. | Pepper Co. |
|---|---|---|
| *Current assets* | | |
| Cash .......................... | $ 60,000 | $ 30,000 |
| Marketable securities .............. | 12,000 | 16,000 |
| Accounts receivable ............... | 19,000 | 25,400 |
| Inventories ....................... | 80,000 | 48,000 |
| Total current assets .............. | $171,000 | $119,400 |
| *Fixed assets* | | |
| Investments....................... | $ 32,000 | $ 40,000 |
| Land, buildings, equipment (net) ..... | 346,000 | 251,200 |
| Total fixed assets ................ | $378,000 | $291,200 |
| *Prepaid expenses* ................... | 10,400 | 3,000 |
| *Total assets* ....................... | $559,400 | $413,600 |
| *Current liabilities* | | |
| Notes payable .................... | $ 7,000 | $16,000 |
| Accounts payable ................. | 32,000 | 31,200 |
| Other current liabilities ............. | 58,000 | 48,000 |
| Total current liabilities ........... | $97,000 | $95,200 |
| *Fixed liabilities* | | |
| Mortgage payable (due in 10 years) ... | $111,600 | $180,000 |
| *Total liabilities* .................... | $208,600 | $275,200 |
| *Net worth* | | |
| Preferred stock (6% cumulative) ...... | $ 84,000 | $ 40,000 |
| Common stock..................... | 120,000 | 68,000 |
| Appropiated surplus ............... | 48,000 | 21,600 |
| Unappropriated surplus ............ | 98,800 | 8,800 |
| Total net worth .................. | $350,800 | $138,400 |
| *Total liabilities and net worth* ........ | $559,400 | $413,600 |

**FIGURE 11.7** Balance sheets for Salt and Pepper Companies.

## QUESTIONS

**11A.1** Balance sheets and income statements for two companies engaged in similar operations are presented in Figures 11.6 and 11.7. Compare the two companies as potential investments, or with respect to their financial health as potential suppliers to your company. Discuss the meaning of each ratio in terms of managerial effectiveness and the financial positions of the companies.

**11A.2** Utilize the basic data in Table 11.4 to determine the values of the ratios listed below for the In-Out Universal Corporation. Industry norms are also listed. Compare the calculated ratios to the industry norms in appraising the economic health of I-O-U. Assume the income-statement values are doubled for a full year's operation, and that 10 workers are employed.

| Ratio | Industry Norms | I-O-U |
|---|---|---|
| Current | 2.0 | |
| Acid test | 1.0 | |
| Equity | 0.8 | |
| Net profit/equity | 15% | |
| Net profit/worker | $2000 | |
| Accounts-receivable turnover: $\dfrac{\text{credit sales}}{\text{average accounts receivable}}$ | 8.0 | |

**11B  Accelerated Cost Recovery System (ACRS)**  Some Canadian engineering economists work for subsidiaries of U.S. Firms and must justify investment proposals to headquarters according to criteria specified by top management. ACRS is the U.S. equivalent of CCA.

This new system went into effect in 1982. It places assets into five classes as follows: Three-year property includes autos, trucks, R & D equipment, and special tools (approximately equivalent to our Class 10). Five-year property includes all other items of machinery and equipment (approximately equivalent to our Class 8). Ten-year property includes most public utility properties and theme parks (approximately equivalent to our Class 6). Fifteen-year utility property includes all other public utility properties. Fifteen-year real property includes all other depreciable real property used in a business. (These are approximately equivalent to our Class 3.)

Each class has a preset table of allowable annual depreciation deductions which are based on a percentage of the asset's first cost. The specific rates, however, are not always the same for each year as is the case in Canada. Table 11.5 indicates the ACRS rates for the five classes of assets.

The ACRS system allows a firm to choose an optional straight line method of depreciation. Three-year property may be depreciated over 3, 5, or 12 years. Five-year property may be depreciated over 5, 12, or 25 years. Ten-year property may be depreciated over 10, 25, or 35 years. Fifteen-year property may be depreciated over 15, 35, or 45 years. If a firm chooses this optional straight line depreciation method, only half (as in Canada) of the normal depreciation can be taken in the year of acquisition, regardless of when the asset was actually acquired. If, for example, a firm purchases a new machine in 1982 for $10,000, it can deduct only $1,000 for 1982. The deductions for 1983, 1984, 1985, and 1986 are $2,000 each. The

ACCELERATED COST RECOVERY SYSTEM TABLES BY PROPERTY CLASS

| Taxable year | 3-year | 5-year | 10-year | *Property class* 15-year utility property | 15-year real property* |
|---|---|---|---|---|---|
| 1 | 25% | 15% | 8% | 5% | 12% |
| 2 | 38 | 22 | 14 | 10 | 10 |
| 3 | 37 | 21 | 12 | 9 | 9 |
| 4 | | 21 | 10 | 8 | 8 |
| 5 | | 21 | 10 | 7 | 7 |
| 6 | | | 10 | 7 | 6 |
| 7 | | | 9 | 6 | 6 |
| 8 | | | 9 | 6 | 6 |
| 9 | | | 9 | 6 | 6 |
| 10 | | | 9 | 6 | 5 |
| 11 | | | | 6 | 5 |
| 12 | | | | 6 | 5 |
| 13 | | | | 6 | 5 |
| 14 | | | | 6 | 5 |
| 15 | | | | 6 | 5 |

*For real property, depreciation in the year of purchase must be computed according to the number of months the property is actually owned. The table above assumes a purchase in January (or the first month of a company's fiscal year). Other tables are available and should be referred to if a piece of real property is acquired in other than the first month of the year.

**TABLE 11.5**

remaining $1,000 is deducted in 1987. Thus, a five-year asset depreciated on a straight line basis is actually written-off in *six* years. (In Canada, under the November 1981 federal budget CCA rules, an asset in Class 13 or 14 with a five-year life would be treated the same way).

American companies may use ACRS, straight-line, double-declining balance, or sum-of-the-years digits methods of depreciation for financial statement purposes, but only ACRS can be used for tax purposes. Hence only ACRS is relevant for engineering economy studies.

# CHAPTER 12

# INCOME TAX CONSIDERATIONS

OVERVIEW

Taxes are a major factor in any profit-seeking venture. *Property, sales, excise,* and/or *income taxes* affect net returns for both individuals and corporations. Types and amounts of taxes vary as governments pursue their *fiscal policies.* In the past few years, *surcharges* and *investment tax credits* have been enacted, rescinded, and reinstated. Other features change too, such as provisions for *capital gains and losses,* options to *carry amounts forward* and *backward,* and capital cost allowance (CCA).

An *effective income tax rate* that represents total corporate tax liability can be developed for after-tax economic evaluations. Special tax provisions and charges for depreciation and/or interest are applied to the before-tax cash flow to determine *taxable income.* Then the taxable income is multiplied by the effective tax rate, and the resulting product is subtracted from the before-tax cash flow to obtain the *after-tax cash flow* for the year. A tabular format is convenient for these calculations and provides information equivalent to a cash-flow diagram. Once the after-tax data are tabulated, economic comparisons are conducted as described in previous chapters.

An after-tax analysis defines the *actual* cash flow expected from a proposal. It may reveal the tax advantages of one proposal over another — advantages which are not part of a before-tax comparison. For instance, one proposal might qualify for an investment tax credit, which would increase its attractiveness over a comparable alternative that does not qualify for the tax deduction. However, comparisons that include tax effects are more complicated because tax laws are very complex. Precise tax considerations require expert assistance, but attention to basic tax provisions provides an adequate evaluation for most situations in the province of engineering economics.

Benjamin Franklin once observed that "in this world nothing is certain but death and taxes." He might have added that attention to both increases your chances of survival and prosperity.

# TAX CONCEPTS

Everyone has an opinion about taxes. Some of the more famous ones include

The art of taxation consists in so plucking the goose as to obtain the largest possible amount of feathers with the smallest possible amount of hissing *(attributed to Jean Baptiste Colbert, 1665)*.

To tax and to please, no more than to love and be wise, is not given to men *(Edmund Burke in a speech, "On American Taxation," in 1774)*.

When I catch myself resenting not being immortal, I pull myself up short by asking whether I should really like the prospect of having to make out an annual income tax return for an infinite number of years ahead *(Arnold J. Toynbee, in Saturday Review, 1969)*.

Corporate income taxes are featured in this chapter. They are a significant factor in the cash flow of any investment proposal. All the analyses in previous chapters were made on a before-tax basis. In most cases before-and after-tax analyses indicate the same order of preference among competing alternatives because the alternatives usually have similar characteristics. However, when some proposals are subject to special tax treatment and others are not, the order of preference can switch abruptly in an after-tax comparison. Also, the after-tax analysis reveals the actual cash flow that results from a proposal.

Tax laws are extremely intricate and subject to frequent changes. Consequently, the intent in this chapter is to present basic tax concepts, not the details of how to calculate the specific amount of taxes due.

## Types of Taxes

Federal, provincial and sometimes city or county taxes are imposed on income, property, and/or transactions. The transfer of wealth through the taxing mechanism is a major concern of governments, and the payment of those taxes is a major concern of income producers, both corporate and individual. The principal types and their relevance to engineering economic studies are described below.

1  *Property taxes* are charged by local governments on land, buildings, machinery and equipment, inventory, etc. The amount of the tax is a function of the appraised value of the assets and the tax rate. Property taxes are usually not a significant factor in an engineering economics study because of their small magnitude compared to income taxes and their similar effect on competing proposals.

2   *Excise taxes,* imposed on the production of certain products such as tobacco and alcohol, rarely affect economic comparisons. Other taxes that are not normally relevant, but may become so in specific situations, are *sales tax* on retail products, *user's tax, value-added tax, unemployment tax,* and *social insurance contributions.*

3   *Income taxes* are levied on personal and corporate income at increasingly higher rates for higher incomes. They are based on net income after deductions allowed for permissible "expenses." The tax effects of different types of expenses on the cash flow of proposals have significant influence on their acceptability. The rest of this chapter is devoted to the examination of income-tax effects.

## Changing Taxes

The federal government controls the monetary and fiscal policy of the nation to influence the level of economic activity. *Monetary policy* influences the availability and cost of credit, and *fiscal policy* deals with government receipts and expenditures. Taxation is the key instrument in fiscal policy. The principal methods for altering government receipts are (1) changing the tax rate, (2) changing the depreciation requirements, and (3) allowing tax credits.

Tax rates imposed on incomes may be raised to dampen the level of economic activity when rapid expansion threatens inflationary consequences. In theory, the reduction in disposable incomes reduces the purchasing power of individuals and thereby decreases demand for goods and services. An associated reduction in after-tax profits by corporations reduces the funds available for new investments and discourages expansion. The reverse, a tax-rate cut, theoretically encourages purchasing and expansion when the fiscal policy attempts to stimulate a depressed economy characterized by high unemployment.

There are changes in tax laws almost every year. Some alter the basic structure. More often the tax rates are changed in response to current fiscal needs.

Engineering economic studies would ideally be based on the tax rates in effect during the lives of the assets being evaluated, but this is an unrealistic expectation. So current or "typical" rates are utilized. The rates utilized in this chapter are representative but not necessarily currently correct.

## CORPORATE INCOME TAXES

Income taxes are due from corporations whenever revenue exceeds allowable tax deductions. Revenue includes sales to customers of goods and services, interest from loans and securities, rents, royalties, and other gains from ownership of capital or property. Deductions embrace a wide range of expenses incurred in the production of revenue: wages, salaries, rents, repairs, interest, taxes, materials, employee benefits, advertising, etc. Also deductible, sometimes under special provisions, are losses from fire and theft, contributions, CCA and depletion, bond interest, research and development expenditures, outlays to satisfy legislated objectives such as pollution control, etc. The difference between the revenue and deductions is taxable income. In general,

*Taxable income = gross income − expenses − interest on debt − capital cost allowance*

and

*Corporate income tax = taxable income × effective tax rate*

## Effective Income Taxes

The corporate tax structure is basically simple, although the tax return form (T2) is not. Corporations were required to pay 37.8% of taxable income to the federal government in 1981. This was determined by deducting the 10% abatement for provincial taxes from the basic federal corporate tax rate of 46% and then adding the "temporary" 5% surtax. (The surtax was originally introduced for the 1980 and 1981 taxation years but has been extended for 1982. It is supposed to decline to 2.5% for the 1983 taxation year.) Thus, the 37.8% is calculated as follows: (46% − 10%)(1 + .05) = 36% (1.05) = 37.8%.

For example, if a corporation had $1,000,000 of taxable income, its federal tax would be: $1,000,000 (.378) = $378,000.

Provincial taxes must also be paid; in Ontario the 1981 rate was 14% and the provincial tax would be:
$1,000,000 (.14) = $140,000.

The total corporate income tax due would be the sum of $378,000 and $140,000, or $518,000. It can be calculated directly as:
$1,000,000 (.518) = $518,000.

Provincial corporate tax rates vary from 0 to 16% and are subject to change by provincial parliaments at any time. See Table 12-1.

**TABLE 12-1   1982 corporate income tax rates.**

| *Province* | *Rates* | |
| --- | --- | --- |
| | *Standard* | *Small Business* |
| Alberta | 11% | 5% |
| British Columbia | 16% | 8% |
| Manitoba | 15% | 10% |
| New Brunswick | 14% | 9% |
| Newfoundland | 16% | 12% |
| Nova Scotia | 15% | 10% |
| Ontario | 14% | Nil |
| Prince Edward Island | 10% | 10% |
| Quebec | 13% | 3% |
| Saskatchewan | 14% | 10% |
| Northwest Territories | 10% | 10% |
| Yukon | 10% | 10% |

Source: Carswell Methuen, *Canadian Tax News*, Volume 10, June 1982.

Except for the provinces of Alberta, Ontario and Quebec, which administer their own corporate income tax systems, the federal government collects the provincial corporate income taxes for the provinces along with the federal taxes.

Within six months after the end of the taxation year, corporation income tax returns must be filed in duplicate, along with financial statements and supporting schedules. For example, if the fiscal year of the corporation ends on December 31, the return must be filed not later than the following June 30.

## Types of Corporations

All corporations are classified as Canadian Controlled Private, Other Private, Public, or Other Corporations for tax purposes. A Canadian Controlled Private Corporation is incorporated or resident in Canada and not controlled by one or more public corporations and/or non-resident persons. Other Private Corporations are resident in Canada but are not public corporations or controlled by a public corporation. Public corporations are resident corporations whose shares are listed on a prescribed Canadian stock exchange or are considered by the Minister of National Revenue to be public corporations. Other corporations are those which do not fall into one of the other three categories. Special provisions apply to corporations which qualify for inclusion in each category.

## Active Business Income

Active business income is income generated by exploration, mining, processing, manufacturing, construction, farming, fishing, wholesaling, retailing, transportation, etc. Thus, it is distinguished from passive investment income from property (such as interest or dividends), income from a non-qualifying business, or income from a personal services business. (For more precise information consult a tax specialist.)

## Interest and Dividend Income Received by a Corporation

Interest income received by a corporation is normally taxed at regular corporate tax rates as ordinary income. However, dividends received by one Canadian public corporation from another are *excluded* from taxable income. Canadian private corporations pay a special tax on dividend income; this tax may be refundable to the corporation if certain conditions are met. Dividends from outside Canada are fully taxable.

## Interest and Dividends Paid by a Corporation

The interest paid by a corporation is deducted from its gross income to obtain taxable income, but dividends are not deductible. Thus, interest is paid with before-tax dollars, while dividends are paid with after-tax dollars.

## Manufacturing and Processing Profits Deduction

There is a manufacturing and processing profits deduction for all active Canadian corporations. It is usually 6% of the manufacturing and processing profits, but is only 5% for firms which qualify for the small business deduction. The term "manufacturing and processing" is not defined in the Income Tax Act but farming, fishing, logging and certain resource activities are *not* included. (For more information, consult Revenue Canada Interpretation Bulletin IT-145R.)

## Small Business Deduction

A small business deduction is available to corporations that were Canadian Controlled Private Corporations throughout an entire taxation year. The small business deduction applies only to the first $200,000 of annual taxable income. This deduction reduces the basic 46% federal tax rate by 21% for income earned from an active business carried on in Canada.

The tax liability for a small active business is calculated as follows: The basic federal 46% rate is reduced by both the 21% small business deduction and the 10% federal tax abatement. This gives a net federal rate of 15%. the provincial tax then must be added. In Manitoba the corporate income tax rate is 10%. Thus, for a Manitoba corporation, the total small business income tax rate would be 46% − 21% − 10% + 10% = 25%. (Businesses which qualify for the Small Business Deduction are exempt from the surtax in 1982 and later taxation years.)

## Investment Tax Credit

The Investment Tax Credit (ITC) is designed to stimulate business investment in certain areas of the country. Parliament varies the ITC depending on current economic conditions. (The federal budget of November 16, 1978 scheduled the ITC to expire on June 30, 1980, but this date has been extended.) So by the time you read this, the ITC may no longer exist, but it could be resurrected some time in the future.

The ITC has been used to allow an immediate tax deduction of a small percentage of the acquisition cost of certain types of assets in the year of acquisition. The rate varies from 7% to 20% depending on the location of the investment. The credit earned in any year must be used to reduce the CCA and UCC amounts. (For the latest ITC information, consult a tax specialist or Revenue Canada.)

For example, if a company invests $100,000 in some assets which qualify for the 10% ITC, a $10,000 credit against taxable income is permitted for that taxation year when the income tax return is filed.

## Incentives

A variety of tax incentives is available from the federal and provincial governments to firms which can qualify. There are approximately 300 incentive programs. These programs are in almost constant state of flux as new ones are created and old ones modified or cancelled. The programs of primary interest to engineers are those for research and development, exports, or special (metric) machinery. Some of the federal programs are briefly mentioned here.*

The Industrial Research Assistance Program (IRAP) encourages applied research in Canada. It will pay the salaries of people working on research projects, for example, up to a maximum of $30,000.

The special Industry and Labour Adjustment Program (ILAP) will help business in specific communities where employment is seriously threatened. Repayable grants are provided by ILAP for developing new projects or for buying new machinery.

The Machinery Program (MACH) will excuse payment of duty over $500 on specific kinds of imported machinery not manufactured in Canada.

The New Technology Employment Program (NTEP) provides wage subsidies to create new jobs in certain fields such as microelectronics. NTEP pays 75% of wages for up to 12 months.

The Program for Export Market Development (PEMD) helps to cover the costs of developing new export markets for Canadian suppliers of goods and services. For example, if a Canadian engineering firm wants to bid on a major international construction project, PEMD will pay $34,000 of the personnel, transportation and consulting, as well as legal and translation costs. PEMD will also pay $25,000 for the preparation of a market penetration plan for a manufacturing firm.

The Program for Industry/Laboratory Projects (PILP) is intended to transform R&D into commercial opportunities. PILP recently funded Lovat Engineering's development of a rock boring and tunneling machine.

## Capital Gains and Losses

The calculation of capital gains and losses is very complex because so many special provisions are involved. The tax rate assigned to capital gains is usually less than that for ordinary income. This preferential rate is allowed in recognition of the risk involved in holding capital assets over a prolonged period of time. The rules are intricate, and our discussion is limited to an overview.

Everything owned is a capital asset *except* property held primarily for sale to customers, including accounts or notes receivable acquired in the course of normal business.

A *gain* is the excess amount realized from the sale of property over its adjusted base (original cost plus or minus certain additions and deductions). A *loss* occurs when the adjusted base exceeds the selling price.

## Corporate Loss Carryback and Carryforward

Corporate non-capital losses can be carried back to the previous year and/or forward to the following five years. Net capital losses, however, can be carried forward until fully applied against capital gains. For example, a net capital loss in 1981 can be used to reduce taxable income from capital gains realized in 1980, and then any remaining losses can be carried forward.

*For more information consult: J. Peter Johnson, *Government Financial Assistance Programs in Canada*, 2nd ed., Butterworths, Toronto, 1982.

# AFTER-TAX ECONOMIC COMPARISONS

All the economic analyses in previous chapters were based on before-tax cash flows. In many situations, before-tax analyses provide adequate solutions. When the alternatives being compared are to satisfy a required function and are affected identically by taxes, the before-tax comparison yields the proper preference. Evaluations of public projects rarely include tax effects and are conducted as before-tax analyses.

Tax effects occasionally cause the preference to switch among alternatives between before- and after-tax evaluations. The principal causes are differences in CCA and special tax regulations such as applicable investment credits. Often, the net return after taxes (the amount actually available) is the main concern. Throughout this chapter, except for Review Exercise 5, we assume that an asset class is never terminated, since this is the normal situation for the on-going concern.*

A simple adjustment of the rate of return calculated without regard for taxes gives a reasonable approximation to the after-tax internal rate of return:

$$IRR_{after-tax} \doteq IRR_{before-tax}(1 - \text{effective income-tax rate})$$

Thus, the after-tax rate of return resulting from a before-tax IRR of 15 percent and an effective income-tax rate of 40 percent would be

$$IRR_{after-tax} \doteq 15\%(1 - 0.4) \doteq 9\%$$

## After-Tax Cash Flow

A tabular approach is convenient for modifying the before-tax cash flow to show the effects of taxes. It is normally sufficient to assume tax payments occur at the end of each period, just as the other cash flows are assumed to occur collectively at the year's end. The number of entries in the table depends on the number of tax considerations involved. The most common are CCA and interest deductions. Table headings based on these tax effects are shown below.

| End of Year (1) | Before-Tax Cash Flow (2) | CCA (3) | Interest on Loan (4) | Taxable Income [(2) − (3) − (4)] (5) | Taxes [(5) x tax rate] (6) | After-Tax Cash Flow [(2) − (6)] (7) |
|---|---|---|---|---|---|---|

## After-Tax Comparison of Proposals

An after-tax evaluation can be made using any of the comparison methods: EAW, PW or IRR. All the precautions discussed for before-tax comparisons are applicable to after-tax analyses. Once the tax effects on cash flows have been determined, the computational procedures and interpretation of results are the same.

---

*For more information on terminating an asset class, see Sidney Davidson, C.L. Mitchell, Clyde P. Stickney, and Roman L. Weil, *Intermediate Accounting*, First Canadian Edition, pp. 443-444, Holt, Rinehart and Winston of Canada, Toronto, 1982.

## Example 12.1    After-Tax Evaluation of a Depreciable Asset

The budget includes $45,000 for the purchase in early 1981 of a new testing machine requested by the maintenance department. All the major investments in the budget are being checked to see if they meet the new required rate of return that has been raised to 12 percent *after taxes*.

The testing machine will have a useful life of 5 years with no salvage value. During the 5 years, it is estimated to save $23,000 per year in maintenance costs while annual operating costs are $7300. The machine is in Class 8 (20% CCA rate). The firm has an effective income-tax rate of 42 percent. Does the proposal to buy the testing machine satisfy the firm's new minimum acceptable rate of return?

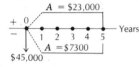

### Solution 12.1

A quick check by the after-tax IRR approximation can be made to see if the proposal is promising. Based on the cash-flow diagram, where savings are considered to be income.

$$PW = -\$45,000 + (\$23,000 - \$7300)(P/A, i, 5) \overset{?}{=} 0$$

At $i$ = 22 percent,

$$PW = -\$45,000 + \$15,700(2.8701) = \$61$$

Using 22 percent as the before-tax rate of return,

$$IRR_{after\text{-}tax} \doteq 22\%(1 - 0.42) \doteq 12.8\%$$

which is just above the required minimum.

The PW of CCA tax shields (deductions) for $1 invested before Friday, November 13, 1981 is

$$
\begin{pmatrix} PW\ of \\ CCA\ tax \\ shields \end{pmatrix} = \begin{pmatrix} PW\ of \\ Year\ 1 \\ shields \end{pmatrix} + \begin{pmatrix} PW\ of \\ Year\ 2 \\ shields \end{pmatrix} + \ldots + \begin{pmatrix} PW\ of \\ Year\ N \\ shields \end{pmatrix} + \ldots
$$

$$
= td \left[ \frac{1}{(1 + i)} + \frac{(1 - d)}{(1 + i)^2} + \ldots + \frac{(1 - d)^{N-1}}{(1 + i)^N} + \ldots \right]
$$

$$
= \frac{td}{(i + d)}
$$

where $t$ = tax rate,

$d$ = CCA rate, and

$i$ = discount rate.

Subtracting the PW of CCA tax shields from the $1 first cost, gives the capital cost tax factor* (CCTF)

$$\text{CCTF} = 1 - td/(i + d)$$

The after-tax PW for this example is

$$\text{PW}_{\text{after-tax}} = (-\$45,000)(\text{CCTF}) + (1 - t)(\$23,000 - \$7,300)(P/A, i, 5)$$

$$= (-\$45,000)[1 - (.42)(.20)/(.12 + .20)] + (1 - .42)(\$15,700)(3.6047)$$

$$= -\$363$$

Thus, the proposal does *not* meet the after-tax minimum acceptable rate of return (MARR) even though the after-tax IRR approximation exceeded it.

To find the actual after-tax internal rate of return for this project, try 11%

$$\text{PW}_{\text{after-tax}} = -(\$45,000) \left\{ 1 - \left[ \frac{(.42)(.20)}{(.11 + .20)} \right] \right\} + (1 - .42)(\$15,700)(3.6958) = \$848$$

Interpolating yields

$$\text{IRR}_{\text{after-tax}} = 11\% + 1\% \left( \frac{\$848}{\$848 + \$363} \right) = 11.7\%$$

## Example 12.2    Depreciable Assets Bought After November 1981

Suppose the data of Example 12.1 are relevant but the testing machine is purchased after November 12, 1981.

### Solution 12.2

If the asset were purchased after November 12, 1981, only one half of the first cost may be added to the undepreciated capital cost (UCC) in the year of acquisition. The other half is added in the following year. The PW of CCA tax shields per dollar invested is now one half of its PW under the previous CCA system plus the other half of its former PW discounted for one year.

$$\begin{array}{l} \text{PW of} \\ \text{CCA tax} \\ \text{shields} \end{array} = 1/2 \left[ \frac{td}{(i + d)} \right] + 1/2 \left[ \frac{1}{(1 + i)} \right] \left[ \frac{td}{(i + d)} \right]$$

$$= \left[ \frac{td}{(i + d)} \right] \left[ \frac{(1 + \frac{1}{2}i)}{(1 + i)} \right]$$

The CCTF now is

$$\text{CCTF} = 1 - \left[ \frac{td}{(i + d)} \right] \left[ \frac{(1 + \frac{1}{2}i)}{(1 + i)} \right]$$

Under the new CCA system, the after-tax PW for our example is

*For a more detailed explanation, see C. Geoffrey Edge and V. Bruce Irvine, *A Practical Approach to the Appraisal of Capital Expenditures*, Second Edition, Hamilton, (Ont.) The Society of Management Accountants of Canada, 1981.

$$PW_{\text{after-tax}} = (-\$45,000) \left\{ 1 - \left[ \frac{(.42)(.20)}{.12 + .20} \right] \left[ \frac{1 + \frac{1}{2}(.12)}{1 + .12} \right] \right\} + (1 - .42)(\$15,700)(3.6047) = -\$996$$

Thus, the effect of the new CCA system is to reduce the after-tax PW of an investment because it reduces the PW of the CCA tax shields.

### Example 12.3   After-Tax Evaluation when an Asset has a Salvage Value

Further investigation of Example 12.1 reveals that the testing machine will have a salvage value of $5,000 at the end of its useful life.

### Solution 12.3

The PW of the salvage value and the PW of the CCA tax shields lost due to salvage value must now be included in calculating the after-tax PW of the testing machine. This is done by adding the product of the single payment PW factor (*P/F*, *i*, *N*), the salvage value, and the CCTF. The PW of the asset becomes

$$\text{New PW} = \text{Old PW} + (P/F, i, N)(\text{Salvage Value})(\text{CCTF})$$

$$= -\$363 + (P/F, .12, 5)(\$5,000)[1 - td/(i + d)]$$

$$= -\$363 + (.56743)(\$5,000)[1 - (.42)(.2)/(.12 + .2)]$$

$$= -\$363 + \$2,092 = \$1,729$$

### Example 12.4   Salvage Value for Assets Acquired after November 1981

Assume the testing machine is purchased after November 12, 1981.

### Solution 12.4

The CCTF used to calculate the after-tax PW of the salvage value and the PW of the tax shields lost is *not* affected by the purchase date of the asset. The purchase date affects the New PW of the asset solely by its effect on the Old PW.

$$\text{New PW} = -\$996 + \$2,092 = \$1,096$$

## After-Tax Replacement Study

Before- and after-tax replacement evaluations are conducted in the same way once the tax effects have been imposed on the cash-flow patterns. There are, however, a couple of points that occasionally cause confusion. One is the use of the undepreciated capital cost (UCC) as the worth of the presently owned asset in a replacement study.

The UCC is the asset's purchase price less its accumulated CCA. This value is the result of Canadian law and is unlikely to be the same as the asset's value in an open market.

### Example 12.5   After-Tax Comparison of a Defender and a Challenger when Revenue is Unknown

A machine has UCC of $10,000 at the beginning of 1983 and 5 years remaining on its orginally estimated useful life. Its operating costs are $19,000 per year. The function performed by the machine will be needed for five more years, at which time it will have a salvage value of $1,000.

A new machine of advanced design can perform the same function as the existing machine for $12,000 per year. This machine is priced at $24,000 and will have a salvage value of $6000 when disposed of at the end of the 5-year use period. Because of the technological advances the old machine can be sold now for only $8000.

The company has a 52 percent effective tax rate. It requires an after-tax rate of return of 20 percent. Both machines are in Class 8. Should the old machine be replaced?

### Solution 12.5

The defender's capital cost for the replacement study is its current salvage (market) value, $8000, and this amount is considered to be an outlay at time zero. As noted in Example 12.4, the CCTF applied to a salvage value does *not* depend on the purchase date.

Since the new machine is purchased after November 12, 1981, only one half of the first cost of the new machine may be added to the undepreciated capital cost (UCC) in the year of acquisition. The other half is added in the next year.

The incremental after-tax PW of replacing the old machine is given by

$$
\begin{aligned}
\text{Incremental PW}_{\text{after-tax}} = \ &-(\text{First Cost}_{\text{new machine}})(\text{CCTF}_{\text{new rule}}) \\
&+ (\text{Current Salvage Value}_{\text{old machine}})(\text{CCTF}_{\text{old rule}}) \\
&+ (1 - t)(\text{Before-tax Operating Savings})(P/A, i, N) \\
&+ (P/F, i, N)(\text{Incremental Salvage Value})(\text{CCTF}_{\text{old rule}})
\end{aligned}
$$

$$
\begin{aligned}
= \ &-(\$24,000)\{1 - [td/(i + d)][(1 + (\tfrac{1}{2}) i)/(1 + i)]\} \\
&+ (\$8,000)[1 - td/(i + d)] \\
&+ (1 - .52)(\$19,000 - \$12,000)(P/A, .2, 5) \\
&+ (P/F, .2, 5)(\$6,000 - \$1,000)[1 - td/(i + d)]
\end{aligned}
$$

$$
\begin{aligned}
= \ &-(\$24,000)\{1 - [(.52)(.2)/(.2 + .2)][(1 + .1)/(1 + .2)]\} \\
&+ (\$8,000)[1 - (.52)(.2)/(.2 + .2)] \\
&+ (.48)(\$7,000)(2.9906) \\
&+ (.40188)(\$5,000)[1 - (.52)(.2)/(.2 + .2)]
\end{aligned}
$$

$$
= -\$825
$$

Thus, the correct decision is *not* to replace the machine.

Alternatively, the EAC of the defender and the challenger can be compared.

$$
\begin{aligned}
\text{EAC}_{\text{after-tax}} (\text{defender}) = \ &[(\$8,000) - (P/F, i, N)(\$1,000)](\text{CCTF}_{\text{old rule}})(A/P, i, N) \\
&+ (1 - .52)(\$19,000)
\end{aligned}
$$

$$
= [(\$8,000) - (.40188)(\$1,000)](.74)(.33438) + \$9,120
$$

$$
= \$11,000
$$

$$\text{EAC}_{\text{after-tax}}(\text{challenger}) = [(\$24,000)(\text{CCTF}_{\text{new rule}})$$
$$- (P/F, i, N)(\$6,000)(\text{CCTF}_{\text{old rule}})](A/P, i, N)$$
$$+ (1 - .52)(\$12,000)$$

$$= [(\$24,000)(.76166) - (.40188)(\$6,000)(.74)](.33438) + \$5,760$$

$$= \$11,276$$

Since the new machine has the higher equivalent annual cost, the old machine should *not* be replaced.

The two methods of analyzing the replacement decision are equivalent methods.

$$\text{Incremental PW}_{\text{after-tax}} = [\text{EAC}_{\text{after-tax}}(\text{defender}) - \text{EAC}_{\text{after-tax}}(\text{challenger})] (P/A, i, N)$$

$$= [\$11,000 - \$11,276](2.9906)$$

$$= -\$825$$

---

### Example 12.6   Investment Tax Credit (ITC)

The replacement question from Example 12.5 has been reopened. Further investigation reveals that the new machine is eligible for a 10% investment tax credit (ITC). Should the old machine be replaced?

### Solution 12.6

The eligible first cost for CCA purposes is reduced by the ITC. The ITC is a *reduction in taxes* equal to the product of the ITC rate $T$ and the new machine's first cost, provided it does not exceed the allowable limit (currently $15,000). This credit is received at the *end* of year 1. Thus, neither the new rule or the old rule CCTF can be applied to the first cost of the new machine.

The incremental after-tax PW of replacing the old machine becomes

$$\text{Incremental PW}_{\text{after-tax}} = -(\text{First Cost}_{\text{new machine}})$$
$$+ (P/F, i, 1)(T)(\text{First Cost}_{\text{new machine}})$$
$$+ (\text{First Cost}_{\text{new machine}})(1 - T)(\textit{New Rule PW CCA tax shields}$$
$$\textit{per \$1 eligible first cost})$$
$$+ (\text{Current Salvage Value}_{\text{old machine}})(\text{CCTF}_{\text{old rule}})$$
$$+ (1 - t)(\text{Before-tax Operating Savings})(P/A, i, N)$$
$$+ (P/F, i, N)(\text{Incremental Salvage Value})(\text{CCTF}_{\text{old rule}})$$

$$= -(\$24,000) + (.83333)(\$24,000)(.1)$$
$$+ (\$24,000)(1 - .1)\{[td/(i + d)][(1 + (\tfrac{1}{2}) i)/(1 + i)]\}$$
$$+ (\$8,000)[1 - td/(i + d)]$$
$$+ (1 - .52)(\$7,000)(2.9906)$$
$$+ (.40188)(\$5,000)[1 - td/(i + d)]$$

$$= \$603$$

Thus, the investment tax credit turns around this replacement decision. Now we should buy the new machine. The investment tax credit does stimulate investment, which is its intended purpose.

## Review Exercises and Discussions

**Exercise 1**   A small Ontario food processing firm invested $100,000 in 1982 for new processing equipment in Class 8. The firm has a taxable income of $180,000. What is its income tax liability before tax credits and how much investment tax credit (ITC) can the firm claim if the new equipment qualifies for the 10% ITC?

**Solution 1**   This firm qualifies for the small business and the manufacturing and processing profits deductions so its effective income tax rate is only 10%. Therefore, its income tax liability is $180,000 (10%) = $18,000.
  The investment tax credit is $100,000 (10%) = $10,000. Since the ITC is less than the limit of $15,000 all $10,000 can be used to reduce the 1982 taxes.
  Thus, the 1982 taxes will be $18,000 – $10,000 = $8,000.

**Exercise 2**   A firm sustained a loss of $175,000 in 1981. It had taxable income and paid taxes in each of the three preceding years as indicated below:

| Year | 1978 | 1979 | 1980 |
|---|---|---|---|
| Taxable income | $50,000 | $75,000 | $25,000 |
| Taxes paid | 9,250 | 16,750 | 4,250 |

How large a tax refund can the firm expect?

**Solution 2**   The firm would submit an amended tax return for 1980, deducting $25,000 of the $175,000 loss. The amended return would indicate the following:

The firm is eligible for an immediate tax refund of $4,250 and has an unused portion of the loss of $175,000 – $25,000 = $150,000 that can be used to offset otherwise taxable income in 1982, or in successive years through 1986 if income in 1982 is less than $150,000.

**Exercise 3**   A portable sawmill will be needed for just 3 years. It has an initial cost of $460,000 and an expected salvage value of $100,000. The mill is expected to generate annual income of $250,000. What is the present worth of the after-tax cash flow for the sawmill when the minimum after-tax rate of return for ventures of this type is 15 percent? The sawmill is in Class 8 and the firm's effective income-tax rate is 54 percent.

**Solution 3**   $PW = -(\$460,000)(CCTF_{new\ rule})$
  $+ (1 - .54)(\$250,000)(P/A, .15, 3)$
  $+ (P/F, .15, 3)(\$100,000)(CCTF_{old\ rule})$

  $= -(\$460,000)\{1-[(.54)(.20)/(.15 + .20)][(1 + .075)/(1 + .15)]\}$
  $+ (.46)(\$250,000)(2.2832)$
  $+ (.65752)(\$100,000)[1 - (.54)(.20)/(.15 + .20)]$

  $= -\$327,314 + \$262,568 + \$45,463 = -\$19,283$

The venture does *not* meet the required rate of return.

**Exercise 4** Further investigation of Example 12.6 reveals that the old machine has a current salvage value of $7,200 instead of the original estimate of $8,000. Should the old machine be replaced?·

**Solution 4** The only difference from the previous PW calculation is that the PW will be reduced by $800 times .74, the old rule CCTF. The new PW is $603 less $592 = $11. Thus, the replacement machine is still more advantageous, but just barely. Note that although the salvage value of the old machine is reduced by $800, this reduction is partially offset by increased tax shields from the corresponding additional $800 starting UCC.

**Exercise 5** A machine was purchased 5 years ago for $50,000. The firm that owns the machine no longer has a need for the function served by the machine, but a buyer is now willing to pay $60,000 for it because machines of this type are no longer available. If the applicable tax rate for the firm is 46 percent, what tax is owed on the abandonment transaction? (Assume the asset is in Class 8.)

**Solution 5** The current UCC of the asset is irrelevant so long as the UCC of Class 8 totals at least $50,000. The excess of $60,000 less the original purchase price of $50,000 is a capital gain. The effective tax on capital gains is ½ of the tax rate on ordinary income. Therefore, the total tax for the transaction is

$$(\tfrac{1}{2})(.46)(\$60,000 - \$50,000) = \$2,300$$

Suppose this asset were the only one in Class 8, which is extremely unlikely. The difference between its $50,000 original purchase price and its UCC would be a recapture of CCA. Recaptures are taxable at ordinary income tax rates.

Assuming this machine was purchased under the old CCA rule, its UCC 5 years later is

$$\$50,000\,(1 - .2)^5 = \$16,384$$

The total tax for the transaction in this case is the sum of the capital gains tax and the recapture tax

$$\$2,300 + (.46)(\$50,000 - \$16,384) = \$17,763.36.$$

# PROBLEMS

**12.1** Three corporations have the following data for 1 year of operation:

| | Macro, Inc. (Blubber Bay, B.C.) | Meso Ltd. (Whiskey Gap, Alta.) | Micro Co. (Come-By-Chance Nfld.) |
|---|---|---|---|
| Sales | $30,000,000 | $3,000,000 | $300,000 |
| Expenses | 15,250,000 | 1,000,000 | 140,000 |
| CCA | 3,000,000 | 750,000 | 60,000 |

What is the effective income-tax rate for each corporation?        *(27% for Micro)*

**12.2**  A corporation has an effective tax rate of 54 percent. Gross revenue for the past year was $8 million. Operating expenses and CCA accounted for $6 million. Interest on outstanding debts was $1.2 million. What amount is left for dividends and surplus after taxes?
*($368,000)*

> *The following basic data pertain to a proposal that is analyzed according to the conditions and objectives of Problems 12.3 through 12.6:*

A proposed investment in Class 10 is expected to produce annual before-tax savings of $13,500. The asset has a first cost of $56,000 and an estimated useful life of 7 years with no salvage value. The effective income-tax rate of the organization is 45 percent. Unless otherwise stated, it is assumed all cash flows occur at the end of a year, and any deductions beyond the $13,500 savings can be applied against other income.

**12.3**  What is the before-tax internal rate of return for the asset described in the basic data? Determine the approximate after-tax IRR from the before-tax figure.  *(15.1% and 8.3%)*

**12.4**  Compute the after-tax internal rate of return if the asset is purchased now.

**12.5**  A 10% investment tax credit is allowed on the asset's purchase price and is taken on the first year's income. The first cost must be reduced by the ITC.

    **12.5a**  What is the after-tax IRR if the asset is purchased before November 13, 1981?
*(11.4%)*

    **12.5b**  What is the after-tax IRR if the asset is purchased after November 12, 1981?

**12.6**  If the purchase of the asset could be considered an operating expense instead of a depreciable investment, what would be the after-tax internal rate of return? Assume there is sufficient income to charge the entire amount in the first year. The savings from the purchase of the asset will still continue for 7 years.

**12.7**  A sales representative made an agreement to purchase a building lot by making six annual payments of $900 each. She was then transferrred to a different territory before she could build a home. When she returned 2 years later, she found she could buy an equivalent lot for $3000 because land values had decreased during her absence. She now feels that she will lose the $1800 she has already paid if she drops her contract to buy the equivalent lot. Assuming that she will suffer no penalty for reneging on the original contract, discuss the "sunk cost" concept as it applies to the situation. What would you advise her to do? Does an assumption that she can invest her savings at 7 percent have any bearing on the situation?

**12.8**  Rimrock Construction Co. is purchasing a new piece of equipment in Class 8 in 1982 for $34,000. The unit is expected to produce annual revenue of $21,000 for each of the next 4 years and will be sold at the end of that time for an expected salvage value of $4000. Maintenance expenses on the equipment are expected to be $2000 for the first year and to increase by $500 per year for each successive year of operation. The company has an effective tax rate of 40 percent and requires an after-tax MARR of 10 percent. What is the present worth of the proposed purchase?  *(PW = $11,481)*

**12.9**  An outmoded paper machine was purchased for $300,000 twelve years ago. Its annual operating costs are $48,000. It is expected to last 8 more years, at which time it will have zero salvage value. A newer model of the paper machine will cost $470,000, have a life of 15 years, and have a negative salvage value of $10,000. The new machine is expected to have average operating costs of $30,000 per year and to be eligible for a 10 percent investment tax credit.

Both machines are in Class 8. The required after-tax rate of return is 10 percent, and the effective tax rate is 40 percent.

**12.9a**   Assuming the old machine has a current salvage value equal to its UCC, what is its after-tax EAC?

**12.9b**   What is the after-tax EAC of the challenger?

**12.10**   An asset purchased for $10,000 that did not qualify for an investment tax credit will have a salvage value of $2000 at the end of its 4-year life. Net annual earnings attributable to the asset are $3200 per year. The asset is in Class 10, and the corporation has an effective tax rate of 40 percent. What is the asset's after-tax IRR?

**12.11**   Determine the after-tax equivalent annual costs for reinforcing the bridge and for the culvert-and-fill approach described in Example 8.4. The minimum acceptable after-tax rate of return is 6 percent. For this problem assume that the bridge is in Class 6 and the culvert is in Class 3. The effective income-tax rate is 35 percent.

**12.12**   Rework Problem 8.2 to determine the after-tax annual costs for machines $A$ and $B$ when the required after-tax rate of return is 8 percent. Both machines are in Class 8. The corporate effective income-tax rate is 50 percent.

**12.13**   Compare the after-tax present worths of the two types of boat landings in Problem 4.25. The wooden deck is in Class 6 and the metal and concrete dock is in Class 3. The required rate of return remains the same and the effective income-tax rate is 30 percent.

**12.14**   Assume the value of the land in Problem 6.14 holds at $20,000 during the study period, and the building is in Class 6. The purchaser's effective income-tax rate is 35 percent. What after-tax internal rate of return can be expected from the purchase?

# EXTENSIONS

**12A   Noncorporate Taxes: What They Are and Why**   Taxes have been levied on individuals throughout recorded history, and probably before. Modest incomes were taxed at about 40 percent at time zero (about 2000 years ago), and the name for a tax collector (publican) in that era was synonymous with "robber." Excessive taxation in England led to the Magna Carta in 1215, and a few hundred years later inequitable taxes contributed to the independence movement in the American colonies. There was no income tax in Canada prior to 1917.

## IDEAL TAXATION

Many changes have been made in the tax laws since 1917. There may be no perfect system of taxation, but economists generally agree on the desirable properties that one should possess. A tax should be:

- *Fair and equal*   People in equal situations should pay equal amounts (horizontal equity), and people in unequal situations should pay according to their capacit (vertical equity).

- *Efficient*   A low ratio of administrative cost to revenue produced is most desirable.
- *Neutral*   The tax should have minimal effect on the total economic system.
- *Certain and predictable*   A person should know what is owed and when.
- *Simple*   Tax laws should be clearly understood and easily complied with.

The vexing problem is to design a system that at once possesses all the desired properties (a no-tax system is eliminated by definition).

The most controversial issue is fairness and equity. An obviously fair tax charges people for services in proportion to the benefits received. This is fine for golf fees and university tuition, but it is difficult to set fixed charges for national defense, the judicial system, etc. Another measure of fairness is the taxpayers' ability to pay. The federal income tax uses "progressive" rates (higher percentages at higher income levels) to make the tax burden equitable. While most people agree in principle as to the fairness of progressive income taxes, there is far less agreement on how steeply the rates should rise.

## TYPES OF TAXATION

For most wage earners, tax calculations are relatively straightforward, but they quickly become more complicated when income is derived from several sources. Then provisions akin to those discussed for corporate taxes become applicable. What individual taxpayers tend to forget is that their tax, just like a corporation's tax, is simply a cost of operation – another disbursement similar to bills for clothing and shelter.

Provinces also collect taxes. An important source of income is the sales tax. This tax is termed "proportional" because the same percentages apply to all purchases. A sales tax has a high rating for simplicity and efficiency, but has mixed ratings for fairness. It is considered more equitable when subsistence expenditures are untaxed.

The property tax is another controversial type of taxation. It has become an emotional issue owing to sharp increases caused by escalating housing prices and mushrooming costs of local government. There is less concern about the fairness of property tax than about the inequity of its administration. Although there is merit in arguments that ownership of property does not necessarily correspond to an ability to pay taxes, more distress is caused by properties of similar value being assessed quite differently for tax purposes.

There are numerous other forms of taxation, ranging from *ad valorem* taxes to import tariffs. All are subject to criticism and reform movements. Since a "tax reform" for most people means getting their own tax burden lightened, a universally appealing tax system is as unlikely as a universal solvent; both are subject to leaks.

## THE NONCORPORATE INCOME TAX ENVIRONMENT

In Canada, the federal and provincial governments levy income taxes on both corporations and individuals. Taxes must be considered when deciding whether or not to engage in business. Taxes also affect where to locate and what form of organization to use for carrying on business activities. There are three major forms of business organization: proprietorship, partnership and corporation. In Canada, about 45% of all businesses are corporations. However, corporations make about 95% of total sales.

A proprietorship is a business owned by one person. In contrast to a corporation, it is simple to organize and subject to little regulation. It has important limitations, however. It is sometimes difficult to raise capital, and the proprietor is personally responsible for the debts of the business.

A partnership can be formed by two or more people. Partnerships are also easier to form than corporations and not subject to as much regulation. *Each* partner is personally responsible for *all* of the debts of the business. Too many partners can make day-to-day managing difficult.

The value of any financial asset, including stocks, bonds and whole firms, depends on the stream of *usable* income produced by the asset. Usable income means income *after taxes*. Proprietorship and partnership business income must be reported and taxed as personal income to the owners, even if it is not actually distributed to them. Most corporations pay taxes on their own income, and shareholders must then also pay taxes on the dividends they receive. Therefore, in all cases, consideration must be given to both *personal* and *corporate* income taxes.

In 1982, federal income tax rates for individuals were as high as 34%. When provincial income taxes are included, the marginal tax rate on an individual's income can be as high as 50%. Corporate income is also taxed heavily. The effective federal rate is 37.8% and provincial rates, which vary from an additional 0 to 16%, can make the top combined rate as high as 53.8%. Because of the magnitude of the tax bite, taxes play an extremely important role in many engineering economy decisions.

It is important to know the basic elements of the tax system. Parliaments (both federal and provincial) change the tax laws frequently. The provisions mentioned here are those in effect in September 1982. Since there was considerable criticism following the federal budget of November 12, 1981, a new budget was introduced in June 1982. Because of these frequent changes in tax law, it is always advisable to consult with a tax specialist *before* taking decisions which have tax consequences.

## INDIVIDUAL INCOME TAXES
Individuals pay taxes on wages and salaries, on investment income (dividends, capital gains on the sale of investments, and interest), and on their profits from proprietorships and partnerships. Our tax rates are *progressive*. That is, the higher the income, the higher the percentage paid in taxes. Rates for 1982 federal income tax range from 6% on the first $1,112 of taxable income to 34% on each dollar of income over $53,376. The tax rate on the last dollar of income is defined as the *marginal tax rate*. Thus, if your taxable income exceeds $53,376, your marginal rate is 34%.

In addition to the federal rate, all provinces impose personal income taxes as well. Except in Quebec, which administers its own individual tax system, provincial taxes are collected by the federal government on the same return. Tax returns must be filed no later than April 30, following the end of the taxation year. See table 12A-1 for more information on provincial tax rates. Table 12A-2 shows a sample income tax calculation for a young engineer working in Ontario.

| Province | Rate |
|----------|------|
| Alberta | 38.5% |
| British Columbia | 44.0% |
| Manitoba | 54.0% |
| New Brunswick | 55.5% |
| Newfoundland | 59.0% |
| Nova Scotia | 56.5% |
| Ontario | 48.0% |
| Prince Edward Island | 52.5% |
| Quebec | Varies |
| Saskatchewan | 51.0% |
| Northwest Territories | 43.0% |
| Yukon | 43.0% |

**TABLE 12A-1**  1982 provincial individual income tax rates as a percentage of the basic federal tax.

Source: Carswell Methuen, *Canadian Tax News*, Volume 10, June 1982.

Taxpayer works in Ottawa for a high tech firm, is married, with 2 children under the age of 18, and earned $34,000 in 1982. His wife and children did not work during the year. He received $1,000 of interest and $200 of dividends.

| | |
|---|---|
| Salary income | 34,000.00 |
| – Employment expenses | 500.00 |
| + Family Allowance payments[a] | 645.84 |
| + Investment income[b] | 1,300.00 |
| *Total Income* | 35,445.84 |
| – Contributions[c] | 4,190.00 |
| *Net Income* | 31,225.84 |
| – Exemptions[d] | 8,010.00 |
| – Deductions[e] | 1,100.00 |
| *Taxable Income* | 22,145.84 |
| Total Federal Tax[f] | 4,313.46 |
| – Dividend Tax Credit[g] | 69.00 |
| *Basic Federal Tax* | 4,244.46 |
| – Federal Tax Reduction[h] | 400.00 |
| *Federal Tax Payable* | 3,844.46 |
| *Ontario Tax Payable*[i] | 2,037.34 |
| *Total Tax Payable* | 5,881.80 |

**TABLE 12A-2**  Example individual income tax calculation.

**NOTES:**

**a.**  Although family allowance payments are usually made to the wife, the spouse who claims the children as dependants must include the payments in income. Generally, the wife still is eligible for the child tax credit, but this family's income level makes them ineligible;

**b.**  The dividends received ($200) are "grossed up" by 50% and this figure is added to the interest to get $1,300;

**c.** The contributions include $3,500 for pension plans (RPP and RRSP), $240 for the Canada Pension Plan, $200 for unemployment insurance premiums, and $250 for union dues;

**d.** The 1982 exemptions are $3,560 for the taxpayer, $3,110 for his wife, and $670 for each child;

**e.** The deductions are $1,000 for interest income and $100 for medical and charitable expenses;

**f.** The federal tax for 1982 is $3,781 on the first $20,016 of Taxable Income and 25% on the rest ($532.46) for a total of $4,313.46;

**g.** The Dividend Tax Credit for 1982 was 34% of the actual dividend, or 23% of the grossed up amount. It is the grossed up figure which is used for calculating taxes;

**h.** The Federal Tax Reduction in 1982 is $200 for the taxpayer plus another $200 for his non-working wife;

**i.** The Ontario Tax for 1982 is 48% of the Basic Federal Tax. Although some taxpayers qualify for Ontario Tax Credits this family's income makes them ineligible for the property, sales, and temporary home heating tax credits.

## TAXES ON DIVIDEND INCOME

Dividend income from Canadian companies which exceeds the $1,000 individual investment income exemption is subject to taxation. There is *double taxation* of dividend income in the hands of the shareholders since corporations pay dividends out of earnings that have already been taxed. To partially offset this, Canada uses the "gross up and tax credit" system. Dividends are first grossed up by fifty percent, and this amount is added to the taxpayer's other taxable income. A dividend tax credit is allowed against the federal tax otherwise payable. In 1982 this credit was 23% of the grossed up dividend. Share dividends are normally taxed the same way as cash dividends. However, share dividends paid by public corporations to shareholders resident in Canada are not taxed when received but are considered to have a nil cost. Therefore, capital gains arise when these shares are sold.

## CAPITAL GAINS TAXES

Assets such as stocks, bonds, and real estate are defined as *capital assets*. If you buy a capital asset and later sell it for more than your purchase price, the profit is defined as a *capital gain*. If you sell it for less than you paid, you suffer a *capital loss*. Thus, if you buy 100 shares of Mitel for $30 per share ($3,000 plus brokerage commission) and later sell them for $40 a share ($4,000 less brokerage commission) you will have a capital gain of $1,000 (excluding commissions). If, on the other hand, you sell them for $20 a share, you will have a capital loss of $1,000.

In either case, half of this gain or loss is included (or deducted) in calculating your income taxes. However, if the capital loss deduction for a given tax year exceeds $2,000, the excess may be applied to other tax years. Since the capital gains tax law went into effect in 1972, the tax applies only to that portion of capital gains realized after December 1971. An exception is made for the family home. Capital gains on the sale of the family's principal residence are exempt from taxation.

## TAXES ON INTEREST AND/OR ORDINARY INCOME

Interest received from Canadian sources totaling more than the $1,000 individual investment income exemption is taxed at the same rate as ordinary employment income. Thus, dividend income and capital gains are taxed at lower effective rates than interest and employment income. Most businesses have at least some flexibility in providing returns to investors in the form of dividends or capital gains. Tables 12A-3 and 12A-4 provide more information. Note the relative tax attractiveness of the different types of income for different tax brackets in Table 12A-4.

|  | Dividends | Capital Gains | Interest |
|---|---|---|---|
| Income | $100.00 | $100.00 | $100.00 |
| Dividend Gross Up | +50.00 | | |
| Less Taxable Gain | | −50.00 | |
| TAXABLE INCOME | 150.00 | 50.00 | 100.00 |
| Federal Tax at 25% | 37.50 | 12.50 | 25.00 |
| Less Dividend Tax Credit | −34.50 | | |
| Basic Federal Tax | 3.00 | 12.50 | 25.00 |
| Ontario Tax at 48% | 1.44 | 6.00 | 12.00 |
| TOTAL TAX PAYABLE | 4.44 | 18.50 | 37.00 |
| INCOME AFTER TAX | 95.56 | 81.50 | 63.00 |

**TABLE 12A-3** Taxation of Canadian Dividend, Capital Gains and Interest and Other Income in 1982.

Note: This table assumes that the same taxpayer mentioned in Table 12A-2 receives another $100 of income. He is in the 25% federal tax bracket. The results are, of course, different for different tax brackets.

| Taxable Income Bracket | Dividends | Capital Gains | Interest |
|---|---|---|---|
| 15,568 – 20,016 | — | 17% | 34% |
| 20,016 – 31,136 | 5% | 18% | 37% |
| 31,136 – 53,376 | 16% | 22% | 44% |
| Over 53,376 | 25% | 25% | 50% |

**TABLE 12A-4** Combined Federal and Ontario 1982 Marginal Tax Rates on Dividends, Capital Gains, and Interest and Ordinary Income for Selected Tax Brackets.

## QUESTIONS

**12A.1** An argument against steep progressive tax scales is that excessive rates discourage people from trying to earn more, thereby making them less productive then they might be. Steep rates are also characterized as disincentives for saving and investing. On the other hand, it is said that the degree of acclivity depends on the bracket from which it is observed. Discuss the progressive tax design as a "cost of operation."

**12A.2** Compare corporate and individual income-tax rates with respect to the properties listed as desirable in a tax.

**12B  *Microcomputer Analysis of Investment Decisions*** This extension presents a microcomputer-based model for the analysis of investment decisions which can be used by anyone with access to a microcomputer and an electronic spreadsheet program.

## MICROCOMPUTERS

The currently available microcomputers, such as the Radio Shack TRS-80, Apple, and Commodore, provide as much computer power as the million dollar computers of twenty years ago. Those monsters required large air conditioned rooms and many specialized personnel. The desktop microcomputers of today are much more robust.

Typical microcomputers use standardized programs, such as *VisiCalc*, so it is not even necessary for the user to know how to program the microcomputer. Because anyone can use a microcomputer with only a few hours of practice, engineering work will soon be changed to an even greater extent than factory work was changed by the industrial revolution.

## ELECTRONIC SPREADSHEETS

The *VisiCalc* program was developed in 1979 and won an award in 1980 as the best microcomputer program of the year. It replaces calculator, pencil, and paper in performing repetitive spreadsheet analyses. It provides a flexible matrix format of Columns and Rows (identified by letters and numbers, respectively) in which information can be entered. Once a spreadsheet has been set up, entering a new data item causes the program to immediately recalculate all the cells in the matrix.

Several other electronic spreadsheets are now on the market. These programs, like *VisiCalc*, have an easy to use symbolic language to tell the computer what to do with the data. They allow for the finished report to be printed as soon as the user is satisfied with it on the video screen. They are also ideal for sensitivity analyses as well as other types of "what if" analyses. Electronic spreadsheet programs are very popular and are causing dramatic changes in the way engineers operate.

## THE NOVEMBER 1981 CCA PROPOSAL

The November 1981 federal budget identified capital cost allowance (CCA) as one of Canada's largest tax expenditures. It also admitted that depreciation of assets is a legitimate business expense and should be deductible in any proper measure of business income. However, one of the budget documents asserted that assets were being written off at much faster rates than warranted by their actual economic lives.[*]

To rectify this, the budget proposed to allow only one-half of the normal full-year's CCA in the year of acquisition for all assets acquired on or after Friday, November 13, 1981. A further rationale for this proposal is that it would have the same result, on average, as exact prorating based on the number of days the asset was owned in the year.

The same budget document asserted that this CCA change would not materially affect the rate of return on most investments.[†] This is technically correct for the accounting rate of return which is a non-discounted cash flow technique. It is calculated by dividing average yearly profits by the average yearly investment. However, the new CCA rule *reduces* the present worth of the discounted cash flows. Thus, the internal rate of return for every Canadian investment proposal is *materially* reduced.

---

[*]Allan J. MacEachen, *The Budget in More Detail*, p. 41, Department of Finance, Canada, November 12, 1981.
[†]Allan J. MacEachen, *op. cit.*, p. 42.

In Canada, the CCA tax shields continue to infinity. Every year there is an allowed deduction and the undepreciated capital cost (UCC) can never reach zero. This tax deduction affects the future cash flows the firm will receive and have available to reinvest. Therefore, most Canadian business firms (about 80%) use the discounted cash flow (DCF) method of analyzing investments.* DCF provides a systematic way of analyzing all investment projects. This method compares the expected present worth of future cash flows of an investment with its first cost. If the comparison shows a positive present worth (PW), the project is usually accepted. Otherwise, it is rejected.

## THE DISCOUNTED CASH FLOW PROGRAM

The DCF program presented here was developed by the authors on a Radio Shack TRS-80 Model III microcomputer, using *VisiCalc*.† After-tax net cash flows from operations are calculated individually for each year in this program. Since the CCA tax shields are included in these net cash flows, the capital cost tax factors (CCTFs) are not relevant to this method. Instead, a tax shield adjustment is added for the CCA tax shields beyond the life of the project. (The explanation of Note 5 below shows how to calculate this tax shield adjustment.)

The formulae for the DCF program are listed in Table 12B.1. The labels for the rows are listed in Column A. Data must be entered in Column B *wherever the word data appears*. Data must be entered in the following rows:
*Row 1.* The first cost of the new asset.

|   | A | B | C | D | E | F |
|---|---|---|---|---|---|---|
| 1 | 1st Cost | data | | | | |
| 2 | Cur. Salv | data | | | | |
| 3 | Net Cost | +B1-B2 | | | | |
| 4 | Rule | data | Note 1 = +B3*(1–B4)+(((.5*B1)–B2)*B4) | | | |
| 5 | Start UCC | Note 1 | Note 2 = +B5-B15+(B4*.5*B1) | | | |
| 6 | CCA Rate | data | Note 3 = @NPV(B8,B19...F19) | | | |
| 7 | Tax Rate | data | Note 4 = $(1/((1+B8)\hat{\ }B9))*B12$ | | | |
| 8 | Disc Rate | data | Note 5 = $(B6*B7)*(-B12+F20)/((B6+B8)*((1+B8)\hat{\ }B9))$ | | | |
| 9 | Life *n* | data | Note 6 = –B3+@SUM(B21...B23) | | | |
| 10 | New Salv. | data | | | | |
| 11 | Ter. Salv | data | | | | |
| 12 | Inc. S. V | +B10-B11 | | | | |
| 13 | | Year 1 | Year 2 | Year 3 | Year 4 | Year 5 |
| 14 | Op. Svgs. | data | +B14 | +B14 | +B14 | +B14 |
| 15 | CCA | +B5*B6 | +B6*B20 | +B6*C20 | +B6*D20 | +B6*E20 |
| 16 | Tax. Inc. | +B14-B15 | +C14-C15 | +D14-D15 | +E14-E15 | +F14-F15 |
| 17 | Taxes | +B7*B16 | +B7*C16 | +B7*D16 | +B7*E16 | +B7*F16 |
| 18 | A.T. Inc. | +B16-B17 | +C16-C17 | +D16-D17 | +E16-E17 | +F16-F17 |
| 19 | NCF | +B15+B18 | +C15+C18 | +D15+D18 | +E15+E18 | +F15+F18 |
| 20 | End UCC | Note 2 | +B20-C15 | +C20-D15 | +D20-E15 | +E20-F15 |
| 21 | PW NCFs | Note 3 | | | | |
| 22 | PW Salv V | Note 4 | | | | |
| 23 | PW TSA | Note 5 | | | | |
| 24 | PW | Note 6 | | | | |

**TABLE 12B.1** Discounted Cash Flow Program.

*C.G. Hoskins and M.J. Dunn, "The Economic Evaluation of Capital Expenditure Proposals Under Uncertainty: The Practice of Large Corporations in Canada," pp. 45-55, *Journal of Business Administration*, Fall 1974.
'A.L. Kahl and W.F. Rentz, "A Microcomputer Analysis of Capital Budgeting Decisions: The Case of the CCA Proposal in the November 1981 Budget," pp. 31-33, *CGA Magazine*, November 1982.

*Row 2.*   The current salvage value of the old asset. Zero is entered if there is no old asset or if the salvage value of the old asset is zero.

*Row 4.*   Zero or one. Zero is entered if the federal budget proposal (new rule) of November 1981 is *not* relevant. One is entered if it is applicable.

*Row 6.*   The capital cost allowance (CCA) rate.

*Row 7.*   The combined marginal federal and provincial income tax rate.

*Row 8.*   The discount rate *i*. This is usually the firm's cost of capital *k*.

*Row 9.*   The remaining years of life *N* of the old asset. It is assumed that the new asset will have the same economic life.

*Row 10.*   The terminal salvage value of the new asset.

*Row 11.*   The terminal salvage value of the old asset. Zero is entered if there is no old asset.

*Row 14.*   The expected before-tax operating saving for Year 1. If these savings are the same for Year 2 through 5, then the program automatically inserts this level value in Columns C through F in row 14. Otherwise, these data must be entered in columns C through F.

Entries in Table 12B.1, other than data or Note # entries, are the formulae that were programmed into *VisiCalc*. For example, the formula for the Value in Column B, Row 3 (Cell B3) is:

Value = +B1-B2,

where      B1 = the data from Cell B1 and

B2 = the data from Cell B2

This Value represents the net first cost of the new asset, which is the first cost (Cell B1) less the current salvage value of the old asset (Cell B2).

When a formula was too long for the format of Table 12B.1, a Note # appears in the cell. The formula is then given beside the corresponding Note # at the upper right of the table.

Note 1 shows the formula for the starting UCC. When the federal budget CCA proposal of November 1981 is *not* relevant, this formula reduces to +B3 (the *net* first cost of the new asset). When the November 1981 budget CCA rule is applicable, the formula becomes (.5*B1) – B2, which is one half of the new asset's first cost less the current salvage value of the old asset.

The November 1981 budget proposal also affects the formula for the first year's ending UCC in Note 2. When the budget proposal is *not* relevant, this formula reduces to +B5 – B15, which is the starting UCC less the first year's CCA. When the November 1981 budget is applicable, the formula becomes +B5 – B15+(.5*B1). That is, the other half of the new asset's first cost must be added.

Note 3 includes the expression @NPV. This is the present worth (present value) function built into *VisiCalc*. It calculates the present worth of the incremental after-tax net cash flows from operations for Years 1-5. These net cash flows are the entries in Cells B19 – F19.

In both Notes 4 and 5 the caret symbol $\hat{}$ appears in the expression $((1+B8)\hat{}\,B9)$. The caret represents exponentiation in *VisiCalc* on the Radio Shack TRS-80 Model III. Other microcomputers may use a different symbol for this function. Since B8 is the project's discount rate *i* and B9 is its economic life *N*, this expression is $((1+B8)\hat{}\,B9) = (1+i)^N$.

The tax shield adjustment is calculated by the formula in Note 5. The starting incremental UCC in year $N+1$ is the ending incremental UCC in year *N* (Cell F20) less the incremental terminal salvage value (Cell B12). This UCC must be depreciated in years $N+1$ through infinity. The PW at the beginning of year $N+1$ for these tax shields is the product of this UCC and the present worth, $td/(i+d)$, of the CCA tax shields for $1 invested before Friday, November 13, 1981. The single payment present worth factor ($P/F$, $i$, $N$) brings this PW back to the beginning of year 1.

$$\begin{array}{l} \text{PW of} \\ \text{Tax Shield} \\ \text{Adjustment} \end{array} = (P/F, i, n) \left[ \left( \begin{array}{c} \text{Starting} \\ \text{UCC} \\ \text{Year } N+1 \end{array} \right) - \left( \begin{array}{c} \text{Incremental} \\ \text{Terminal} \\ \text{Salvage Value} \end{array} \right) \right] td/(i+d)$$

$$= \text{Formula of Note 5}$$

*VisiCalc's* @SUM function in Note 6 sums the entries in cells B21, B22, and B23. These entries are, respectively, the PW of the incremental after-tax net cash flows from operations, the PW of the terminal incremental salvage value, and the PW of the incremental tax shield adjustment.

The current version of this program requires that columns be added or deleted if the economic life of the investment is greater or less than 5 years. Care must be taken to insure that the formulae in the columns follow the scheme presented in Table 12B.1 when any addition or deletion is made. The authors would appreciate comments from readers who try this program on *VisiCalc* or any other electronic spreadsheet.

*Results*

To demonstrate the model, assume that Engeco, Ltd. has a machine which could be operated for five more years. This machine could be sold today for $5,000. After five more years of operation, however, it would be worthless.

A new machine can be purchased for $25,000 and would have an estimated salvage value of $3,000 in five years. This machine would generate the same before-tax operating revenues as the present machine, but the before-tax operating savings are expected to be $8,250 annually. Engeco's cost of capital for such a project is 15%, and its effective marginal tax rate is 52%.

The first question to be decided is whether Engeco should replace the machine, assuming that the November 1981 budget proposal does *not* apply. The second question is whether the budget proposal will change the decision to invest in the machine. Both machines are assumed to be in CCA Class 8, which as a CCA rate of 20%.

Cell B24 of Table 12B.2 shows a present worth of $266. Thus, under the old rules, Engeco would buy the new machine.

However, if the new rule applies, Engeco would *not* buy the machine because the present worth would now be −$219. This is shown in Cell B24 of Table 12B.3.

The only difference in data between Tables 12B.2 and 12B.3 is a one, instead of a zero, in Cell B4. Entering this single change caused *VisiCalc* to recalculate the entire table.

## IMPLICATIONS

The present worth in this example becomes negative because of the change in the method of calculating the capital cost allowance proposed in the November 1981 federal budget. Thus, the effect of this change in fiscal policy is to *discourage* investment in Canada. This was an unwise policy change during recessionary times when investment should be stimulated to create jobs.

## QUESTIONS

**12B.1** Use the electronic spreadsheet model in Table 12B.1 on a microcomputer to

| | A | B | C | D | E | F |
|---|---|---|---|---|---|---|
| 1 | 1st Cost | 25000 | | | | |
| 2 | Cur. Salv | 5000 | | | | |
| 3 | Net Cost | 20000 | | | | |
| 4 | Rule | 0 | | | | |
| 5 | Start UCC | 20000 | | | | |
| 6 | CCA Rate | .2 | | | | |
| 7 | Tax Rate | .52 | | | | |
| 8 | Disc Rate | .15 | | | | |
| 9 | Life $n$ | 5 | | | | |
| 10 | New Salv. | 3000 | | | | |
| 11 | Ter. Salv | 0 | | | | |
| 12 | Inc. S. V | 3000 | | | | |
| 13 | | Year 1 | Year 2 | Year 3 | Year 4 | Year 5 |
| 14 | Op. Svgs. | 8250 | 8250 | 8250 | 8250 | 8250 |
| 15 | CCA | 4000 | 3200 | 2560 | 2048 | 1638 |
| 16 | Tax. Inc. | 4250 | 5050 | 5690 | 6202 | 6612 |
| 17 | Taxes | 2210 | 2626 | 2959 | 3225 | 3438 |
| 18 | A.T. Inc. | 2040 | 2424 | 2731 | 2977 | 3174 |
| 19 | NCF | 6040 | 5624 | 5291 | 5025 | 4812 |
| 20 | End UCC | 16000 | 12800 | 10240 | 8192 | 6554 |
| 21 | PW NCFs | 18249 | | | | |
| 22 | PW Salv V | 1492 | | | | |
| 23 | PW TSA | 525 | | | | |
| 24 | PW | 266 | | | | |

**TABLE 12B.2** Engeco Ltd., Machine Replacement Decision, Old Rule.

| | A | B | C | D | E | F |
|---|---|---|---|---|---|---|
| 1 | 1st Cost | 25000 | | | | |
| 2 | Cur. Salv | 5000 | | | | |
| 3 | Net Cost | 20000 | | | | |
| 4 | Rule | 1 | | | | |
| 5 | Start UCC | 7500 | | | | |
| 6 | CCA Rate | .2 | | | | |
| 7 | Tax Rate | .52 | | | | |
| 8 | Disc Rate | .15 | | | | |
| 9 | Life $n$ | 5 | | | | |
| 10 | New Salv. | 3000 | | | | |
| 11 | Ter. Salv | 0 | | | | |
| 12 | Inc. S. V | 3000 | | | | |
| 13 | | Year 1 | Year 2 | Year 3 | Year 4 | Year 5 |
| 14 | Op. Svgs. | 8250 | 8250 | 8250 | 8250 | 8250 |
| 15 | CCA | 1500 | 3700 | 2960 | 2368 | 1894 |
| 16 | Tax. Inc. | 6750 | 4550 | 5290 | 5882 | 6356 |
| 17 | Taxes | 3510 | 2366 | 2751 | 3059 | 3305 |
| 18 | A.T. Inc. | 3240 | 2184 | 2539 | 2823 | 3051 |
| 19 | NCF | 4740 | 5884 | 5499 | 5191 | 4945 |
| 20 | End UCC | 18500 | 14800 | 11840 | 9472 | 7578 |
| 21 | PW NCFs | 17613 | | | | |
| 22 | PW Salv V | 1492 | | | | |
| 23 | PW TSA | 676 | | | | |
| 24 | PW | −219 | | | | |

**TABLE 12B.3** Engeco Ltd., Machine Replacement Decision, New Rule.

determine if the old machine in Example 12.5 should be replaced.

**12B.2**   Construct a seven year model analogous to the model in Table 12B.1.

**12B.3**   Suppose that Engeco's existing machine and new machine would last for seven years instead of five. Assume that the annual before-tax operating savings also last seven years and that the terminal salvage values are unchanged by the extended life. Use an electronic spreadsheet on a microcomputer to determine if Engeco should replace the old machine under the new CCA rule.

# CHAPTER 13

# EFFECTS OF INFLATION

OVERVIEW

Inflation causes prices to rise and decreases the purchasing power of a unit of money with the passage of time. Deflation has the opposite effect. Inflation rates are measured by the Wholesale Price Index, Implicit Price Index, and Consumer Price Index, the last being the most quoted. The impact of inflation has become more severe in recent years, suggesting the desirability of including inflation effects in analyses.

Real-dollar (constant purchasing power) or actual-dollar (future exchange) cash flows can be used in an analysis. The latter is recommended for its practicality, understandability, and versatility. The MARR used in a study must be consistent with the method of handling inflation. The same solution results from calculations using either real or actual dollars.

The most convenient way to account for inflation is to estimate real-dollar cash flows and apply a uniform escalation rate to them to convert them to actual dollars. However, since not all prices escalate uniformly or at the same rates, explicit rate estimates for certain cash flow components may be necessary. Actual-dollar cash flow for all components may be converted back to real dollars by discounting at the general inflation rate or at a customized composite rate.

An after-tax evaluation provides a more accurate assessment of the effects of inflation because it accounts for cash flow components that are not responsive to inflation – loan repayments, leases, and CCA. In an inflation-prone economy it becomes even more imperative to conduct inflation-sensitive evaluations in order to detect proposals that promise savings in high-inflation operations.

*288*

## CONCEPTS OF INFLATION

Inflation is a general increase in the price level. Equivalently, inflation results in a decline over time in the purchasing power of a unit of money. An individual perceives inflation as higher prices for food, cars, and other purchased commodities and services. In the case of food, inflation is a creeping increase in the cost of a necessity. It is worrisome but tends to seem inevitable. For larger purchases made at longer intervals, escalations are more startling and possibly more dismaying. In both cases inflation has eroded the purchasing power of savings and earnings, if interest rates and salary raises have not kept pace with general price trends. The same effects are felt by business and government.

Deflation is the opposite of inflation. The last time prices declined in Canada was in 1953. During the next 25 years prices rose by 147 percent. A dollar worth 100 cents in purchasing power in 1953 shrank to a worth of only 40 cents by 1978. And the decline continues. The causes and consequences of high inflation rates are examined in Extension 13A.

## MEASURING INFLATION

Inflation is difficult to measure because the prices of different goods and services do not increase or decrease by the same amount, nor do they change at the same time. The calculation of a general inflation rate is further complicated by geographical differences in prices and changeable buying habits of consumers. Government statisticians attempt to overcome these difficulties by collecting data that profile the types and amounts of expenditures made by a middle-income family. Prices for these goods are obtained monthly and averaged according to demographic distributions. Then the prices are weighted according to the expenditure proportions of the typical family. The result is the *Consumer Price Index* (CPI).

Statistics Canada compiles several indexes to measure inflation. The Consumer Price Index reveals the effect of retail price changes on a selected standard of living. The *Wholesale Price Index* (WPI) measures inflation at the wholesale level for both consumer and industrial goods, but not services. The *Implicit Price Index* (IPI) is designed to show the effect of general price-level changes on the Gross National Product (GNP), the total market value of all goods and services produced by a nation's economy. The CPI is the most-used measure of prices.

Although the indexes measure price changes that have already occurred, they are useful in projecting future price trends. The historical data suggest the general movement of costs. If an index moves from 200 to 216 in 1 year, the rate of increase is $(216 - 200)/200 = 0.08$, or 8 percent. Since a trend over several periods is usually a better indicator for inflation expectation, an annual compound rate of growth is calculated. For an index that has risen from 176 to 216 over the last 3 years, the price trend or inflation rate $f$ is

$$176(1 + f)^3 = 216$$
$$(1 + f)^3 = 216/176 = 1.2273$$
$$1 + f = \sqrt[3]{1.2273} = 1.071$$
$$f = 0.071 \quad \text{or} \quad 7.1\%$$

# IMPACT OF INFLATION ON ECONOMIC EVALUATIONS

Years ago when inflation was a modest 2 to 4 percent per year, it was generally ignored in economic evaluations of proposals. It was argued that all proposals were affected similarly by price changes and there was too little difference between current and future costs to influence the order of preference. These arguments lose substance when inflation reaches double-digit levels and some goods and services escalate much more rapidly than others.

Once analysts recognize that inflation has an impact on most investment opportunities and therefore deserves consideration in their appraisals, they must decide on the most appropriate method with which to include it. There are two basic methods, with a number of refinements available for each.

1 Eliminate inflation effects by converting all cash flows to money units that have constant purchasing power, called *constant* or *real* dollars. This approach is most suitable for before-tax analysis, when all cash flow components inflate at uniform rates.
2 Estimate cash flows in the amount of money units actually exchanged at the time of each transaction. These money units are called *future, then-current,* or *actual* dollars. The actual-dollar approach is generally easier to understand and apply, and is more versatile than the real-dollar method.

In an analysis by either method it is critical that the assumptions made in determinig the cost of capital, and hence the minimum acceptable rate of return, correspond to inflation rates used in the study. As we observed in Chapter 9, the weighted average of costs of all sources of funds acquired by an organization sets the lower bound for the organization's MARR. To this is added a premium to account for the risk of investing in a proposal. Anticipation of future inflation affects expectations of returns on invested capital and the degree of risk that is acceptable. In effect, this anticipation is accounted for by investors adding an increment to the cost of capital to offset the effects of inflation. This offset is reflected in the MARR. This offset is not needed for constant or real dollar analyses.

Until the middle 1960s, 7 percent was considered to be a reasonable cost of money for a corporation. What little inflation occurred prior to that period was largely compensated by productivity increases. As inflation increased, investors sought higher returns as compensation for buying power lost to price escalation. Since a firm's cost of money is intimately linked to the rate of return that investors deem satisfactory for their investment, the cost of capital rises in accordance with experienced and expected inflation.

The inflation adjustment to the cost of capital, which manifests itself in the minimum acceptable rate of return, must be consistent with the estimates of future cash flows used in economic evaluations. If the MARR includes an increment for 5 percent inflation, but estimates of future costs are based on a higher inflation rate, a study would be biased toward accepting proposals. Conversely, if cash flow is stated in real dollars and the MARR contains an inflation adjustment, a proposal is penalized by excessive discounting. The bias results because inflating cash flows and discounting them are counteracting procedures.

## Example 13.1 Inconsistency between Inflation Estimates for the Cost of Capital and for Cash Flow

A proposal with an initial cost of $2000 is expected to produce net returns of $850 per year for 3 years in *real* dollars. The minimum acceptable rate of return has been raised from 10 percent to 15 percent in response to an adjustment in the cost of capital based on anticipation of 5 percent inflation during the next few years. Should the proposal be accepted?

### Solution 13.1

If the cash flow were estimated in real dollars of constant purchasing power and the MARR were adjusted for inflation, the proposal would be rejected because its present worth would be negative:

$$PW = -\$2000 + \$850(P/A, 15, 3)$$
$$= -\$2000 + \$850(2.2832) = -\$59$$

This evaluation unfairly penalizes the proposal because the MARR is based on the assumption that the cash flow will state the *actual* amount received each year. Real dollars can be converted to actual dollars by inflating them to an amount that is equivalent in purchasing power to their value today. For 5 percent annual inflation, the future cash flow equivalent to constant purchasing power of $850 a year is

| End of Year | Real Dollars (No Inflation) | | 5% Inflation | | Actual Dollars (Inflated Cash Flow) |
|---|---|---|---|---|---|
| 0 | −$2000 | | | | |
| 1 | 850 | × | 1.05 | = | $893 |
| 2 | 850 | × | $(1.05)^2$ | = | 937 |
| 3 | 850 | × | $(1.05)^3$ | = | 984 |

The inflated cash flow indicates that it would take $984 three years from now to acquire goods that could be purchased today for $850. When the inflated receipts are discounted at the inflation-adjusted MARR, the proposal has an acceptable present worth:

$$PW = -\$2000 + \$893(P/F, 15, 1) + \$937(P/F, 15, 2) + \$984(P/F, 15, 3)$$
$$= -\$2000 + \$893(0.86957) + \$937(0.75614) + \$984(0.65752)$$
$$= \$132$$

The proposal merits approval.

## BEFORE-TAX, CONSTANT-VALUE COMPARISONS

Actual-dollar flow indexed to a base year is frequently used to compare economic performance in different years. For instance, 1978 could be the base year for measuring the productivity of a firm. If the Consumer Price Index were used to convert actual-dollar flow in future years to real-dollar amounts in the base year, the output and input figures in 1979 would be deflated to their 1978 worth by using a CPI "deflator":

$$\text{CPI deflator}(1979 \rightarrow 1978) = 1 + \frac{\text{CPI}(1979) - \text{CPI}(1978)}{\text{CPI}(1978)}$$

$$= 1 + \frac{185.5 - 170.0}{170.0} = 1.091$$

Then an output of, say, $426,000 in 1979 actual dollars would be deflated to $426,000/ 1.091 = $390,000 to compare it on an equivalent basis to an output of, say, $377,000 in 1978. Output has thus increased by $390,000 − $377,000 = $13,000 for the year *in constant terms.*

It is generally easier to estimate future costs in constant dollars because the estimator is familiar with today's values. It is a simple matter to convert estimates in real-dollar flow to actual-dollar flow when inflation is assumed to be a constant rate. Consider the two proposals shown below for which the estimates have been made in real dollars.

|  | COST | CASH FLOW, REAL DOLLARS | | | | |
|---|---|---|---|---|---|---|
|  | *Year 0* | *Year 1* | *Year 2* | *Year 3* | *Year 4* | *PW at 12%* |
| Proposal *A* | −$10,000 | $4000 | $4000 | $4000 | $4000 | |
| Proposal *B* | −14,000 | 5500 | 5500 | 5500 | 5500 | |
| *Net difference* | −$4,000 | $1500 | $1500 | $1500 | $1500 | $556 |

The net difference might also have been estimated in actual dollars to show what receipts would have to be in years ahead to equal today's purchasing power. If inflation during the next 4 years is expected to be 6 percent per year, a consistent estimator would place the net difference as

|  | COST | CASH FLOW, ACTUAL DOLLARS | | | |
|---|---|---|---|---|---|
|  | *Year 0* | *Year 1* | *Year 2* | *Year 3* | *Year 4* |
| Net difference be- tween proposal *A* and proposal *B* | −$4000 | $1590 | $1685 | $1787 | $1894 |

The procedure for evaluating proposals stated in actual dollars is to convert them to real dollars. Doing so to the actual dollars above, by applying the ($P/F$, 6%, $N$) factor, naturally converts them to the previously given real dollars. By either approach the present worth of the additional investment in proposal *B* is $556.

The same present worth is obtained by determining a combined discount rate that represents both the minimum required rate of return and the inflation rate. Let $i$ = rate of return and $f$ = inflation rate; then the combined rate is $(1 + i)(1 + f) - 1$. For the rates from the previous examples, where $i$ = 12 percent and $f$ = 6 percent,

$$Combined\ interest\text{-}inflation\ rate = (1.12)(1.06) - 1 = 1.1872 - 1$$
$$i_f = 0.1872 \quad or \quad 18.72\%$$

Applying this rate to the given net difference expressed in actual dollars produces the same present worth as previously calculated, and confirmed in Table 13.1.

| Year, $N$ | Cash Flow in Actual Dollars | (P/F, 18.72, N) | Present Worth |
|---|---|---|---|
| 0 | $-\$4000$ | 1.00000 | $-\$4000$ |
| 1 | 1590 | 0.84237 | 1339 |
| 2 | 1685 | 0.70964 | 1195 |
| 3 | 1787 | 0.59786 | 1068 |
| 4 | 1894 | 0.50372 | 954 |
| | | | $\$ 556$ |

**TABLE 13.1**
Combined interest-inflation rate applied to an actual-dollar cash flow to obtain the before-tax present worth.

## Example 13.2 Equivalence of Real-Dollar and Actual-Dollar Cash Flow in a Before-Tax Analysis

A productive asset can be purchased for $120,000. It will have no salvage value at the end of its 6-year useful life. Operating costs will be $12,000 per year while it provides a revenue of $40,000 annually. Estimates are based on current economic conditions without consideration of price or cost escalations. Evaluate the proposed purchase according to the real-dollar data and actual-dollar cash flow when the inflation rate is 8 percent. The MARR is 15 percent without an adjustment for inflation, and taxes are not included in the analysis.

## Solution 13.2

The real-dollar cash flow is composed of an immediate $120,000 outlay followed by net receipts of $40,000 - $12,000 = $28,000 at the end of each of the next 6 years. This flow, discounted at 15 percent, yields

$$PW = -\$120,000 + \$28,000(P/A,\ 15,\ 6)$$
$$= -\$120,000 + \$28,000(3.7844) = -\$14,037$$

Real dollars are converted to actual dollars by applying the inflation factor $(1 + f)^N$ to each of the annual receipts, where $N$ equals the year in which the receipt occurs. The resulting actual-dollar cash flow is discounted by the combined interest inflation rate $i_f$ to obtain the present worth of the "then-current" dollars; $i_f = (1.15)(1.08) - 1 = 0.242$. The calculations are shown in Table 13.2.

The present worths from Table 13.2 and the PW formula agree, of course, because $(P/F,\ 24.2,\ N) = (P/F,\ 8,\ N)(P/F,\ 15,\ N)$. The combined interest-inflation rate thus represents an inflation-adjusted MARR applied to inflation-adjusted cash flow.

| End of Year, N | Real-Dollar Cash Flow | Inflation Factor, f=8% (F/P, 8, N) | Actual-Dollar Cash Flow | Combined Interest-Inflation Factor(P/F, $i_f$, N) | Present Worth of Cash Flow |
|---|---|---|---|---|---|
| 0 | −$120,000 | | −$120,000 | | −$120,000 |
| 1 | 28,000 | 1.0800 | 30,240 | 0.80516 | 24,348 |
| 2 | 28,000 | 1.1664 | 32,659 | 0.64827 | 21,172 |
| 3 | 28,000 | 1.2597 | 35,272 | 0.52196 | 18,410 |
| 4 | 28,000 | 1.3604 | 38,091 | 0.42025 | 16,007 |
| 5 | 28,000 | 1.4693 | 41,141 | 0.33838 | 13,921 |
| 6 | 28,000 | 1.5868 | 44,430 | 0.27244 | 12,105 |
| | | | | | −$14,037 |

TABLE 13.2 Present worth of actual-dollar cash flow when discounted by the combined interest-inflation factor to determine its real-dollar equivalence.

## AFTER-TAX ACTUAL CASH FLOW COMPARISONS

Two weaknesses limit the usefulness of the preceding approach: Tax effects are ignored and no provision is made for differences in escalation rates among price and cost components.

Tax effects are significant because deductions allowed for depreciation and loan interest are *not responsive* to inflation. That is, CCA is based strictly on the purchase price of an asset, not its inflation-elevated replacement price, and interest payments on loans are set by contract in actual dollars that are not subject to correction for inflation. Because borrowed money is received in real dollars and is repaid in actual dollars, borrowers benefit from inflation unless lenders require an inflation-adjusted interest rate.

*Price instability* is a condition in which prices for goods and services do not change proportionately over time. Earlier in this chapter differences in escalation rates were observed for hospital service, hamburger, and TV sets. When price instability is significant for factors in an economic study, it can affect the preference among alternatives. For instance, two alternatives with identical real-dollar cash flows would be equally promising, but if the revenue for one of them resulted from energy savings that inflated 20 percent annually, while revenue for the other came from labor savings that escalated 10 percent per year, the energy-saving proposal would be preferred.

| Time, t (1) | BTCF, Actual Dollars (2) | (CCA) (3) | Taxable Income (2)−(3)=(4) | Taxes at 40% (5) |
|---|---|---|---|---|
| 0 | −$120,000 | | | |
| 1 | 30,240 | $12,000 | $18,240 | $ 7,296 |
| 2 | 32,240 | 21,600 | 10,640 | 4,256 |
| 3 | 35,272 | 17,280 | 17,992 | 7,197 |
| 4 | 38,091 | 13,824 | 24,267 | 9,707 |
| 5 | 41,141 | 11,059 | 30,082 | 12,033 |
| 6 | 44,430 | 8,847 | 35,583 | 14,233 |

TABLE 13.3 PW calculation procedure for an after-tax analysis which includes components that are not responsive to inflation.

## Nonresponsive Charges in After-Tax Analysis

Loans and leases that specify actual-dollar cash flows benefit borrowers and lesees when inflation rises faster than anticipated in the agreements. The reverse is true during deflation, when interest rates and costs drop below those agreed to in contracts. The significance of nonresponsive cash flows is demonstrated in Example 13.3.

---

### Example 13.3   Difference in After-Tax Present Worth Caused by Nonresponsive Cash Flows during Inflationary Periods

The proposal described in Example 13.2 is to be subjected to an after-tax analysis. Both earnings and expenses are responsive to the general inflation rate of 8 percent. The asset is purchased at the beginning of 1982 and is in Class 8. The tax rate is 40 percent.

### Solution 13.3

An after-tax evaluation performed according to the procedures described in Chapter 12 does not reveal the effect of nonresponsive cash flow components.

The calculations below correct for inflation-induced loss of purchasing power through the use of actual-dollar cash flows. A modified real-dollar approach is developed in a later section to reaffirm the equivalence of real- and actual-dollar analyses.

Actual-dollar, before-tax cash flow (BTCF) based on 8 percent inflation is shown in column 2 of Table 13.3. CCA charges in column 3 are subtracted from column 2 to get the taxable income for the year in column 4. Taxes are calculated in column 5 and deducted from the BTCF to reveal the actual-dollar, after-tax cash flow (ATCF) in column 6. It is then necessary to convert the actual dollars back to real dollars, as shown in columns 7 and 8. Finally, the real-dollar ATCF is discounted at the inflation-free 15 percent rate to yield the present worth, column 10. The present worth includes the CCA tax shield adjustment calculated at the combined interest-inflation rate of 24.2 percent because the CCA tax shields for years seven through infinity are in actual dollars.

| ATCF, Actual Dollars (2)−(5)=(6) | Inflation Factor, (P/F, 8, N) (7) | ATCF, Real Dollars (6)×(7)=(8) | Discount Factor, (P/F, 15, N) (9) | Present Worth (8)×(9)=(10) |
|---|---|---|---|---|
| −$120,000 | | −$120,000 | | −$120,000 |
| 22,944 | 0.92593 | 21,245 | 0.86957 | 18,474 |
| 27,984 | 0.85734 | 23,992 | 0.75614 | 18,141 |
| 28,075 | 0.79383 | 22,287 | 0.65752 | 14,654 |
| 28,384 | 0.73503 | 20,863 | 0.57175 | 11,928 |
| 29,108 | 0.68059 | 19,811 | 0.49718 | 9,849 |
| 30,197 | 0.63017 | 19,029 | 0.43233 | 8,227 |
| | | CCA Tax Shield Adjustment = | | 1,068 |
| | | | | −$37,658 |

**TABLE 13.4**
Calculation of the present worth of a proposal when revenue inflates at 20 percent and expenses at the general inflation rate of 8 percent. After-tax actual dollars are deflated at the combined interest-inflation rate, $i_f$ = 24.2 percent.

| | BTCF IN ACTUAL DOLLARS | | | |
| End of Year, N (1) | Revenue at f=20%, $40,000(F/P, 20, N) (2) | Expenses at f=8%, $12,000(F/P, 8, N) (3) | Net Revenue (2)−(3)=(4) | CCA (5) |
|---|---|---|---|---|
| 0 | | $120,000 | −$120,000 | |
| 1 | $48,000 | 12,960 | 35,040 | $12,000 |
| 2 | 57,600 | 13,997 | 43,603 | 21,600 |
| 3 | 69,120 | 15,116 | 54,004 | 17,280 |
| 4 | 82,944 | 16,325 | 66,619 | 13,824 |
| 5 | 99,532 | 17,632 | 81,900 | 11,059 |
| 6 | 119,436 | 19,042 | 100,394 | 8,847 |

The same PW solution would have resulted from discounting column 6 by the combined interest-inflation factor, 24.2 percent. However, columns 7 to 9 descriptively display how the actual-dollar ATCF is converted to real dollars to allow discounting at the unadjusted MARR, 15 percent. It should be apparent that inflation has not increased the real value of the net revenue; column 2 shows the number of actual dollars required in each year to equal the buying power of $28,000 per year in real dollars. Therefore, actual-dollar cash flow must be discounted by an inflation-adjusted MARR.

The present worth of the proposal is lower when inflation is accounted for because the CCA charges do not escalate in tandem with revenue. The result is higher annual taxes. Consequently, a more realistic evaluation is obtained from actual-dollar, after-tax data when inflation is significant.

## Price Instability in an After-Tax Analysis

There are often one or more components in a cash flow stream that have escalation rates prominently different from the general inflation rate. The flow patterns for such components may be stated as specific estimates of actual-dollar transactions or in terms of specific inflation rates that vary from the general rate. Specific enumeration of annual flows permits year-by-year variations in the rate of escalation, whereas assigning a specific inflation rate commits the cash flow to a continuous growth pattern. Both options are accommodated by the procedure demonstrated in Example 13.4.

### Example 13.4  Evaluation of a Proposal in which Cash Flow Components Escalate at Different Rates

The conditions for the proposal described in Example 13.3 remain the same, except for the inflation rate of revenue. It is now believed that revenue will escalate at a 20 percent rate while expenses will continue to increase at the general inflation rate of 8 percent. Determine the present worth under the new assumption.

### Solution 13.4

Recall from Example 13.2 that the net receipts of $28,000 per year resulted from

| Taxable Income (4)−(5)=(6) | Taxes at 40% (7) | ATCF, Actual Dollars (4)−(7)=(8) | Discount Factor, $i_f$=24.2% (P/F, 24.2, N) (9) | Present Worth (8)×(9)=(10) |
|---|---|---|---|---|
| | | −$120,000 | | −$120,000 |
| $23,040 | $ 9,216 | 25,824 | 0.80516 | 20,792 |
| 22,003 | 8,801 | 34,802 | 0.64827 | 22,561 |
| 36,724 | 14,690 | 39,314 | 0.52196 | 20,521 |
| 52,795 | 21,118 | 45,501 | 0.42025 | 19,122 |
| 70,841 | 28,336 | 53,564 | 0.33838 | 18,125 |
| 91,547 | 36,619 | 63,775 | 0.27244 | 17,375 |
| | | CCA Tax Shield Adjustment = | | 1,068 |
| | | | | −$ 436 |

annual revenue of $40,000 and annual expense of $12,000; then actual-dollar revenue in Table 13.4 (column 2) is obtained by applying an inflation factor of (*F/P,* 20, *N*) for each *N* year, and actual expense (column 3) in year *N* is $12,000 (*F/P,* 8, *N*). Taxable income is the difference between revenue and the sum of expenses plus CCA (column 6). After-tax actual dollars are discounted at the combined interest-inflation rate of 24.2 percent (column 9) to determine the present worth of the revised proposal (column 10).

It is no surprise that the proposal's PW increases notably, compared to Example 13.3, from the disproportionately rapid rise in revenue. The rationale for using the general inflation rate to discount actual dollars to their real-dollar equivalency is that the overall inflation rate is the weighted average of all price escalations and is therefore a reasonable standard for uniformly deflating all cash flow components.

The general inflation rate may not be the most appropriate discount factor to use in certain studies. A unique inflation-factor index, a composite inflation rate for a given firm or area, could be calculated for any organization from the weighted average of price changes that the organization expects for its operations. Because escalations vary with geography and product mix, a customized inflation factor would more accurately represent future cash flow expectations. The composite rate is calculated from forecasted inflation rates for critical cash flow components weighted according to the proportion of utilization of each component. An example of the computation and use of a custom-built composite inflation index is given in Review Exercise 2.

# AFTER-TAX MODIFIED CASH FLOW COMPARISON

It is also possible to utilize real dollars for an after-tax evaluation under the conditions stipulated for the proposal in Example 13.4. To do so, it is necessary to modify all components that inflate or deflate at a rate different from the general inflation rate. In Example 13.4, revenue escalates faster than the general inflation rate, and CCA charges are constant (which means they deflate with respect to the general inflation rate). Therefore, these revenue and CCA components must be modified to make their value correspond to

**TABLE 13.5** Modified real-dollar analysis of the proposal described in Example 13.4. The special interest rate for revenue is $(1.20/1.08) - 1 = 0.1111$ (where $g = 20$ percent and $f = 8$ percent) and $i^*$ for depreciation charges is $(1.08/1.00) - 1 = 0.08$ (where $g = 0$ and $f = 8$ percent). Revenue is inflated at 11.11 percent annually (column 2), and depreciation charges are deflated at 8 percent per year (column 5). After-tax cash flow (column 8) is discounted at MARR = 15 percent to obtain the present worth (column 9).

| | BTCF IN MODIFIED REAL DOLLARS | | | |
|---|---|---|---|---|
| End of Year, N (1) | Revenue, $i^*=0.1111$, $\$40,000(1 + i^*)^N$ (2) | Expenses (3) | Net Revenue (4) | Modified CCA, $i^* = 0.08$, $CCA, (1 + i^*)^{-N}$ (5) |
| 0 | | | −$120,000 | |
| 1 | $44,444 | $12,000 | 32,444 | $11,111 |
| 2 | 49,382 | 12,000 | 37,382 | 18,519 |
| 3 | 54,869 | 12,000 | 42,869 | 13,717 |
| 4 | 60,965 | 12,000 | 48,965 | 10,161 |
| 5 | 67,738 | 12,000 | 55,738 | 7,527 |
| 6 | 75,264 | 12,000 | 63,264 | 5,575 |

the real-dollar value of expense, which is the only component expected to escalate at the general inflation rate.

Real-dollar equivalence can be calculated with the geometric-series factor introduced in Extension 2A. An explicit growth rate $g$ higher than the general inflation rate $f$ conforms to case 1:

$$i^* - \frac{1 + g}{1 + f} - 1$$

When $g$ is less than $f$, case 3 applies:

$$i^* = \frac{1 + f}{1 + g} - 1$$

The special interest rate $i^*$ is then used in the expression $(1 + i^*)^N$ to inflate or deflate applicable cash flow components. The resulting after-tax cash flow is discounted at a MARR that has *not* been adjusted for inflation.

Table 13.5 shows a real-dollar analysis that corresponds to the actual-dollar analysis given in Table 13.4. Both methods produce the same present worth for the identical data. Either approach can be utilized, but the actual-dollar procedure is more descriptive, is easier to comprehend, facilitates irregular cash flows, and is generally more convenient to apply.

# DECIDING WHEN AND HOW TO CONSIDER INFLATION

Including the effect of inflation is a second-order refinement for economic evaluations; the first-order refinement was including the effect of taxes on basic cash flow. Many proposals do not deserve the additional inflation refinement because their cash flows are too small, are immune from inflation, escalate in concert with competing proposals, or are so uncertain that fine tuning of cash flow is not justified. Other proposals, especially those subject to a wide range of price escalations among cash flow components, are obvious candidates for inflation-sensitive analyses. An indication of the sensitivity of a decision to

| Taxable Income (4)−(5)=(6) | Taxes at 40% (7) | ATCF in Modified Real Dollars (4)−(7)=(8) | Present Worth, MARR=15%: (8)(P/F, 15, N) (9) |
|---|---|---|---|
| | | −$120,000 | −$120,000 |
| $21,333 | $ 8,533 | 23,911 | 20,792 |
| 18,863 | 7,545 | 29,837 | 22,561 |
| 29,152 | 11,661 | 31,208 | 20,521 |
| 38,804 | 15,522 | 33,443 | 19,122 |
| 48,211 | 19,284 | 36,454 | 18,125 |
| 57,689 | 23,076 | 40,188 | 17,375 |
| | CCA Tax Shield Adjustment = | | 1,068 |
| | | | −$   436 |

the effects of inflation can be obtained by using the *sensitivity analysis* techniques presented in the next chapter.

In an inflation-prone economy the rewards from implementing proposals that reduce rapidly escalating costs are great. High rankings for these proposals rely on inflation being included in their evaluation. It is critically important that inflated cash flows be discounted according to an appropriate inflation adjustment to the minimum acceptable rate of return; a common error is to discount actual dollars at a MARR based on real-dollar values. Actual-dollar analysis is recommended for most applications, owing to its practicality, and an after-tax analysis is recommended because it reveals the effect of cash flow components that are not responsive to inflation.

The tedious mechanics of manually including inflation and tax effects in an analysis is alleviated by the use of computers. Appropriate programs can be readily written because the analysis procedure is systematic. Estimating future cash flows and inflation rates is a more serious difficulty, particularly in tense times when prices spurt ahead spasmodically as a result of shortages, political events, and other causes of economic turbulence. However, these same disturbances strongly underline the importance of considering inflation effects for major economic evaluations.

## Review Exercises and Discussions

**Exercise 1**   The rise in the Consumer Price Index from 1966 to 1979 is shown in Table 13.6. What return on investment would be required to have a real rate of return of 7 percent during the 1978 through 1980 period?

**Solution 1**   The compound rise in the CPI for 3 years starting in 1978 was

$$160.8(1 + f)^3 = 210.6$$

| Year | CPI | Year | CPI | Year | CPI |
|------|------|------|-------|------|-------|
| 1966 | 83.5 | 1971 | 100.0 | 1976 | 148.9 |
| 1967 | 86.5 | 1972 | 104.8 | 1977 | 160.8 |
| 1968 | 90.0 | 1973 | 112.8 | 1978 | 175.1 |
| 1969 | 94.1 | 1974 | 125.0 | 1979 | 191.2 |
| 1970 | 97.2 | 1975 | 138.5 | 1980 | 210.6 |

**TABLE 13.6** Record of Consumer Price Index figures.

$$f = \sqrt[3]{\frac{210.6}{160.8}} - 1 = 0.094 \quad \text{or} \quad 9.4\%$$

Combining the real interest rate and the inflation rate yields an inflation-adjusted rate of return of $(1.07)(1.094) - 1 = 0.171$ or 17.1 percent.

**Exercise 2** A company has developed its own inflation-factor index to allow closer evaluation of future cash flows. The index was prepared by categorizing costs of production, determining the proportion spent in each category, and forecasting an inflation rate for each category according to local conditions. Then the inflation-factor index was calculated as the weighted average of all the inflation factors. The result is shown below.

| Cost Factors | Budget Proportion | Inflation Rate, % | Weighted Rates |
|---|---|---|---|
| Labor (for the company work force) | 0.25 | 8 | 2.0 |
| Material 1 (raw materials) | 0.10 | 5 | 0.5 |
| Material 2 (subassemblies) | 0.10 | 15 | 1.5 |
| Energy (electricity, fuel, etc.) | 0.25 | 20 | 5.0 |
| General services (general inflation rate) | 0.30 | 10 | 3.0 |
| Inflation-factor index | | | 12.0% |

A proposal is being evaluated to reduce labor costs and material waste by the purchase of automated equipment. The equipment is expected to be in service for 3 years with no salvage value. To simplify this example, straight-line depreciation is used, and the tax rate for the company is 50 percent. Data from the proposal are summarized below.

| | |
|---|---|
| *Annual revenue* | |
| Net savings in labor | $60,000 |
| Net savings in material | $140,000 |
| First cost | $150,000 |
| *Annual costs* | |
| Additional energy required | $70,000 |
| Added maintenance expense | $30,000 |

Evaluate the proposal.

**Solution 2** After-tax calculations that include the effects of the unique individual inflation rates are shown in Table 13.7. Each revenue and cost component is projected from real dollars to actual dollars by its exclusive inflation rate (maintenance falls within the general-service category, where the inflation rate is 10 percent). Note that the BTCF in actual dollars is lower than in real dollars because expenses increase at a faster rate than savings. Actual dollars are converted back to real dollars in the ATCF by applying the inflation-factor index, 12 percent.

| Year, N | BTCF, Real dollars | BTCF, Actual dollars | Depre-ciation | Taxable Income | Taxes at 50% | ATCF, Actual dollars | ATCF, Real dollars at $f$ = 12% |
|---|---|---|---|---|---|---|---|
| 0 | −$150,000 | −$150,000 | | | | −$150,000 | −$150,000 |
| 1 | 100,000 | 94,800 | $50,000 | $44,800 | $22,400 | 72,400 | 64,646 |
| 2 | 100,000 | 87,234 | 50,000 | 37,234 | 18,617 | 68,617 | 54,701 |
| 3 | 100,000 | 77,624 | 50,000 | 27,624 | 13,812 | 63,812 | 45,421 |

**TABLE 13.7** After-tax cash flow using exclusive inflation factors and an inflation-factor index.

The BTCF in actual dollars for annual net revenue in years 1, 2, and 3 is determined from the following formula by employing a different inflation rate for each cash-flow component:

$$\text{BTCF(actual dollars)} = \$60,000(F/P, 8, N) + \$140,000(F/P, 5, N)$$
$$- \$70,000(F/P, 20, N) - \$30,000(F/P, 10, N)$$

The proposal is evaluated by the rate-of-return method. A preliminary before-tax rate of return *without considering inflation* shows a promising value of

$$(A/P, i, 3) = \frac{\$100,000}{\$150,000} = 0.66667$$

for which $i$ is about 45%. A more realistic assessment, *still not considering inflation,* is obtained from an after-tax rate of return calculated as shown below.

$$(A/P, i, 3) = \frac{\$100,000 - \$50,000(0.5)}{\$150,000} = 0.5 \quad \text{and} \quad \text{IRR} = 23.4\%$$

The rate of return calculated *when inflation effects are included* drops still lower:

$$\text{PW} = -\$150,000 + \$64,646(P/F, i, 1) + \$54,701(P/F, i, 2)$$
$$+ \$45,421(P/F, i, 3) \overset{?}{=} 0 \quad \text{at IRR}$$

At $i$ = 5 percent,

$$\text{PW} = -\$150,000 + \$61,568 + \$49,615 + \$39,236 = \$419$$

At $i$ = 6 percent,

$$\text{PW} = -\$150,000 + \$60,987 + \$48,684 + \$38,136 = -\$2193$$

IRR = 5.2%

The reason for the drop is twofold: Depreciation charges are not responsive to inflation and the costs (energy and services) in the proposal increase at a higher inflation rate than the savings (labor and material).

# PROBLEMS

**13.1**  Calculate the compound interest rate for the CPI during the entire period shown in Table 13.6.

**13.2**  Net cash flow from the purchase of an asset for $1000 is expected to be responsive to inflation. The inflation rate is forecast to be 5 percent for the next 3 years. Based on this forecast, the expected cash flow in actual dollars is shown below.

| Year | 0 | 1 | 2 | 3 |
|---|---|---|---|---|
| Cash flow | −$1000 | $400 | $600 | $500 |

**13.2a**  What is the combined interest-inflation rate if the organization expects a 10 percent return on investments?                                                                  *(15.5%)*
**13.2b**  Using this interest rate, calculate the present worth.                        *($121)*
**13.2c**  What cash flow estimates in real dollars would produce the same present worth when discounted at 10 percent?
**13.2d**  Do you feel it is a better practice to estimate future cash flow in "then-current" actual dollars or in "now-current" real dollars? Why?

**13.3**  Assume a firm has an inflation-adjusted rate of return of 24 percent. The general inflation rate is 10 percent. Explain why the firm's real required rate of return is *not* 14 percent. What is it?

**13.4**  A $10,000 investment can be made today that will produce savings of $2000 annually for the next 7 years. There is no salvage value involved. Calculate the present worth of the investment at MARR = 10 percent. Show that the same PW results when the real-dollar savings inflate at 8 percent annually. Apply the combined interest-inflation rate to discount the actual-dollar cash flow.                                      *(PW = − $263)*

**13.5**  The general inflation rate is 8 percent, and a company requires a real rate of return of 10 percent. A machine purchased for $10,000 will have no salvage value at the end of its 7-year useful life. It is expected to produce a revenue of $2000 the first year, with annual increases of 20 percent in subsequent years. Operating costs are $1000 in year 1 and will rise in proportion to the general inflation rate.

**13.5a**  Calculate the actual-dollar cash flow, convert it to real dollars, and determine the present worth.                                                                        *(PW = −$291)*
**13.5b**  Show that the solution for Problem 13.5a can also be obtained by discounting the actual-dollar cash flow at $i_f$.
**13.5c**  Use the special interest rate $i^*$ for a geometric series to calculate a modified revenue and show that the resulting PW at $i$ = 10 percent is the same as determined in Problem 13.5a.
**13.5d**  Calculate the after-tax PW if the machine is in Class 8, the tax rate is 50 percent, and the after-tax required rate of return is 5 percent.

**13.6**  A proposal in real dollars will produce a revenue of $110,000 annually for the next 10 years. It will require an initial investment of $150,000 in depreciable equipment that will be fully written off in 10 years by straight-line depreciation; no investment credit is applicable. Operating costs will be $52,000 per year. In addition, facilities will be leased for $6000 per year for 5 years; then the lease will be renegotiated for 5 more years at a constant annual charge of $6000(1 + f)^5$. The general inflation rate over the study period is expected to be 6 percent. The firm is subject to a tax rate of 46 percent and requires an after-tax rate of return of 4 percent. What is the present worth of the proposal?        *(PW = $137,762)*

**13.7** Sales of a new product are expected to grow at a 12 percent compound rate for the next 3 years. Current sales are $1.2 million. The price of the product should increase at the national inflation rate of 6 percent per year. Production-cost categories and associated expected inflation rates are shown below.

| Production-Cost Category | Current Total Cost | Inflation Rate, % |
|---|---|---|
| Materials | $200,000/year | 9 |
| Energy | 150,000/year | 12 |
| Labor | 150,000/year | 8 |
| All other | 100,000/year | 6 |

Assume that depreciation charges for assets associated with production of the product amount to $200,000 per year. The company's effective tax rate is 45 percent.

**13.7a** Assuming that marketing, overhead, and other allowable tax deductions associated with the product amount to 50 percent of the production costs, determine the after-tax cash flow without considering inflation (the initial investment is the sum of the depreciation charges.)

**13.7b** What is the before-tax rate of return when inflation is ignored?

**13.7c** What is the after-tax rate of return when inflation is ignored?

**13.7d** Determine the after-tax cash flow when it is assumed that price and production costs will inflate at the given unique rates while other costs rise at the inflation-factor index rate based on production costs only.

**13.7e** What is the internal rate of return for the cash flow pattern in Problem 13.7*d*?

# EXTENSIONS

***13A*** **Causes and Consequences of Inflation**   The Canadian Senior dictionary defines inflation as "a sharp and sudden rise in prices resulting from an excessive expansion in paper money or bank credit." A more succinct description is "too much money chasing too few goods."

Some economists trace the cause of inflation to more money being poured into the economy than the economy is worth. The real wealth of a nation is the goods and services it produces. Money is merely a convenient symbol of wealth, the amount of which is controlled by the government, and governments often feel impelled to create more money (or credit) to pay for old debts and new social programs. When money is generated at a faster rate than the growth in goods and services, it is subject to the old economic law that the more there is of something, the cheaper it becomes. In the case of money, cheaper means it loses purchasing power.

Other economists blame inflation on

- Increases in producers' costs that are passed along to customers, sometimes with disproportionate escalations that push prices up—called *cost-push* inflation
- Excessive spending power of consumers, sometimes obtained at the expense of savings, that pulls prices up—called *demand-pull* inflation
- Impact of international forces on prices and markets, most notably the escalation of oil prices
- Unresponsive prices that never decline, regardless of market conditions, because wages set by union contracts and prices set by some very large firms never fall
- Inflation psychology that leads consumers to "buy ahead," often on easily obtained credit, in the belief that prices will inevitably inflate and loans can be repaid in cheaper dollars

Because there are so many probable roots of inflation, there is no consensus on how to bring it down.

Inflation first became serious in the mid 60s, but few realized how dangerous it was. So strong enough measures to restrain it were not adopted. Among the remedies later attempted were price and wage controls, contraction of the money supply, credit restrictions, reduction in demand by raising taxes, enlarged supply of goods through greater productivity stimulated by investment incentives, and wage-price guidelines backed by political persuasion. Lack of success in applying the remedies has been attributed to inconsistency in applying them, inadequate time allowed for a remedy to become effective, and inattention to other factors while concentrating on just one remedy.

Everyone is affected to some degree by inflation. The effects may be immediate and conspicuous, like a hike in rent. Other effects are subtle but pervasive, and they influence decisions both on and off the job. As a consequence of an inflation-prone economy:

- The general standard of living declines as savings and investments are eroded. People on fixed incomes suffer the brunt of the decline. Wage earners are afflicted by "tax creep" when their inflated incomes push them into higher tax brackets, unless tax brackets are fully indexed for inflation.
- Confidence in the economy declines, with a resulting increase in petty crime, political instability for incumbents, greater unemployment, and spreading discontent.
- Business decisions are distorted by efforts to cope with inflation, and the ability of business to compete in foreign markets declines.

Given the disparity of views on causes of and remedies for inflation, and the omnifariousness of its consequences, frustrations in coping with it are understandable. Concerns of engineering economists for the productivity of capital and resources force attention to government efforts to control inflation. These efforts take the form of revised tax regulations, such as new rules for depreciation accounting, fluctuations in interest rates, investment incentives aimed at particular product areas, and other provisions that can modify the cash flow of affected proposals. As inflation elevates costs, it also escalates the value of cost-conscious analysis.

**QUESTION**

**13A.1** According to Drs. Sullivan and Bontadelli,*

> At a time when the most productive use of capital is so important, it would be foolish to ignore the anticipated effects of inflation and take the risk of losing competitive position because of indifference (or ignorance) in this regard. Omitting inflation from engineering economy studies is the same as assuming that the monetary unit is a constant-valued measure of worth. This is clearly out of tune with the present and expected future conditions in the business environment.

Do you agree? Why?

**13B Inflation and Income Taxes** It is interesting to note what can happen to income taxes under inflation. Suppose you had a taxable income of $10,000 and your tax bill was $2,000. Then inflation causes prices to double. Because your income is tied to a cost of living index, it rises to $20,000. However, your taxes will now jump to $5,000 because your income has boosted you into a higher tax bracket. Although your after-tax income has increased from $8,000 to $15,000 your *real* income has actually declined. Since prices doubled, $15,000 this year purchases the same goods and services as $7,500 did last year. You need $16,000 after tax to stay even with inflation. If this happens to everyone, the government will get a larger share of the national product.

In Canada this was avoided by indexing the personal exemptions and tax brackets. This indexing was based on increases in the Consumer Price Index for the 12 month period ending September 30 of the year preceding the taxation year. Since all the provinces except Quebec have rates which are a percentage of the federal rates, taxes for all Canadians living outside Quebec are indexed. (In Quebec the National Assembly must vote changes in the tax rates.) The June 1982 federal budget limited this indexing to 6 percent for 1982 and 5 percent for 1983.

*W. G. Sullivan and J. A. Bontadelli, "The Industrial Engineer & Inflation," *Industrial Engineering*, March 1980.

# CHAPTER 14

# SENSITIVITY ANALYSIS

OVERVIEW

Sensitivity analysis provides a second look at an economic evaluation. It questions whether the original estimates adequately represent the future conditions that could affect a proposal if it were implemented. Its purpose is to assist decision makers. By considering the extent to which critical elements can deviate from original estimates before a preference is reversed, either from acceptance to rejection or between competing alternatives, the decision maker gets a better "feel" for the situation—how sensitive it is.

A sensitivity analysis can be performed with PW, EAW, or IRR calculations using after-tax or before-tax cash flows. The sensitivity of any of the elements used in the calculations can be checked. Analyses can be displayed on sensitivity graphs that show the affects of percentage variations for key parameters. The graphs are useful because they consolidate analytical data in a single, easily understood display.

Several formats are suitable for sensitivity studies. Cash-flow factors can be investigated individually or in pairs, as in an isoquant. More- or less-favorable estimates can bracket the original estimates to obtain a range of values for a proposal's worth. All the approaches are geared to the question, "What if?"

WHAT IF?

Lurking behind every meaningful decision are "what if" doubts: What if sales differ from forecasts? What if cash flow doesn't follow the planned pattern? What if a new, far better challenger becomes available? What if inflation is higher than expected? What if shortages disrupt operations? For major decisions the list of "what ifs" is discouragingly long, but decisions still have to be made. To escape inertia caused by nagging doubts, decision makers have to first accept the realization that they will seldom, if ever, know all conditions with absolute certainty. Then they can focus on one or more critical factors and investigate what would happen to a proposal as a result of variations in those factors. That is the purpose of sensitivity analysis.

*Sensitivity analysis involves repeated computations with different cash flow elements and analysis factors to compare results obtained from these substitutions with results from the original data.* If a small change in an element leads to a proportionately greater change in the results, the situation is said to be sensitive to that assumption or variable. In an economic study, the critical point is the level at which an analysis factor causes an economic proposal to change from acceptable to not acceptable, or that reverses a preference between alternatives.

An informal sensitivity assessment is natural for most decisions. The amount of analysis time that a decision deserves was examined in Example 1.2. Variability in cash flow estimates and the effects of different values of $i$, $N$, $P$, and $S$ were considered in several chapters. In this chapter, formal procedures for evaluating deviations from basic data are discussed, with emphasis on the value of graphical representations.

Consideration of the sensitivity of assumptions begins at the preproposal stage, where it is decided whether ideas for improvements are worthy of further development, and continues to the proposal presentation stage, where a case is made for the final acceptance or rejection decision. The role of sensitivity analysis for proposal planning, evaluation, and presentation is explored in the following examples.

## Example 14.1 What If an Investment Is Made that Increases Fixed Costs?

An engineer has suggested an improvement in a production line that requires a substantial investment. This alteration will increase the fixed cost of producing the products. While it can be shown that the alteration improves quality and reduces variable costs, the question remains whether future sales revenue will provide sufficient additional income to make the investment worthwhile.

Figure 14.1 displays the considerations involved, in the form of a breakeven chart (traditional breakeven analysis and conventional breakeven charts are presented in Chapter 16). The annual cost of the proposed improvement is represented by an increase in the fixed cost of production. This increase raises the total production cost, which is the sum of variable costs and fixed cost. Total cost increases as a function of annual output volume, as does sales revenue when the output is sold. Potential variations in costs and revenue are shown by shaded areas. If it is reasonable to expect sales revenue to increase enough to offset the added fixed costs, or if the proposal will decrease variable costs enough to pay for itself, or if a combination of greater sales revenue and lower variable costs will produce a large enough positive cash flow, the proposal merits further development.

It is doubtful that a chart would be drawn to enunciate the prospective operation variables in the example. The sensitivity analysis would more likely be a mental evaluation or preliminary calculation to confirm that receipts or savings could

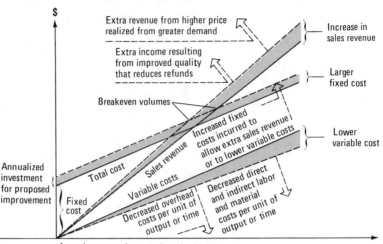

**FIGURE 14.1** Possible results of an investment that increases fixed cost to improve quality and reduce variable costs. The critical factor is whether output volume will be sufficient to support the investment.

plausibly be expected to cover the investment. Then the idea would emerge from the preproposal to the proposal stage.

### Example 14.2   What If Demand for Services and Labor Costs Change?

In most service industries, demand fluctuates in response to local or national trends. Inflation, unemployment, size of harvests, and other conditions that cannot be confidently forecasted affect the cash flow of a proposal. In deciding whether to introduce a new labor-intensive service, a company is concerned about the demand for the new service and possible increases in labor costs.

The nature of the service to be offered suggests that demand might exceed the basic estimate by 10 percent or fall short of expectation by 10 percent. Labor costs could increase by 5 percent or 10 percent over original estimates. The effect of these variations is analyzed by calculating the present worth of the project at each level of anticipated demand and labor costs. Results of the calculations are shown in Table 14.1.

| LABOR COSTS | DEMAND LEVEL | | |
|---|---|---|---|
| | *Decrease of 10%* | *Original Data* | *Increase of 10%* |
| Basic Data | $250,000 | $300,000 | $420,000 |
| Increase of 5% | 255,000 | 310,000 | 440,000 |
| Increase of 10% | 265,000 | 325,000 | 465,000 |

Present worth of project

**TABLE 14.1** Present worth of a proposal as it is affected by changes in demand and increases in labor costs.

From the table it appears that PW is not very sensitive to labor costs; it is unlikely that a labor-cost estimating error will lead to a "wrong" decision because the proposal's PW does not rise disproportionately to labor costs. However, a 10 percent increase or decrease in demand causes a pronounced change in the present worth, a variation of 17 to 43 percent from the basic data. This sensitivity indicates that more study may be justified to provide assurance that the demand level used in the original data is supportable.

Graphs, charts, and tables are often prepared to explain the sensitivity of proposals to key decision makers. The data for the visual aids is generated by substituting different values for the critical variables in formulas used during proposal analysis. The purpose of pictorial presentations is to clarify the considerations that are pertinent to a proposal's acceptance and to present analysis results in a digested but readily understood format.

### Example 14.3   What If Profit Increases?

Annual reports from corporations, government reports, news magazines, and other publications that deal with economic statistics use bar graphs, pie charts, and myriad other pictorial devices to display economic relationships. The purpose may be to influence, explain, or educate. When they portray the financial effect of different assumptions, they are agents for sensitivity analysis.

An attention-getting display of how an investment grows as a function of capital structure, operating success, and dividend policy is shown in Figure 14.2. It is a form

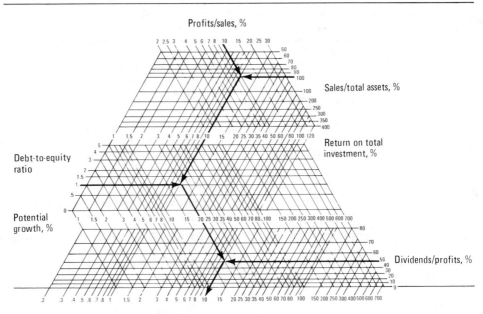

**FIGURE 14.2**   Trilinear representation of factors affecting investment growth. Bold lines indicate paths based on:

$$10\% \frac{\text{profit}}{\text{sales}} \rightarrow 100\% \frac{\text{sales}}{\text{assets}} \rightarrow 10\% \text{ return on investment}$$

$$10\% \text{ return on investment} \rightarrow 1.0 \frac{\text{debt}}{\text{equity}} \rightarrow 20\% \text{ potential growth}$$

$$20\% \text{ potential growth} \rightarrow 50\% \frac{\text{dividends}}{\text{profits}} \rightarrow 10\% \text{ rate of investment growth}$$

of *trilinear* chart, a nomograph based on trigometric features of equilateral triangles. It facilitates a sensitivity analysis by providing a range of values for each variable and the paths that relate the variables to each other. In effect, it is a graphical calculator that simplifies an examination of factors that contribute to return on capital.

The top segment of the chart shows return on investment determined from the profit-to-total-asset ratio. Potential growth for the investment is the product of the return given by the top segment and the debt-to-equity ratio (a ratio of 1.0 means that total assets are represented equally by debt and ownership funds, which doubles the rate of return when equity is the only concern). The lower segment shows the rate by which the investment grows as a result of the percent of profits left in the firm after paying dividends. Various combinations of inputs that could produce a given number for a certain parameter can be tested by tracing different paths through the chart.

# SENSITIVITY OF A SINGLE PROPOSAL

Assume a decision is to be made about a business opportunity based on the following estimates and tentative before-tax analysis:

| *Economic Factors* | *PW for a 10-Year Study Period at i = 13%* |
|---|---|
| Annual receipts ($35,000) | +$189,917 |
| First cost ($170,000) | −170,000 |
| Salvage value ($20,000) | +5,892 |
| Annual disbursements ($3000) | −16,279 |
| *Net PW* | +$9,530 |

The first cost is the most reliably known value in the problem, owing to its immediacy. The other factors could vary considerably over the 10-year period, owing to unforeseeable deviations from anticipated conditions. Even the study period may be inappropriate if the asset's useful life is shorter than 10 years (or longer than 10 years), or if the function it serves does not continue to yield the stated receipts for the full study period. And the 13 percent rate of return might be questioned. Should it be higher to compensate for inflation and the risk of losing invested capital? Or should it be lower?

## Sensitivity Graph

Such questions are collectively examined by constructing a sensitivity graph as shown in Figure 14.3. Curves are generated by substituting various values for one factor in the PW formula,

$$PW = -(\text{first cost}) + (\text{salvage value})(P/F, i, N) + (\text{receipts} - \text{disbursements})(P/A, i, N)$$

while holding the values of all other factors constant. The abscissa of the graph is the

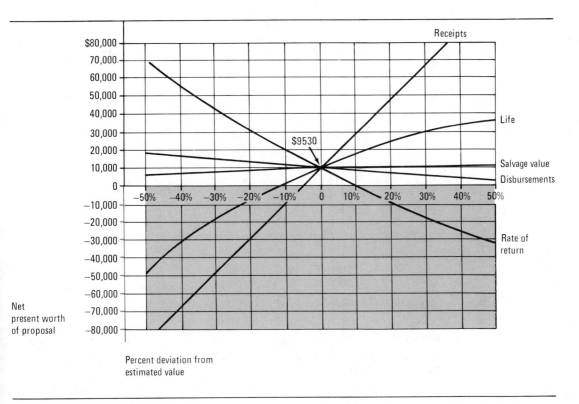

**FIGURE 14.3**   Sensitivity graph of the effect on a proposal's net PW when factors deviate from their original estimates.

percentage deviation from original values. This dimensionless scale puts all the factors in the same perspective to allow direct comparison of curve shapes. A steeper rising or falling curve indicates greater sensitivity of the proposal's worth to that factor.

The sensitivity graph reveals that deviations of up to 50 percent of the original estimates for salvage value and annual disbursements will not affect the acceptance of the proposal. The other factors—minimum acceptable rate of return, number of years the proposal will stay in effect, and amount of annual receipts—could switch the verdict to the do-nothing alternative if they deviate by only 10 percent from the original estimates. This condition suggests that extra care be given to forecasts of future business conditions that could affect income flow or the continued demand for the asset purchased.

## Isoquant

The life of the asset and the size of receipts are not controlled by the analyst, as is the interest rate used in the comparison. The timing and amount of the cash flows are functions of the operating environment. Since these are the two most sensitive factors in the evaluation of the proposal, the limiting combinations for accepting or rejecting the proposal are graphed as an *isoquant* in Figure 14.4. The isoquant forms an *indifference line* which indicates the combinations of the proposal's duration and size of receipts that make the present worth of the proposal neither positive nor negative (indifference condition) when the other factors are unchanged. Thus, a reduction in the life of the asset from 10 to 8 years must be accompanied by an increase in annual receipts for 8 years of at least $36,859 − $35,000 = $1859 for the proposal to be minimally acceptable at $i = 13$ percent:

$$PW \doteq 0 = -\$170,000 + \$20,000(P/F, 13, 8) + (\$36,859 - \$3000)(P/A, 13, 8)$$
$$0 = -\$170,000 + \$20,000(0.37616) + \$33,859(4.7987)$$

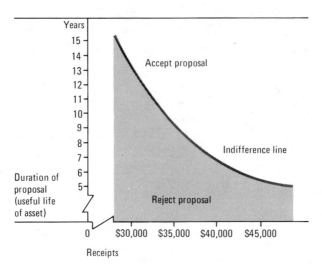

**FIGURE 14.4** Isoquant showing combinations of the proposal's life and annual receipts at which the present worth is zero. Any combination that falls above the indifference line indicates the proposal is acceptable when other factors remain constant.

## Acceptance-Rejection Zones

A chart divided into acceptance and rejection zones based on more than one parameter of a proposal combines the sensitivity-graph format with an isoquant. Two or three critical parameters can be selected for the sensitivity study. If two are chosen, a formula is written to determine the present or annual worth of the proposal in which one parameter is associated with the $x$ axis of a graph and the other with the $y$ axis. The intent of the formulation is to develop an expression relating values of parameter $x$ and parameter $y$ that generate zero present worth or annual worth. The resulting expression is represented by a line on the sensitivity graph. Percentage changes from the original data that occur on one side of the line maintain a positive worth for the proposal, while changes that fall on the other side cause a negative worth.

### Example 14.4   Two-Parameter Sensitivity Study

The proposal pictured in Figures 14.3 and 14.4 is to be tested for its sensitivity to annual receipts and disbursements. The intent is to determine how large a joint percentage change in these critical parameters can be sustained without rejecting the proposal; it will be rejected if the equivalent annual worth is negative. Develop a sensitivity graph that identifies the acceptance and rejection zones.

## Solution 14.4

Letting $x$ represent a percentage change in receipts and $y$ a percentage change in disbursements, the equivalent annual worth for the proposal is

$$
\begin{aligned}
\text{EAW} &= -\$170{,}000(A/P, 13, 10) + \$35{,}000(1 + x) \\
&\quad - \$3000(1 + y) + \$20{,}000(A/F, 13, 10) \\
&= -\$170{,}000(0.18429) + \$35{,}000 + \$35{,}000x - \$3000 \\
&\quad - \$3000y + \$20{,}000(0.05429) \\
&= \$1757 + \$35{,}000x - \$3000y
\end{aligned}
$$

where $x$ and $y$ represent percent changes from the original data.

The proposal will be profitable, and therefore acceptable, so long as $\text{EAW} > 0$, or

$$
x > \frac{3000}{35{,}000}\, y - \frac{1757}{35{,}000} \qquad \text{so} \qquad x > 0.0857y - 0.0502
$$

When this inequality is plotted on a graph with $x$ and $y$ axes scaled in percent, the indifference line separates the chart into acceptance and rejection zones. The acceptance zone is on one side of the line where $\text{EAW} > 0$, and the rejection zone is on the other side. The near-vertical slope of the line indicates that the proposal is

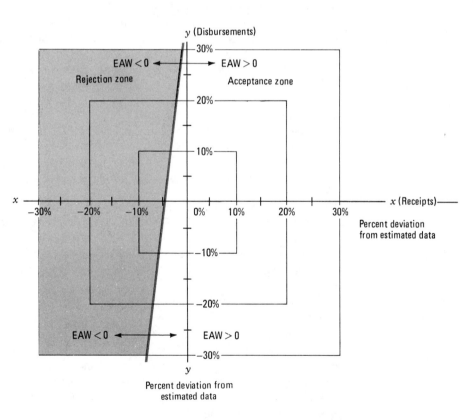

**FIGURE 14.5**
Sensitivity graph of the percentage change for two factors (receipts and disbursements) that define acceptance and rejection zones for a proposal when all other factors are held constant.

highly sensitive to changes in the $x$ factor (receipts), and quite insensitive to the $y$ factor, as is obvious from a comparison of the magnitude of annual receipts relative to annual disbursements.

The center of the sensitivity graph in Figure 14.5 represents the original conditions for the proposal, where EAW = $1757. At $x = -5$ percent and $y = 0$,

EAW = $1757 + $35,000(-0.05) - $3000(0.0) = $7

At $y = -5$ percent and $x = 0$,

EAW = $1757 + $35,000(0.0) - $3000(-0.05) = $1907

Thus the sensitivity study clearly emphasizes the criticality of an accurate forecast of future receipts.

## Range of Estimates

An intensive assessment of a proposal's cash flow is provided by a scenario approach that asks "What if the future is more or less favorable than originally estimated?" By bracketing the most likely cash flow condition with optimistic and pessimistic scenarios, the analyst exposes the shortcomings and strengths of the proposal. Each element of the proposal is questioned with respect to conditions envisioned for the bleak and promising scenarios. Most elements will probably vary from initial estimates, but some may be stable. The sensitivity of the proposal to each scenario is revealed by comparing the PW, EAW, or IRR of the three sets of data.

The range is developed from:

1 *An objective estimate* The most likely cash flow and the one that would be used if only a single estimate were made
2 *A more-favorable estimate* An optimistic appraisal based on an advantageous interpretation of future events
3 *A less-favorable estimate* A pessimistic assessment of the future that adversely affects the cash flow

Neither the more- nor less-favorable estimate is based on an extreme—the best or worst that could conceivably happen. They assess the outcomes of border conditions that are reasonably likely to occur. The three-estimate approach is also applicable to uncertainties besides price; analyses based on ranges of possible levels of activity, such as utilization rates and output quantities, or levels of performance may be more useful than single-estimate evaluations.

Item-by-item estimates are more credible than collective estimates. Additional work is required to develop estimates for smaller cash-flow categories, but the resulting summations are more likely to be accurate than block estimates, and the effort expended makes the analyst better informed about the situation. The cost of extra calculations and estimating is usually insignificant compared with the value of even a small improvement in the decision process. Therefore, when price instability casts doubt on future cash flows, or operating levels cannot be anticipated with any assurance, an evaluation encompassing a range of itemized estimates is a sound practice.

## Example 14.5  Range of Estimates that Reflect Uncertain Future Prices for a Training Proposal

A proposal has been made to introduce a training program to improve a production process which relies primarily on manual operations. New motions and fixtures for individual operators are expected to lower manufacturing costs from their present level by about $50,000 per year. It is difficult to predict the benefits of the training proposal because the size of the savings depends on the scale of operations and prices, which are functions of the marketplace and general economic conditions.

A range of estimates for possible future conditions is shown. Should the training program be adopted?

| Items Estimated | Less-Favorable Estimate | Objective Estimate | More-Favorable Estimate |
|---|---|---|---|
| Additional units produced annually | 60,000 | 75,000 | 100,000 |
| Price/unit | $2 | $3 | $3.50 |
| Annual income | $120,000 | $225,000 | $350,000 |
| Duration of income | 5 years | 6 years | 7 years |
| Training cost/year | $45,000 | $35,000 | $30,000 |
| Required period of intensive training | 2 years | 2 years | 1 year |
| Operating expenses of new process | $90,000 | $160,000 | $275,000 |
| Investment in consumable supplies | $30,000 | $30,000 | $30,000 |

## Solution 14.5

A before-tax analysis using a 15 percent required rate of return is conducted by calculating the present worth of the cash flows for the three possible conditions: less favorable (LF), objective estimate (OE), and more favorable (MF).

$$PW(LF) = (\$120,000 - \$90,000)(P/A, 15, 5) - \$45,000(P/A, 15, 2) - \$30,000$$
$$= \$30,000(3.3521) - \$45,000(1.6257) - \$30,000$$
$$= \$100,563 - \$73,157 - \$30,000 = -\$2594$$

$$PW(OE) = (\$225,000 - \$160,000)(P/A, 15, 6) - \$35,000(P/A, 15, 2) - \$30,000$$
$$= \$65,000(3.7844) - \$35,000(1.6257) - \$30,000$$
$$= \$245,986 - \$56,900 - \$30,000 = \$159,086$$

$$PW(MF) = (\$350,000 - \$275,000)(P/A, 15, 7) - \$30,000(P/A, 15, 1) - \$30,000$$
$$= \$75,000(4.1604) - \$30,000(0.8696) - \$30,000$$
$$= \$312,030 - \$26,087 - \$30,000 = \$255,943$$

Although there is a chance the training program will result in a small loss if things go unfortunately, the opportunity for a very large gain under more favorable conditions makes the proposal very attractive. The three-phase analysis admits the chance of low returns and shows how good returns can be if things turn out favorably.

# SENSITIVITY OF ALTERNATIVES

An alternative ($A2$) has been developed to accomplish the same mission as the proposal ($A1$) described by the sensitivity relationships in Figure 14.3. Both alternatives are expected to have the same revenue, but proposal $A2$ has a lower first cost. However, the annual disbursements for $A2$ will increase significantly each year as shown by the following cash-flow estimates:

| Factor | Alternative 1 | Alternative 2 |
|---|---|---|
| Annual receipts | $ 35,000 | $ 35,000 |
| First cost | 170,000 | 116,400 |
| Salvage value (year 10) | 20,000 | 0 |
| Annual disbursements | 3,000 | $3000 the first year and increasing by $2500 each year |

On the basis of the given estimates and a study period of 10 years with $i = 13$ percent, both alternatives have about the same PW:

$$PW(A1) = \$9530$$

$$PW(A2) = -\$116{,}400 + [\$35{,}000 - (\$3000 + \$2500)(A/G, 13, 10)](P/A, 13, 10)$$
$$= -\$116{,}400 + [\$32{,}000 - \$2500(3.5161)](5.4262)$$
$$= \$9540$$

Therefore, a preference for one or the other rests on the interpretation given to the annual cash flows. Since both alternatives are assumed to produce the same receipts, and disbursements can usually be estimated quite accurately, the most questionable feature remaining is the study period. A sensitivity graph for the alternatives' possible useful lives is given in Figure 14.6.

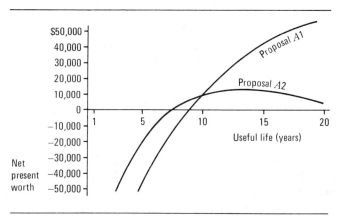

**FIGURE 14.6**
Sensitivity of two proposals to deviations from their estimated life.

The graph indicates that *A*2 is preferred to *A*1 when the likelihood is that the proposals will have lives of less than 10 years. At $N = 7$, neither proposal is profitable. Proposal *A*1 offers much larger gains should the life extend beyond 10 years.

The most critical cash flow elements that distinguish one alternative from another are usually quite evident. If one alternative has an exceptionally large salvage value, estimates for $N$ and $i$ should be scrutinized. An after-tax evaluation of proposals where one alternative has a particularly favorable loan arrangement suggests close inspection of interest rates. Any of the elements so picked for further examination can be graphed.

Often a graph will assist in a decision by narrowing the judgments that have to be made. For instance, growth rate is frequently a debatable parameter. Growth may be a function of inflation as it affects certain cash flow elements or a function of the rate of service expansion, as in higher production rates needed to satisfy increasing demand for a product. Growth rate is shown on the $x$ axis of Figure 14.7, where the present worths of three alternatives are graphed. Intersections of the plotted lines indicate the range of growth over which each alternative is preferred. Where proposals are presented in this fashion, it is not necessary to substantiate the selection of a certain growth rate for the study; the managers who are responsible for the final selection can use their personal judgment as to which alternative best serves their vision of future conditions. Also, the decision makers do not have to fret over a specific growth rate; they just have to pick a range in which they expect it to fall.

**FIGURE 14.7**
Sensitivity comparison of present worths of three alternatives that have different growth rates. Alternative *A* is preferred if the anticipated growth rate is less that $G_1$, and alternative *C* is the choice when growth is expected to exceed $G_2$. Between $G_1$ and $G_2$, alternative *B* has the highest present worth.

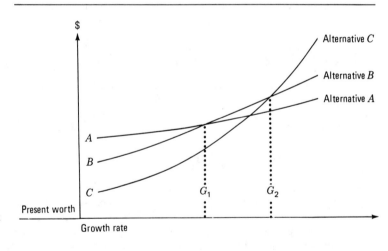

## REVIEW EXERCISES AND DISCUSSIONS

**Exercise 1**  A would-be engineer spent so much time seeing movies while she was enrolled in engineering school that she never passed the differential-equations course. After she dropped out, she inherited $100,000 on her twenty-first birthday (perhaps that is why she did not bother to study much). She greeted this inheritance as a chance to satisfy her passion for flicks by leasing a soon-to-be vacant supermarket and converting it into a CinemaCenter comprising four small theaters in the one building. Based upon what she remembered from the engineering economics course she took before leaving school, she prepared the following cost estimates:

| | |
|---|---|
| Renovation cost | $80,000 |
| Contingency fund | $10,000 |
| Estimated life of renovations | 9 years |
| Salvage value | 0 |
| Annual operating cost (365 days/year) | $62,000 |
| Annual lease expense | $42,000 |
| Other annualized expenses | $16,000 |
| Desired annual profit | $35,000 |

The CinemaCenter will have 280 deluxe seats in the four projection areas and an elaborate lobby. Income per moviegoer should average $3.35, including net profit from refreshments purchased.

The most questionable estimate involved in this economic evaluation is the number of people who will attend the shows. She has been told that she will be lucky to have a 50 percent utilization rate. What percentage of capacity is necessary to break even (assuming receipts accumulate to year-end totals and the local cost of capital is 12 percent)? What influencing factors should be considered in forecasting utilization rates?

**Solution 1**   The percentage of seats occupied by paying customers $X$ needed to break even when the desired profit is not included as a cost is found from

$$0 = (\$3.35)(280)(365)(X) - (\$80,000 + \$10,000)(A/P, 12, 9) - \$62,000 - \\ \$42,000 - \$16,000$$
$$= \$342,370X - \$90,000(0.18768) - \$120,000$$

and,

$$X = \frac{\$16,891 + \$120,000}{\$342,370} = 0.4 \quad or \quad 40\%$$

If the estimated 50 percent attendance figure is realistic, the CinemaCenter appears to have a decent chance of surviving, so long as no profit is expected. To achieve the $35,000-per-year profit goal, the utilization rate must exceed 50 percent. Factors to consider in forecasting the chances of bettering 50 percent include the number and success of competitors, demographic data on the number of people in age groups most likely to attend the type of movies to be shown, and the average wage and spending habits of the local population.

---

**Exercise 2**   Data for a training program are shown on page 319. The expected duration of the program is 6 years. Both benefits and costs are uncertain. Analyze the desirability of the program from the given data.

| | BENEFIT | | | COST | | | | PRESENT WORTH | | | | | |
| | | | | | | | | EXPECTED | | MINIMUM | | MAXIMUM | |
| Year | Min. | Exp. | Max. | Min. | Exp. | Max. | (P/F, 10, N) | B | C | B | C | B | C |
|---|---|---|---|---|---|---|---|---|---|---|---|---|---|
| 1 | 0 | 0 | 5 | 10 | 15 | 25 | 0.90909 | 0 | 13.6 | 0 | 9.1 | 4.5 | 22.7 |
| 2 | 5 | 10 | 15 | 10 | 10 | 15 | 0.82645 | 8.3 | 8.3 | 4.1 | 8.3 | 12.4 | 12.4 |
| 3 | 15 | 20 | 25 | 5 | 5 | 10 | 0.75132 | 15.0 | 3.8 | 11.3 | 3.8 | 18.8 | 7.5 |
| 4 | 20 | 30 | 30 | 4 | 5 | 8 | 0.68302 | 20.5 | 3.4 | 13.7 | 2.7 | 20.5 | 5.5 |
| 5 | 10 | 20 | 25 | 3 | 5 | 6 | 0.62092 | 12.4 | 3.1 | 6.2 | 1.9 | 15.5 | 3.7 |
| 6 | 5 | 15 | 20 | 2 | 5 | 5 | 0.56448 | 8.5 | 2.8 | 2.8 | 1.1 | 11.3 | 2.8 |
| *Totals* | | | | | | | | 64.7 | 35.0 | 38.1 | 26.9 | 83.0 | 54.6 |

**Solution 2**  The *expected* benefit-to-cost ratio based on the most likely values is

$$B/C = \frac{64.7}{35.0} = 1.85 \quad \text{and} \quad B - C = 29.7$$

which makes the program acceptable. As is apparent in the table, the B/C ratios under all three conditions are greater than 1.0. However, if maximum cost occurred while the benefit was at a minimum, then

$$B/C(\text{worst condition}) = \frac{38.1}{54.6} = 0.70 \quad \text{and} \quad B - C = -16.5$$

The worst combination might be excused from consideration if supporting evidence could be collected to show that the chance is very remote that the highest cost would accompany the lowest benefit.

---

**Exercise 3**  Review Exercise 3 of Chapter 13 described a proposal in which the cost factors were subject to individually unique inflation rates. Since forecasting future inflation rates is always an "iffy" proposition, a sensitivity analysis is appropriate. Based on the data from the original problem (summarized below), develop a sensitivity graph for deviations from initial inflation estimates.

---

PROPOSAL TO PURCHASE AUTOMATED EQUIPMENT DESIGNED TO
REDUCE LABOR COSTS AND MATERIAL WASTE

---

*Automated equipment*
  $P = \$150,000$
  $S = 0$
  $N = 3$ years
*Annual revenue*
  Net savings in labor = $60,000; $f = 8\%$
  Net savings in material = $140,000; $f = 5\%$
*Annual costs*
  Additional energy required = $70,000; $f = 20\%$
  Added maintenance expense = $30,000; $f = 10\%$
Effective tax rate = 50%; straight-line depreciation

---

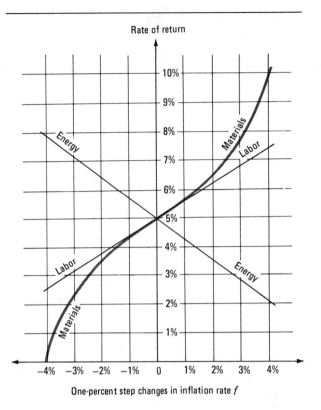

**FIGURE 14.8**
Sensitivity graph of different inflation rates on the IRR of the proposal described in Review Exercise 3 of Chapter 13.

The critical cost factors subject to unique inflation rates are labor, material, and energy. The effects of deviations from the expected inflation rates are determined by calculating an IRR for each percent change in the inflation rate of one factor while all other conditions are held constant. The curves shown in Figure 14.8 consolidate the results of all the computations.

The intersection of the curves is at the IRR calculated previously for the most likely inflation rates. The most sensitive cost element is material because it has a proportionately much larger dollar value than the other factors in the proposal; an increase in the inflation rate from 5 to 9 percent doubles the rate of return (savings from decreased use of material are worth more as the price of the material goes up). Energy is almost as sensitive, owing to its much higher starting inflation rate, even though it is applied to a factor only half as large as material.

# PROBLEMS

**14.1** A company has a debt-to-equity ratio of 3:1. Annual sales are 150 percent of total assets and provide a rate of return on total investment of 9 percent. If a growth rate on investment of 25 percent is desired, use the trilinear chart to determine what percent of profit can be paid in dividends and what percent profit is expected from sales.

*(Profit/sales = 6%; dividend/profit = 30%)*

**14.2** An isoquant is to be developed for program $A$ in Problem 6.8. It will relate the two most sensitive factors: the life of the program and expected volume. Using $i = 8$ percent, $N = 4$, and $P = \$10,000$, what is the dollar value of the specified point on the isoquant? *($3019)*

**14.3** A project will have a life of 10 years and is to be evaluated at a social discount rate of 9 percent. It has an initial cost of $1 million, and expected annual costs are $100,000. However, it is possible that these annual costs could consistently increase by $10,000 each year or decrease by $5000 per year. The most likely annual benefits are $350,000, but there is a chance that benefits will decrease by $25,000 per year.

   **14.3a** What is the worst possible B/C that could occur with the given scenario?
*(B/C = 0.868)*

   **14.3b** What maximum first cost could be incurred for an acceptable project in which annual cash flows follow the expected (most likely) estimates? *(P = $1,604,400)*

**14.4** The purchase of rental property in a neighborhood where real-estate prices are increasing rapidly is being considered. The following estimates have been developed for a preliminary before-tax analysis:

| | |
|---|---|
| First cost | $50,000 |
| Annual income from rent | $6,000 |
| Annual maintenance | $1,000 |
| Investment period | 6 years |
| Resale value | $60,000 |
| Cost of capital | 10% |

   **14.4a** Given that the first cost of the property and the investment period are fixed, construct a sensitivity chart showing the effect of changes in all the other elements on the EAW.

   **14.4b** Construct a sensitivity chart for joint variation within a $\pm 30$ percent range of annual income and cost of capital; indicate the acceptance and rejection zones.

**14.5** A proposal is described by the following estimates: $P = \$20,000$; $S = 0$; $N = 5$; and net annual receipts $= \$7000$. A rate of return of 20 percent is desired on such proposals. Construct a sensitivity graph of the life, annual receipts, and rate of return for deviations over a range of $\pm 20$ percent. To which element is the decision most sensitive? *(Annual receipts)*

**14.6** Tennis enthusiasts in a small town want indoor courts to allow them to play tennis during bad weather. Someone suggested that they band together to form a corporation to build and operate a profit-making tennis facility. Two courts with a small lounge could be built for $125,000, not including land. The facility would have a 10-year life and a salvage value of $20,000. Annual operating expenses would be $23,000.

   **14.6a** At a charge of $7 per hour for playing time on a court, how many hours would the courts have to be rented each year for the investors to break even on construction and operating costs, assuming a rate of return of 10 percent? *(3006 hours)*

   **14.6b** Develop a graph of the utilization rate required to yield rates of return between 10 and 25 percent. Assume the facility will be open 14 hours per day for 320 days each year. Would you recommend the investment? Why?

**14.7** Three designs to perform the same function have the cost patterns indicated:

*Design 1* Initial cost is $12,000, and annual expenses are uniform at $4000 per year.

*Design 2* A low initial cost of $5000 is possible because refinements will be made while the facility is in operation. The first year's operating and refinement cost will be $7500, and it will decrease by $500 each year.

*Design 3*   Initial cost is $15,000, with annual disbursements that start at $2000 and increase by $1000 each year.

The principal uncertainty in the evaluation is how long the function will be needed for which the designs were developed. All the designs could perform the function for 12 years, if the function lasts that long, and none of the designs would have any salvage value at any time. Determine the range of life over which different designs would be preferred when the minimum attractive rate of return is 11 percent.

**14.8**   An aluminum company has to decide whether to install a new type of "air float" conveyor for extra thin aluminum sheets or to retain their conventional conveyors. A pilot test reveals that the float conveyor moves the sheets faster and reduces damage, but maintenance costs to keep it operating properly may be high. The amount of savings expected from the new design depends on the quantity of aluminum sheeting produced in the future and the reliability of the new equipment. The engineering department has provided the following estimates:

| | |
|---|---|
| First cost | $180,000 |
| Economic life | 4 years |
| Annual maintenance expense | $40,000 |
| Annual savings | $100,000 |

There is no realizable salvage value because the cost of removing the equipment would about equal the scrap value. The company uses a minimum attractive rate of return of 12 percent.

**14.8a**   Because there is still some doubt about the effectiveness of the air float conveyor design, some of the analysts feel a higher rate of return should be required for the project. Make an isoquant of the maximum first cost that could be incurred to earn rates of return between 5 and 25 percent.

**14.8b**   Assuming the life, maintenance cost, and savings may vary as much as 50 percent on both sides of the given estimate, develop a graph of the effects of individual variations on the net present worth of the project. Do you recommend that the new conveyor system be installed? Why?

**14.9**   Current mail-sorting operations on one line at a mail distribution center cost about $1 million per year. A newly developed and essentially unproved but promising system for sorting mail by automatic address readers is being considered. Although the devices have been tested and approved in laboratories, there is still doubt about how they will perform in regular service. Questionnaires describing less-than-favorable and more-than-favorable operating conditions were sent to people familiar with the devices and the mail-distribution process. Consensus data from the two scenarios and the most likely estimates are shown below:

| Factors Estimated | Pessimistic Estimate | Most Likely Estimate | Optimistic Estimate |
|---|---|---|---|
| First cost, including installation | $2,112,000 | $985,000 | $915,000 |
| Life, years of full utilization | 2 years | 2 years | 6 years |
| Annual maintenance and minor repair | $221,000 | $81,000 | $75,000 |
| Annual operating cost and standbys | $929,000 | $714,000 | $588,000 |

Calculate the range of EAC and discuss the results. MARR = 10 percent.

$$[EAC(P) = \$2,155,713; \; EAC(ML) = \$1,007,238; \; EAC(O) = \$781,593]$$

**14.10** There is considerable doubt about the need for and performance to be obtained from a new process developed by the R&D department. A decision about launching a small-scale pilot project is being evaluated. Three estimates of possible outcomes of the pilot project are given below.

|  | *Objective Estimate* | *Less Favorable Estimate* | *More-Favorable Estimate* |
|---|---|---|---|
| Income/year | $200,000 | $150,000 | $250,000 |
| Expenses/year | $80,000 | $80,000 | $90,000 |
| Start-up cost | $300,000 | $350,000 | $300,000 |
| Life of project | 3 years | 1 year | 4 years |
| Salvage value | $100,000 | $50,000 | $100,000 |

**14.10a** What is the present worth of each possible future when the minimum attractive rate of return is 15 percent?

**14.10b** What other considerations could affect the decision to launch the pilot project? Should the money already invested in research and development be a consideration? Why?

**14.10c** Compare the range-of-estimates method of evaluation with sensitivity analysis.

**14.11** Three revenue-producing projects are being considered. Estimates of future returns are uncertain because the projects involve new products. The initial investment is expected to provide adequate production capability for any reasonable project life, and the lives of all projects are considered to be equal. Regardless of useful life, there will be no salvage value.

*Project I* has a first cost of $200,000 and uniform annual net revenue of $65,000.

*Project O* has a low initial cost of $100,000 and will return $50,000 the first year, but net revenue will decline each year by an amount $0.5G$, where $G$ is a uniform gradient.

*Project U* has a high initial cost of $250,000 and also returns $50,000 the first year, with the expectation that net revenue will increase by an annual uniform amount $G$.

Compare the three projects by constructing sensitivity graphs according to the following assumptions, and discuss the results.

**14.11a** Let the project life be 6 years and $G = \$7500$ to test project preference for sensitivity to minimum rates of return up to 25 percent.

**14.11b** Let the project life be 6 years and MARR = 12 percent to test project preference for sensitivity to values of $G$ from 0 to $15,000.

**14.11c** Let MARR = 12 percent and $G = \$7500$ to test project preference for sensitivity to project life.

# CHAPTER 15

# INDUSTRIAL PRACTICES

OVERVIEW

This chapter builds on previously introduced concepts to examine more closely the perspective of industrial organizations toward investment financing and customized procedures for selecting the most promising proposals.

Investment funds are acquired *internally* from depreciation (CCA) and retained earnings, and *externally* by borrowing capital or selling equity. Tax deductions allowed for interest payments enhance the attractiveness of debt financing. A higher *leverage factor* (ratio of debt to total assets) generally produces higher after-tax returns on equity when business conditions are favorable, but it lowers returns when conditions are unfavorable. Leasing rather than borrowing or using equity funds to buy an asset is another alternative.

Many industrial organizations utilize customized economic evaluation procedures, often complemented by worksheet forms. A *request for expenditure* (RFE) includes supporting analysis documents and a letter of justification which explains the proposed investment. *Postauditing* is a systemized follow-up on approved RFEs to appraise the accuracy of previous estimates in order to improve future estimations.

The "moment of truth" in engineering economics is the final decision to fund or reject a proposed investment. Industrial practices attempt to make the judgment convenient, consistent, and credible.

# SOURCE OF FUNDS

Securing capital is a prerequisite to implementing an acceptable proposal. Ideas for profitable investments are generated and data are collected to support or refute the investment proposals on the assumption that funds will become available to carry out the best ones. These funds can be generated internally or acquired from external sources.

The amount of *internal funds* available for investment during a given time period is the positive difference between cash receipts and all cash disbursements for that period. The disbursements include operating expenses, interest charges, taxes, and dividends, but *not* CCA. The flow of funds is shown in Figure 15.1. The influx of *external funds* is mainly from *debt* (bonds, mortgages, short-term notes, etc.) and *equity* (issues of common or preferred stock and other forms of partial ownership).

One of the best ways to cultivate funding sources is to have profitable operations or activities that strongly promise future profits. Even then there may be a scarcity of capital owing to inflated prices for new investments and the worldwide tightening of capital supplies. Mr. F. W. Searby, a director of McKinsey & Company, described the plight of not-so-profitable capital-intensive companies as follows:

> In the last 20 years, industrial companies in basic industries have substantially increased their debt in absolute terms and, perhaps what is more important, in relation to their

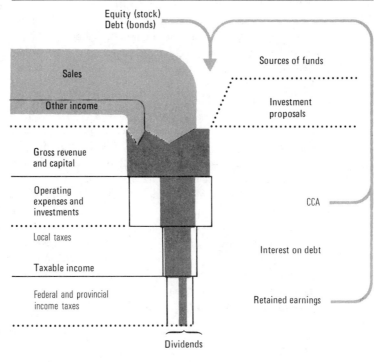

**FIGURE 15.1** Flow of funds into, through, and out of an industrial organization. New funds are derived from borrowing or selling equity. Sources of internal funds are depreciation charges and retained earnings.

equity. Capital requirements as measured by assets to sales are up; return on capital is down; the financing burden as measured by the dividend yield demanded by the market is up; and the total bite on profits taken by interest payments is also up.*

# STRATEGIC CONSIDERATIONS CONCERNING FUNDING SOURCES

The management of an industrial enterprise works for the owners. In smaller firms the managers may be the owners. Either in the role of an owner or representing owners, management has the responsibility of conducting operations in ways that financially benefit the equity holders. Owners receive gains from successful corporate operations in two forms: dividend payments and increases in the value of their stock. Each of the four main sources of funds shown in Figure 15.1 has its own effect on returns to equity holders.

CCA is the least controversial source of funds for new investments. Investments in replacements for worn assets and new processes to update production functions are customary practices.

*Retained earnings* come from after-tax income that could be distributed to shareholders as dividends. Expenditures of retained earnings are judged by the effect they have on the market price of stock. Stock prices typically reflect current earnings per share and the growth potential of a firm. If the stock market is confident that a firm is building up to a more profitable position, the stock price can rise even when the earnings are modest and no dividends are declared over a prolonged period.

*Equity financing* results from selling part ownership in a firm. When additional shares are issued and sold, and profits do not increase, there is a dilution of earnings.

*Debt financing* does not dilute ownership, and it offers certain tax advantages, but the incurred indebtedness can be an onerous drain on finances during periods of low economic activity. Example 15.1 illustrates some of the considerations involved in an equity-versus-debt financing decision.

---

**Example 15.1   A Decision to Borrow Funds or to Sell Equity**
Two brothers own and operate a vegetable cannery valued at $300,000. They have an opportunity to buy a firm which now supplies most of their warehousing and distribution services. Only an insignificant amount of the to-be-acquired firm's assets is depreciable because the warehouses and equipment are leased. An annual saving of $28,000, exclusive of financing costs, should result from the acquisition. There are insufficient equity funds to meet the $100,000 purchase price.

The needed funds can be secured from a bond issue or by selling 25 percent control of the firm. The 20-year bonds would carry 8 percent annual interest. Which source of funds would provide the greater return to the brothers on their equity when their effective income-tax rate is 40 percent?

---

*From F. W. Searby, "Return to Return on Investment," *Harvard Business Review*, March–April 1975.

## Solution 15.1

The bond expense would amount to an annual interest charge of $100,000(0.08) = $8000 and a commitment to have $100,000 available in 20 years to retire the debt. If the brothers' tax rate is assumed to remain unchanged, the annual after-tax return from the acquisition would be

$$\text{Net annual return} = \text{before-tax returns} - \text{interest payments} - \text{taxes}$$
$$= \$28,000 - \$100,000(0.08) - (\$28,000 - \$8000)(0.4)$$
$$= \$28,000 - \$8000 - \$8000 = \$12,000$$

which provides an *additional*

$$\text{Return on equity} = \frac{\$12,000}{\$300,000} = 0.04 \quad \text{or} \quad 4\%$$

when the acquisition is made from funds obtained by borrowing.

If they sell one-quarter interest in their organization for $100,000 and invest that amount in the firm, the brothers' equity is still ($100,000 + $300,000)(0.75) = $300,000. The annual $28,000 saving now comes from ownership funds for which no interest is owed and no tax deductions are allowed:

$$\text{Net annual return} = \$28,000 - \$28,000(0.4) = \$16,800$$

The brothers' share is then $16,800(0.75) = $12,600 which provides an additional

$$\text{Return on equity} = \frac{\$12,600}{\$300,000} = 0.042 \quad \text{or} \quad 4.2\%$$

Both return-on-equity figures require interpretation. The return provided by borrowing $100,000 does not include provisions for paying off the debt. A sinking fund that draws interest at the same rate as the loan would require annual payments from the revenue earned by the investment of

$$\text{Annual redemption reserve} = \$100,000(A/F, 8, 20) = \$2185$$

which reduces the net return to $12,000 − $2185 = $9815. This figure is less than the net return for the brothers when they sell one-quarter ownership, but it represents *only* the return from the investment in the distribution service. The brothers would also have to share the profit from their regular cannery operations with the new owners.

If it is assumed the brothers had an after-tax return on investment of 15 percent before acquiring the distribution service, the total return on equity when $100,000 is borrowed would be

$$\text{Return on equity by debt financing} = \frac{\$300,000(0.15) + \$9815}{\$300,000}$$

$$= 0.183 \quad \text{or} \quad 18.3\%$$

The preacquisition profit due the brothers is reduced by one-fourth through the sale of equity, because the new owners share the total returns. The resulting proportion of the brothers' share of total returns after the acquisition would be

Return on equity after selling 25% ownership =

$$\frac{\$45,000 - \$45,000(0.25) + \$12,600}{\$300,000}$$

$$= 0.155 \quad \text{or} \quad 15.5\%$$

which is slightly better than the preacquisition return on equity but less than that afforded by debt financing. In addition, the brothers would have to share their management prerogatives with the new owners. The effect on managerial decision making is not a major consideration in selling a small block of shares in a large corporation, but the sale of a controlling interest or even a significant minority interest can create an uneasy leadership situation. Therefore, the brothers would probably be wise to employ debt financing.

# FINANCIAL LEVERAGE

The *financial structure* of a firm describes the way its assets are financed: via long-term debt, short-term credit, preferred stock, and/or common equity. Debt and credit represent obligations to repay borrowed amounts and to send regular interest payments outside the firm. Both loans and preferred stock represent claims on the income of a firm before common stock. Common equity includes common stock, capital surplus, and retained earnings.

*Financial leverage* is the ratio of total debts to total assets. A firm having assets of $50 million and debts of $20 million has a *leverage factor* of 0.4. Higher leverage means more money is owed outside the firm, and this allows a higher rate of return on the amount owners have invested, but it also increases the firm's *financial risk*—uncertainty about future returns to a firm's owners as a result of the financing of assets by debt or preferred stock.

The effects of different leverage factors on the percentage return on equity when earnings vary as a function of economic conditions are portrayed in Table 15.1. Three states of financial leverage are shown for total assets of $1 million with equity proportions of $1 million, $600,000, and $300,000. When all the assets are composed of equity holdings, the after-tax rate of return on investment is equal to half the before-tax rate of return, with the effective income-tax rate at 50 percent. Under unfavorable business conditions causing low sales, the percentage return on equity drops as the leverage factor increases. The trend is reversed when favorable business conditions allow high sales. At average sales, when the before-tax rate of return equals the interest rate for borrowed funds, all three leverage positions result in the same after-tax return on equity investments. In general, *whenever favorable business conditions allow a before-tax rate of return greater than the interest rate on debt, the higher the leverage factor, the higher the after-tax percentage return on equity.*

A highly leveraged firm produces attractive return-on-investment figures during periods of prosperity, yet it can quickly become a target for management criticism or a victim of bankruptcy during a recession. Lenders are often a determinant of the degree of leverage a firm can attain. The credit standing of a borrower is reduced by excessive borrowing, and lenders attempt to protect their loans by limiting the leverage to certain norms. The norms vary among industries with respect to the stability of incomes, and within an industry according to the confidence lenders have in a firm's management; service industries and public utilities typically have very high debt-to-asset ratios (0.6+), and manufacturing has relatively low leverage (0.3 to 0.4). A thriving business can expand faster with the infusion of debt funding, and a sick business may recover more rapidly with the aid of borrowed funds, but a firm weathers brief spells of adversity better when it is less leveraged and not obligated to pay off large debts.

---

### Example 15.2 Sensitivity of the Rate of Return to Financial Leverage
Develop a sensitivity graph for the firm depicted in Table 15.1, and discuss its message.

### Solution 15.2
Table 15.1 provides a range of estimates based on scenarios for debt-to-asset ratios of 0, 0.4, and 0.7. The sensitivity graph in Figure 15.2 portrays the effect of these ratios on the rate of return owners can expect from a range of rates earned on total assets. The intersection of the three ratio lines is at the point where return on total assets equals the interest cost of debt, 8 percent. At this point, the return on net worth (common equity) is 4 percent regardless of the degree of leverage. When opera-

| FINANCIAL LEVERAGE (IN $1000 UNITS) | LEVERAGE FACTOR = 0: EQUITY = 1000 AND DEBT = 0 | | | LEVERAGE FACTOR = 0.4: EQUITY = 600 AND DEBT = 400 | | | LEVERAGE FACTOR = 0.7: EQUITY = 300 AND DEBT = 700 | | |
|---|---|---|---|---|---|---|---|---|---|
| *Economic Conditions* | *Low Sales* | *Average Sales* | *High Sales* | *Low Sales* | *Average Sales* | *High Sales* | *Low Sales* | *Average Sales* | *High Sales* |
| Rate of return before taxes and interest | 2% | 8% | 14% | 2% | 8% | 14% | 2% | 8% | 14% |
| Net earnings before interest and taxes | $20 | $80 | $140 | $20 | $80 | $140 | $20 | $80 | $140 |
| Interest on debt at $i = 8\%$ | 0 | 0 | 0 | $32 | $32 | $32 | $56 | $56 | $56 |
| *Taxable income* | $20 | $80 | $140 | −$12 | $48 | $108 | −$36 | $24 | $84 |
| Taxes at effective tax rate of 50%* | $10 | $40 | $70 | −$6 | $24 | $54 | −$18 | $12 | $42 |
| *Available for equity returns* | $10 | $40 | $70 | −$6 | $24 | $54 | −$18 | $12 | $42 |
| Percentage return on equity | 1% | 4% | 7% | −1% | 4% | 9% | −6% | 4% | 14% |

*Assumes losses are carried back and result in tax credits.

**TABLE 15.1** Equity holders' returns under different leverage factors and economic conditions when assets total $1 million (shown in units of $1000).

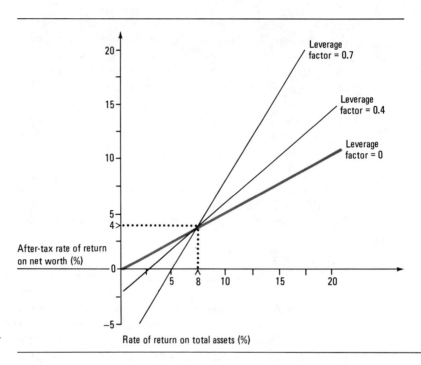

**FIGURE 15.2**
Relationship between rates of return on total assets and owners' assets under different leverage factors.

tions afford a return on assets greater than 8 percent, the debt-financed portion of the assets pays its interest cost and contributes its surplus to the owners of the firm.

## LEASING

Over 3000 years ago, Phoenician shipowners engaged in leasing. Today virtually any asset can be leased. The leasing of capital equipment has grown enormously in the last decade. There are many reasons why leasing may be more attractive than purchasing. These may include:

- Use of an asset's services if a firm lacks cash or borrowing capacity to purchase the asset
- Less effect on future borrowing capacity than debt financing
- Imposition of fewer financial restrictions than accompany a loan for the purchase of a comparable asset
- Possible reductions in the risk of obsolescence and escalation in ownership costs due to inflation
- Tax advantages under certain conditions

The most frequently cited reasons for leasing are income-tax advantages and the freeing of working capital by enabling the acquisition of needed equipment without going into debt.*

*T. L. Ward, "Leasing During Inflation: A Two-Edged Sword," *Industrial Engineering*, March 1980.

## Types of Leases

A lease is a contract between the owner of an asset, called a *lessor,* and a *lessee* who makes periodic payments for the right to use the asset. When there is also a lender involved who furnishes capital to the lessor to purchase the asset, the lease is said to be *leveraged.*

An *operating lease* can be canceled by either the lessee or lessor at any time after due notice has been given. A commitment by both parties to specified charges for the use of an asset for a definite period is a *financial lease.* Temporary use of vehicles, computers, and furniture typify operating leases. More expensive assets are usually subject to financial leases: real estate, railway cars, airplanes, and construction equipment.

It is common practice for a firm that needs certain equipment to get a price agreement from the manufacturer or distributor and then find a lessor who will purchase the equipment. A commitment is made to pay to the lessor a specified rental that will assure the lessee use of the equipment for the period needed and provide an adequate return on the lessor's investment. It is also possible for a firm to sell an asset it already owns and lease it back from the buyer. This *sale and leaseback* arrangement allows a firm to obtain cash and still have the use of its asset.

## Lease or Buy

The comparison methods presented in previous chapters are applicable to the lease-or-buy question. The two alternatives can be evaluated according to their PW, EAW, or IRR. An after-tax analysis is usually more revealing. The *lease* alternative typically includes the following elements:

Cash flow (lease) = revenues − operating expenses − rental costs
$$− \text{(tax rate)(revenues − expenses − rentals)}$$

Particulars for the calculations depend on the specific lease arrangement, such as who pays maintenance costs, and which tax provisions are applicable.

An operating lease is normally considered to be an expense that is deductible from taxable income in the year it occurs. However, leases are subject to several criteria that determine their eligibility as deductions. For instance, a rental agreement cannot qualify as an operating lease if it transfers ownership to the lessee at the end of the lease term or has a bargain purchase option. As is the case for most tax questions, expert advice is needed when a situation does not fit standard prescriptions (see Review Exercise 2).

The degree of protection from obsolescence and inflation a lessee achieves by leasing an asset depends on the contract. The lessor is also aware of the risks. A lease appears as a "bargain" to a lessee who views the future differently than the lessor and perceives an advantage. Which way the risk shifts as a result of the lease, if it shifts at all, is a function of forecasting ability.

---

### Example 15.3   Leasing versus Buying

A construction company must obtain a piece of heavy equipment to work on a long-term project. The initial cost is $100,000. The equipment is in Class 8, and will have no salvage value at the end of its 10-year useful life.

The equipment can be purchased or it can be leased. The lease has an annual charge of $20,000 and an option to buy the equipment at the end of the eighth year for $5,000. Assume that the lease payments are tax deductible and that the option is exercised. The company's effective tax rate is 40 percent and its after-tax cost of debt is 10 percent. Compare the two alternatives, assuming that the equipment is eligible for special CCA treatment. Namely, that the old CCA rule for first cost will be permitted.

## Solution 15.3

The Lease versus Buy decision is a difficult one to analyze. The appropriate discount rate to use is controversial. Some recommend using a discount rate as high as the weighted average cost of capital and others recommend the after-tax cost of debt. Still others recommend different discount rates for different cash flows.

For this particular problem, which has no salvage value, calculate the PW of the costs of immediate purchase versus leasing at the after-tax cost of debt. If the lease is more attractive under this method, then leasing is preferred.

Table 15.2 shows that the $73,333 PW of the cost of immediate purchase exceeds the $65,730 PW of leasing. Therefore, lease the equipment.

| | CASH PURCHASE | | | LEASE-BUY OPTION | | | |
|---|---|---|---|---|---|---|---|
| End of Year | Annual CCA (1) | Tax Saving (2) | PW of Cash Flow (3) | Annual Lease Charge (4) | CCA (5) | Tax Saving (6) | PW of Cash Flow (7) |
| 0 | | | -$100,000 | | | | 0 |
| 1 | $ 20,000 | $ 8,000 | 7,273 | -$ 20,000 | | $ 8,000 | -$10,909 |
| 2 | 16,000 | 6,400 | 5,289 | -20,000 | | 8,000 | -9,917 |
| 3 | 12,800 | 5,120 | 3,847 | -20,000 | | 8,000 | -9,016 |
| 4 | 10,240 | 4,096 | 2,798 | -20,000 | | 8,000 | -8,196 |
| 5 | 8,192 | 3,277 | 2,035 | -20,000 | | 8,000 | -7,451 |
| 6 | 6,554 | 2,621 | 1,480 | -20,000 | | 8,000 | -6,774 |
| 7 | 5,243 | 2,097 | 1,076 | -20,000 | | 8,000 | -6,158 |
| 8 | 4,194 | 1,678 | 783 | -20,000 (5,000)* | | 8,000 | -7,931 |
| 9 | 3,355 | 1,342 | 569 | | $1,000 | 400 | 170 |
| 10 | 2,684 | 1,074 | 1,518† | | 800 | 320 | 452† |
| Totals | | | -$73,333 | | | | -$65,730 |

*$5000 cost at the end of year 8 to exercise the buy option for the equipment.
†Includes Tax Shield Adjustments $1104 (Col. 3) and $329 (Col. 7). See Note 5, Extension 12B.

**TABLE 15.2** Comparison of acquiring the 10-year use of a $100,000 asset with no salvage value by cash purchase and by lease with an option to buy for $5000 after 8 years. Tax savings (2) for the cash purchase result from multiplying the annual CCA (1) by the 40 percent tax rate; the total discounted cash flow (3) is the sum of the present worths of total tax savings plus the purchase price. Tax savings (6) for the lease-buy plan result from the 40 percent tax rate multiplied by the annual lease cost (4) or CCA (5), and the present worth of the cash flow (7) is the net summation [(6) + (4)] discounted at 10 percent.

# DECISION-MAKING PRACTICES FOR INDUSTRIAL INVESTMENTS

A comparison of investment alternatives follows the general procedures previously introduced. Specific procedures vary among industrial organizations. Some are content to compare proposals simply by the payback criterion. Others have specially developed procedures to account for their unique situations. Many utilize preprinted forms to standardize the comparisons.

The economic decision process gets more structured as the size of an organization increases. Larger firms specify channels of successive screenings for proposals and provide printed instructions and worksheets for analyses. Examples and descriptions of typical industrial practices are presented in the following sections.

## Request for Expenditure

Proposals for investments normally originate with operating personnel or staff analysts. These personnel observe deficiencies in the present system and conceive ways to overcome them. Improvements may be directed toward *cost reduction* or *profit expansion,* and may or may not require commitments of capital. For instance, a training program for cost reduction is "expensed," or classified as an operating cost, when no durable assets are required to conduct it. Similarly, a change in packaging styles designed to increase sales could be an expense if only cosmetic alterations are involved, or a capital cost when new equipment is needed to produce redesigned containers. A list of proposed objectives is shown in Table 15.3.

|  | *Categories of Proposed Expenditures* |  |  |
|---|---|---|---|
| **1** | Cost reduction | **7** | Process modernization |
| **2** | Profit improvement | **8** | Replacement of equipment or materials |
| **3** | Additional capacity, new plant | **9** | Energy conservation |
| **4** | Redesign or new product | **10** | Metrication |
| **5** | Product improvement |  |  |
| **6** | Plant modernization |  |  |

**TABLE 15.3** Objectives of investment proposals for industrial operations.

After preliminary data have been collected to confirm that an idea for cost reduction or profit expansion is worth pursuing, a proposal for expenditure is typically turned over to a staff engineer or analyst. If the initial assessment of the proposal is encouraging, firmer cost and demand figures are generated. These figures are based on estimates from engineering design, operations, purchasing, marketing, and other departments that would be involved in the proposed project in some way. Checklists of easily overlooked costs are often provided as reminders. An example is shown in Table 15.4.

A form to show the advantage of a proposed replacement or cost-reduction plan is given in Figure 15.3. In addition to the comparison of operating costs required on the form, the present and proposed facilities or equipment are described by model number, anticipated usage, net value or installed cost, and estimates of useful life and salvage value.

---

### COST AND OPERATING SPECIFICATIONS FOR EXPENDITURE REQUESTS

---

1 *Land*  Acquisition cost, legal and escrow fees, title search, etc.
2 *Buildings*  Architectural design costs, contractor construction billings, transfer costs, waste treatment, power, fire control, heating and ventilating, elevators, loading docks, etc.
3 *Grounds*  Grading and drainage, sidewalks, parking lots, art, fencing, utility tunnels, lighting, sprinklers, landscaping and landscape-architect fees, etc.
4 *Machinery and equipment*  Invoice prices, taxes, freight, installation costs, utility conenctions, consultant fees, building modifications, material-handling systems, spare parts, down time during replacement, maintenance costs, output rates over time, insurance, utility usage rates and other operating costs, etc.
5 *Dies, molds, fixtures*  Invoice price, freight, internal and external labor costs, modifications, associated materials, etc.
6 *Materials and supplies*  Type, price and discounts, delivery time and reliability of deliveries, build-up-to-capacity costs, storage, equipment modifications, handling requirements, protection, associated equipment required, inspection costs, etc.
7 *Labor*  Number, wages, skills, training costs, tools needed, affirmative action, overtime, and typical employment costs as indicated below.

**TABLE 15.4** Checklist of cost categories to be accounted for in the preparation of a request for expenditure.

| Standard Wage | Incentives | Hourly Additives | Vacation, Shift Premiums, Allowances | Fringe Benefits | Employment Cost |
|---|---|---|---|---|---|
| $5.184 | $1.058 | $2.504 | $2.624 | $3.20 | $14.57 |

## Investment Analysis

When no capital outlays are required, a request for expenditure (RFE) is based on just operating costs of the type shown in Figure 15.3, plus estimates of expanded profits, if appropriate. Some firms use only the payback criterion for relatively small investments, say up to $500; if the cost data meet the before-tax payback criterion, the RFE is transmitted to the screening group that decides which requests are funded.

Larger investments are usually subjected to a discounted cash-flow analysis. Again the type of analysis and what is included vary among organizations. For instance, some analyses use continuously compounded interest, and firms that process large quantities of raw materials may require a "working-capital cost" to be charged against any investment that increases the amount of inventory held.

Three methods of analyzing investments in use by large corporations in different industries are shown in Figures 15.4 to 15.6. They are designed to assure the uniformity of RFE preparations and to provide sufficient information for deciding which requests are most deserving. In essence, the forms are programmed routines for conducting the after-tax computations described in Chapter 12; only minor variations are added to customize the procedure.

Figure 15.4 is a cash-flow worksheet that utilizes the data collected from the "operating advantage" form shown in Figure 15.3. Irregular expenses (column 4) and depreciation or depletion charges (column 5) are subtracted from the annual savings in column 3 to determine the taxable profit (column 6). Columns 7, 8, and 9 are the tax effects and lead to the after-tax cash flow in column 10. When the amount invested is entered as a negative

# OPERATING COST COMPARISON: REPLACEMENT OR COST REDUCTION

| | PRESENT | PROPOSED | (PRESENT − PROPOSED) DIFFERENCE | EFFECT ON VOLUME IN UNITS |
|---|---|---|---|---|
| Direct Labor _____ @ _____<br>Hrs.　　Rate | _____ | _____ | _____ | |
| Indirect Labor _____ @ _____<br>Hrs.　　Rate | _____ | _____ | _____ | INCREASE　　DECREASE |
| Other Labor _____ @ _____<br>Hrs.　　Rate | _____ | _____ | _____ | _____　_____ |
| Subtotal Labor _____ | _____ | _____ | _____ | |
| Benefits @ _____ % of Labor | _____ | _____ | _____ | OTHER |
| | _____ | _____ | _____ | |
| Maintenance Costs _____ | _____ | _____ | _____ | |
| Tooling Costs _____ | _____ | _____ | _____ | |
| Materials & Supplies _____ | _____ | _____ | _____ | |
| Down Time Cost _____ | _____ | _____ | _____ | Attach Supporting Documents |
| Utilities (power, air, etc.) _____ | _____ | _____ | _____ | _____ |
| Floor Space (in m²) _____ | _____ | _____ | _____ | COST BENEFITS IN SUBSEQUENT YEARS. |
| Subcontracting Costs _____ | _____ | _____ | _____ | |
| Inventory (incr/decr) _____ | _____ | _____ | _____ | YR 2 $ _____ |
| Safety _____ | _____ | _____ | _____ | YR 3 _____ |
| Start-up Costs _____ | _____ | _____ | _____ | YR 4 _____ |
| Training Costs _____ | _____ | _____ | _____ | YR 5 _____ |
| Software Costs _____ | _____ | _____ | _____ | YR 6 _____ |
| Other _____ | _____ | _____ | _____ | YR 7 _____ |
| | _____ | _____ | _____ | |
| | _____ | _____ | _____ | |
| | _____ | _____ | _____ | |
| TOTALS | $ _____ | $ _____ | _____ | Prepared by　　Date |
| Cost Benefits of Project—First Year (Present Minus Proposed) | | | $ _____ | |

**FIGURE 15.3**　Cost-analysis worksheet for a replacement or cost-reduction proposal.

CASH FLOW FROM OPERATIONS

| 1 | 2 | 3 | 4 | 5 | 6 | 7 | 8 | 9 | 10 | 11 |
|---|---|---|---|---|---|---|---|---|---|---|
| | | | | | | Taxes Paid | | | Cash Flow | |
| Calendar Year | Year No. | Operating Advantage Form xxx | Expense Portion of Project | Tax Depreciation & Depletion | Taxable Profit Col 3 Less 4 & 5 | Normal Tax | Tax Credits | Total Col 7 Less 8 | Annual Col 3 Less 9 | Cumulative |
| | -3 | | | | | | | | | |
| | -2 | | | | | | | | | |
| | -1 | | | | | | | | | |
| Zero Point | | | | | | | | | | |
| | 1 | | | | | | | | | |
| | 2 | | | | | | | | | |
| | 3 | | | | | | | | | |
| | 4 | | | | | | | | | |
| | 5 | | | | | | | | | |
| | 6 | | | | | | | | | |
| | 7 | | | | | | | | | |
| | 8 | | | | | | | | | |
| | 9 | | | | | | | | | |
| | 10 | | | | | | | | | |
| | 11 | | | | | | | | | |
| | 12 | | | | | | | | | |

Date: _____, 19 _____          Division: _____          RFE No. _____

Prepared by: _____          Plant: _____          Payback: _____

**FIGURE 15.4** Worksheet for calculating the after-tax cash flow and payback period before discounting.

CALCULATION OF PROFITABILITY INDEX (INTEREST RATE)

**Capital Costs**

| Year (Actual) | Relative to Zero | Trial No. 1 0% Interest Rate — Actual Amount | Trial No. 2 10% Interest Rate — Factor | Trial No. 2 — Present Worth | Trial No. 3 25% Interest Rate — Factor | Trial No. 3 — Present Worth | Trial No. 4 40% Interest Rate — Factor | Trial No. 4 — Present Worth |
|---|---|---|---|---|---|---|---|---|
| | -3 | | 1.285 | | 1.873 | | 2.736 | |
| | -2 | | 1.162 | | 1.459 | | 1.834 | |
| | -1 | | 1.052 | | 1.136 | | 1.230 | |
| Zero Point | | | 1.000 | | 1.000 | | 1.000 | |
| | 1 | | .952 | | .885 | | .824 | |
| | 2 | | .861 | | .689 | | .553 | |
| | 3 | | .779 | | .537 | | .370 | |
| | 4 | | .705 | | .418 | | .248 | |
| | 5 | | .638 | | .326 | | .166 | |
| Totals A | | | | | | | | |

Cash Outflow

**Operating Benefits**

| Relative to Zero | 10% Factor | 25% Factor | 40% Factor |
|---|---|---|---|
| -3 | 1.285 | 1.873 | 2.736 |
| -2 | 1.162 | 1.459 | 1.834 |
| -1 | 1.052 | 1.136 | 1.230 |
| Zero Point | 1.000 | 1.000 | 1.000 |
| 1 | .952 | .885 | .824 |
| 2 | .861 | .689 | .553 |
| 3 | .779 | .537 | .370 |
| 4 | .705 | .418 | .248 |
| 5 | .638 | .326 | .166 |
| 6 | .577 | .254 | .112 |
| 7 | .522 | .197 | .075 |
| 8 | .473 | .154 | .050 |
| 9 | .428 | .119 | .034 |
| 10 | .387 | .093 | .023 |
| 11 | .350 | .073 | .015 |
| 12 | .317 | .057 | .010 |
| Totals B | | | |
| Ratio A/B | | | |

Cash Inflow

Interpolation Chart

Profitability Index (%)

Ratio (A/B)

PROFITABILITY INDEX = 

RFE No. _____   Date: 

Plant: _____   Div.: 

FIGURE 15.5 Worksheet for determining the profitability index of an investment proposal. The present worth of capital costs and operating benefits are summed to obtain A/B ratios at different interest rates. The A/B ratios are then graphed to indicate the profitability-index percentage.

337

value in the "zero point" row, the cumulative total in column 11 reveals the payback period—the number of years before the cumulative cash flow switches from negative to positive. This payback is the flow in actual dollars rather than time-value dollars.

A convenient worksheet for calculating the rate of return, called the *profitability index*, is shown in Figure 15.5. The after-tax cash flow as developed in the last column of Figure 15.4 is the input for the "actual amount" column in the "operating benefits" section of Figure 15.5. Receipts and disbursements that occur irregularly before the nominal implementation date, the zero point, are listed in the negative-year rows; the regular cash flow is listed below the zero-point row. Similarly, regular and irregular investments are listed in the "capital costs" section. Then values in the "actual amount" column (PW at 0 percent interest rate) are multiplied in trial 2 by the present-amount factors for 10 percent. As long as the $A/B$ ratio at the bottom of the trial column is less than 1.0, another trial is needed. The present-amount factors for each trial are multiplied by the "actual amount" figures to obtain trial values. The given interest factors are based on mid-period continuous compounding, and consequently are different than the factors given in Appendix B.

The profitability index is determined from the sums of the discounted capital cost $A$ and the operating benefits $B$. $A/B$ ratios are calculated for each trial interest rate up to a rate which produces a ratio greater than 1.0. The profitability index lies between the interest rate which produced the last $A/B$ ratio less than 1.0 and the next larger one. The actual index percentage is determined graphically by plotting the $A/B$ ratios on the "interpolation chart." The profitability index is indicated by the point where the line connecting the plotted $A/B$ ratios crosses the vertical 1.0 line on the interpolation chart. The return on investment is the percentage obtained by reading across from that intersection to the vertical scale on the left.

### Example 15.4   Investment Analysis for a Profit-sharing Company

A proposed investment will have an initial outlay, including freight charges, of $11,000. It is expected to produce cost savings of $5000, $7000, $9000, $8000, and $6000 over the next 5 years. At the end of the fifth year it will have a salvage value of $1000.

The company has a profit-sharing plan by which 35 percent of before-tax earnings are distributed among employees. This proportion of earnings is thus an operating expense to the company.

A "capital investment evaluation" worksheet is used to analyze proposals. It is based on straight-line depreciation, a 50 percent income-tax rate, and interest rates for discrete compounding periods. The proposal is to be evaluated by the six-step procedure given in Figure 15.6.

### Solution 15.4

In "step 1" of Figure 15.6, the purchase price and associated costs are recorded. The $11,000 total is the amount $X$ used in "step 3."

Cost savings, lease payments avoided, and other net benefits are entered in column $P$ at "step 2"; nonrecurring expenses are deducted in the year they occur. Depreciation in column $D$ results from

$$\text{Annual depreciation} = \frac{\text{total capital cost }(X) - \text{residual value}}{\text{depreciable life}}$$

## STEP NUMBER 1

| INVESTMENT | | COST |
|---|---|---|
| ACQUISITION PRICE | (a) | 10,500 |
| FREIGHT | (b) | 500 |
| INSTALLATION | (c) | |
| | (d) | |
| TOTAL CAPITAL | (x) | 11,000 |

DEPRECIABLE LIFE — five — YRS
RESIDUAL VALUE — 10 % — $ 1000

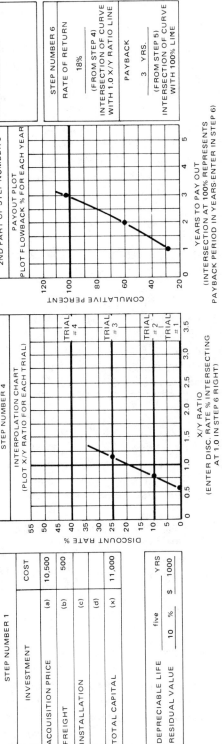

## PROJ. DESCRIPTION

**STEP NUMBER 6**

RATE OF RETURN — 18%
(FROM STEP 4)
INTERSECTION OF CURVE WITH 1.0 X/Y RATIO LINE

PAYBACK — 3 YRS.
(FROM STEP 5)
INTERSECTION OF CURVE WITH 100% LINE

**2ND PART OF STEP NUMBER 5**

PAYOUT PLOT
PLOT FLOWBACK % FOR EACH YEAR

YEARS TO PAY OUT
(INTERSECTION AT 100% REPRESENTS PAYBACK PERIOD IN YEARS-ENTER IN STEP 6)

**STEP NUMBER 4**

INTERPOLATION CHART
(PLOT X/Y RATIO FOR EACH TRIAL)

X/Y RATIO
(ENTER DISC. RATE % INTERSECTING AT 1.0 IN STEP 6 RIGHT)

## STEP NUMBER 2 / STEP NUMBER 3

| YEAR | COST BENEFITS (P) | (LESS) DEPRE-CIA-TION (D) | NET COST BENEFITS (P–D)=C | AFTER PROFIT SHARING (Cx.65)=E | AFTER-TAX EARNINGS (Ex.50)=A | TRIAL 1 0 Disc. Rate AFTER-TAX CASH FLOW (A+D)=B | TRIAL 2 10% Disc. Rate FAC-TOR f1 | CASH VALUE B(f1) | TRIAL 3 25% Disc. Rate FAC-TOR f2 | CASH VALUE B(f2) | TRIAL 4 40% Disc. Rate FAC-TOR f3 | CASH VALUE B(f3) |
|---|---|---|---|---|---|---|---|---|---|---|---|---|
| 1st | 5000 | 2000 | 3000 | 1950 | 975 | 2975 | .91 | 2707 | .80 | 2380 | .71 | |
| 2nd | 7000 | 2000 | 5000 | 3250 | 1625 | 3625 | .83 | 3009 | .64 | 2320 | .51 | |
| 3rd | 9000 | 2000 | 7000 | 4550 | 2275 | 4275 | .75 | 3206 | .51 | 2180 | .36 | |
| 4th | 8000 | 2000 | 6000 | 3900 | 1950 | 3950 | .68 | 2686 | .41 | 1620 | .26 | |
| 5th | 6000 | 2000 | 4000 | 2600 | 1300 | 3300 | .62 | 2046 | .33 | 1089 | .19 | |
| 6th | | | | | | | .56 | | .26 | | .13 | |
| 7th | | | | | | | .51 | | .21 | | .10 | |
| TOTALS | | | | | Y1 | 18,125 | Y2 | 13,654 | Y3 | 9588 | Y4 | |
| RATIOS | | | | | X/Y | 0.61 | X/Y2 | 0.81 | X/Y3 | 1.15 | X/Y4 | |

## FIRST PART OF STEP #5

CUMULATIVE CASH FLOW BACK

| AMOUNT (CUM B) | CUM B X | YEAR |
|---|---|---|
| 2975 | .27 | 1st |
| 6600 | .60 | 2nd |
| 10,875 | .99 | 3rd |
| 14,825 | 1.35 | 4th |
| | | 5th |

REF. NO.

PREPARED BY — DATE

**FIGURE 15.6** Completed worksheet for determination of the rate of return on invested capital and the payback period for a profit-sharing organization.

This charge is deducted from amounts in column $P$ to obtain net cost benefits $C$. The portion of these benefits available to the company for capital recovery is 65 percent, $E$. After-tax earnings $A$ result from applying a 50 percent effective income-tax rate to the company's profit share. The after-tax cash flow $B$ is earnings $A$ plus the depreciation charges $D$.

In "step 3" the after-tax yearly values $B$ are multiplied by single-payment present-worth interest factors to obtain the equivalent cash flow at different interest rates. The sums of the discounted values $(Y_1, Y_2, Y_3)$ are the present worths of the net benefits and are the denominators for $X/Y$ ratios representing each interest rate. The $X/Y$ ratio is simply

$$\frac{X}{Y} = \frac{\text{investment at time zero}}{\text{PW of net benefits}} \qquad \text{at } i = ?$$

The rate of return is determined graphically in "step 4." At the point where the line connecting $X/Y$ ratios crosses the vertical line at $X/Y = 1.0$, the value of $i$ that makes $X = Y$ is identified.

Similarly, for the graph in "step 5," the cumulative values of the after-tax cash flow at $i = 0(B)$ are divided by the investment $X$ to obtain ratios to plot. The payback period is interpolated from the crossing point of the line connecting the plotted ratios and the horizontal 100 percent line.

Resulting interpolated values for the return on investment, 18 percent, and the payback period, 3 years, are recorded in "step 6."

## Letter of Justification

Most industrial organizations require submission of an explanatory letter along with the economic analysis of a proposed investment. A typical summary sheet for a request for expenditure (RFE) is shown in Figure 15.7. The key figures from the analysis are displayed, and space is provided for approvals from the staff engineers and managers responsible for budgeting.

The accompanying written justification explains the reasons for the RFE. It describes the origin of the problem or the opportunity for which the RFE is submitted, and how the proposal will be implemented if approved. Intangible factors not included in the analysis are discussed. Supplementary data on related effects of the proposal are also supplied if pertinent to the decision.

## Postaudits

Following the progress of a design from the drawing board through construction to on-the-job performance is a natural progression to engineers. They take pride in their designs, welcome the opportunity to make modifications to improve performance, and realize they will be able to make future designs better by knowing what was previously successful and what failed. Follow-ups on capital investments tend to be neither as extensive nor as rigorous. Engineering economists would be well served by the same monitoring instincts displayed in other engineering pursuits.

LETTER OF JUSTIFICATION                                              RFE No.

Description of Request:

Budget Spending  19 _____$ _____        Budget Total  19 _____ $ _____

|  | Total Investment | 19 ____ | 19 ____ | 19 ____ | 19 ____ | 19 ____ |
|---|---|---|---|---|---|---|
| Investment: Capital |  |  |  |  |  |  |
| Expense |  |  |  |  |  |  |
| Total Authorized Working Capital |  |  |  |  |  |  |
| Future Obligations |  |  |  |  |  |  |
| Total Justified |  |  |  |  |  |  |
| Benefit: Sales |  |  |  |  |  |  |
| Operating Profit after Tax |  |  |  |  |  |  |
| Cash Flow from Operations |  |  |  |  |  |  |
| % Return on Capital Employed after Tax |  |  |  |  |  |  |

| Type of RFE | PI | Payout |
|---|---|---|
|  |  |  |

Most Critical Assumptions

Prepared by _____        Sponsored by _____

| Date | Dept. | Staff Review Signature |  | Approvals Signature |  | Date |
|---|---|---|---|---|---|---|
|  |  |  |  |  |  |  |
|  |  |  |  |  |  |  |
|  |  |  |  |  |  |  |
|  |  |  |  |  |  |  |

FIGURE 15.7  Summary page for a letter of justification to support a request for expenditure.

The purpose of auditing investments is not to punish those who approved the proposals any more than quality-control inspections are intended to penalize a production process. The aim is to improve future analyses. How else can analysts learn whether their estimated cash flows are realistic? Many factors influence estimated receipts and disbursements; some are easily overlooked unless brought to attention by postaudits.

Cost-reduction proposals tend to be more accurately estimated than profit-expansion proposals because costs are more controllable than sales volume and market prices.* Yet the savings generated by implementing a lower-cost process or by replacing a higher-cost asset cannot be checked because the performance of the replaced assets cannot be determined for the latest operating conditions. A good indication is provided, however, by the comparison of estimated operating costs to the actual costs of the replacement.

A major advantage of a systematized postaudit program is the availability of the most recent cost data for categories not itemized in cost-accounting records. Maintenance costs for various types of machines, operating efficiency during training periods, labor costs for specific activities such as installation or set-up activities, and other data utilized in preparing requests for expenditure would be available from postaudits. The more complete computer-based management information systems that are spreading throughout industry promise to make such information conveniently accessible.

## Review Exercises and Discussions

**Exercise 1**  The owners of land with geothermal potential are seeking capital to develop the property. They feel that $10 million is necessary. That amount should yield annual revenue of $5 million for a prolonged period of time. Potential financing is from the sale of common stock on which buyers will expect a return of about 12.5 percent, preferred stock on which the annual dividend rate would have to be 10 percent, or a loan on which interest would be 12 percent. The effective tax rate will be 50 percent.

Evaluate the financing alternatives.

**Solution 1**  The relative impact of the financing plans on income to the owners of the land is shown in Table 15.5. Since the capitalization rate for common stock is expected to be 12.5 percent, stock dividends would consume $10,000,000 \times 0.125 = \$1,250,000$ annually, which requires before-tax net revenue of $\$1,250,000/0.50 = \$2,500,000$. Given the expectation of a $5 million annual revenue, the common shareholders must own 50 percent of the company to accommodate their 12.5 percent return. The original owners of the land would then receive $1,250,000 per year for the use of their property.

Returns to the owners would be higher if they issue preferred stock or borrow. A more complete analysis would investigate the sensitivity of the financing alternatives to differences in revenue.

**Exercise 2**  An asset can be purchased for $80,000 and will have a 10-year useful life. A suggested lease arrangement is to pay $28,000 for the first 4 years and then make annual payments of $1500 for the remaining 6 years. Evaluate the suggestion.

*According to J. L. Bower, *Managing the Resource Allocation Process*, Harvard, Cambridge, Mass., 1970.

**TABLE 15.5**
Comparison of financing through $10 million obtained by sales of common stock, sales of preferred stock, and a loan at an interest rate of 12 percent. Preferred stock pays dividends of 10 percent, and new common stock accounts for 50 percent of the company's shares.

| | $10 Million from Com- mon Stock | $10 Million from Pre- ferred Stock | $10 Million from a Loan |
|---|---|---|---|
| Before-tax cash flow | $5,000,000 | $5,000,000 | $5,000,000 |
| Annual interest expense | 0 | 0 | −1,200,000 |
| Taxable income | $5,000,000 | $5,000,000 | $3,800,000 |
| Taxes at 50% | −2,500,000 | −2,500,000 | −1,900,000 |
| Earnings after taxes | $2,500,000 | $2,500,000 | $1,900,000 |
| Preferred dividend | 0 | −1,000,000 | 0 |
| Earnings on common equity | $2,500,000 | $1,500,000 | $1,900,000 |
| Income to new shareholders | −1,250,000 | 0 | 0 |
| Income to original owners | $1,250,000 | $1,500,000 | $1,900,000 |

**Solution 2** A closer look at the lease is needed. It is probable that Revenue Canada would consider the described "lease" as a disguised purchase aimed at reducing the total tax paid by the two parties. Conditions of the "lease" suggest that the lessee is actually assuming an ownership position for the asset as a consequence of the large initial payments and minimal subsequent payments. The payment schedule would produce a fine return to the lessor, and the lessee's expenses would provide larger and earlier deductions from income than allowed for CCA of a comparable purchased asset. The lease plan is feasible only if it could be proved that the asset did indeed lose almost its entire value in 4 years.

# PROBLEMS

**15.1** The owner of a drive-in restaurant believes there is a good potential for another drive-in at a nearby town. She has $40,000 of capital with which to expand the business. Using this amount she can open a new operation which should yield a gross income before taxes of $8000. She feels that a conservative study period of 10 years is reasonable. The restaurant is a Class 6 asset. The salvage value is expected to be $10,000.

After checking with a bank, she finds that she can borrow $20,000 at 16 percent interest per year on the unpaid balance. The loan extends for 10 years and would be repaid in 10 equal annual installments.

If her effective income-tax rate is 40 percent for the period, which means of financing is the most attractive?

**15.2** A corporation plans to buy out a supplier and needs $2 million in new capital to do so. The proportion of equity to debt financing will be 40:60 for the acquisition. The current cost of equity capital is 14 percent after taxes, and it is 12 percent before taxes for debt financing. The effective income-tax rate is 55 percent.

  **15.2a** What is the minimum amount of before-tax earnings necessary per year from the purchase to justify raising the required capital?   *($392,000)*

  **15.2b** What minimum after-tax earnings should be expected?   *($180,000)*

**15.3** A consulting engineer has a 10-year contract to monitor waste discharges from several mills located on a small bay. Since the contract also calls for a hydrographic study of the area, a boat will be needed. A properly equipped craft can be purchased for $20,000. At the end of the 10-year study it can likely be sold for 10 percent of its purchase price. Moorage and maintenance costs will be $400 per year. The boat is a Class 7 asset. The engineer's effective income-tax rate is 40 percent.

A loan for the entire amount, requiring annual payments of $2590, can be obtained. Interest charges during each year of the loan are shown below.

| Year | 1 | 2 | 3 | 4 | 5 | 6 | 7 | 8 | 9 | 10 |
|---|---|---|---|---|---|---|---|---|---|---|
| Interest | $1000 | $921 | $837 | $749 | $657 | $561 | $459 | $353 | $241 | $123 |

It would also be possible to lease an adequate boat from a marina on the bay. A 10-year lease that allows use of a boat whenever needed, if a 2-day warning is given, will cost $3000 per year. Maintenance and moorage fees are included in the lease cost. Operating expenses will be the same under both plans.

**15.3a** What are the present worths of the costs of the two plans for the use of a boat when the after-tax cost of debt is used?

**15.3b** What other factors might be considered in the comparison of the two plans? Would a higher required rate of return, say 10 percent after taxes, affect the decision? Why?

**15.4** Would you rather have net earnings before taxes of $70,000 when you have no debt or $45,000 before interest payments and taxes when you are leveraged at 0.8? Assume the interest on debt is 10 percent and in both cases the total assets are $500,000 and the effective tax rate is 50 percent. What is the return on investment under both conditions? *[ROI(LF = 0) = 7%]*

**15.5** A corporation has an effective tax rate of 45 percent. Its annual earnings total $2 million. For a leverage factor of 0, the after-tax percentage return on equity is 6.6 percent. If the leverage factor had been 0.6 and the interest rate for debt 9 percent, what would the after-tax percentage return on equity be? *(ROE = 9.07%)*

**15.6** A portable drilling rig can be purchased for $85,000 or leased at the rate of $30,000 per year. Operating costs will be the same for either alternative except that insurance and maintenance costs of $5000 per year are paid by the leasing organization under the lease agreement; these costs are handled as operating expenses for a purchased rig. If purchased, the rig will have a salvage value of $10,000 at the end of its 4-year useful life, and it will be in Class 8. Financing of the purchase will be by a $15,000 immediate down payment and equal installments at the end of each year on a loan which charges interest at the rate of 10 percent, compounded annually, on the unpaid balance. Lease payments are to be made at the beginning of each of the 4 years the rig will be leased. Compare the two alternatives at a tax rate of 30 percent.

**15.7`** A cost-reduction proposal to equip a locomotive with remote radio control is being developed. Because the radio-control equipment, which costs $28,000, can be considered an operating expense, no depreciable assets are involved.

Two operators are now employed to shuttle scrap-weighing cars between the scrap yard and the steel-making furnace. By equipping the locomotive with remote radio-control equipment, the need for one operator each shift is eliminated. The locomotive is utilized

4000 hours per year. Operators are paid $9 per hour including fringe benefits. Installation costs for the controls are expected to be $2000. There have been significant improvements in remote-control systems since the company had its unpleasant experience with a radio-controlled locomotive 10 years ago.

Complete the form in Figure 15.7 to justify the request for expenditure.

# SECTION FOUR

# ECONOMIC DECISIONS Over 100 years

ago a delightful and prophetic paper appeared in the *Journal of the Statistical Society*.* It was written by William Farr, Esq., M.D., D.C.L., F.R.S., and bore the inclusive title "On the Valuation of Railways, Telegraphs, Water Companies, Canals, and other Commercial Concerns, with Prospective, Deferred, Increasing, Decreasing, or Terminating Profits." The following excerpts from that treatise reveal the century-old roots of engineering economic evaluation concepts:

> The value of things depends to some extent on their utility. . . . Goods are in general good things: they give life, health, and strength; they yield enjoyment to the highest faculties as well as the lowest wants of human nature. . . . The value of a thing bears no definite or constant relation to its excellence in an aesthetic sense, or to its high place in philosophy. . . . Thus it is found in every case value expressed in money is measured by the mind, and that its price is practically fixed by the concurrence of the seller and the buyer. . . .
>
> As the same thing differs in value at different distances in space, so its value— expressed in money—differs in time. It may be worth 1,000£ if paid for in ready money, but if payable in a year's time it may be worth 905£: due in fourteen year's time it may only be worth 505£ . . .
>
> If there is risk, that is valued by the doctrine of probabilities; thus, if in a lottery there

*Volume XXXIX, London, September 1876.

347

are one thousand prizes of 1£ and forty blanks, the value of one thousand and forty tickets of 1£ will only be 1,000£. The same result, the same depreciation of value, may be caused by risk as is caused by remoteness of payment; and as both risks and profits vary, and their combination produces corresponding effects on the values involved, several of these combinations are conveniently included in the rates of interest.

The value of annuities at constant risk diminishes with the factor of risk. Thus let an annuity of 4£ in perpetuity be equivalent to 4 percent interest on 100£, then it will be worth twenty-five years' purchase; but if there is a constant risk equivalent to 1/105, it will be worth only twenty years' purchase. The risk rate enters into the dividends of all commercial undertakings; so rate of dividends includes the ordinary profit of capital at no risk, and the insurance premium to cover such normal risk as the concern is exposed to.

The views expressed by Dr. Farr are forerunners of contemporary economic decision making. He recognized the time value of money and the influence of uncertainty on the cost of capital. His words also implied concern for intangible values and risk considerations. These implications are the theme for Section Four.

An investment proposal has to satisfy a series of criteria before it is fully accepted. To start with, it must pass the test of technological feasibility—an engineering criterion. Then it has to meet the economic criterion of producing a sufficient return on investment, and it is still subject to financial criteria that ration capital to only the most deserving requests for expenditure. Those that survive eventually face the decisive hurdle of management approval. The final review, buttressed by information from previous screenings, ascertains how well a proposal supports future plans of the organization. These plans involve risks and intangible factors which affect a proposal's attractiveness. Although risks and intangible influences cannot be documented as convincingly as most cash flow elements, they may be conclusive in the final decision on acceptability.

The chapters in this section progress from consideration of known production criteria to recognition of the role of risk in immediate and successive decisions, and conclude with decision-making techniques that accommodate both tangible and intangible elements. The purpose of mastering these refinements to Dr. Farr's concepts is to make engineering economic decision making as complete as possible, to allow better understanding of the opportunities, and to develop evaluation consistency that in the long run will maximize returns.

# CHAPTER 16

# BREAKEVEN ANALYSIS

OVERVIEW

Many economic comparisons are a form of breakeven analysis. The lease-or-buy question from Chapter 15 could be rephrased to ask at what level of service or period of time does leasing become more expensive than buying. The point where the two alternatives are equal is the *breakeven point*. Most sensitivity studies involve an *indifference* level for a given cash flow element at which two alternatives are equivalent—the breakeven point for the given element. The choice between the two then rests on a judgment as to which side of the breakeven point the element will likely register.

In this chapter breakeven analysis is directed to the point at which operations just break even, neither making nor losing money; changes in operations are evaluated according to their affect on this point. Breakeven analysis, known also as cost-volume-profit analysis, is widely used for financial studies because it is simple and extracts useful insights from a modest amount of data. The studies necessarily include an examination of production costs and operating policies.

Costs which remain relatively constant regardless of the level of a firm's activity are *fixed costs FC*. Per-unit *variable costs VC* are proportional to *output n*. *Profit Z* is the difference between *total revenue* ($TR = nSP$, where $SP$ = selling price and *total cost* $TC = nVC + FC$). The *breakeven point BEP* occurs when $Z = 0$. Profit may be increased by raising or lowering $SP$, cutting $TC$ or combinations thereof.

In linear breakeven charts, $BEP = FC/(SP - VC)$, where $SP - VC$ is the *contribution per unit.* Breakeven charts can be constructed for single or multiple product analysis.

*Dumping* is the practice of selling a product at a lower price in a separate market to increase plant utilization.

In a nonlinear breakeven analysis, the average total cost is the sum of ever-declining average fixed cost and the typically saucer-shaped average-variable-cost function. The average-total-cost curve is intersected at its lowest point by the rising marginal-cost curve. Similarly, the point of maximum profit occurs where marginal revenue equals marginal cost. The effects of inflation on breakeven analyses are examined in Extension 16A.

# COST AND COMPETITIVENESS

Most organizations strive for profits. They do so through a close scrutiny of their internal operating costs and strict attention to their competitive position. Even intentionally non-profit organizations must follow the same policy if they are to achieve excellence. The cost-revenue-profit relationships are exposed by breaking down a unit of output into its component dollar values.

The rectangular block in Figure 16.1(a) represents a unit of output. This output can be a product, such as an automobile, or it can be a service, such as collecting garbage from a subscriber. The unit is divided into three segments which classify the producer's interests. The overall height or price for which it can be sold is a function of the consumer's regard for the item.

## Fixed Costs

Those costs which remain relatively constant regardless of the level of activity are known as *fixed costs* or *indirect costs*. This description implies that the fixed level is maintained whether output is nil or at 100 percent capacity. In some cases this assumption is not valid; fixed costs may tend to increase as output increases, and they can vary with time. However, the change is usually not significant for short-run studies.

Some of an organization's expenditures which can be considered as fixed are shown in Figure 16.1(b). These costs may be thought of as "preparation" expenses. They arise from measures taken to provide the means to produce a product or service. Before painters can paint a house, they have to have paint brushes. Whether they paint one house or a dozen with the brushes, the expense has already been incurred and shows as a fixed cost. The painter's insurance and advertisements for work would also be indirect costs.

## Variable Costs

Those costs which are generally proportional to output are called *variable costs* or *direct costs*. Such costs are relatively easy to determine, because they are directly associated with a specific product or service. When there is no output, variable costs are zero. The input material and the time required to make a unit give rise to variable costs. For example, the specific type and quantity of paint painters use in painting a house is a variable cost. The more houses they paint, the more paint they use; the quantity used is a function of their output. In a similar manner, the time they spend painting is a direct cost.

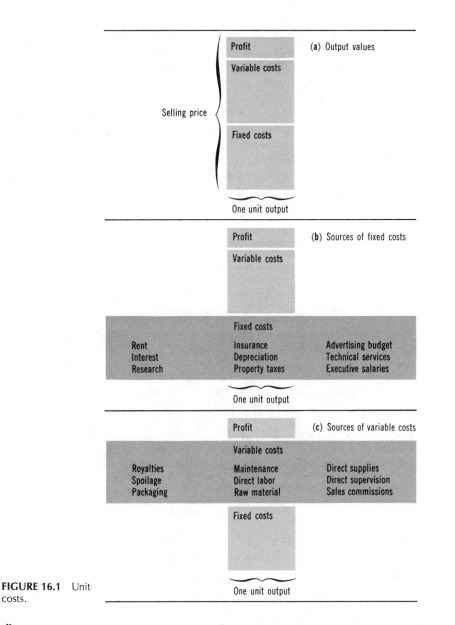

**FIGURE 16.1** Unit costs.

## Profit

The dimension of quantity must be included to examine the competitive aspects of profit. A single unit of output is relatively immune to competition. In isolated instances, a fair-sized output distributed in a local area to satisfy a peculiar need is also shielded from competition. However, as output quantity expands, competition is an increasingly apparent factor. Profit is the cause and effect of competitiveness.

A profit (or loss) figure attracts a great amount of attention. It is a handy yardstick of success. Like a thermometer, it only measures the level achieved; it does not control the source it measures. Unlike a thermometer, however, continued low readings may convince the financial temperature takers to eliminate the source.

There are basically three ways to increase profit: (1) increase the selling price, (2) increase the value to increase sales, and (3) decrease the selling price to increase sales. The profit-expansion descriptions are oriented to consumer's interests. The issues become more complicated when we look at them from the producer's viewpoint. Figure 16.2 shows some of the consequences of selling-price manipulations.

The original price-cost-quantity conditions are shown in Figure 16.2(a). *Total revenue* is the product of *n* units sold at selling price *SP*. *Total cost* is the sum of variable and fixed costs incurred in producing *n* units. *Profit* is the difference between revenue and total cost (when revenue exceeds costs).

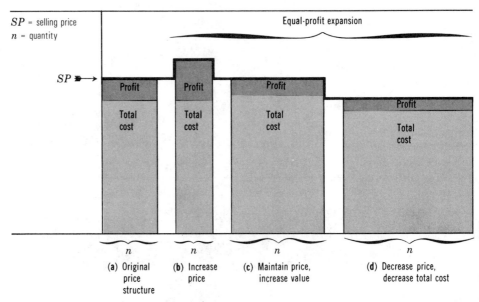

**FIGURE 16.2**    Methods for expanding profit.

Figure 16.2(b) through (d) shows increased profit. The shaded profit areas of (b), (c), and (d) are equal and are larger than the profit in (a). The dangers and limitations of profit-expansion methods are as follows:

*Increased selling price*    Competing products or services set an upper limit to price increases.* Ultimately, this limit is controlled by the consumers. Their willingness to pay is a function of the value they expect to receive and their loyalty to a product. Prices higher than competing products of equivalent value will reduce the number of units sold. The shrinking share of the market eventually causes a decline in total profit.

*Conditions of *free competition* are assumed: Similar products or services are available from a number of vendors.

*Unchanged selling price*  One way to increase profit without changing the selling price is to sell more units by increasing the value. The greater value perceived by the consumer can result from better quality, more quantity, or more effective advertising. All these measures increase the total cost for the producer. Higher total cost leads to a lower margin of profit per unit sold. If the market is unstable, a very low profit margin can seriously limit recuperative powers during market fluctuations.

A straightforward means to increase profit while holding prices constant is to reduce total costs. Such a task is the continuous aim of engineers and managers. The obstacle is that it becomes increasingly difficult to make more and more savings in an established operation. At first it is easy. When a product or service is new, it meets a high current demand which compensates for operational inefficiencies. As competition forces the price down, the "fat" is removed from operations. Further effort to reduce costs meets diminishing returns. It is like trying to make a horse run faster. A small whip may help at first, but using ever larger whips fails to force proportional returns in greater speed.

*Reduced selling price*  New areas of cost reduction are exposed by changing the level of operations or capacity. A greater output often allows new methods to be incorporated. Some of the savings resulting from the new methods are passed on to consumers in the form of a lower selling price. In theory, the decreased price should lead to the sale of more units, which in turn satisfies the conditions for incorporating the new methods.

Limitations are inherent throughout the cost reduction-lower price-increased sales cycle. Cost reductions are limited by minimum levels of quality, maximum levels of expenditure for new equipment, and basic labor or material costs that resist lowering. Reduced prices may be an insufficient incentive to attract enough new sales. However, with reasonable care the cycle rewards the producer and leads to a better standard of living for the consumer.

# BREAKEVEN COMPARISONS

After a decision has been made to pursue a venture that promises to be beneficial, a subsequent decision is usually required to select the best tactic to accomplish the venture's purpose. One method of accomplishment seldom stands out as the best possible when all angles are considered. Assuming the choice among methods has been narrowed to those that can perform the desired function adequately, it is still likely that different alternatives are better over certain ranges of activity. A breakeven comparison detects the range over which each alternative is preferred. Then the decision maker has only to decide the most likely range of future operations to select the proper method to complete the venture. This practice was illustrated for sensitivity analysis in Chapter 14.

A "make-or-buy" decision is frequently encountered. It occurs when an item can be made in-house at a lower variable cost than the purchase price for that item from a vendor. The point at which the alternatives are equal depends on the first cost required to begin the in-house production. This situation was illustrated in Figure 1.6 and was used to point out the dangers of suboptimization.

A similar problem arises in a decision to lease or buy an asset. The costs of ownership (purchase price, installation cost, etc.) must be added to operating costs in comparing an owned item to one that is leased. Any fixed-cost investment to lower variable costs with respect to a strictly direct-cost alternative depends on the time period required to pay off the investment from variable-cost savings. One advantage of diagraming a breakeven comparison, as shown in Figure 16.3, is the attention focused on the breakeven point *BEP*, which designates the level of activity and implies the time period separating the preference for alternatives. The more conventional practice of comparing costs at a specified level of activity was described in Chapter 15.

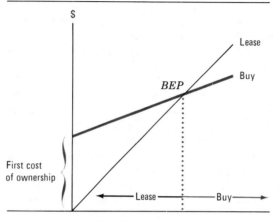

FIGURE 16.3 Lease-or-buy comparison.

# BREAKEVEN CHARTS

The best known breakeven model relates fixed and variable costs to revenue for the purpose of profit planning. The name *breakeven chart* is derived from the concept it depicts, the volume or level at which revenue and total cost of operations exactly break even. At this point, one additional unit made and sold would produce a profit. Until the breakeven point is attained, the producer operates at a loss for the period.

## Standard Format

Properties of a typical breakeven chart are displayed in Figure 16.4. The vertical scale shows the revenue and costs in monetary units. The horizontal scale indicates the volume of activity during the period pictured. The units of volume can be in sales dollars, number of units produced and sold, or the output quantity expressed as a percentage of total capacity.

The horizontal line in the chart shows the fixed costs *FC*, which are constant throughout the range of volume. The sloping line originating at the intersection of the fixed-cost line and the vertical axis represents variable costs *VC* plus the fixed costs. For linear relationships, variable costs are directly proportional to volume; each additional unit produced adds an identical increment of cost. The sum of variable and fixed costs is the total cost *TC*. The sloping line from the origin of the graph is the revenue line. Total Revenue *TR* is also assumed to be directly proportional to the number of units produced and sold at price *SP*.

*selling price*

The breakeven point $BEP$ occurs at the intersection of the total-cost and revenue lines. It thus specifies the dollar volume of sales and the unit volume of output at which an operation neither makes nor loses money. The vertical distance between the revenue line and the total-cost line indicates a profit $Z$ to the right of $BEP$ and a loss to the left.

A block cost diagram used in the discussion of profit expansion is shown alongside the breakeven chart in Figure 16.4. For an output volume of $n$, the costs, revenue, and profit are the same in both formats. The breakeven chart further indicates the profit or loss expectation at levels of output other than the specific quantity $n$. This feature helps explain such statements as, "A very low profit margin can seriously limit recuperative powers during market fluctuations." "A very low profit margin" means that the output is barely on the profit side of the breakeven point. An unstable market could easily cause sales to fall below point $BEP$ and show a loss for the period.

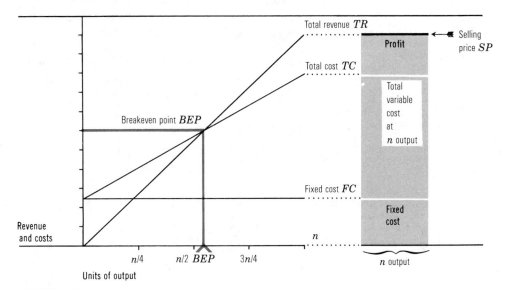

**FIGURE 16.4**  Standard format for breakeven charts.

## Algebraic Relationships

The graphic format is convenient for clarifying or presenting economic relationships. It is possible to obtain quantities for particular conditions by scaling values from the chart. However, the same conditions can be easily quantified by formulas. Calculations generally provide greater accuracy. Using the symbols already defined, we have

$$\text{Total revenue/period} = TR = nSP$$
$$\text{Total cost/period} = TC = nVC + FC$$
$$\text{Gross profit/period} = Z = TR - TC = n(SP - VC) - FC$$

where $n$ can also be a fraction of total capacity when $SP$ and $VC$ represent total dollar volume at 100 percent capacity.

At the breakeven point, profit equals zero. To determine the output to just break even, we have, at $BEP$,

$$Z = 0 = TR - TC = n(SP - VC) - FC$$

and, letting $n = BEP$,

$$BEP = \frac{FC}{SP - VC}$$

The term $SP - VC$ is called *contribution*. It indicates the portion of the selling price that contributes to paying off the fixed cost. At $n = BEP$ the sum of contributions from $BEP$ units equals the total fixed cost. The contribution of each unit sold beyond $n = BEP$ is an increment of profit.

To observe breakeven-chart relationships, assume an airline is evaluating its feeder routes. These routes connect smaller cities to major terminals. They are seldom very profitable themselves, but they feed passengers into the major flights which yield better returns. One feeder route has a maximum capacity of 1000 passengers per month. The contribution from the fare of each passenger is 75 percent of the $120 ticket price. Fixed costs per month are $63,000.

To find the average percentage of seats that must be sold on each flight to break even, the cost and revenue data could be converted to the graphical breakeven format shown in Figure 16.5. The same information displayed in the breakeven chart is supplied by the following calculations:

Total maximum revenue per month is

$$nSP = 1000 \times \$120 = \$120,000$$
$$\text{Total contribution} = 0.75 \times \$120,000 = \$90,000$$

$$BEP \text{ (\% of capacity)} = \frac{FC \times 100\%}{\text{contribution}}$$

$$= \frac{\$63,000}{\$90,000} 100\% = 70\%$$

or,

$$BEP \text{ (passengers)} = \frac{FC}{SP - VC} = \frac{\$63,000}{0.75 \times \$120}$$

$$= 700 \text{ passengers/month}$$

Assuming a tax rate of 40 percent, the net profit at full capacity is

$$
\begin{aligned}
\text{Net profit} &= Z(1 - t) \qquad\qquad\qquad \text{where } t = \text{Tax rate} \\
&= (TR - TC)(1 - t) \\
&= [n(SP - VC) - FC](1 - t) \\
&= [1000(0.75 \times \$120) - \$63,000](0.60) \\
&= \$27,000 \times 0.60 = \$16,200
\end{aligned}
$$

A gross-profit line is shown in the lower right corner of the chart, starting at $BEP$. Net profit is a fraction of $Z$ which depends on the tax rate for the total earnings of the organization.

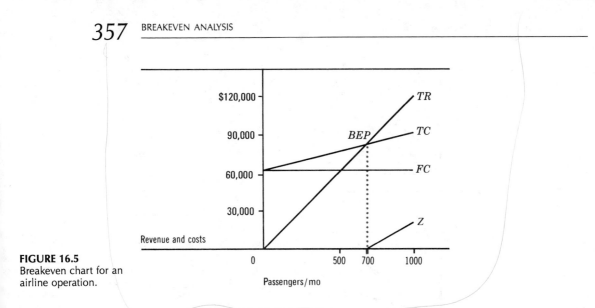

**FIGURE 16.5**
Breakeven chart for an airline operation.

# LINEAR BREAKEVEN ANALYSIS

A breakeven chart displays cost-volume-profit relationships that hold only over a short run. Over the long run, the relationships are altered by internal factors (new products, production facilities, etc.) and external impacts (competition, state of the general economy, etc.). Many of the internal activities that affect long-run changes are initiated from analyses of current cost-volume-profit conditions. Thus, a breakeven analysis is like a medical checkup; the physical examination reveals the current state of health and provides clues about what should be done to become or stay healthy.

## Breakeven-Point Alternatives

Any change in costs or selling price affects the breakeven point. We observed the gross effects of profit expansion as a function of selling price. Now we can consider the interaction of revenue, variable costs, and fixed costs in terms of output.

A lower breakeven point is a highly desirable objective. It means the organization can meet fixed costs at a lower level of output or utilization. A sales level well above the breakeven output is a sign of healthiness. Three methods of lowering the breakeven point are shown in Figure 16.6. The original operating conditions are shown as light lines and are based on the following data:

$$VC = \$7/\text{unit}$$
$$SP = \$12/\text{unit}$$
$$TR(\text{at } n = 100 \text{ units}) = \$1200$$
$$TC(\text{at } n = 100 \text{ units}) = \$1100$$
$$FC = \$400$$
$$BEP = 80 \text{ units}$$

The bold lines depict the measures necessary to reduce the breakeven point by half, from 80 to 40 units.

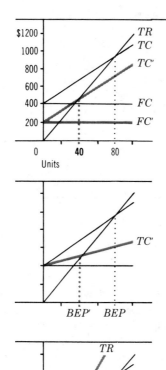

**Fixed-cost reduction:** By reducing the fixed costs by half, $BEP$ is halved. Therefore the new fixed cost $FC'$ is

$$FC' = \frac{\$400}{2} = \$200$$

and the new breakeven output $BEP'$ becomes

$$BEP' = \frac{FC'}{SP - VC}$$

$$= \frac{\$200}{(\$12 - \$7)\text{ per unit}} = 40\text{ units}$$

**Variable-cost reduction:** Knowing that $BEP'$ should equal 40 units, we can solve for the associated $VC'$ by

$$BEP' = \frac{FC}{SP - VC'}$$

$$\text{or } VC' = SP - \frac{FC}{BEP'} = \$12 - \frac{\$400}{40}$$

$$= \$12 - \$10 = \$2/\text{unit}$$

**Selling-price increase:** Raising the selling price $SP'$ increases the slope of the revenue line and augments the contribution. The contribution' required for $BEP'$ to equal 40 units is

$$\text{Contribution}' = \frac{FC}{BEP'} = \frac{\$400}{40}$$

$$= \$10/\text{unit}$$

which leads to

$$SP' = VC + \text{contribution}'$$
$$= \$7 + \$10 = \$17$$

**FIGURE 16.6**
Breakeven alternatives.

## Margin of Profit and Dumping

The perspective from which an organization views its breakeven point depends on its particular circumstances at the time of review. A firm struggling to get its products accepted in the market would have concerns different from those of a producer that has already captured a large share of the market. The struggling firm is likely beset with problems of cash availability to meet its fixed costs, while the dominant producer probably seeks investments to maintain or expand its sales.

Consider the alternatives available to a firm producing package waste-disposal units that sell for $35,000 each. Variable costs are $20,000 per unit, and fixed costs are $600,000. The plant can produce a maximum of 80 units per year. It is currently operating at 60 percent capacity. The firm is contemplating the effects of reducing the selling price by $2000 per unit, adding a feature to each unit which will increase the variable costs by $1000, and allocating an extra $120,000 per year for advertising. These actions are designed to sell enough additional units to raise plant utilization to 90 percent.

Under current conditions,

$$BEP = \frac{FC}{SP - VC} = \frac{\$600,000}{\$35,000 - \$20,000} = 40 \text{ units}$$

Since the company now sells $0.60 \times 80 = 48$ units per year, the gross annual profit is

$Z$ = units sold beyond $BEP \times$ contribution/unit
   $= (48 - 40)\$15,000 = \$120,000$

The ratio of gross annual profit to fixed costs is

$$\frac{Z}{FC} = \frac{\$120,000}{\$600,000} = 0.20$$

and may be thought of as a margin of profit or safety. The same ratio can be obtained by

$$\text{Margin of profit} = \frac{n - BEP}{BEP} = \frac{48 - 40}{40} = 0.20$$

where $n$ is the number sold during the period.

Both the current conditions (dotted lines) and the anticipated conditions (solid lines) are displayed in Figure 16.7. As graphed, $BEP$ increases, as a result of the added expenditures, to

$$BEP' = \frac{\$600,000 + \$120,000}{\$33,000 - \$21,000} = \frac{\$720,000}{\$12,000} = 60 \text{ units}$$

and the gross profit expected at 90 percent capacity also increases to

$Z = [(0.90 \times 80) - 60](\$33,000 - \$21,000)$
  $= 12 \text{ units} \times \$12,000/\text{unit} = \$144,000$

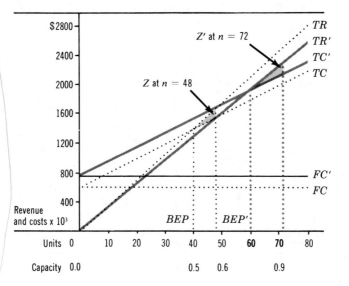

**FIGURE 16.7** Original and anticipated conditions for profit improvement from increased plant utilization.

but the margin of profit remains unchanged at

$$\frac{Z}{FC} = \frac{\$144,000}{\$720,000} = 0.20$$

The firm could also follow a course of action in which only one or two of the alternatives are pursued. If the advertising budget is eliminated but price and modifications are retained, the same profit ($144,000) would be obtained at an output of

$$n = \frac{Z + FC}{SP - VC} = \frac{\$144,000 + \$600,000}{\$33,000 - \$21,000}$$

$$= \frac{\$744,000}{\$12,000/unit} = 62 \text{ units}$$

and

$$BEP = \frac{\$600,000}{\$12,000/unit} = 50 \text{ units}$$

which makes the margin of safety (62 − 50)/50, or 0.24.

There are, of course, many factors to consider in such a decision. If the market is stable, the margin of profit is less important. Some alternatives are easier to implement than others. Some outcomes are more certain than others.

Still another alternative would be to sell a portion of the output at a reduced price. This practice is called *dumping.* It can be accomplished by selling to foreign markets at a lower price or by selling the same product at different prices under different names. There are many dangers in this practice, but if it works, profit will increase because of the increased plant utilization.

Figure 16.8 illustrates dumping applied to the original data on waste-disposal-unit sales: 48 units are sold at the regular selling price ($SP$ = $35,000) to account for 60 percent utilization. If 100 percent utilization could be achieved by *dumping* the remaining capacity at a sales price $SP'$ of $25,000 per unit, the gross profit would increase from $120,000 to $280,000.

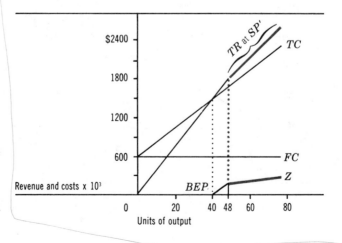

**FIGURE 16.8** Effects of dumping on price, cutting profit, and utilization.

## Multiproduct Alternatives

More than one product can be shown on a breakeven chart. Including a whole product line allows the decision maker to evaluate the combined effect of the product mix on plant utilization, revenue, and costs. A slightly different format for the breakeven chart accentuates the effect of multiple products. This type of graph is displayed in Figure 16.9 and is called a *multiproduct profit* or *contribution chart*.

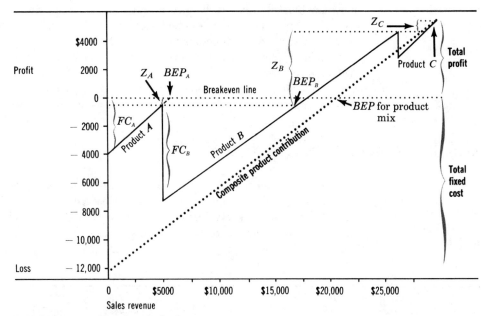

**FIGURE 16.9** Multiproduct profit chart.

The chart is constructed by plotting fixed costs as a loss on the vertical axis. The horizontal axis denotes sales revenue. At zero sales the only costs associated with a product are the negative preparation costs or fixed costs. As production and sales develop, each unit sold makes a contribution toward paying off the fixed costs. When enough units have been sold to pay these costs, the breakeven point is reached and the contribution from further sales is profit.

Three products, *A*, *B*, and *C*, are represented in Figure 16.9. The plotted values are based on the following assumptions made for the period shown in the chart:

|  | PRODUCT | | |
|---|---|---|---|
|  | *A* | *B* | *C* |
| Selling price per unit | $8.00 | $5.40 | $4.00 |
| Contribution per unit | $6.00 | $3.00 | $3.00 |
| Fixed cost | $4000 | $7000 | $1000 |
| Number of units sold | 600 | 4000 | 400 |

Product $A$ is entered in the chart by marking its fixed costs ($4000) on the negative side of the breakeven line at zero sales revenue. The total contribution of $A$ is 600 units times $6 per unit equals $3600. Subtracting the fixed costs from the total contribution leaves a loss of $400 from total sales of $4800.

The remaining products are dealt with in a similar manner. Each fixed cost is entered as a vertical line attached to the highest point on the contribution line for the preceding product. The results are cumulative. The distance the last contribution segment extends above the breakeven line is the total plant profit. The dotted line extending diagonally across the chart is the composite contribution line. The point at which this line crosses the plant breakeven line establishes the sales volume at which fixed costs are exactly covered.

The value of multiproduct breakeven charts lies in their use for product comparisons. The portion of fixed costs borne by each product is easily observed. A product is preferred when its contribution line is steeper than the composite contribution line. Such considerations are important in decisions to add new products or drop old ones.

## NONLINEAR BREAKEVEN ANALYSIS

Cost and revenue functions do not always follow convenient linear patterns. More often than not, realistic cost relationships develop a nonlinear pattern as typified by Table 16.1. The first four columns in the table relate output $n$ to total fixed cost $FC$, total variable cost $TVC$, and total cost $TC$. The right side of the table shows average and marginal costs derived from the figures tabulated on the left.

| Total Product, $n$ | Total Fixed Cost, $FC$ | Total Variable Cost, $TVC$ | Total Cost, $TC$ | Average Fixed Cost, $FC/n$ | Average Variable Cost, $TVC/n$ | Average Total Cost, $TC/n$ | Marginal Cost, $\Delta TC/\Delta n$ |
|---|---|---|---|---|---|---|---|
| 0 | $3000 | $ 0 | $ 3000 | — | — | — |  |
| 1 | 3000 | 700 | 3700 | $3000 | $700 | $3700 | $ 700 |
| 2 | 3000 | 1300 | 4300 | 1500 | 650 | 2150 | 600 |
| 3 | 3000 | 1800 | 4800 | 1000 | 600 | 1600 | 500 |
| 4 | 3000 | 2400 | 5400 | 750 | 600 | 1350 | 600 |
| 5 | 3000 | 3100 | 6100 | 600 | 620 | 1220 | 700 |
| 6 | 3000 | 3900 | 6900 | 500 | 650 | 1150 | 800 |
| 7 | 3000 | 4900 | 7900 | 429 | 700 | 1129 | 1000 |
| 8 | 3000 | 6200 | 9200 | 375 | 775 | 1150 | 1300 |
| 9 | 3000 | 7800 | 10,800 | 333 | 867 | 1200 | 1600 |

**TABLE 16.1**   Total and average cost data for a firm's operations over a given time period.

Characteristic patterns of average and marginal costs based on Table 16.1 are pictured in Figure 16.10 and discussed below.

*Average fixed cost*   Since fixed costs are independent of output, their per-unit amount declines as output increases. This feature is recognized when business people speak of "higher sales spreading the overhead."

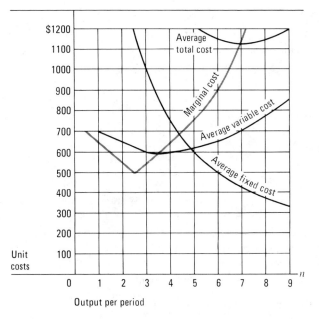

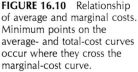

**FIGURE 16.10**   Relationship of average and marginal costs. Minimum points on the average- and total-cost curves occur where they cross the marginal-cost curve.

*Average variable cost*   The typical saucer-shaped average-cost curve declines at first, reaches a minimum, and then increases thereafter. It reflects the law of diminishing returns, Initially, combining variable resources $TVC$ with fixed resources $FC$ produces increasing returns, but a point is reached where more and more variable resources must be applied to obtain each additional unit of output. Stated another way, a fixed plant is underemployed when its output is below the minimum average-cost point. As output expands, more complete utilization of the plant's capital equipment will make production more efficient. But continually increasing variable costs will eventually create a condition in which overcrowding and overutilization of equipment impair efficiency.

*Average total cost*   Because average total cost is simply the sum of average fixed and average variable costs, it shows the combined effects of spreading out fixed charges and diminishing returns from variable resources.

*Marginal cost*   The key to the cost pattern in Figure 16.10 is contained in marginal-cost concepts. Marginal cost is calculated from either $TC$ or $TVC$ as the extra increment of cost required to produce an additional unit of output. If the last increment of cost is smaller than the average of all previous costs, it pulls the average down. Thus, *average total cost declines until it just equals marginal costs. Equivalently, the rising marginal-cost curve also pierces the average-variable cost curve at its minimum point.*

## Marginal Revenue and Profit

Both nonlinear revenue and cost schedules may be expressed as formulas. When such equations are available, their analysis is not much more difficult than that of linear models. Since an assumption of linearity makes all monetary increments constant over an extended range of output, nonlinear models call more attention to marginal relationships.

   *Marginal revenue* is the additional money received from selling one more unit at a specified level of output. For linear revenue functions, the marginal revenue is a constant value $SP$. That is, for each additional unit sold, the total revenue is increased by $SP$ dollars. Consequently, a greater output automatically increases the total profit.

When the linear relationship is replaced by an expression such as

Selling price $= SP = 21,000n^{-12}$ dollars/units

the price of each unit is not so obvious. Such expressions are examined with differential calculus. For the price function above, the rate of change of revenue with output is

$$\text{Marginal revenue} = \frac{dTR}{dn} = \frac{d(nSP)}{dn} = \frac{d(21,000n^{1/2})}{dn}$$

$$= 10,500n^{-1/2}$$

Figure 16.11(a) shows a decelerating revenue rate and linear costs. Decreasing marginal revenue could result from a policy of lowering prices in order to achieve a higher plant utilization. The nonlinear revenue curve fixes two breakeven points. Between these two points the firm operates at a profit. Outside the breakeven points a loss is incurred, as shown in the profit chart, Figure 16.11(b).

The graphs are based on the following data:

$n = 1$ unit produced and sold/period
$VC = \$1000$/unit
$FC = \$100,000$/period
$SP = \$21,000n^{-1/2}$/unit

Using the formula for total revenue and the selling-price function, $TR = nSP = 21,000n^{1/2}$, leads to a gross-profit equation of

$$Z = TR - TC = TR - (nVC + FC)$$
$$= 21,000n^{1/2} - 1000n - 100,000$$

Knowing that $Z = 0$ at a breakeven point allows the value or values for $BEP$ to be determined by rearranging the terms for $Z$:

$$Z = 0 = -10^3n - 10^5 + 21(10^3n^{1/2})$$

or

$$10^3n + 10^5 = 21 \times 10^3n^{1/2}$$

Squaring each side of the equation and dividing by $10^6$ results in

$$n^2 + 200n + 10^4 = 441n$$

and by collecting terms,

$$n^2 - 241n + 10^4 = 0$$

This expression can be solved with the quadratic formula.*

*For an equation in the quadratic form $Ax^2 + Bx + C = 0$, $x = \dfrac{-B \pm \sqrt{B^2 - 4AC}}{2A}$.

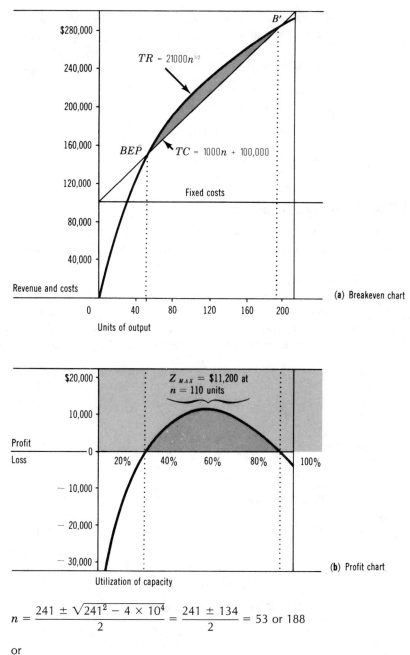

**FIGURE 16.11**
Nonlinear breakeven charts for decreasing marginal revenue and linear costs.

$$n = \frac{241 \pm \sqrt{241^2 - 4 \times 10^4}}{2} = \frac{241 \pm 134}{2} = 53 \text{ or } 188$$

or

$BEP$ = 53 units and $BEP'$ = 188 units

The point of maximum profit is especially important when two breakeven points are present. As indicated in Figure 16.11(b), the rate of profit is increasing to the left of the point of maximum profit, and decreasing to the right. The rate of change of profit with respect to output is *marginal profit*. At the point of maximum profit, the rate of change (and the marginal profit or slope of the profit line) is zero. Therefore, to find this point, differentiate the profit equation, set the derivative equal to zero, and solve for $n$:

$$\frac{dZ}{dn} = \frac{d(21{,}000n^{1/2} - 1000n - 100{,}000)}{dn} = 0$$

$$= 10{,}500n^{-1/2} - 1000 = 0$$

$$n = \left(\frac{10{,}500}{1000}\right)^2 = 110 \text{ units}$$

## Marginal Cost and Average Unit Cost

As production increases, the total cost per unit may also increase, owing to greater maintenance needs, overtime payments to workers, and general inefficiency caused by congestion during stepped-up operation. Under these conditions there is an increasing *marginal cost* (rate of change of total cost with output).

One possible pattern of marginal costs and linear revenue is shown in Figure 16.12. There could be many patterns: two breakeven points (as in Figure 16.11), decreasing marginal costs owing to savings realized from quantity purchases or near-capacity mechanized production, nonlinear functions for both revenue and costs, etc.

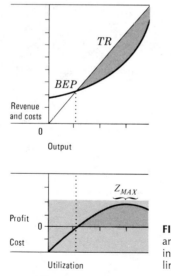

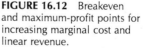

**FIGURE 16.12** Breakeven and maximum-profit points for increasing marginal cost and linear revenue.

The feature points of a breakeven analysis are determined in the manner described previously. To find *BEP*, set the profit equation equal to zero and solve for $n = BEP$. Differentiate the profit equation, and set the derivative equal to zero to solve for the output that produces maximum gross profit. In doing so, it is interesting to note that

$$\frac{dZ}{dn} = \frac{d(nSP - nVC - FC)}{dn} = 0$$

$$= \frac{d(nSP)}{dn} - \frac{d(nVC + FC)}{dn} = 0$$

or

$$\frac{d(nSP)}{dn} = \frac{d(nVC + FC)}{dn}$$

*Marginal revenue = marginal cost*

*at the operating level that produces maximum profit.* This means that when the change in revenue from one additional sale equals the change in cost of producing one more unit, the point of maximum profit is attained. Graphically, this point is at the output at which the vertical distance between the total-cost curve and the revenue curve is greatest. If marginal revenue and marginal cost were plotted, the output for maximum profit would be at the intersection of the two curves.

For linear functions, the *average unit cost* is

$$\frac{nVC + FC}{n} = VC + \frac{FC}{n} \quad \text{where } n = \text{a specific output}$$

In this case the average unit cost continually decreases with increasing output. For nonlinear costs this condition is not necessarily true. If the average cost goes through a minimum point and then increases, the slope of the curve will be zero at the output for lowest average unit cost:

$$\frac{d(VC + FCn^{-1})}{dn} = 0$$

$$\frac{dVC}{dn} - \frac{FC}{n^2} = 0$$

$$\frac{dV}{dn} = \frac{FC}{n^2}$$

From this equation and the maximum-profit equation it is clear that for nonlinear relationships the point of minimum average unit cost does not necessarily coincide with the maximum-profit point (see Review Exercise 4).

## APPLYING BREAKEVEN ANALYSES

A breakeven analysis often tends to oversimplify the decision environment. This is an attribute for presentation purposes and for gross evaluations. It can also be a shortcoming for problems in which detailed measures are needed. A decision to lower the breakeven point for an operation can result from a study of total revenue and costs, but the study alone seldom reveals the in-plant operations that engineers and managers must conduct to implement the decision. The inability to identify tactical procedures is not really a defect of a breakeven analysis; it merely indicates that decision makers should be aware of the limitations of the approach in order to apply it appropriately.

The validity of a breakeven chart is directly proportional to the accuracy of the data incorporated in the chart. When several products are lumped together and represented by one line on a chart, there is a distinct possibility that poor performance by one product may go undetected. A firm should have a good cost-accounting system, but data from past performance are not always indicative of future performance. However, examining graphs of previous breakeven conditions calls attention to developing trends in revenues and costs.

Breakeven relationships imply where engineering efforts can be of most use to an organization. Field or factory-floor engineers can observe the present state of financial affairs and use those observations to guide their cost-control activities. As an engineer's managerial responsibilities increase, the interplay of price, cost, and quantity become of greater concern. Then the combined effect of the system's operations and the underlying economic principles merge to steer strategic decisions.

# REVIEW EXERCISES AND DISCUSSIONS

**Exercise 1**  An engineering consulting firm won a contract to design and supervise construction of a sewage-treatment plant at a remote location. The installation phase will last at most 2 years, and two engineers from the firm will supervise on-site operations. They will need both living accommodations and an office. Three alternatives are available, with the costs shown below.

1  Rent a building with furnished living accommodations and an office: $3000 per month including upkeep and utilities.
2  Buy two furnished trailers to live in and rent an office: The purchase price of a house trailer is $24,000 per trailer (the seller will buy back a used trailer for 40 percent of its purchase price any time within 2 years); trailer upkeep, site rental, and utilities are $200 per trailer per month; and office rental is $800 per month.
3  Buy three trailers: Two house trailers as in alternative 2 and a smaller one to serve as an office, purchased for $16,000 from the same seller.

If all the alternatives provide adequate facilities, which one do you recommend?

**Solution 1**  Total costs $TC$ for the three alternatives are calculated as

$TC(1) = \$3000n$ where $n$ is the number of months needed
$TC(2) = (2 \times \$24,000)0.6 + [(2 \times \$200) + \$800]n = \$28,800 + \$2100n$
$TC(3) = [(2 \times \$24,000) + \$16,000]0.6 + (3 \times \$200)n = \$38,400 + \$600n$

As is apparent in Figure 16.3, $TC(1) = TC(2)$ at $n = 16$ months; $TC(1) = TC(3)$ at $n = 16$ months; and $TC(2) = TC(3)$ at $n = 16$ months. The decision thus narrows to a choice between alternatives 1 and 3, which, in turn, depends on the engineers' estimate of how long the project will take. If it takes longer than 16 months, 3 is preferred. Otherwise, 1 is less expensive. The convenience offered by the rented building (alternative 1 has upkeep and utilities paid, no trade-in hassles, etc.) would likely sway the decision.

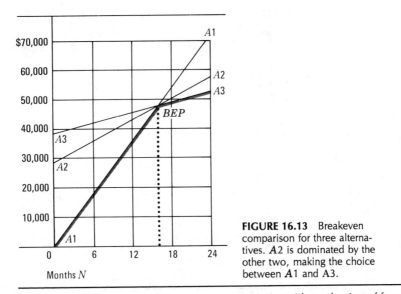

**FIGURE 16.13** Breakeven comparison for three alternatives. $A2$ is dominated by the other two, making the choice between $A1$ and $A3$.

**Exercise 2**   A fertilizer plant is operating at capacity with production of four mixes which have a total sales volume of $2 million. The sales and production-cost figures for mixes $W$, $X$, $Y$, and $Z$ are as shown:

|  | Mix W | Mix X | Mix Y | Mix Z | Totals |
|---|---|---|---|---|---|
| Percentage of total sales | 10 | 20 | 30 | 40 | 100 |
| Contribution (% of $SP$) | 45 | 40 | 45 | 35 |  |
| Fixed cost charged | $70,000 | $180,000 | $210,000 | $220,000 | $680,000 |
| Profit | $20,000 | −$20,000 | $60,000 | $60,000 | $120,000 |

Recognizing the loss incurred with product $X$, the company is considering dropping the product or replacing it with another mix. If the product is dropped without a replacement, the new sales and cost figures are estimated to develop as follows:

|  | Mix W | Mix Y | Mix Z | Totals |
|---|---|---|---|---|
| Percentage of total sales | 15 | 35 | 50 | 100 (for $R$ of $1,800,000) |
| Contribution (% of $SP$) | 45 | 45 | 35 |  |
| Fixed cost charged | $100,000 | $250,000 | $290,000 | $640,000 |

Construct a multiproduct profit chart to compare the two alternatives.

**Solution 2**   The anticipated and original conditions are displayed in Figure 16.14 in a slightly different form of multiproduct breakeven chart. In this version the first entry is made at zero revenue and the point of maximum fixed cost. Then the contributions of each product are plotted progressively to the right. All other interpretations are the same for the two forms of multiproduct charts.

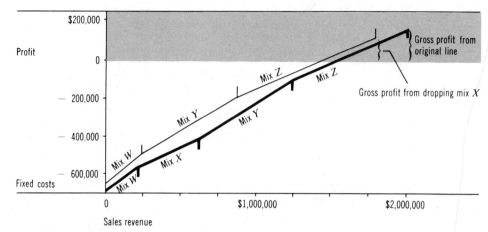

Sales revenue

**FIGURE 16.14** Multiproduct contribution chart showing reduced profit from the revised mix.

The new product line without mix $X$ would be less profitable than the former line:

|  | *Mix W* | *Mix Y* | *Mix Z* | *Total* |
|---|---|---|---|---|
| Profit | $21,500 | $33,500 | $25,000 | $80,000 |

The main reason gross profit falls from $120,000 to $80,000 is that most of the fixed costs carried by mix $X$ did not disappear with its elimination from the product line; capital cost allowance, taxes, engineering services, and other indirect costs are still required to run the batching plant, and their magnitude is not reduced appreciably by dropping mix $X$. The situation is further aggravated by having the largest sales increase occur for mix $Z$, which has a lower contribution rate than the product eliminated.

**Exercise 3** A manufacturing company produces several different products that are manufactured on the same equipment but are marketed individually. An audit of one product reveals the data shown in Table 16.2; all figures are corrected to a base year to avoid distortion by inflation or the general economy. The portion of manufacturing overhead allocated to the product as its fixed cost is $400,000.

Analyze the product's life-cycle costs and revenues.

| CUMULATIVE OUTPUT, COST, AND REVENUE | | | |
|---|---|---|---|
| *Product Life, Age* | *Output, Units* | *Variable Cost* | *Revenue Earned* |
| Year 1 | 1000 | $ 80,000 | $ 200,000 |
|  | 2000 | 112,000 | 400,000 |
|  | 3000 | 134,000 | 600,000 |
| Year 2 | 4000 | 160,000 | 780,000 |
|  | 5000 | 190,000 | 930,000 |
| Year 3 | 6000 | 252,000 | 1,050,000 |
|  | 7000 | 352,000 | 1,160,000 |
| Year 4 | 8000 | 480,000 | 1,270,000 |

**TABLE 16.2** Life-cycle pattern of output, costs, and income.

**Solution 3**   Fixed cost chargeable to the product totals $400,000 and is included in the analysis as shown in the second column of Table 16.3 (p. 406). Variable costs were high during the start-up period, dropped as production became more efficient and climbed during the third and fourth years as a result of "relearning" when production runs were not continuous, owing to declining sales. Although average fixed cost drops consistently with additional output, the average variable and total cost figures show the effect of increasing production costs.

Marginal costs, collected for increments of 1000 units of output, focus attention on key output levels. The lowest marginal cost occurred in the first year (at 3000 units) when the annual production rate was highest. At about 5000 units, marginal cost equaled the average variable cost at its lowest point. Average total cost bottomed out near 7000 units, where it equaled marginal cost. At about this same level, rising marginal costs met the dropping marginal revenues to signal the point of maximum profit. The decline in marginal revenue, stated in 1000-unit increments, is attributed to pressure from competitors.

Unless variable costs can be slashed or prices increased, the product is a candidate for termination or remodeling. Production factors that will influence the decision include the expected utilization of manufacturing facilities for other products, labor and material availability, and resource requirements (both money and time) for restoring productivity or producing a revamped product.

---

**Exercise 4**   A monthly record of operating expenses and revenue for a new manufacturing plant is posted in the manager's office. The purpose is to detect any changes in cost-revenue relationships and to establish the plant's operating pattern.

The graphic results of several months' operations are depicted in Figure 16.15. The pattern appears to indicate that as the output becomes greater, marginal costs increase and

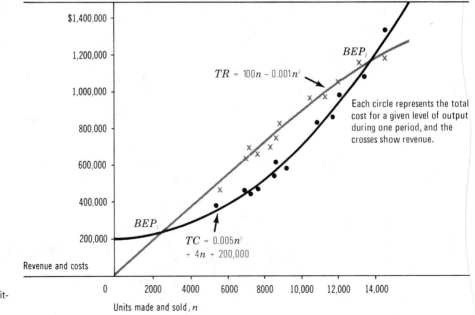

$$TR = 100n - 0.001n^2$$

Each circle represents the total cost for a given level of output during one period, and the crosses show revenue.

$$TC = 0.005n^2 + 4n + 200,000$$

Revenue and costs

Units made and sold, $n$

**FIGURE 16.15**
Production data and fitted curves.

| Out-put (n units) | Fixed Cost (FC) | Total Variable Cost (TVC) | Total Cost, TC (TC = TVC + FC) | Incremental Marginal Cost (1000 units) | Average Fixed Cost (FC/n) |
|---|---|---|---|---|---|
| 0 | $400,000 | 0 | $400,000 | | |
| 1000 | 400,000 | $80,000 | 480,000 | $80,000 | $400 |
| 2000 | 400,000 | 112,000 | 512,000 | 32,000 | 200 |
| 3000 | 400,000 | 134,000 | 534,000 | 22,000 | 133 |
| 4000 | 400,000 | 160,000 | 560,000 | 26,000 | 100 |
| 5000 | 400,000 | 190,000 | 590,000 | 30,000 | 80 |
| 6000 | 400,000 | 252,000 | 652,000 | 62,000 | 67 |
| 7000 | 400,000 | 352,000 | 752,000 | 100,000 | 37 |
| 8000 | 400,000 | 480,000 | 880,000 | 128,000 | 50 |

**TABLE 16.3** Product cost and revenue patterns over a 4-year product life.

marginal revenue decreases. The belief is confirmed by formulas developed for curves that fit the data.

The selling price of finished units varies according to $SP = (100 - 0.001n)$ dollars per unit. The price behavior is attributed to lower per-unit quotes given for large orders. Fixed costs are considered reasonable at $200,000 per month. The variable costs, $VC = (0.005n + 4)$ dollars per unit, also appear competitive. The plant is designed to produce 12,000 units per month.

Based on the given data, calculate the level of output which produces the greatest profit, the least average unit cost, and the breakeven points. On a graph, show the curves for average unit cost, marginal cost, marginal revenue, and marginal profit.

**Solution 4**   Maximum profit occurs where marginal revenue equals marginal cost, as shown in Figure 16.16 (p. 408) and the computations below.

$$\text{Marginal revenue} = \frac{d(nSP)}{dn} = \frac{d(100n - 0.001n^2)}{dn} = 100 - 0.002n$$

$$\text{Marginal cost} = \frac{d(nVC + FC)}{dn} = \frac{d(0.005n^2 + 4n + 200,000)}{dn} = 0.01n + 4$$

At maximum profit, $100 - 0.002n = 0.01n + 4$, so

$$n = \frac{96}{0.012} = 8000 \text{ units}$$

For an output of 8000 units,

$$Z = TR - TC = 100n - 0.001n^2 - 0.005n^2 - 4n - 200,000$$
$$= -0.006n^2 + 96n - 200,000$$
$$Z_{8000} = -0.006(8000)^2 + 96(8000) - 200,000 = \$184,000$$

| Average Variable Cost (TVC/n) | Average Total Cost (TC/n) | Total Revenue (TR) | Incremental Marginal Revenue (1000 units) | Total Production Profit (TR − TC) |
|---|---|---|---|---|
| 0 | | 0 | | |
| $80 | $480 | $200,000 | $200,000 | −$280,000 |
| 56 | 256 | 400,000 | 200,000 | −112,000 |
| 45 | 178 | 600,000 | 200,000 | 66,000 |
| 40 | 140 | 780,000 | 180,000 | 220,000 |
| 38 | 118 | 930,000 | 150,000 | 340,000 |
| 42 | 109 | 1,050,000 | 120,000 | 398,000 |
| 50 | 107 | 1,160,000 | 110,000 | 408,000 |
| 60 | 110 | 1,270,000 | 110,000 | 390,000 |

The output for maximum profit is also located by the point at which the marginal profit is zero:

$$\text{Marginal profit} = \frac{dZ}{dn} = \frac{d(-0.006n^2 + 96n - 200,000)}{dn} = 0$$

$$0 = -0.012n + 96$$

$$n = \frac{96}{0.012} = 8000 \text{ units}$$

The minimum average cost occurs where the output satisfies the relation

$$\frac{dVC}{dn} = \frac{FC}{n^2}$$

$$\frac{d(0.005n + 4)}{dn} = \frac{200,000}{n^2}$$

$$0.005n^2 = 200,000$$

$$n = 6325$$

At $n = 6325$, the average cost is $67.20 per unit, as determined from the average-cost formula ($0.005n + 4 + 200,000/n$), and as shown in Figure 16.16.

The breakeven output is calculated from the gross profit, where $Z = 0$. Thus,

$$Z = 0 = -0.006n^2 + 96n - 200,000$$

$$n = \frac{96 \pm \sqrt{(96)^2 - 4 \times 0.006 \times 200,000}}{2 \times 0.006}$$

$$BEP = n = \frac{96 \pm 66.4}{0.012} = 2467 \text{ and } 13,533 \text{ units}$$

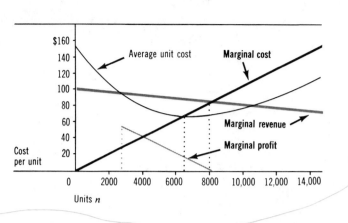

**FIGURE 16.16**
Average and marginal
economic relationships.

## PROBLEMS

**16.1** "Do you mean you would charge me $68.75 to ride home with you? You're out of your mind! The bus costs only $51. By air it's just $66.50. Look at those figures again," implored Gaston.

"Look, Gassie," said Alphonse, "I *know* what it costs me to drive my car. I keep records, complete ones. It's all right here. You look again."

Alphonse handed the paper to Gaston. On it were written the costs of operating a car for 3 years, the length of time Alphonse expected to keep his car before trading it in:

| | |
|---|---:|
| Gasoline (40,000 miles at 7.2¢/mile) | $2880 |
| Oil and grease | 200 |
| Tires | 280 |
| Repairs and maintenance | 800 |
| Insurance | 900 |
| License fees and property taxes | 180 |
| Depreciation in value ($7200−$3400) | 3800 |
| Average interest on investment at 6% interest | |
| ($3800/2 + $3400)(0.06)(3) | 954 |
| Total cost for 3 years | $9994 |

Cost per mile = $9994/40,000 miles = 25¢/mile

"Ok, Alphie, let's assume your figures are correct. But you haven't used them right. You say the 550-mile trip costs $137.50. It doesn't. Your car isn't going to lose more value because you drive it an extra 550 miles. Your license fee doesn't go up. Your insurance premium is the same. You still have to pay interest. The only thing this trip will cost you is gas and oil. That's only about 7.7 cents per mile . . . say, $42 for the trip, my share being about $21."

"So you say," retorted Alphonse. "I say I use up my tires. I'm going to have to make repairs sooner. Go hitchhike if you want to be cheap."

"I just might do that. I also thought of catching the plane so I could get home in time for a party Saturday night. However, I will forgo the party and give up a relaxing bus ride to keep you company, if you will be reasonable. Now let's look at that list again, Alphie, and remember that car of yours is going to get older whether I ride in it or not. My contribution is clear profit to you. You've got to go home anyway."

"So have you," replied Alphonse, settling more firmly into his bargaining position.

**16.1a** What is Gaston's fair share of the cost if he rides home with Alphonse? Why?

**16.1b** How do you reconcile the counterarguments that Gaston's share of the trip is pure profit to Alphonse and, conversely, whatever Gaston can save compared to the bus price is pure profit to him?

**16.2** Two alternative methods* of crude-oil processing in a producing oil field are available: a manual tank battery (MTB) and an automated tank battery (ATB). Tank batteries are composed of heaters, treaters, storage tanks, and other equipment, which remove salt water and sediment from crude oil prior to its entrance into pipelines for transport to an oil refinery.

Fixed costs for a tank-battery installation include depreciation, taxes, etc. Variable costs that increase in direct proportion to the volume of oil being processed include chemical additives and heating cost. In addition, there are constant costs independent of volume. All these costs are tabulated below.

|  | *ATB* | *MTB* |
| --- | --- | --- |
| Annual cost of labor and maintenance | $5485 | $7921 |
| Fixed annual cost of depreciation and taxes | 4064 | 2375 |
| Variable cost per barrel of oil processed | 0.0114 | 0.0081 |

At what level of oil production is the automatic tank battery preferred?

$$(B = 226,000 \ barrels/year)$$

**16.3** An import company buys foreign-made sewing machines for $80 per unit. Fixed costs of the operation are $140,000 per year. The sewing machines are sold on commission by door-to-door sales representatives who receive 40 percent of the selling price for each machine sold. At what price should the machines be sold to allow the importers to break even on a shipment of 5000 sewing machines? $(SP = \$180)$

**16.4** A privately owned summer camp for youngsters has the following operating data for a 12-week session:

| Charge per camper | $120/week |
| --- | --- |
| Variable cost per camper | $80/week |
| Fixed costs | $48,000/season |
| Capacity | 150 campers |

**16.4a** What is the total number of campers that will allow the camp to just break even?

$$(BEP = 100 \ campers)$$

**16.4b** What is the profit for the 12-week season if the camp operates at 80 percent capacity? $(Z = \$9600)$

**16.4c** What profit would result if the camp stayed open 2 weeks longer and averaged 75 campers paying a reduced rate of $100 per week during the extended season? What might go wrong with the plan? $(Z_{extra} = \$3000)$

**16.5** A manufacturer of hand-operated power tools can produce a convenient attachment for use with his line of tools at an estimated annual fixed cost of $9000 and variable costs of $3.75 per attachment. He can also buy the complete attachment custom-made for

*Adopted from E. J. Ferguson and J. E. Shamblin, "Break-Even Analysis," *Journal of Industrial Engineering,* April 1967.

his line of tools at a price of $6 per attachment for the first 5000, and $3.15 for all units purchased beyond the 5000-unit breakoff point. At what increments of unit sales should he purchase or manufacture the attachment? What factors other than cost might influence the decision?

**16.6** A lake resort includes 5 three-bedroom cabins which rent for $90 a night, 25 two-bedroom cabins which rent for $70 a night, and 15 single and 15 double rooms in the lodge which rent for $30 and $50 a night, respectively. The cost of cleaning a rental and preparing for new occupants is $20 for a cabin and $12 for a room. Annual fixed costs for operating the resort are $376,000 for the 200-day season. The average stay at the resort is 2 days, and utilization closely follows the proportion of available rooms and cabins.

**16.6a** What percentage of resort capacity must be rented each night to break even?

**16.6b** How many rooms and cabins must be rented each day to make an annual profit of $64,000?

**16.7** Sales of a desk lamp that wholesales at $4 per lamp have been disappointing. The contribution of each lamp sold is $1.50. It is planned to increase the advertising budget by $0.22 per lamp and reduce the price to spur sales. Twice as much will be allocated for advertising as for price reduction. Current gross profit is $50,000 on sales of 100,000 lamps per year. How many lamps must be sold under the proposed conditions to double the profit? *(n = 171,000 units)*

**16.8** A product currently sells for $12. The fixed costs are $4 per unit, and 10,000 units are sold annually for a gross profit of $30,000. A new design will increase variable costs by 20 percent and fixed costs by 10 percent, but sales should increase to 12,000 units per year. What should the selling price be to keep the same profit ($30,000)? *(SP' = $12.17)*

**16.9** A boat marina now sells new boats of only one make. The boats are divided into classes by size: *A*, *B*, and *C*. With an average value placed on the accessories sold with each boat, the accounting figures for annual turnover are

| Type | Average P | Average V | Number Sold |
|------|-----------|-----------|-------------|
| A | $ 400 | $ 300 | 300 |
| B | 900 | 500 | 175 |
| C | 2200 | 1200 | 100 |

Adding a new, fancier line of boats, enlarging the display area, and increasing the sales staff could change the cost and sales figures to

| Type | Average P | Average V | Number Sold |
|------|-----------|-----------|-------------|
| A | $ 450 | $ 350 | 425 |
| B | 1000 | 600 | 200 |
| C | 2400 | 1200 | 75 |
| D | 3600 | 2000 | 50 |

The additional expense of carrying the extra line of boats would double the present $100,000 fixed-cost charge for the original line.

**16.9a** What is the composite contribution for each line?

**16.9b** Should the new line be added?

**16.10** A consulting engineer was asked by some of her clients to produce a book on "tilt-up" construction. Her costs for preparation—artwork, typesetting, plates, etc.—came to $12,000. For each 1000 books printed, the variable costs—paper, printing, binding, etc.—will be $4000. She believes the number of books she will sell depends on the price she lists for the book. Her estimates show that the following number of books would sell at the prices shown:

| Number of Books Sold | Price per Book |
| --- | --- |
| 2000 | $20.00 |
| 4000 | 14.00 |
| 10,000 | 7.00 |

**16.10a** What price will give her the greatest profit?                    *(SP = $14)*

**16.10b** An advertising agency claims that a $20,000 promotion plan for the book would double the sales at any of the prices listed above. If the engineer accepts their forecast, what price should she use?                    *(Z = $48,000 at SP = $14)*

**16.11** A plant produces products 1, 2, and 3 at annual rates of 10,000, 7000, and 5000 units, respectively. Product 1 accounts for 30 percent of the plant's revenue, with a 40 percent contribution on its selling price. Product 2 has fixed costs of $35,000 and a contribution rate of $0.5SP$, where $SP$ is the selling price. The fixed costs for product 3 are $20,000, while it accounts for 30 percent of the total sales revenue, with the same contribution rate as the composite contribution rate. Total fixed costs for the plant are $80,000, and total sales amount to $250,000.

**16.11a** What is the plant breakeven revenue?
**16.11b** What is the profit for each product?

**16.12** Another alternative for the fertilizer batching plant described in Review Exercise 2 is to replace mix $X$ with a new mix $XX$. By replacing mix $X$ with mix $XX$, the following operating figures are expected:

| | Mix W | Mix XX | Mix Y | Mix Z | Totals |
| --- | --- | --- | --- | --- | --- |
| Percentage of total sales | 10 | 15 | 30 | 45 | 100(on $2 million) |
| Contribution (% of *SP*) | 45 | 50 | 45 | 35 | |
| Fixed cost charged | $70,000 | $140,000 | $210,000 | $275,000 | $695,000 |

**16.12a** Calculate the expected profit from the total product line which includes mixes *W, XX, Y,* and *Z.*                    *(Profit = $130,000)*
**16.12b** A *composite contribution rate*, as shown by the sloping dotted line in Figure 16.9, is the sum of each product's contribution, weighted according to its percentage of total sales. That is,

$$\text{Weighted contribution} = \text{product contribution} \times \frac{\text{product sales}}{\text{total sales}}$$

Then, the composite contribution rate is the sum of the weighted contributions, and the total contribution is the composite contribution rate times total sales, which makes the gross profit equal the total contribution less the fixed cost.

Calculate the composite contribution rate, and use it to reaffirm the gross product computed in Problem 16.12*a*.

**16.13** What are some of the dangers faced by a firm that engages in dumping to increase its plant utilization?

**16.14** A small company manufactures rubber matting for the interiors of custom carts. During the past year a revenue of $202,000 from sales was earned with the current costs given below.

| *Current Operating Costs* | |
| --- | --- |
| Direct material | $51,000 |
| Direct labor | 42,000 |
| Maintenance | 11,000 |
| Property taxes and depreciation | 17,000 |
| Managerial and sales expenses | 35,000 |

The forecast for the next year is a drastic drop in custom-cart sales, which is expected to limit mat sales to $90,000. There is insufficient time to develop new markets before next year. With a skeleton force for the reduced production, anticipated operating costs are shown below:

| *Expected Operating Costs* | |
| --- | --- |
| Direct material | $28,000 |
| Direct labor | 23,000 |
| Maintenance | 7,000 |
| Property taxes and depreciation | 17,000 |
| Managerial and sales expense | 35,000 |

The company can operate at an apparent loss, or mats can be purchased from a large supplier and resold to the custom-cart builders at a price that will just meet purchase and handling costs. Either alternative will retain the market for the company until the following year, when sales are expected to be at least equal to last year. Which of the two alternatives is the better course of action?

**16.15** Assume the variable cost in Table 16.1 is composed completely of labor and represents one week's operation of the firm. Suppose the firm is currently producing 4 units per week with 12 employees (the average wage is $200 per week). The manager recognizes that the firm should operate at a level of 7 or 8 units of output per week to minimize total cost. At a weekly production level of 8 units, variable cost allows an employment level of $6200/$200 per employee = 31 employees at a continued average wage of $200 per week. It thus takes $31 - 12 = 19$ employees to double the output produced by the original work force producing 4 units per week. Or, put differently, the original 12 employees accounted for $4/12 = 0.33$ units of output apiece, whereas the next 19 employees would account for $(8 - 4)/(31 - 12) = 0.21$ output units each. Do the original 12 deserve higher pay than the next 19 employees? Discuss wage policy as a function of marginal cost.

**16.16** A company is being organized to produce a new type of one-piece fishing rod and reel to be called the Fish Machine. One million dollars has been budgeted for fixed costs over a 3-year period, including the advertising budget. Sales in the first year are expected to be 20,000 units, and the units will be priced to recover one-half the fixed cost. Second-year sales are expected to be double those of the first year. After all fixed costs have been recovered, the selling price of the Fish Machine may have to be reduced to encourage more sales. In the third year production will be upped to 50,000 units, and variable costs are expected to rise sharply because production facilities will be operating over their design capacity. The expected total variable cost pattern is given below.

| $n$ | $TVC$ | $n$ | $TVC$ | $n$ | $TVC$ |
|---|---|---|---|---|---|
| 10,000 | $320,000 | 50,000 | $1,050,000 | 90,000 | $2,160,000 |
| 20,000 | 520,000 | 60,000 | 1,260,000 | 100,000 | 2,500,000 |
| 30,000 | 700,000 | 70,000 | 1,540,000 | 110,000 | 2,860,000 |
| 40,000 | 880,000 | 80,000 | 1,840,000 | | |

**16.16a** Prepare a graph of marginal cost, average variable cost, and average total cost.
**16.16b** How much total profit would result if the price could be held at the original level for 3 years?
**16.16c** Assume that the selling price holds at the original level for 2 years but then it must come down to meet competition from larger manufacturers that have entered the market. During the third year prices must be dropped by 10 percent to sell each additional increment of 10,000 Fish Machines. What is the total profit for 3 years? Show that the maximum profit would be obtained if production were terminated at the output where marginal revenue equals marginal cost.

**16.17** A company manufactures industrial clips for assembly work. The marginal revenue has been determined to be

Marginal revenue $= 100 - 0.02n$

where $n$ is the number of clips produced. Variable costs plus fixed costs are calculated by the formula

Total cost $= 2n^2 \times 10^{-4} + 10,000$

Compute the production in clips per year for the following:

| | | |
|---|---|---|
| **16.17a** Minimum unit cost of sales | | *(n = 7071 clips)* |
| **16.17b** Production for maximum profit | | *(n = 4902 clips)* |
| **16.17c** Breakeven volume | | *(n = 9700 and 100 clips)* |

**16.18** Assume that a company can sell all the units it produces, but costs are subject to diminishing returns. Its revenue and cost functions (in thousands of dollars) are

$$TR = \frac{3n}{4} \quad \text{and} \quad TC = \frac{n^3 - 8n^2 + 25n + 30}{25}$$

**16.18a** Construct a graph of the cost and revenue curves with the breakeven points indicated.
**16.18b** At what output $n$ will profit $Z$ be maximum?

# EXTENSION

**16A  Effects of Inflation on Breakeven Analysis**  Moderate inflation rates do not affect breakeven volumes as severely as they affect returns from individual proposals, but they are still influential. One reason why they are less affected is that fixed cost is not responsive to inflation. Since fixed cost is largely composed of capital cost allowance, taxes, and contracts that are typically renegotiated annually (janitorial services, administrative salaries, maintenance agreements, etc.), there is no continuous impact of inflation. In contrast, variable costs and prices are consistently influenced by inflation and tend to rise accordingly.

Effects of escalations on the cost-volume-price relationship can be accounted for by linear or continuously compounded growth. A linear inflation model is conveniently used when inflation rates are moderate and the time taken to reach breakeven volume is short. This model is examined because it is simple, yet conceptually complete.

To the symbols already defined for breakeven analyses ($SP$ = price/unit, $VC$ = variable cost/unit, $FC$ = fixed cost/period, $n$ = number of units produced, and $BEP$ = breakeven volume), the following are added:

$M = SP - VC$ = contribution margin at beginning of analysis period
$N$ = output or production rate per period (normally 100% utilization)
$a$ = inflation rate per period for variable cost $VC$
$b$ = escalation rate per period for selling price ($SP$)
$t$ = time  ($t = 0$ at start of period, and $t = 1$ at end of period)

Then $n = Nt$ and $BEP = Nt^*$, where $t^*$ is the time when breakeven occurs.

Knowing that revenue equals total cost at $BEP$, the effect of inflation on price ($SPbt$) and variable cost ($VCat$) at time $t$ is included in the breakeven relationship as

$$\int_{t=0}^{t^*} (SP + SPbt)N\, dt = FC + \int_{t=0}^{t^*} (VC + VCat)N\, dt$$

By integrating and rearranging terms,

$$\frac{t^{*2}\,(SPbN - VCaN)}{2} + t^*\,(SPN - VCN) - FC = 0$$

Note that if there is no inflation, $a = b = 0$, and the first term in the above equation is eliminated to give

$$t^*(SPN - VCN) = FC$$

and, since $t^* = BEP/N$,

$$\frac{BEP}{N}\,(SP - VC)N = FC \quad \text{or} \quad BEP = \frac{FC}{SP - VC} = \frac{FC}{M}$$

Solving for $BEP$ in the quadratic equation after substitution for $t^*$ yields

$$BEP = \frac{-MN \pm \sqrt{M^2N^2 + 2\,(SPb - VCa)NFC}}{SPb - VCa}$$

As an illustration of the linear inflation model, let $a = 0.5$ percent/month and $b = 1$ percent/month for the feeder airline situation described in Figure 16.5. Given $SP = \$120$/unit, $VC = \$30$/unit, $FC = \$63,000$/month, and $N = 1000$ units (seats available) per month, without inflation

$$BEP = \frac{FC}{M} = \frac{\$63,000}{\$120 - \$30} = 700 \text{ units/month}$$

When the price of a ticket is going up faster than the variable cost ($b > a$), the breakeven point goes down, as shown by

$$BEP = \frac{-90(1000) \pm \sqrt{(90)^2(1000)^2 + 2[120(0.01) - 30(0.005)](1000)(63,000)}}{120(0.01) - 30(0.005)}$$

$$= \frac{-90,000 \pm \sqrt{8100 \times 10^6 + 2(1.20 - 0.15)(63 \times 10^6)}}{1.05}$$

$$= \frac{-90,000 \pm 90,732}{1.05} = \frac{732}{1.05} = 697 \text{ units/month}$$

When the percentages are reversed ($a = 1$ percent and $b = 0.5$ percent), prices are still climbing faster than costs in terms of dollar amounts, and

$$BEP = \frac{-90,000 + 90,209.75}{0.30} = 699 \text{ units/month}$$

For the given data the change in the breakeven point is slight, mainly because the contribution margin per unit is so large. The effect of inflation is more pronounced when the contribution margin is small and the production rate is high.

The quadratic relationship affords the possibility of two breakeven points. This may occur when $M$ is greater than $\sqrt{Z(VCa - SPb/N}$. Whenever $SPb$ is greater than $VCa$, profit continually increases as production increases beyond the breakeven point.

A compound inflation model is developed similarly to the previous model. From

$$\int_{t=0}^{t^*} SPe^{bt} \, dn = FC + \int_{t=0}^{t^*} VCe^{at} \, dn$$

the breakeven point $BEP$ can be determined by integration and numerical solution techniques.*

## QUESTION

**16A.1**  For an annual production rate of 150,000 units, the fixed cost is $200,000 a year. The selling price is $10 per unit, and the contribution margin is $2 per unit.

**16A.1a**  Solve for $BEP$ when inflation is not considered.      *(BEP = 100,000)*

**16A.1b**  Solve for $BEP$ when both $VC$ and $SP$ inflate at a 20 percent annual rate by applying the linear inflation model.      *(BEP = 94,097)*

---

*See D. G. Dhavale and H. G. Wilson, "Breakeven Analysis with Inflationary Cost and Prices," *The Engineering Economist*, Winter 1980.

**16A.1c**  What is the breakeven point when prices escalate at 20 percent per year and variable cost inflates at 10 percent? (Use the linear inflation model.) *(BEP = 85,410)*

**16A.1d**  What is *BEP* when $a = 20$ percent and $b = 10$ percent, when the linear inflation model is applied?

# CHAPTER 17

# EXPECTED VALUE

OVERVIEW

*Risk* is the chance of loss. As applied to engineering economics, risk is the chance that cash flow will fall short of expectation. In previous evaluations we have assumed cash flow to be known with certainty, although sensitivity analysis questioned the effect of cash flow deviations and the cost of capital when risk is considered. In this chapter, risk is a specified dimension for investment decisions. It is quantified as the probabilities of occurrence of different cash flows.

At least some risk is inherent in any economic decision. Inputs and outputs for short-term investment alternatives are usually subject to less variability than long-term investment proposals. Risk analysis is appropriate when *significant* outcome variations are likely for different future states and *meaningful* probabilities can be assigned to those states.

Probability principles govern risk analyses. Both objective and subjective probability estimates are utilized in economic evaluations. Future states are usually defined by independent probabilities. The widely used *expected-value* measure of preference is a weighted average of outcomes—the sum of the products of outcomes from independent states multiplied by their associated probabilities of occurrence. *Investment-risk profiles* and *acceptable-investment diagrams* are graphic aids that assist in the evaluation of expected values. Other criteria such as the *most probable future* and *aspiration level* may influence the final selection of the preferred alternative. Investments to avoid risk are considered in Extension 17A.

# RECOGNIZING RISK

Economic analyses in previous chapters were based on the assumption that complete information was available and that any uncertainty connected with a comparison could be tolerated. Thus, a salvage value assigned today is expected to be valid, say, 15 years hence. A positive cash flow of $1000 per year in a comparison model presupposes that exactly $1000 will become available each period on schedule. Unfortunately, real-world conditions do not always follow the models developed to represent them.

Variability is a recognized factor in most engineering and management activities. People are expected to possess individual skills and temperaments, and to behave impetuously when exposed to some situations. The properties of materials vary over time. Seemingly identical machines exhibit diverse operating characteristics. Environmental factors are never constant, and economic conditions change irregularly. But recognizing variability is much easier than including its consequences in economic comparisons.

Risk analysis recognizes the existence of variability and accordingly provides ways to select a preferred alternative. Consideration of inflation, sensitivity analysis, and comparisons based on a range of estimates were modifications of assumed certainty suggested earlier to deal with unpredictable future events. In this chapter probability theory and associated management-science tools are introduced. They are applied to discounted cash flows and decision models. Such analyses contribute to a more complete economic evaluation when there are *significant* risks involved that can be represented by the assignment of *meaningful* probabilities.

# INCLUDING RISK IN ECONOMIC ANALYSES

The problem-solving and decision-making process depicted in the first two figures in this book set the framework for decisions under risk. Every decision of any consequence has overtones of risk. Sometimes the risk is so remote that it can be disregarded as a factor. Even when risk is recognized, it may have to be ignored because of insufficient data for evaluation or because the evaluation would require too much time or money. Such secondary attention to risk factors is neither laziness nor stupidity; it is often a necessity. If every decision were subject to a searching appraisal of risk, management functions would grind along at an intolerably slow pace.

## Definition of the Problem

The investigation leading to a problem definition should give strong hints as to the appropriateness of including risk considerations in the evaluation. Objectives that can be satisfied almost immediately are not as subject to change variations that intrude over extended time periods. Narrow objectives bounded by limited means of accomplishment effectively exclude risk by confining the problem and solution to known quantities. Risk enters into the decision situation when current activities are projected into a distant future, and the resulting activities are subject to conditional influences.

## Collection of Data

Collecting data is a more demanding task when risk effects are to be considered. The first obstacle is the identification of possible alternatives. Both the obvious and the subtle warrant consideration. Creative effort is commonly considered a virtue in developing alternatives and is subordinated to statistical and accounting efforts in assessing outcomes. This is a mistaken belief. Both phases benefit from creativity, and both rely on documentation. Moreover, the knowledge acquired in one phase is bound to contribute to the other phases.

In comparing a problem to a tree (Figure 17.1), the main branches might be alternative solutions, and the outcomes the secondary branches and twigs. Assessment of these outcomes includes (1) the identification of future states or conditions, (2) the prediction of the probability of each state, and (3) the determination of returns associated with each state. Future states can be anticipated, but they cannot be controlled. Noncontrollable conditions may include weather, economic or technological developments, political legislation, world affairs, whims of buyers, and so forth. A key question is to decide which states are relevant to the problem objectives.

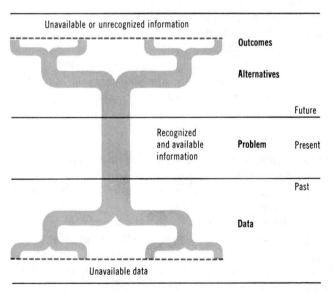

**FIGURE 17.1** Problem tree linking data sources to alternative outcomes. The problem results from a current situation which has roots in the past and outcomes in the future.

To continue the problem-tree analogy illustrated in Figure 17.1, the roots of the tree or problem lie in the past and constitute the source material. Some information about the outcomes is obtained by investigating the roots. Other information is available from the structure of the limbs, or alternatives. The least promising alternatives can be pruned out, thereby reducing the effort required for outcome assessments to reasonable limits.

A shortage of pertinent information is a common handicap in risk evaluation. This condition is depicted in Figure 17.1 by the cutoff lines bounding the problem tree. Lack of information may be due to a scarcity of historical data or the inability to decipher past trends in terms of future outcomes. Failure to identify promising alternatives can be traced to unavailability of data or to simply having overlooked a course of action that should have been apparent. Estimating distant outcomes is at best precarious with good information; without applicable data it becomes more heroic than rational.

## Formulating the Model

A natural reaction to risk is to adopt a conservative stance. Conservatism in economic evaluations often takes the form of overly pessimistic estimates of future cash flows or requiring an abnormally high rate of return (or an exceptionally short payback period) when there is a significant likelihood that an investment might fail. Both approaches are informal attempts to ration capital to proposals that have better chances of profitability. The weakness of such informal weighting is the subjectivity of the assigned risk penalties. It would be difficult to explain to someone why, for instance, a 5 percent boost in the minimum required rate of return is realistic for one proposal and not another. For the 5 percent penalty to be meaningful, it should be associated with specific receipts or expenditures that are doubtful. If this is done, only slightly more definitive data are required to utilize a formal model of risk.

The decision-making literature offers many models of risk to choose from. Taken one at a time, each appears logical. Taken as a group, they may blend into a maze of diverse solution paths, difficult to decipher for a particular application. The models presented in this chapter and Chapter 18 are limited to future states defined by discrete probabilities. They are sufficient for most practical problems.

## Evaluation

The selection of the most advantageous alternative can be compared with a simple weight balance. Each alternative is weighed. Rewards are balanced against outlays. Opportunity costs are compared to operating costs. The alternative that best meets the decision criteria on the economic balance is chosen.

The inclusion of risk factors does not automatically increase the accuracy of a study. Probabilities representing risk appear on both sides of the economic balance. Sometimes they can decidedly swing the balance to one side. The important point is to realize that some evaluations are trivial or misleading without risk considerations, while others will not benefit from the additional effort required to include risk. The ability to distinguish between the two comes from confidence nourished by familiarity and practice.

Including risk in an analysis can be likened to adding a small flashlight to a key ring; it can be a novelty and a conversational gambit, or it can be used for illumination.

# PROBABILITY ESTIMATES

A formal evaluation of risk is feasible when the likelihood of possible futures can be estimated, and associated outcomes from alternative courses of action can be identified.

The first step is to determine categories of future states that affect the alternatives being compared. If the questionable aspect is expected market conditions, the states might be low sales, average sales, and high sales, defined by specific ranges such as annual sales below $50,000, $50,000 to $125,000, and over $125,000. Finer categories for expected sales could be very low, low, average, high, and very high, with corresponding dollar ranges declared. The breadth of categories appropriate for risk analysis depends mostly on how much the outcomes of alternatives vary between states; when cash flows do not differ much over a wide spectrum of possible future operating conditions, a smaller number of states adequately defines the problem. After the future states are identified and bounded, cash flow outcomes can be estimated by assuming each state, in turn, is sure to occur.

The next step in risk analysis is to determine the probability that each state will actually occur. The sources may be objective or subjective. Objective evidence of probability is usually in the form of historical documentation or common experience. It is readily accepted that a coin has two sides and a die has six. A reasonable person would not question the assignment of a probability of 0.50 to the occurrence of a head on the flip of a coin or a probability of 1/6 for an ace from the roll of a die (assuming that both the coin and die were fair or unbiased and that they were tossed or rolled in a fashion that assured an equal chance for all possible outcomes; equivalently, probability data for economic studies are assumed to be impartial and intrinsic). This type of information is *prior* (also known as *a priori*) knowledge.

In practice, prior knowledge of probabilities is seldom possible. Most of the time it is necessary to look at past records of events and use this empirical knowledge as a basis for current probabilities. However, vigilance is required to determine the relationship of historical records to the present action; seemingly unrelated events could influence each other. On the other hand, the records of one machine can sometimes be used to predict the performance of a similar machine. Experimental and other measurements that provide *after the fact* (*a posteriori*) probabilities are necessarily approximate, but they can still be the basis for practical applications.

Subjective probability estimates are derived from opinions based on general experience and knowledge that pertain to the situation under consideration. It has been academically disputed whether "guesstimates" of likelihood qualify as legitimate probability relationships, but the practice is well established for decision-making applications. Any subjective estimate suffers some from the bias and ignorance of the estimator, since no one predicts perfectly, but even purely intuitive valuations often have surprising roots in fact when their lineage is probed.

## PROBABILITY CONCEPTS

Betting in poker is a decision under risk. By keeping track of the cards played and relating them to the known distribution of card values in a complete deck, a betting policy can be developed to theoretically maximize returns. However, it takes considerable discipline to abide by the policy consistently and to do it long enough for the laws of probability to have effect. Somewhat the same problems affect economic decisions under risk. Each event has a single outcome and an associated probability of occurrence. It can be discouraging when an undesirable outcome occurs that had odds against it of 99 to 1, but in the long run probability theory promises that, if the odds are accurate, the temporary disappointment will be replaced by satisfaction when the same situation is replicated a number of times.

Events can be either statistically independent or dependent. Statistical *dependence* means that the probability of an outcome is dependent on or influenced by the occurrence of some other event, whereas an *independent* event is not affected by the occurrence of any other event. Dependent events are discussed in Chapter 18.

The probabilities of mutually exclusive independent events can be added. The probability of drawing a queen from an honest deck of cards is the sum of the probabilities of all four queens in the deck. In functional notation this would appear as

$$P(Q) = P(Q_S) + P(Q_H) + P(Q_D) + P(Q_C)$$

where $P$ is probability, $Q$ means queen, and the subscripts stand for the four suits in the deck. And the numerical values are

$$P(Q) = \frac{1}{52} + \frac{1}{52} + \frac{1}{52} + \frac{1}{52} = \frac{1}{13} = 1/13 \quad \text{or} \quad 0.077$$

Intuitively, the probability of not drawing a queen is 1 minus the probability of drawing a queen:

$$P(\cancel{Q}) = 1 - P(Q) = 1 - \frac{1}{13} = \frac{12}{13} \quad \text{or} \quad 0.923$$

because the outcomes are mutually exclusive and collectively exhaustive (add up to 1.0). Mutually exclusive sets are also additive. The probability that a card will be either a spade or a heart is

$$P(S + H) = P(S) + P(H) = \frac{13}{52} + \frac{13}{52} = \frac{26}{52} \quad \text{or} \quad 0.5$$

---

### Example 17.1 Additive Probabilities

The output of a machine has been classified into three grades: superior (A), passing (B), and failing (C). The items in each class from an output of 1000 items are 214 in A, 692 in B, and 94 in C. If the run from which this sample was taken is considered typical, the probability that the machine will turn out each grade of product is

$P(A) = 214/1000 = 0.214$
$P(B) = 692/1000 = 0.692$
$P(C) = 94/1000 = 0.094$

What is the probability of making *at least* a passable product?

### Solution 17.1

The probability of producing a passable product includes the set of superior and passing grades.

$$P(A + B) = P(A) + P(B) = 0.214 + 0.692 = 0.906$$

or

$$P(A + B) = P(\cancel{C}) = 1 - P(C) = 1 - 0.094 = 0.906$$

The probability that two or more independent events will occur together or in succession is the product of all the individual probabilities. In terms of the deck of cards, the probability of drawing the queen of hearts twice in a row (provided the queen is reinserted in the deck and the deck is reshuffled) is

$$P(Q_H Q_H) = P(Q_H)P(Q_H) = 1/52 \times 1/52 = 1/2704$$

The same reasoning applies to drawing any predesignated cards in a predesignated order or to drawing the same predesignated cards simultaneously from more than one deck.

A probability tree provides a pictorial representation of sequential events. In the probability tree of Figure 17.2 a new deck is used for each draw, and each suit is considered a set. The probability of drawing three hearts in a row is represented by the double line in the probability tree. By formula, this action is equal to

$$P(H_1 H_2 H_3) = P(H_1)P(H_2)P(H_3) = 0.25 \times 0.25 \times 0.25 = 0.015625$$

The same probability is evident for the sequence of drawing two hearts in a row and then drawing any predesignated suit on the third draw.

The probability of not drawing a heart in two consecutive draws is

$$P(\cancel{H})^2 = [1 - P(H)]^2 = (1 - 0.25)^2 = (0.75)^2 = 0.5625$$

It is shown in the tree by the sum of the probabilities in shaded circles which end the paths containing no hearts. Then the probability of at least one heart in two draws is the sum of the probabilities in the light circles and is equal to 0.4375.

---

### Example 17.2   Multiplication of Probabilities

A series of samples from the output of a machine reveals that 4 items out of every 100 sampled are defective. Thus, $P = 0.04$. For an order of 5 items taken directly from the machine without preliminary inspection, what is the probability that the order will be filled without containing a defective item?

### Solution 17.2

The probability of no defects, $P(0)$, in an order of five is

$$P(0) = (0.04)^0(0.96)^5 = (0.96)^5 = 0.82$$

Further, the probability that the order has not more than one defective is

$$P(1) = 0.82 + 5(0.04)^1(0.96)^4 = 0.82 + 0.17 = 0.99$$

---

## EXPECTED VALUE

*Expected value* is a standard measure for economic comparisons involving risk. It incorporates the effect of risk on potential outcomes by means of a weighted average.

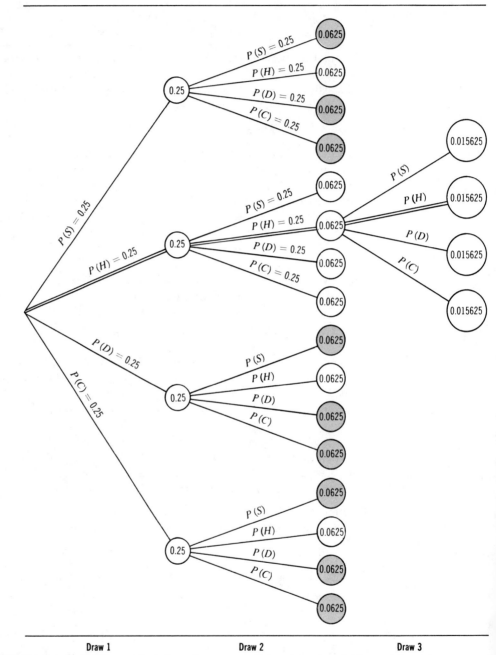

**FIGURE 17.2** Probability tree for independent events which registers the suit of a card drawn from a complete deck. The sum of the independent probabilities in each column of circles is 1.0 and represents all possible outcomes. By extension of the tree to include three draws (the incomplete column on the right), the probability of at least two hearts ($H$) in three draws is 10 × 0.015625 = 0.156.

Outcomes are weighted according to their probability of occurrence, and the sum of the products of all outcomes multiplied by their respective probabilities is the expected value, EV:

$$EV(i) = \sum_j P_j O_{ij}$$

where $P_j$ is the independent probability of future $j$, $\sum P_j = 1.0$, and $O_{ij}$ is the outcome of alternative $i$ for future $j$.

As a common example of the expected-value approach, consider the coin-flipping game: A coin is flipped, and if it comes up *heads* you win the coin, but when *tails* show you lose. Let the coin be a "fair" dime; then the probability of a head or a tail is, of course, 0.5, and the expected value of winnings from the game is

$$EV(\text{flipping dimes}) = P(H)(\$0.10) + P(T)(-\$0.10) = 0.5(\$0.10) + 0.5(-\$0.10) = 0$$

The given probabilities of future states are collectively exhaustive (both heads and tails are accounted for, and $\sum P = 0.5 + 0.5 = 1.0$); an outcome is associated with each future state (the gain or loss of a dime); and the expected value is the long-term expectation from repeated performances under the same conditions.

A profit-seeking individual or organization prefers a positive expected value, when gains are plus and losses are minus. In comparing alternatives, the one with the highest EV is preferred, other things being equal. For instance, a variant of the coin-flipping game might be to pay $1 for the chance to flip two coins. The payoff could be to win $2 for two heads, $1 for two tails, and to win nothing when the coins split head and tail. The expected-value calculation,

$$EV = P(H_1 H_2)(\$2 - \$1) + P(H_1 T_2)(-\$1) + P(T_1 H_2)(-\$1) + P(T_1 T_2)(\$1 - \$1)$$

$$= 0.25(\$1) + 0.25(-\$1) + 0.25(-\$1) + 0.25(0) = -\$0.25$$

shows that this is not a very good game to get into because the *average* loss per play is 25 cents. But the *actual* outcome for any given gamble is a gain of a dollar, a loss of a dollar, or no change.

The appropriateness of the expected-value model for a once-in-a-lifetime decision is questionable. Other decision criteria such as those presented in Chapter 18 would enter the verdict. However, truly unique decisions do not occur too often in actual practice; alternatives vary individually as to amounts, possible futures, and probabilities, but their evaluation is based on a consistent long-term objective of profit maximization or cost minimization. Since most industries and governments are long-lived, and new investment projects are being continually initiated, expected value is a rational measure for most comparisons that recognize risk.

## Payoff Tables

A format for organizing and displaying outcomes of alternative courses of action is called a *payoff table*. Each row in the table represents an alternative with its outcomes arranged in columns according to respective future states. In the payoff table on page 426, the present worths of two new products, $A$ and $B$, are shown for three states of sales success during a 3-year marketing period.

| | STATE OF MARKET ACCEPTANCE | | |
|---|---|---|---|
| *Alternative* | *Rejection* | *Average* | *Domination* |
| Product *A* | −$50,000 | $200,000 | $500,000 |
| Product *B* | −200,000 | 100,000 | 1,000,000 |

The initial cost of developing product *A* is $50,000, and this amount would be lost if the product were rejected by consumers. If product *A* received average acceptance, the expected gain would be $200,000, and if it dominated the market, the payoff would be $500,000. Product *B* would cost four times as much as product *A* to put into production, but if it became a best seller it would double *A*'s profit. Because production costs for *B* are higher, an average demand would result in only half the payoff expected from *A*.

Some conclusions might be drawn from just the payoffs included in the table. For instance, a loss of $200,000 could be considered disastrous to the company, while a loss of $50,000 would at least be tolerable. With such a severe penalty for failure, alternative *B* would practically be eliminated regardless of the potentially large payoff. However, even more meaningful observations can be made by including the relative likelihood of each outcome. The payoff table below has been modified to incorporate probability factors.

| | OUTCOME AND RISK | | |
|---|---|---|---|
| *Product* | *P(R) =0.1* | *P(A) =0.6* | *P(D) = 0.3* |
| *A* | −$50,000 | $200,000 | $ 500,000 |
| *B* | −200,000 | 100,000 | 1,000,000 |

It might have been necessary to assign probabilities to each outcome of each alternative, but it is assumed that products *A* and *B* are similar enough to possess the same consumption pattern. In the example both products have a probability of 0.1 of rejection, 0.6 of normal demand, and 0.3 of booming acceptance. If all the possible futures are included, the sum of probabilities will equal 1.0.

After concluding that the future states are indeed representative, the probability assignments are realistic, and outcomes are estimated as accurately as possible, calculation of the expected values is easy; and preference among alternatives is clearly distinguished. For the comparison between product *A* and product *B*,

$$EV(A) = 0.1(-\$50,000) + 0.6(\$200,000) + 0.3(\$500,000)$$
$$= \$265,000$$

$$EV(B) = 0.1(-\$200,000) + 0.6(\$100,000) + 0.3(\$1,000,000)$$
$$= \$340,000$$

Product *B* is clearly preferred, assuming all other factors affecting the decision are equal.

### Example 17.3  Expected Value of Risky Alternatives

A process line that will continue to be needed for 3 years has annual costs of $310,000, which are expected to remain constant. A novel redesign for the line has been suggested. The new approach will cost $150,000 to install and has a 50 percent chance of cutting annual operating costs to $210,000. However, there is a probability of 0.25 that annual costs for the redesigned line will increase, from $210,000 for the first year, by $20,000 or $75,000 in each of the next 2 years. If a 12 percent rate of return is required, should the new design be installed?

### Solution 17.3

Equivalent annual costs for each future state of the redesigned process line are

$$\text{EAC(at } P = 0.5) = \$150,000(A/P, 12, 3) + \$210,000$$
$$= \$150,000(0.41635) + \$210,000 = \$272,453$$

$$\text{EAC(at } P = 0.25) = \$150,000(A/P, 12, 3) + \$210,000 + \$20,000(A/G, 12, 3)$$
$$= \$272,453 + \$20,000(0.9245) = \$290,943$$

$$\text{EAC(at } P = 0.25) = \$150,000(A/P, 12, 3) + \$210,000 + \$75,000(A/G, 12, 3)$$
$$= \$272,453 + \$75,000(0.9245) = \$341,790$$

These costs are inserted in a payoff table, as shown below, where the calculated expected values indicate that the redesign should be attempted even when there is one chance in four of increasing the process-line costs.

| | EQUIVALENT ANNUAL COSTS | | | |
|---|---|---|---|---|
| Alternative | P(0.5) | P(0.25) | P(0.25) | Expected Value |
| No change | $310,000 | $310,000 | $310,000 | $310,000 |
| Redesign | 272,453 | 290,943 | 341,790 | $294,410 |

## Investment-Risk Profiles

The range-of-estimates approach (Chapter 14) can be modified to reflect risk. Probabilities of occurrence are assigned to each future state in the range. Then all possible combinations of outcomes are collected, and their dollar amounts and joint probabilities are calculated. The result is an *investment-risk profile* that reveals the likelihood for an investment to realize various net present-worth returns.

Assume an investment proposal for income expansion requires an initial outlay of $200,000. The most likely outcome is for after-tax returns to amount to $100,000 per year for 4 years. There is no salvage value, and the minimum attractive rate of return is 9 percent. Under the assumption of certainty,

$$\text{PW} = -\$200,000 + \$100,000(P/A, 9, 4)$$
$$= -\$200,000 + \$100,000(3.2396) = \$123,960$$

A risk analysis of the same proposal recognizes that the most likely cash flow has just a probability of 0.5 of occurrence. A pessimistic appraisal of the future concedes returns might amount to only $50,000 per year. Under the most optimistic assessment, returns could total $125,000 per year. The probabilities of pessimistic and optimistic returns materializing are 0.3 and 0.2, respectively. The duration of returns is also questionable;

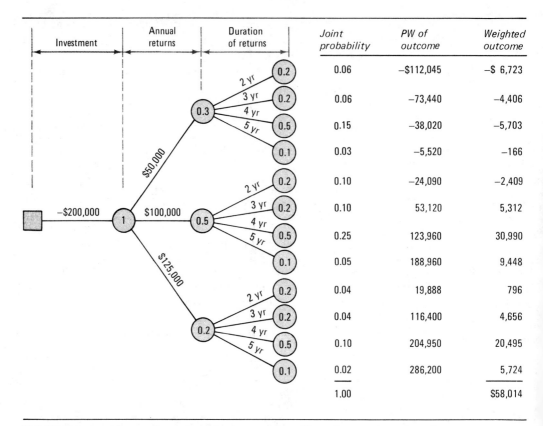

| | | | Joint probability | PW of outcome | Weighted outcome |
|---|---|---|---|---|---|
| | | | 0.06 | −$112,045 | −$ 6,723 |
| | | | 0.06 | −73,440 | −4,406 |
| | | | 0.15 | −38,020 | −5,703 |
| | | | 0.03 | −5,520 | −166 |
| | | | 0.10 | −24,090 | −2,409 |
| | | | 0.10 | 53,120 | 5,312 |
| | | | 0.25 | 123,960 | 30,990 |
| | | | 0.05 | 188,960 | 9,448 |
| | | | 0.04 | 19,888 | 796 |
| | | | 0.04 | 116,400 | 4,656 |
| | | | 0.10 | 204,950 | 20,495 |
| | | | 0.02 | 286,200 | 5,724 |
| | | | 1.00 | | $58,014 |

**FIGURE 17.3**   Decision-tree format for an investment-risk profile analysis. Node entries indicate probabilities for the economic factors noted on lines leading to the nodes. Each burst represents one economic condition subject to risk.

probabilities for 2, 3, 4, and 5 years are, respectively, 0.2, 0.2, 0.5, and 0.1. These data are summarized on the decision-probability tree shown in Figure 17.3.

The joint probability for each outcome is the product of the independent probabilities representing each factor involved in the outcome. These probabilities are entered in the nodes of the probability-decision tree, and the factors are labeled on the lines connecting the nodes. For example, the joint probability of returns of $50,000 per year for 2 years (top of the column in Figure 17.3) is 0.06. It results from multiplying the probability of the definite investment (1.0) by the probabilities of $50,000 returns (0.3) and a 2-year period (0.2).

Present worths of the outcomes are calculated by the usual procedures. The value listed at the top of the "PW of outcome" column, based on a required rate of return of 9 percent, is computed as

$$PW(P = 0.06) = -\$200,000 + \$50,000(P/A, 9, 2)$$
$$= -\$200,000 + \$50,000(1.7591) = -\$112,045$$

The weighted value of this present worth is the top entry of the last column on the right in Figure 17.3, and is the product

Joint probability($i$) × PW(outcome $i$) = 0.06 × −$112,045 = −$6,723

The remaining outcomes are computed similarly. The sum of these values is the expected value of the proposal, EV = $58,014. For the given probabilities of occurrence, the expected value is much less than the present worth based on the most likely outcomes. Although the probability estimates are quite likely subject to some error, the exercise of calculating an investment profile contributes to a more complete analysis and a better appreciation of the factors involved in the proposal.

## INVESTMENT-RISK DECISION CRITERIA

An investment-risk profile highlights more than just the expected value. When the outcomes and related probabilities are graphed, a proposal's prospects are clearly displayed for capital-budgeting discussions. The data from Figure 17.3 are graphed in Figure 17.4. Lines connect the outcome-risk points to better define the cumulative probability distribution of net present values. The connected points make it quite evident that the proposal has a probability greater than 0.4 of showing a loss.

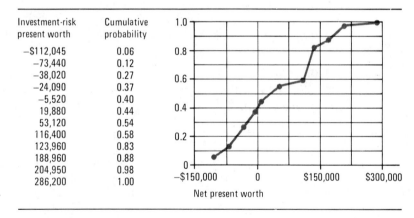

| Investment-risk present worth | Cumulative probability |
|---|---|
| −$112,045 | 0.06 |
| −73,440 | 0.12 |
| −38,020 | 0.27 |
| −24,090 | 0.37 |
| −5,520 | 0.40 |
| 19,880 | 0.44 |
| 53,120 | 0.54 |
| 116,400 | 0.58 |
| 123,960 | 0.83 |
| 188,960 | 0.88 |
| 204,950 | 0.98 |
| 286,200 | 1.00 |

**FIGURE 17.4**
Tabulated data and graph of an investment-risk profile.

### Acceptable-Investment Diagram

Another graphic display to assist in the evaluation of alternatives subject to risk is called an *acceptable-investment diagram* (AID). Its format is a horizontal axis representing rates of return and a vertical axis scaled to show the probability an investment will surpass a given rate of return. Criteria for an acceptable investment are blocked off in the chart by setting limits for:

**1** The required probability that an investment's rate of return exceeds a minimum percentage (loss coefficient)

**2** The desired probability that an investment's internal rate of return will exceed an attractive level (payoff coefficient)

**3** A line connecting the two coefficients, called an *aspiration level*

Any investment-risk profile that does not intrude on the reject area defined by the listed limits is considered an acceptable investment; its risk-return potential is greater than the minimum risk-return requirements.

### Example 17.4  Application of an AID

An investment of $1000 for 1 year has the possible after-tax returns shown. The probability of each outcome is estimated, and the internal rate of return is apparent.

| Return (Outcome) | Rate of Return, % | Probability of Outcome | Probability Investment's IRR Will Exceed Rate of Return |
|---|---|---|---|
| $900 | −10 | 0.05 | 0.95 |
| 1050 | 5 | 0.15 | 0.80 |
| 1150 | 15 | 0.40 | 0.40 |
| 1300 | 30 | 0.30 | 0.10 |
| 1500 | 50 | 0.10 | 0.00 |

The investors seek proposals that provide a probability of 0.95 that they will not lose more than 5 percent, and a 0.30 likelihood that their rates of return will be greater than 15 percent. Use an AID to determine the acceptability of the $1000 investment proposal.

### Solution 17.4

The reject area for the acceptable-investment diagram in Figure 17.5 results from lines connecting the loss coefficient horizontally to the ordinate, the loss coefficient

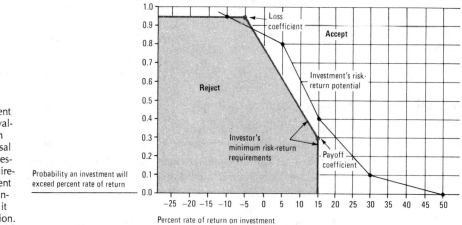

**FIGURE 17.5** Acceptable-investment diagram (AID) for evaluating the risk-return potential of a proposal according to the investor's risk-return requirements. The investment proposal shown is unacceptable because it enters the reject region.

diagonally to the payoff coefficient, and the payoff coefficient to the abscissa. The sloping line is the implied aspiration level relating desired returns to allowable risk. The investment's risk-return potential is represented by lines connecting the rates of return associated with their probabilities of occurrence.

Because part of the risk-return curve crosses the reject area, the investment is not acceptable according to the given criteria. Investments passing these criteria can be further evaluated on other merits such as timing of returns, capital availability, and the decision criteria discussed next.

## Auxiliary Decision Criteria

Once an investment-risk profile is developed, there are several ways to appraise its desirability. The basic criterion, as already observed, is *maximization of expected returns*, which is determined by expected-value calculations. Other criteria include the *most probable future* and the *aspiration level*. These criteria are illustrated by reference to Table 17.1.

|            | POSSIBLE NET PRESENT WORTHS OF PROPOSALS | | | | | |
|------------|---------|------|--------|--------|--------|--------|
| *Alternative* | −$1000 | 0 | $1000 | $2000 | $3000 | $4000 |
| A | 0 | 0.11 | 0.26 | 0.22 | 0.02 | 0.39 |
| B | 0.29 | 0.18 | 0.07 | 0 | 0 | 0.46 |
| C | 0.14 | 0.10 | 0.11 | 0.37 | 0.28 | 0 |

**TABLE 17.1** Probability of returns from three equal-size, equal-life investments.

According to the most-probable-future criterion, the investment that has the greatest return for the most probable future is preferred. The most probable futures for the alternatives in Table 17.1 are

| *Most Probable Future* | *PW at Most Probable Future* |
|---|---|
| Alternative $B: P = 0.46$ | $4000 |
| Alternative $A: P = 0.39$ | 4000 |
| Alternative $C: P = 0.37$ | 2000 |

They indicate a preference for *B*, because its maximum return, though the same as that of alternative *A*, has a greater probability of occurrence. This criterion thus assumes the future with the highest probability is *certain* to occur, and the alternative with the highest return for its "certain" future is best.

An *aspiration level* is based on a minimum amount that will satisfy a decision maker. The rationale behind an aspiration level is to achieve assurance that the investment will "at least return a respectable amount" or "surely not lose money." For the sample data from Table 17.1 and an aspiration level of $2000, we have

| Alternative | Probability of Return of $2000 or More |
|:-----------:|:--------------------------------------:|
| C | $0.37 + 0.28 = 0.65$ |
| A | $0.22 + 0.02 + 0.39 = 0.63$ |
| B | $0.46 = 0.46$ |

Alternative $C$ is preferred because it has a higher cumulative probability of providing $2000 and more. If the aspiration level had been to "at least make some money," alternative $A$ would be selected because it has a probability of $0.26 + 0.22 + 0.02 + 0.39 = 0.89$ of having returns greater than zero, which is larger than that of any other alternative.

Since alternative $A$ would also be selected by the maximum-expected-return criterion [because EV($A$) = $2320, EV($B$) = $1620, and EV($C$) = $1550], any of the alternatives in Table 17.1 could receive the nod of approval by one criterion or another. This should cause no dismay; it merely demonstrates the importance of a decision maker's perspective, the theme of Chapter 19.

# REVIEW EXERCISES AND DISCUSSIONS

**Exercise 1** The Owlglass Company is considering the manufacture of two mutually exclusive types of sunglass clip-on attachments. One clip-on design is specifically devised for Owl frames only and would not fit the eyeglass frames produced by other manufacturers. The other type is adaptable to competitors' frames but would not fit as securely or be color-coordinated with Owl frames. The investment required to get into the production of either design is $100,000. Estimates of net annual receipts for a 4-year market period are $43,000 for Owl-only clip-ons, and $50,000 for general-purpose clip-ons.

Because the "captive" market for clip-ons designed to fit and complement Owl frames appears to have less risk, management decides that the general-purpose clip-on proposal should be evaluated at a risk-adjusted rate of return 8 percent greater than the regular 10 percent required rate. What effect does this decision have on the economic analysis?

**Solution 1** The present worths of the two proposals are calculated using a 10 percent discount for the clip-ons that fit only Owl frames $O$, and 18 percent for general-purpose clip-ons $G$:

$$PW(O) = -\$100,000 + \$43,000(P/A, 10, 4)$$
$$= -\$100,000 + \$43,000(3.1698) = \$36,301$$

$$PW(G) = -\$100,000 + \$50,000(P/A, 18, 4)$$
$$= -\$100,000 + \$50,000(2.6952) = \$34,760$$

The risk-adjusted discount rate switches the preference from general-purpose to Owl-only clip-ons. An engineering economist should question whether the 8 percent addition to the required rate of return fairly represents the perceived risk.

**Exercise 2**  A construction company has determined that it costs $8700 to prepare a bid for a major construction project. It even costs $500 to decide not to submit a bid. The annual profit earned from winning a bid for a major construction project is $400,000. For such projects the competition is severe and the chance of submitting the lowest bid is small. How often must the company's bids win to make the bidding worthwhile?

**Solution 2**  Outcomes from the alternatives of bidding and not bidding are shown below for the future states of winning and losing.

|  | Win Bid P(W) | Lose Bid P(L) |
|---|---|---|
| *No Bid* | −$500 | −$500 |
| *Bid* | $400,000 | −$8700 |

How often the company must win a bid to break even on its bidding can be determined from a graph as shown in Figure 17.6. A "win" occurs when $P(W) = 1$, and a bid is lost when $P(W) = 0$. As indicated by the no-bid line, the outcome is constant because there is no chance of winning when no bid is submitted. The point where lines representing the bid and no-bid options cross is the indifference or breakeven point.

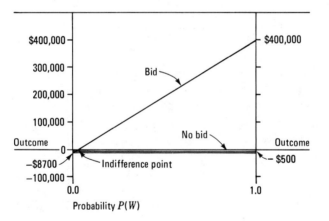

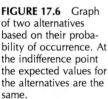

**FIGURE 17.6**  Graph of two alternatives based on their probability of occurrence. At the indifference point the expected values for the alternatives are the same.

By letting $P(W)$ and $P(L) = 1 - P(W)$ be the probabilities for the two future states (win and lose), the indifference probability can be calculated from

$$\text{EV(no bid)} = \text{EV(bid)}$$
$$P(W)(-\$500) + [1 - P(W)](-\$500) = P(W)(\$400,000) + [1 - P(W)](-\$8700)$$

to yield

$$P(W) = \frac{\$8700 - \$500}{\$400,000 + \$8700} = 0.02$$

which means the construction company must win just over 2 percent of the times it submits bids for new projects. From a slightly different viewpoint, it means that a project is worth bidding on when there is at least a 2 percent chance that the submitted bid will be chosen.

**Exercise 3**  Owing to the lack of other suitable land, a mill is forced to construct its new settling ponds for waste disposal along the bank of a river. The stream has no dams to control its flow. Flood-level records for the last 70 years reveal that the river rose above the minimum required height of the settling-pond walls 42 times. Therefore, the economic analysis must include not only construction costs but also the risk of flood damage. Building the walls higher increases the initial investment but lowers the threat of flooding. Engineering calculations for the cost of higher retaining walls in 2 m increments and the expected damage from floods of different crests are shown in the table below.

| River Levels above Minimum Wall Height in Range, m | Year the River Crests in Given Range above Wall Height, m | Probability of River Cresting in Range above Height, m | Flood Damage when River Crests above Walls | Cost to Construct Walls to Height, m |
|---|---|---|---|---|
| 0-2 | at $m$ = 0:  14 | 14/70 = 0.20 | $ 70,000 | $135,000 |
| 2-4 | at $m$ = 5:  14 | 14/70 = 0.20 | 105,000 | 200,000 |
| 4-6 | at $m$ = 10:  8 | 8/70 = 0.11 | 150,000 | 280,000 |
| 6-8 | at $m$ = 15:  6 | 6/70 = 0.09 | 200,000 | 370,000 |
| Over 8 | at $m$ = 20:  0 | 0/70 = 0.0 | 0 | 450,000 |

The settling ponds are expected to be needed for 10 years before the process can be improved sufficiently to eliminate the need for special waste treatment. A rate of return of 10 percent is used by the mill to evaluate such mandated investments. To what height should the retaining walls be built to minimize annual costs?

**Solution 3**  The initial cost of the settling ponds is translated to an equivalent annual cost by the capital-recovery factor. For the minimum wall height ($m$ = 0), the equivalent annual investment cost is

EAC(investment at $m$ = 0) = $135,000($A/P$, 10, 10) = $135,000(0.16275) = $21,971

Equivalent annual investment costs for successively higher retaining walls are calculated similarly.

Data arranged for the calculation of expected values of flood damage for alternative wall heights are shown in Table 17.2. The outcomes in the payoff table indicate damages expected from floods exceeding a given wall height by amounts $m$. Thus, for the minimum wall height, flood waters will cause damage 3 years in every 5 years, on the average, to produce an expected value of

EV($m$ = 0) = $70,000(0.20) + $105,000(0.20) + $150,000(0.11) + $200,000(0.09)
= $14,000 + $21,000 + $16,500 + $18,000
= $69,500

which, when added to the equivalent annual investment cost, makes a total expected cost for the minimum-height settling-pond walls of $21,971 + $69,500 = $91,471. Expected

| Wall Height above Minimum, $m$ | PROBABILITY OF RIVER CRESTING ABOVE WALL HEIGHT IN RANGE, METRES | | | | Expected Value | Equiva- lent Annual Investment | Total Expected Annual Cost |
| | 0-2 $P = 0.20$ | 2-4 $P = 0.20$ | 4-6 $P = 0.11$ | 6-8 $P = 0.09$ | | | |
|---|---|---|---|---|---|---|---|
| 0 | $70,000 | $105,000 | $150,000 | $200,000 | $69,500 | $21,971 | $91,471 |
| 2 | 0 | 70,000 | 105,000 | 150,000 | 39,050 | 32,550 | 71,600 |
| 4 | 0 | 0 | 70,000 | 105,000 | 17,150 | 45,570 | 62,720 |
| 6 | 0 | 0 | 0 | 70,000 | 6,300 | 60,218 | 66,518 |
| 8 | 0 | 0 | 0 | 0 | 0 | 73,238 | 73,238 |

Flood damage from incremental river levels above alternative settling-pond wall heights, $m$.

**TABLE 17.2**   Payoff table (shaded) for five alternative wall heights for settling ponds. Total expected annual costs are the sums of expected flood damages and equivalent annual investment costs.

values for other wall heights are calculated in the same manner, as indicated in the shaded area of Table 17.2. Note that the probabilities do not add up to 1.0 because river levels below $m = 0$ (probability = 0.40) have no bearing on the flood-damage expectations.

The settling-pond retaining-wall height that minimizes total annual cost is 4 m above the minimum level.

**Exercise 4**   The most likely cash flow for a cost-reduction proposal is for an investment of $4000 to produce after-tax present-worth savings of $1200 per year for 5 years. The net present worth is

PW(most likely) = −$4000 + $1200(5) = $2000

Upon further investigation it appears that the initial investment has probabilities of 0.4 of being as high as $5000, and 0.6 of being $3000. The after-tax present worths of annual savings could amount to $2000, $1200, or $800 with respective probabilities of 0.2, 0.3, and 0.5. Determine the investment-risk profile and the expected value of the proposal.

**Solution 4**   If $I$ and $S$ represent investment and savings levels, respectively, then the pattern of possible future outcomes is shown in the table. There is a 20 percent chance the proposal will lose money, but the expected value is $2000.

| Possible Futures | Net After-Tax Present Worth | Joint Probability | Weighted Outcome |
|---|---|---|---|
| $S(P = 0.2)I(P = 0.6)$ | $2000(5) − $3000 = $7000 | (0.2)(0.6) = 0.12 | $ 840 |
| $S(P = 0.3)I(P = 0.6)$ | 1200(5) − 3000 = 3000 | (0.3)(0.6) = 0.18 | 540 |
| $S(P = 0.5)I(P = 0.6)$ | 800(5) − 3000 = 1000 | (0.5)(0.6) = 0.30 | 300 |
| $S(P = 0.2)I(P = 0.4)$ | 2000(5) − 5000 = 5000 | (0.2)(0.4) = 0.08 | 400 |
| $S(P = 0.3)I(P = 0.4)$ | 1200(5) − 5000 = 1000 | (0.3)(0.4) = 0.12 | 120 |
| $S(P = 0.5)I(P = 0.4)$ | 800 5) − 5000 = −1000 | (0.5)(0.4) = 0.20 | −200 |
| | | 1.00 | $2000 |

## PROBLEMS

**17.1**  Given a fair coin,

**17.1a**  What is the probability of at least one head in three tosses?   *(0.875)*

**17.1b**  What is the probability of flipping a tail, a head, and a head in that order?   *(0.125)*

**17.1c**  What is the probability of flipping at most two heads in three tosses?   *(0.875)*

**17.2**  In the example used in the chapter, the probability of drawing a queen was 1/13, and the probability of a heart was 1/4. The probability of drawing a queen *or* a heart is called a *union*, because the two sets overlap; they are not mutually exclusive. Therefore, when the probabilities of the two sets are added the portion that overlaps must be subtracted. By this means we arrive at the formula for the probability of drawing a queen or a heart,

$$P(Q + H) = P(Q) + P(H) - P(QH) = 1/13 + 1/4 - 1/52 = 4/13$$

**17.2a**  Show the union by a sketch of the overlapping heart and queen sets.

$$[P(H + Q) = 4/13]$$

**17.2b**  Let three overlapping sets be $A$, $B$, and $C$. Sketch the sets, and determine a formula for $P(A + B + C)$.

**17.3**  A new product introduced by Up-and-Up, Inc. has been so successful that the company is now considering ways to expand production. It can do so by adding facilities or by increasing the utilization of present facilities. The choice depends on forecasts of future market trends for the new product.

The best available probability estimates for future demand are 0.1 to decline slightly from current sales, 0.3 to remain constant, and 0.6 to increase rapidly. If a major expansion of facilities is undertaken now, Up-and-Up should be able to capture most of the new demand before competitors can gear up for production. However, the company would suffer considerable loss from unused capacity if the demand fails to increase or declines. The conservative alternative is to increase utilization of existing facilities from the present 85 percent rate to 100 percent, but there is no way to meet higher levels of potential demand with existing production capacity.

The equivalent annual worths expected to result from each alternative according to each level of future demand are shown in the payoff table below.

|  | *Decline* $P(D) = 0.1$ | *Constant* $P(C) = 0.3$ | *Increase* $P(I) = 0.6$ |
|---|---|---|---|
| Add new facilities | $-\$1,800,000$ | $-\$50,000$ | $\$900,000$ |
| Increase utilization | $-\$100,000$ | $\$100,000$ | $\$400,000$ |

**17.3a**  Calculate the expected values.

**17.3b**  What other factors might affect the decision?

**17.4**  How would you explain the reason for using the expected-value measure to evaluate a unique engineering design project that is unlikely ever to be repeated again in exactly the same form?

**17.5**  A logging company must decide the most advantageous duration for a paving project. The beginning date of the project has been definitely set. A critical-path analysis has shown that three project durations are feasible. If the paving is completed in 4 months, the basic project cost will be $80,000. A 5-month duration will allow construction savings of $20,000, and it will cost an extra $40,000 over the basic cost to crash the project to 3 months. However, transportation expenses can be cut by $10,000 over the 4-month schedule if the paving is done in 3 months, and an extra transportation expense of $15,000 will be incurred for an extension of the paving time to 5 months.

Since the project must be completed during a period of expected foul weather, the extra expense due to possible weather conditions should also be considered. Weather records indicate that the probabilities for mild rain, heavy rain, and wind and rain are, respectively, 0.3, 0.5, and 0.2. The costs that must be included for these conditions are given in the following table:

| Weather conditions | 3 Months | 4 Months | 5 Months |
|---|---|---|---|
| Mild rain | $10,000 | $15,000 | $ 5,000 |
| Heavy rain | 10,000 | 40,000 | 60,000 |
| Wind and rain | 15,000 | 55,000 | 65,000 |

Which duration has the lowest expected total cost?

*[Total cost (4 months) = $115,500]*

**17.6**  There are several methods available to discover defective welds. A company has investigated two methods. Method 1 costs $0.50 per inspection and detects defects 80 percent of the time. Method 2 costs $2.00 per test, but it always detects a defective weld. When a defective weld goes undetected, the estimated cost to the company is $30.00 for replacement and other incidental costs. The probability of a defective weld is 0.05. Using the expected-value criterion, determine whether method 1 or 2 should be used, or whether the company is better off with no inspection procedure.  *(Method 1: $0.80)*

**17.7**  An investment is being considered that requires $1 million and commits the money for 10 years. During that period it is equally likely that the annual returns from the investment will be $100,000, $150,000, and $200,000. The probability is 0.75 that the salvage value will be $300,000, but there is one chance in four that it will be zero. A minimum rate of return of 10 percent is expected.

**17.7a**  Construct an investment-risk profile for the proposal on a chart in which the horizontal axis registers the net PW and the vertical axis is a probability scale ranging from 0 to 1. Draw the curve to show the probability of returns equal to or less than the scaled PWs.

**17.7b**  How could the investment-risk profile contribute to the economic evaluation of the million-dollar investment?

**17.8**  Three mutually exclusive alternatives are described by the data below, which show the probabilities of earning four rates of return.

| Alter-native | RATE OF RETURN | | | |
|---|---|---|---|---|
| | -5% | 0 | 10% | 20% |
| A | 0.3 | 0.1 | 0.2 | 0.4 |
| B | 0.0 | 0.3 | 0.5 | 0.2 |
| C | 0.15 | 0.15 | 0.4 | 0.3 |

**17.8a**  Which alternative would be selected using the most-probable-future criterion? Why?                                                                                       *(A)*

**17.8b**  Which alternative would be selected using the expected-value criterion? What is the EV?                                                                          *(C, 9.25%)*

**17.8c**  Which alternative would be selected if the decision maker had an aspiration level of 10 percent? Why?                                                              *(C)*

**17.8d**  Construct an acceptable-investment diagram with a loss coefficient of −5 percent at $P = 0.7$ and a payoff coefficient of 10 percent at $P = 0.3$. Which alternative would be eliminated by the AID?                                                          *(B)*

**17.9**  A payoff table (in thousands of dollars) is given below for three investments of equal size and duration.

| Alternative | Boom (P = 0.3) | So-so (P = 0.5) | Bust (P = 0.2) |
|---|---|---|---|
| A | 1000 | 200 | −500 |
| B | 300 | 400 | 0 |
| C | 400 | 600 | −300 |

Which alternative would you select? Why?

**17.10**  A cost-saving modification to an existing process is being evaluated. The savings will affect products I and II. The rate of return earned by the investment in the modification depends on how much the process is utilized, which depends on the market conditions for future sales of the two products. Three future states have been identified: *good,* with IRR = 20 percent; *average,* with IRR = 10 percent; and *bad,* with IRR = −5 percent. Since there are two products involved, the maximum possible rate of return under good conditions is 20 percent + 20 percent = 40 percent. The probability of each future for both products is given below.

| Product | FUTURE Good | Average | Bad |
|---|---|---|---|
| I | 0.20 | 0.70 | 0.10 |
| II | 0.40 | 0.30 | 0.30 |

**17.10a**  What is the expected value of the cost-saving modification?            *(20%)*

**17.10b**  Draw an investment profile for the proposal on an acceptable investment diagram. The ordinate is the probability the investment will exceed the percentage return, and the horizontal axis is the rate of return. The investment criteria are to limit losses to 5 chances in 100 of −10 percent return and to be 90 percent sure that the internal rate of return is at least 20 percent. Should the proposal be accepted? Why?

# EXTENSION

***17A  Investments to Avoid Risk***  For a given set of alternatives there are two ways to modify exposure to risk: (1) alter the probabilities of the applicable future states or (2) make different future states applicable. Both possibilities are usually costly to implement. For instance, the probabilities for future demand of a product could be changed by advertising; the amount of change is typically a function of the amount invested. When probabilities are immune to manipulation, as in the case of weather in a given locality, the odds can be altered by switching operations to a different locality. It may even be possible to effectively omit a future state by eliminating its effect on the alternatives, as would happen to an adverse weather state when an outdoor activity is moved indoors. And there is almost always a recourse to insurance, the conventional reaction to risk that does not reduce the danger but mitigates the damage.

## CHANGING THE ODDS

An adequate investment can essentially eliminate risk in unique cases. Ski resorts can make provisions for artificial snow in anticipation of a dry winter. Investments are made in massive irrigation projects to eliminate the danger of drought. On a smaller scale, the selection by a city engineer of a storm drain sized to handle the maximum expected runoff is an attempt to nullify risk.

A more typical response in avoiding risk is a compromise. Even if the cause or penalty associated with a risk can conceivably be eliminated, the cost may be prohibitive. Yet the effects of risk often can be limited to a tolerable level by a reasonable expenditure. We dealt with this compromise when we considered benefit-cost ratios for public projects. Similarly, the city engineer could select a storm-drain size which balances the extra costs of larger-diameter sewers against damages that could occur in exceptional storms.

A quality-assurance program is a form of self-protection that attempts to control the probability of error with respect to the cost of increased vigilance. In a production process the cost of defective output is balanced against the cost of a procedure capable of reducing the chance of defects; an inspection plan is often used to guard against inferior quality. Consider the case of a company which received a contract to build 3000 precision instruments of a new type. The terms of the contract strongly suggest an inspection system to avoid the risk of supplying defective instruments; the penalty clause states damages of $300 per faulty unit.

Inspection equipment which would limit undetected faulty units to 0.5 percent could be purchased for $19,000. It would have no value after termination of the 3-year contract. A trained operator for the testing equipment would have to be paid $7000 per year, and operating costs would amount to $1000 annually. Assuming a desired rate of return of 10 percent, the annual cost of inspection would be

| | |
|---|---|
| Testing machine: $19,000(A/P, 10, 3) = $19,000(0.40212)$ | $ 7,640 |
| Operator | 7,000 |
| Operation | 1,000 |
| *Total cost of inspection* | $15,640 |

In addition to the inspection costs, there is still a penalty for the few defective instruments which pass undetected and adjustment or reworking costs for the detected faulty instruments:

$$\text{Annual cost of penalty} = \frac{3000 \text{ instruments}}{3 \text{ years}} 0.005 \times \$300/\text{instrument} = \$1500$$

Annual adjustment, reworking, and scrap costs =
$$X - 0.005 \times 1000 \text{ instruments/year} \times C_{av}/\text{instrument}$$

*where* $X$ = percentage of defective instruments produced
$C_{av}$ = average cost of reworking a defective instrument to enable it to pass inspection

Then the total cost of the inspection program is the sum of inspection, penalty, and reworking costs. Setting the cost of reworking at $C_{av}$ = \$50 per instrument, we have

$$\text{Total cost} = \$15,640 + \$1500 + (X - 0.005) \times 1000 \times \$50$$
$$= \$17,140 + (X - 0.005) \times \$50,000$$

By equating the cost of the inspection program to the penalty cost of no inspections, we get

$$\text{Cost of vigilance} = \text{cost of error}$$
$$\$17,140 + (X - 0.005) \times \$50,000 = X \times 1000 \times \$300$$
$$X = 6.8\%$$

$X$ represents the percentage of defective units produced at which the two costs are equal. If the production capabilities can limit the percentage of defective instruments to 6.8 percent or less, the investment in this inspection program is unwarranted from strictly a cost viewpoint. However, reputation and other intangible considerations should influence the decision. It would also be wise to explore other inspection programs which are not so precise in detecting errors, but are less expensive investments.

### SPREADING THE RISK
The dichotomy of risk costs is again apparent in the use of an insurance program which transfers the burden of risk. Paying a premium to an insurer is an investment made to avoid the consequences of a specific disaster. The amount of the premium should reflect the potential magnitude of the disaster in proportion to the probability of its occurrence (plus administrative costs and profit). For a disaster which could cause damages of \$100,000 per year with a probability of 0.001, it would be reasonable to expect an annual premium cost of at least \$100,000 × 0.001 = \$100.

The reason insurance programs are so prevalent is that they spread the cost of protection over a period of time and transfer the risk of a financial calamity to a group better prepared to meet the payment. Just because the chance of a disaster is one in a thousand, it cannot be stated in exactly what year it will occur or even that it could not occur 2 years in a row. Premiums prorate the disaster shock to the pooled assets of the absorbing insurance company.

A program of self-insurance is followed by some companies for specific risks. Such a policy presumes sufficient resources to cover potential damages and is usually limited to minor risks. Accident liability is a popular area for self-insurance.

Investments may be made to reduce premiums for a group insurance policy or to reduce the probability of risk for a self-insurance policy. Annual investments in a plant safety program are aimed at reducing the probability of accidents. They should result in less damage payment for the self-insured or lower premiums for group insurance.

A feasible amount to spend for a risk-reduction investment can be estimated from insurance rates. Companies which sell insurance normally have a great deal of experience to draw on in setting rates. These rates may be used as estimates of risk for related situations as described in the following example.

The owners are considering an automatic sprinkling system for a warehouse. The company insuring the warehouse will reduce the annual $12,000 fire-insurance premium by one-third if the system is installed. The owners estimate that opportunity costs incurred as a result of a serious fire, such as relocation expenses, disruption of deliveries, and loss of reputation, would amount to one-half the value of the warehouse. Using the insurance company's evaluation for the extent of risk reduction, the expected value of annual savings in opportunity costs from the installation would be $12,000 \times 1/2 \times 1/3 = $2000.

If annual taxes and maintenance costs for the sprinklers are $1000, the life of the proposed system is 20 years, and capital is worth 15 percent, a feasible price for the sprinkler system could be determined from the following equality:

$P(A/P, 15, 20)$ = premium reduction + opportunity-cost reduction

− annual taxes and maintenance

$$P = \frac{\$12,000 \times 1/3 + \$2000 - \$1000}{0.15976} = \$31,300$$

## QUESTIONS

**17A.1** A resident engineer on a construction project has been troubled with parts received from a supplier. Eight percent of the parts have been defective. The scrap and reworking costs for each item average $12. At least 2000 parts will be used over the next 2 years. Two methods have been suggested to reduce the risk of defective parts:

1 Visual inspection by part-time labor would reduce the risk by half. The labor cost would be $500 per year.
2 Only 0.5 percent defective parts would be accepted if gages were purchased for $180 and a worker were trained to use them. The training cost would be $60, and an annual wage for the inspection time would total $700.

Which of the alternatives would be adopted if a 10 percent rate of return is considered acceptable?

**17A.2**   A private golf course lies in a hollow beside a river. Every other year the river rises to a level that prohibits play. The loss of revenue and damage to the course average $8000 each time the river rises to this level. A new clubhouse has been constructed on higher ground, but flood data indicate a 1/20 chance the river will reach a level which will inundate the facility. The owners estimate that a flood of this magnitude would cause $40,000 damage to the clubhouse.

**17A.2a**   How much could the course owners afford to pay for a levee that would protect them from the biennial damage? The required rate of return is 8 percent, and the economic life of the levee is expected to be 30 years.

**17A.2b**   What would be a reasonable annual premium for a full-coverage flood-insurance policy on the clubhouse?

**17A.2c**   Compare the premium in Problem 17A.2b with a self-insurance policy the owners could follow of laying aside 1/20 × $40,000 = $2000 per year in anticipation of a major flood.

# CHAPTER 18

## DECISION TREES

OVERVIEW
Utilizing the expected-value criterion presented in Chapter 17, decisions involving risk are analyzed in this chapter with decision trees. The graphic quality of decision trees contributes to comprehensive analysis and cogent communications. Nonrepetitive decisions involving substantial outcomes exposed to risk are well served by the systematic evaluation methodology promoted by decision trees.

Conditional probabilities are the basis for a *discounted-decision-tree* analysis. A graphic tree format displays the effects of successive decisions occurring at timed intervals during a study period. Computations begin with expected values calculated for the most distant decision and roll back to the present by accepting the preferred alternative at each distant decision as a certain outcome for the next closer decision. A completed backward pass discloses the present worth of each immediate course of action.

Additional information about a decision is used in *Bayesian analysis* to revise the probability of a future event. The *value of perfect information* for estimating occurrences of future independent states reveals how much could be spent to obtain better forecasts.

## PROBABILITY CONCEPTS

Independent events and their probability relationships were examined in Chapter 17. These relationships were applied to evaluate risk-affected situations according to the expected-value criterion. Independent outcomes that could logically be expected for each alternative course of action were displayed in a payoff table or in a decision-tree format

(Figure 17.3). In this chapter the same general approach to economic risk is followed, but possible rewards from obtaining additional information are incorporated in the decision tree. In the process, some events become dependent on the occurrence of other events.

## Dependent Events

An event is termed *statistically dependent* when its occurrence is affected by the occurrence of one or more other events. For instance, your probability of becoming a millionaire 10 years from now might be 0.9 if you were given $500,000 next year. The event of becoming a millionaire would thus be dependent on the receipt of $500,000. If the probability of receiving $500,000 is 0.01, then your likelihood of being a millionaire in 10 years according to this specific situation is

$P$(becoming a millionaire *and* receiving $500,000)

$= P$(making a million *given* $500,000) $\times P$(receiving $500,000)

$= 0.90 \times 0.01 = 0.009$

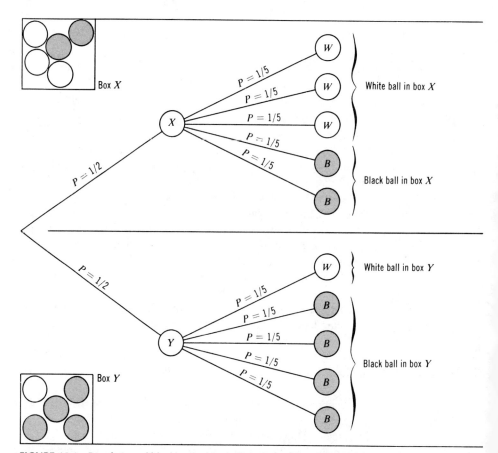

**FIGURE 18.1** Population of black and white balls in boxes $X$ and $Y$. Each burst of probability-labeled lines represents additional available information.

The millionaire status obviously depends on the likelihood of the occurrence of the $500,000 acquisition.

Dependent relationships are illustrated by the classic "balls in a box" example depicted in Figure 18.1. Two boxes, labeled $X$ and $Y$, contain black and white balls. Box $X$ contains three white and two black balls, while box $Y$ holds one white and four black balls. The probability of drawing a ball of a given color clearly depends on which box is chosen for the draw.

The *marginal probability* of drawing a white ball in this situation is 0.4 [the sum of the probabilities of individual white balls, $P(W) = 1/2 \times 1/5 = 1/10$]. Even though two events may be related, a marginal probability refers to just one of the dependent events. From the probability tree in Figure 18.1, it is clear that the probability of drawing a white ball is affected by the box from which it is drawn. Therefore the two events (drawing from one of the boxes and drawing a white ball) are related, but the marginal probability of drawing a white ball is still 0.4, because there are 10 balls with an equal probability of selection on the initial draw, and 4 of them are white.

What is the probability that a black ball will be drawn from box $Y$? This *conditional probability* is expressed symbolically as $P(B|Y)$, where the vertical line is read "given." From inspection of the probability tree, there are four chances in five that a black ball will be selected from box $Y$. Expressed as an equation, the conditional probability that a black ball will be drawn from box $Y$ is equal to the probability that a black ball will occur in box $Y$ divided by the probability that the draw will be made from box $Y$. Thus

$$P(B|Y) = \frac{P(BY)}{P(Y)} = \frac{0.4}{0.5} = 0.8$$

## Example 18.1   Conditional Probability

The number of defective and acceptable items received in a shipment from two different companies is shown in the table below.

|            | Company C1 | Company C2 | Total  |
|------------|-----------:|-----------:|-------:|
| Defective  | 500        | 1000       | 1,500  |
| Acceptable | 9500       | 4000       | 13,500 |
|            | 10,000     | 5000       | 15,000 |

What is the probability of receiving a defective item from company $C1$?

## Solution 18.1

The marginal probability of a defective item in the entire shipment is $1500/15,000 = 0.10$, but the conditional probability of a defective item, given that it was supplied by company $C1$, is 0.05. This result could be obtained logically by dividing the number of defective items $D$ in the portion of the shipment supplied by company $C1$ (500) by the total number received from company $C1$ (10,000). It could also be calculated by formula:

$$P(D|C1) = \frac{P(DC1)}{P(C1)} = \frac{500/15,000}{10,000/15,000} = \frac{1}{20}$$

The *joint probability* that two dependent events will occur is given by the general equation

$$P(AB) = P(A|B) \times P(B) \qquad \text{or} \qquad P(B|A) \times P(A)$$

It is readily apparent that this is a restatement of the formula used to calculate conditional probabilities. In the illustration of black and white balls in boxes $X$ and $Y$, the joint probability that a ball will be black and will come from box $Y$ is

$$P(BY) = P(B|Y) \times P(Y) = 0.8 \times 0.5 = 0.4$$

Similar applications to other joint probabilities for this situation can be verified by referring to Figure 18.1.

## Bayesian Analysis

The opportunity to update and refine probability forecasts by taking advantage of additional information is a powerful analytic tool. Original objective or subjective probability assignments are developed from current knowledge to anticipate possible future outcomes. As time passes, we often have access to new information about the events we are predicting. The concept of revising prior probability estimates to reflect new data is attributed to Thomas Bayes. His basic formula, $P(A|B) = P(AB)/P(B)$, was described in connection with the calculation of conditional probability. The routine followed in finding posterior probabilities is based on this basic formula. The sequence of operations follows this pattern: The equality

$$P(AB) = P(B|A) \times P(A)$$

can be rewritten as

$$P(BA) = P(A|B) \times P(B)$$

which provides the equality

$$P(B|A) \times P(A) = P(A|B) \times P(B)$$

which can be converted to

$$P(B|A) = \frac{P(A|B) \times P(B)}{P(A)}$$

and the marginal probability of $A$ is

$$P(A) = P(A|B_1) \times P(B_1) + \cdots + P(A|B_x) \times P(B_x) + \cdots + P(A|B_n) \times P(B_n)$$
$$= \sum_x P(A|B_x) \times P(B_x)$$

The correct use of this routine allows an event $B$ to be reevaluated when new information concerning the outcome of $A$ becomes available.

The illustration in Figure 18.1, black and white balls in boxes $X$ and $Y$, will be adapted to illustrate a Bayesian analysis. Assume that the content of each box is known but the identity of the boxes is unknown. This situation is equivalent to knowing the outcome of two possible futures without being certain which future will occur.

In this case we want to identify which box is $X$ and which is $Y$. Since the two boxes are indistinguishable, there is an equal opportunity that either could be nominated as $X$ or $Y$.

## EVENT 1

The first event is a random selection of one of the boxes. The prior probability of this event is represented by the probability tree of Figure 18.2.

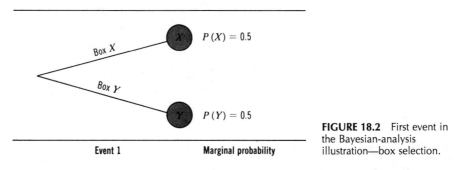

| Event 1 | Marginal probability |

**FIGURE 18.2**   First event in the Bayesian-analysis illustration—box selection.

## EVENT 2

Next a ball is drawn from whichever box was picked in event 1. We will assume that it is a black ball. Since we know the proportion of black to white balls in each box, we can calculate the probability of drawing a black ball, given that it came from a designated box. In box $X$ three of the five balls are white, so the conditional probability for the top branch of an expanded probability tree is 0.6. The likelihood of drawing a ball of a given color from a given box is shown by the joint probability for each branch of the tree. The complete tabulation of joint probabilities (collectively exhaustive) totals to 1.0, but we are interested primarily in the probabilities relating to black balls, because our first draw was black. The sum of the probabilities pertaining to black balls is the marginal probability of drawing a black ball and is shown in the last column of Figure 18.3.

The posterior probability of identifying the boxes, based on the additional information derived from the draw, is calculated by Bayes basic formula. Box $Y$ is arbitrarily used in the formula to give

$$P(Y|B) = \frac{P(YB)}{P(B)} = \frac{0.4}{0.6} = 0.67$$

Thus the added data have allowed us to revise our probability estimate from 0.5 to 0.67 that the selected box is indeed box $Y$.

## EVENT 3

Now assume that another ball is drawn from the same box and is black. Conditional probabilities for this draw are calculated on the basis of the four balls remaining in the box after the first draw. Then the joint probabilities are determined for two successive black draws from either box. These procedures are depicted in the third section of the probability tree in Figure 18.4.

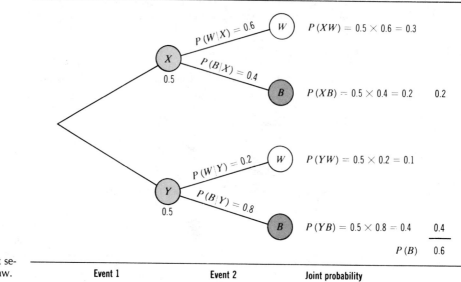

**FIGURE 18.3** Box selection and first draw.

A further revision of the likelihood that the chosen box is box $Y$ now becomes

$$P(Y|B_1B_2) = \frac{P(B_1B_2Y)}{P(B_1B_2)} = \frac{0.3}{0.35} = 0.857$$

Suppose the second draw had revealed a white rather than a black ball. This possibility is represented by the dotted lines in the probability tree. A format for revising the probability that the draws ($B_1$ and $W_2$) were from box $Y$ is given in the following table:

| *Event 1* | *Event 2* $= B_1$ | *Event 3* $= W_2$ | $P(E1E2E3)$ |
|---|---|---|---|
| $P(X) = 0.5$ | $P(B_1|X) = 0.4$ | $P(W_2|B_1X) = 0.75$ | $0.5 \times 0.4 \times 0.75 = 0.15$ |
| $P(Y) = 0.5$ | $P(B_1|Y) = 0.8$ | $P(W_2|B_1Y) = 0.25$ | $0.5 \times 0.8 \times 0.25 = \underline{0.10}$ |
| | | | $0.25$ |
| | $P(Y|B_1W_2) = \dfrac{0.10}{0.25} = 0.40$ | | |

We would intuitively suspect that a reversed order of the draws ($W_1$ and $B_2$) would not alter our revised probability. This suspicion is confirmed by the following values:

| *Event 1* | *Event 2* $= W_1$ | *Event 3* $= B_2$ | $P(E1E2E3)$ |
|---|---|---|---|
| $P(X) = 0.5$ | $P(W_1|X) = 0.6$ | $P(B_2|W_1X) = 0.5$ | $0.5 \times 0.6 \times 0.5 = 0.15$ |
| $P(Y) = 0.5$ | $P(W_1|Y) = 0.2$ | $P(B_2|W_1Y) = 1.0$ | $0.5 \times 0.2 \times 1.0 = \underline{0.10}$ |
| | | | $0.25$ |
| | $P(Y|W_1B_2) = \dfrac{0.10}{0.25} = 0.40$ | | |

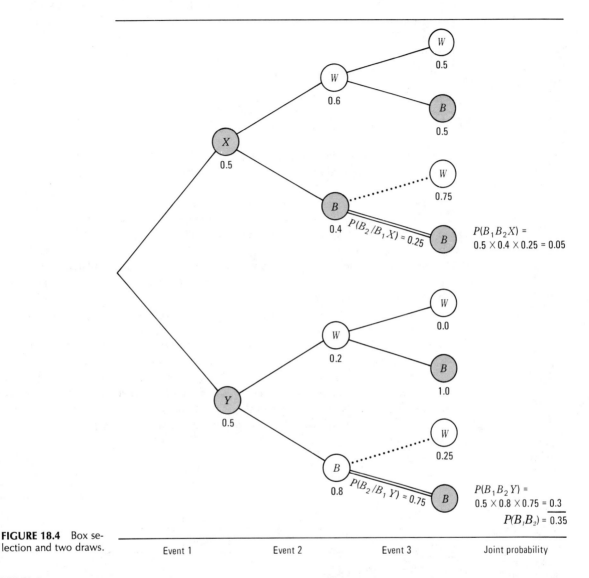

**FIGURE 18.4** Box selection and two draws.

| Event 1 | Event 2 | Event 3 | Joint probability |
|---------|---------|---------|-------------------|

**EVENT 4**

As a final possibility, again assume that the first two balls drawn were black, and now a third black ball is picked from the same box. We have obviously been drawing from box $Y$, because box $X$ originally contained only two black balls. Although formal calculations are unnecessary in this case, the conclusion is verified easily by recognizing that

$P$(3 black-ball draws | box $X$) = 0.4 × 0.25 × 0.0 = 0.0

and

$P$(3 black-ball draws | box $Y$) = 0.8 × 0.75 × 0.67 = 0.4

which makes the marginal probability of three successive black draws 0.0 + 0.4 = 0.4,

so

$$P(\text{box } Y \mid 3 \text{ black-ball draws}) = \frac{0.4 \times 0.5}{0.4 \times 0.5} = 1.0$$

# DECISION TREES

The tree structure in Figure 18.4 displays probabilities, but it does not represent a decision situation. A decision tree has three components:

1  Decision alternatives with associated future events
2  Outcomes for each alternative, given the occurrence of each future event
3  The probability of the occurrence of each event

A convenient set of symbols to graphically portray the decision situation represents decision points as squares and outcomes as circles. Then dotted lines between squares and circles symbolize different courses of action, and solid lines from the circles represent the possible consequences of the actions. The decision criterion is the expected value of alternatives at each decision point.

Suppose it costs $100 to play the game of picking which box is $X$ and $Y$ when the contents of the boxes are known, but outwardly the boxes are identical. Success in naming a box correctly is rewarded by winnings of $180 (net gain of $80 since it costs $100 to play the game). Because the boxes are indistinguishable to the gambler, there is a 50-50 chance of guessing correctly. The expected value from repeatedly playing the game is −$100 + 0.5($180) = −$10 per play. A decision-tree representation of the gamble is shown in Figure 18.5.

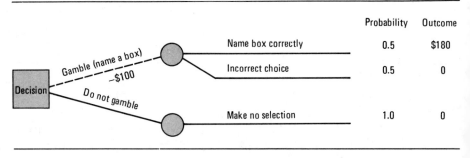

**FIGURE 18.5**
Decision tree for a gamble to select box $X$ or $Y$ when the ante is −$100 and the payoff for correctly selecting the named box is $180.

Now assume another option has been added to make the game more interesting (and because no one wants to play the original game). A gambler can select one ball from either box for a sampling fee of $25. Then, after the charge is paid and a ball is drawn, the original conditions of the game apply: an ante of $100 to guess which box is which. The advantage of the sampling draw for the gambler is to gain additional information before making a selection between boxes. The question is whether the additional information provided by the draw can change the expected value of the game to the gambler's favor. The sequential alternatives are displayed in Figure 18.6.

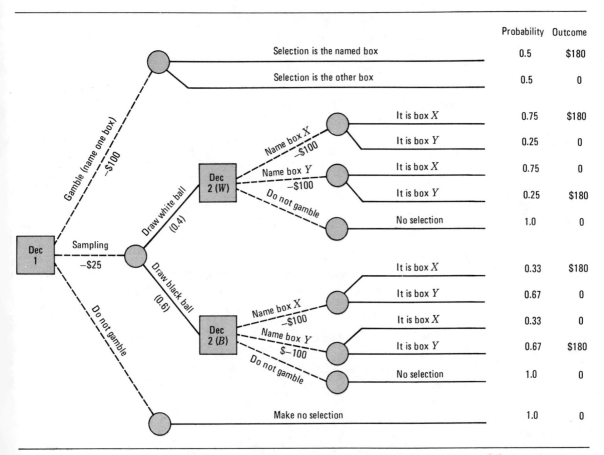

|  | Probability | Outcome |
|---|---|---|
| Selection is the named box | 0.5 | $180 |
| Selection is the other box | 0.5 | 0 |
| It is box $X$ | 0.75 | $180 |
| It is box $Y$ | 0.25 | 0 |
| It is box $X$ | 0.75 | 0 |
| It is box $Y$ | 0.25 | $180 |
| No selection | 1.0 | 0 |
| It is box $X$ | 0.33 | $180 |
| It is box $Y$ | 0.67 | 0 |
| It is box $X$ | 0.33 | 0 |
| It is box $Y$ | 0.67 | $180 |
| No selection | 1.0 | 0 |
| Make no selection | 1.0 | 0 |

**FIGURE 18.6** Expanded decision tree for the pick-a-box gamble. Probabilities are based on the boxes described in Figure 18.1. Payoffs are the same as in Figure 18.5, but there is an added option of sampling one ball from a box before deciding to ante $100 for the chance to select a box. The fee for sampling is $25.

Probabilities for the sampling option are based on the known distribution of black and white balls in boxes $X$ and $Y$. For instance, once a white ball is drawn, the probability it was drawn from box $X$ is

$$P(X|W) = \frac{P(W|X)\,P(X)}{P(W|X)\,P(X) + P(W|Y)\,P(Y)} = \frac{P(XW)}{P(XW) + P(YW)}$$

$$= \frac{0.6\,(0.5)}{(0.6)(0.5) + (0.2)(0.5)} = \frac{0.3}{0.3 + 0.1} = 0.75$$

Similarly, the probability of drawing a white ball for the sample when the identity of the boxes is unknown is

$$P(W) = P(W|X)\ P(X) + P(W|Y)\ P(Y)$$
$$= (0.6)(0.5) + (0.2)(0.5) = 0.4$$

or, since there are four white balls among the ten in the two boxes, $P(W) = 4/10 = 0.4$.

Given the probabilities and the payoffs for each outcome, the expected value of the sampling option is calculated by "rolling back" from decision point 2 to decision point 1. This means the expected values from point 2 are calculated first, and the most profitable alternatives become the outcomes for point 1.

A payoff table for decision point 2($W$) (a white ball drawn as the sample) is shown below.

| | *It Is Box X*<br>*P(X\|W)=0.75* | *It Is Box Y*<br>*P(Y\|W)=0.25* | *Expected*<br>*Value* |
|---|---|---|---|
| Pick box $X$ | $180 − $100 = $80 | −$100 | $35 |
| Pick box $Y$ | −$100 | $180 − $100 = $80 | −$55 |
| Refuse gamble | 0 | 0 | 0 |

The preferred alternative is clearly to pick box $X$ when a white ball is drawn. By equivalent calculations, the box should be identified as $Y$ at decision point 2($B$) when a black ball is drawn because the expected value of this choice is

$$EV(Y \text{ given } B) = (\$180 − \$100)(0.67) + −\$100(0.33) = \$20$$

as opposed to naming the box $X$ for an expected value of −$40 or quitting after the draw at no additional gain or loss.

A pruned decision tree is shown in Figure 18.7. It displays the expected values for the original gamble and the outcomes for the sampling alternative. These outcomes are based

**FIGURE 18.7** Pruned decision tree showing the expected values for two alternatives and the rolled-back outcomes from decision points 2($W$) and 2($B$) as determined from Figure 18.6. Expected value of the sampling alternative is $1, making it the preferred course of action for the given data.

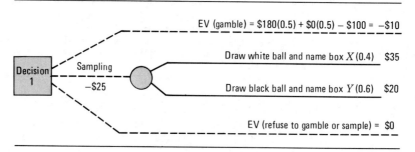

EV (gamble) = $180(0.5) + $0(0.5) − $100 = −$10

Draw white ball and name box $X$ (0.4)   $35

Sampling   
−$25

Draw black ball and name box $Y$ (0.6)   $20

EV (refuse to gamble or sample) = $0

Decision 1

on selecting the most advantageous alternatives from decision points 2($W$) and 2($B$). Given the likelihood of drawing a black or white ball for the sample, the expected value of the sampling alternative is

$$EV(\text{sampling}) = \$35(0.4) + \$20(0.6) − \$25 = \$1$$

Thus the option to buy a sample for $25 converts the long-term gain of the gamble from negative to positive, albeit barely profitable. The actual outcome of each round of gambling would be a loss of $25 + $100 = $125 or a gain of $180 − $125 = $55. Over a large number of rounds, the gambler averages a $1 gain per round.

The value of information gained from sampling is the difference between the expected value of the sampling alternative and the *next best alternative*. For the "pick-a-box" decision, the alternative of refusing to gamble is compared to the gamble-with-sampling alternative to indicate

Value of sampling information = $1 − $0 = $1

# DISCOUNTED DECISION TREES

Discounted cash flows, probabilities, and expected values are combined in a tree format to generate a graphic *discounted decision tree*. Its unique feature is its capacity to display future decision points—times in the future when a decision maker can appraise actual outcomes from earlier decisions to decide if a previously determined course of action should be modified to cope with current conditions.

A discounted decision tree shows decisions separated by time intervals and susceptible to external influencing factors. Branches radiate from an initial decision point to indicate the primary alternatives. Each main branch is divided to show foreseeable outcomes associated with possible future events. Then the events are rated with respect to their probable occurrence. When gains can be maximized by introducing new alternatives at a future date, a second decision point is established. A succession of decision points can extend to the limit of forecasting ability. The time value of monetary outcomes is effected by discounting the outcomes to a common point in time.

## Formulation of a Discounted Decision Tree

A warehousing problem of a small novelty manufacturing company will serve to illustrate a decision tree for successive decisions. The company is relatively new and has captured a limited segment of the novelty market. It must have additional storage space to meet customer demands and to allow more flexible production scheduling. A primary decision has been made to secure additional inventory storage.

An initial investigation has revealed the availability of only one suitable rental warehouse, and it is available only if leased for 10 years. The warehouse has more space than is immediately required, but the company feels that some of the space could be sublet if desired. Estimates solicited from building contractors confirm that the construction of a new warehouse of equivalent size would amount to more than the $23,000 per year lease cost.

Another alternative is to build a small warehouse now and enlarge it if future business activity warrants expansion. The owners feel that in 3 years they will know whether the company's growth will support the addition. In order to evaluate the alternatives, estimates were made of possible business patterns and the likelihood of each. Their optimistic forecasts are shown in Table 18.1.

| Growth Pattern | Probability |
|---|---|
| No increase in activity for 10 years | 0.15 |
| No increase for 3 years, but an expanded growth rate during the next 7 years | 0.15 |
| Increasing growth for the next 3 years, but no increase during the following 7 years | 0.14 |
| Increasing activity for the full 10 years | 0.56 |

**TABLE 18.1** Growth patterns.

The owners place the probability for increased growth during the next 3 years at 0.56 + 0.14 = 0.70. If the growth materializes, they can use more room than is available in the anticipated small warehouse. Therefore, if they initially decide to build, they will have to make a decision in 3 years about whether to add to the small warehouse or find other means to obtain extra storage space. At that time the conditional probability that the company will continue to grow is 0.56/0.70 = 0.80. The spectrum of forecasts and alternatives can be summarized in a decision tree as shown in Figure 18.8.

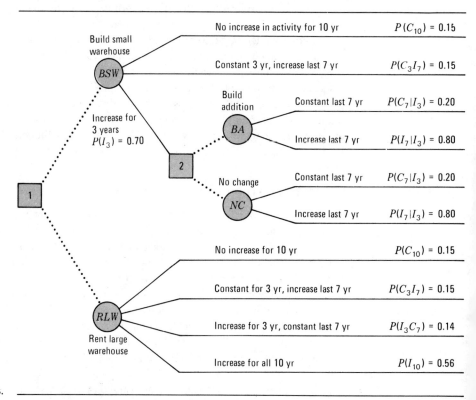

**FIGURE 18.8**
Decision tree with alternatives and forecasts.

## Outcomes

The outcomes for the warehouse proposals are rated according to expected costs. Initial building costs for a small warehouse should be accurate, but the estimated price for an addition is less firm because of possible changes in building conditions at the time of construction. Yearly rental fees for the leased warehouse are a fixed amount. Other annual costs are less certain. Savings, net positive cash flows, could result if the entire capacity is not required for the company's inventory and the extra portion is rented. Conversely, additional costs are incurred when a lack of storage space forces production runs below the economical lot size or causes out-of-stock costs in supplying customers. Estimates of net annual costs for the outcomes of each alternative are tabulated in the decision tree of Figure 18.9.

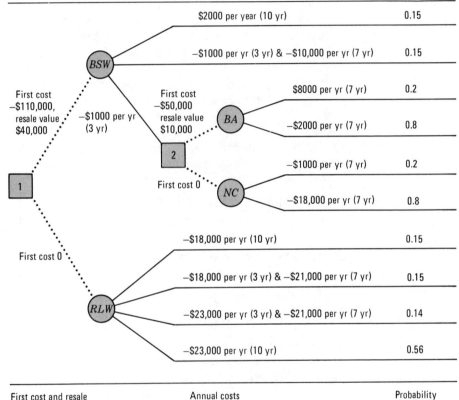

**FIGURE 18.9** Costs associated with warehouse alternatives.

| First cost and resale value of alternatives | Annual costs | Probability |
|---|---|---|

The cash-flow estimates shown in the figure include the first costs associated with each alternative and the annual costs related to the outcomes. Building a small warehouse, *BSW*, has a first cost of $110,000 and a resale value of $40,000 after 10 years; renting a large warehouse, *RLW*, has no initial cost. The second decision point 3 years in the future is a choice between building an addition, *BA*, at a cost of $50,000 with a $10,000 resale value, and making no change, *NC*. Net annual returns comprise repairs, taxes, insurance, leasing expense, and opportunity costs, as well as the savings from subletting when possible. The lease for the rental warehouse states an annual charge of $23,000, which includes taxes, insurance, and repairs. If there is no increase in the company's activities, this annual charge can be defrayed by $5000 from subletting extra space. Less rental income is anticipated when the company needs part or all of the space to handle its own increasing activity. The two periods of returns, 3 and 7 years, correspond to the original growth patterns indicated in Figure 18.8.

# Evaluation

Two types of calculations are involved in evaluating alternatives. The present values of receipts and expenditures are determined for each outcome and are then weighted according to their probability of occurrence. This procedure amounts to finding the expected value of the present worth of the outcomes. These expected values are compared at a decision point to select the most advantageous alternative.

Comparisons are made in a reverse chronological order. That is, the most distant decision point from time zero is evaluated first. The selected alternative from the first decision then becomes an input to the next decision. The backward pass through successive points is continued until the primary decision is resolved.

For the warehouse example, the discounting procedure begins at decision point 2. At this point in time, 3 years away from the primary decison, the company must decide whether to build an addition to the plant or make no change. The outcomes of each of these two alternatives depend on the level of business activity during the last 7 years of the study period. We shall assume that the company uses an interest rate of 12 percent. The present worths of the four outcomes at decision point 2 are calculated as shown.

$$PW(BA{:}C_7) = -\$50{,}000 + \$10{,}000(P/F,\ 12,\ 7) + \$8000(P/A,\ 12,\ 7)$$
$$= -\$50{,}000 + \$10{,}000(0.45235) + \$8000(4.5637)$$
$$= -\$8{,}966$$

$$PW(BA{:}I_7) = -\$50{,}000 + \$10{,}000(P/F,\ 12,\ 7) + -\$2000(P/A,\ 12,\ 7)$$
$$= -\$54{,}603$$

$$PW(NC{:}C_7) = -\$1000(P/A,\ 12,\ 7) = -\$1000(4.5637) = -\$4{,}564$$

$$PW(NC{:}I_7) = -\$18{,}000(P/A,\ 12,\ 7) = -\$82{,}142$$

These present worths at decision point 2 are entered in a payoff table as shown in Figure 18.10, where the calculated expected values indicate a preference for the alternative to build an addition, $BA$.

| | COMPANY GROWTH PATTERNS | | |
| *Alternative* | *Constant (0.2)* | *Increase (0.8)* | *Expected Value (Costs)* |
|---|---|---|---|
| $BA$ | −$8966 | −$54,603 | −$45,476 |
| $NC$ | −4564 | −82,142 | −66,626 |

**FIGURE 18.10** Payoff table for decision point 2.

Decision point 1 also has two alternatives. Since we have already considered decision point 2, we shall continue on this branch of the decision tree. The initial cost of building is $110,000, with an expected resale value of $40,000 after 10 years. Four outcomes may occur from this course of action. Company activity could increase or remain constant for the entire 10 years, or it could increase the first 3 years and then level off or continue to increase the remaining 7 years. A comparison, assuming end-of-year returns and a 12 percent interest factor, is shown below.

$$PW(BSW{:}C_{10}) = -\$110{,}000 + \$40{,}000(P/F,\ 12,\ 10) + \$2000(P/A,\ 12,\ 10)$$
$$= -\$110{,}000 + \$40{,}000(0.32197) + \$2000(5.6502)$$
$$= -\$85{,}821$$

$$PW(BSW{:}C_3I_7) = -\$110{,}000 + \$40{,}000(P/F,\ 12,\ 10) + -\$1000(P/A,\ 12,\ 3)$$
$$+ -\$10{,}000(P/A,\ 12,\ 7)(P/F,\ 12,\ 3)$$
$$= -\$110{,}000 + \$40{,}000(0.32197) + -\$1000(2.4018)$$
$$+ -\$10{,}000(4.5637)(0.71178) = -\$132{,}007$$

$$PW(BSW{:}I_3C_7) = -\$110{,}000 + \$40{,}000\ (P/F,\ 12,\ 10) + -\$1{,}000(P/A,\ 12,\ 3)$$
$$+ -\$50{,}000(P/F,\ 12,\ 3) + \$10{,}000(P/F,\ 12,\ 10)$$
$$+ \$8{,}000\ (P/A,\ 12,\ 7)(P/F,\ 12,\ 3)$$
$$= -\$110{,}000 + \$40{,}000(0.32197) + -\$1{,}000(2.4018)$$
$$+ -\$50{,}000(0.71178) + \$10{,}000(0.32197) + \$8{,}000(4.5637)(0.71178)$$
$$= -\$105{,}905$$

$$PW(BSW{:}I_{10}) = -\$110{,}000 + \$40{,}000(P/F,\ 12,\ 10) + -\$1{,}000(P/A,\ 12,\ 3)$$
$$+ -\$50{,}000(P/F,\ 12,\ 3) + \$10{,}000(P/F,\ 12,\ 10)$$
$$+ -\$2{,}000\ (P/A,\ 12,\ 7)(P/F,\ 12,\ 3)$$
$$= -\$138{,}389$$

Equivalent calculations applied to the other main fork of the decision tree give the present worths of annual costs associated with leasing a large warehouse.

$$PW(RLW{:}C_{10}) = -\$18{,}000(P/A,\ 12,\ 10) = -\$18{,}000(5.6502) = -\$101{,}704$$

$$PW(RLW{:}C_3I_7) = -\$18{,}000(P/A,\ 12,\ 3) + -\$21{,}000(P/A,\ 12,\ 7)(P/F,\ 12,\ 3)$$
$$= -\$18{,}000(2.4018) + -\$21{,}000(4.5637)(0.71178)$$
$$= -\$111{,}448$$

$$PW(RLW{:}I_3C_7) = -\$23{,}000(P/A,\ 12,\ 3) + -\$21{,}000(P/A,\ 12,\ 7)(P/F,\ 12,\ 3)$$
$$= -\$123{,}457$$

$$PW(RLW{:}I_{10}) = -\$23{,}000(P/A,\ 12,\ 10) = -\$129{,}955$$

Grouping the outcomes from the two alternatives into a payoff table yields the values in Figure 18.11.

From this analysis it is apparent that the most economical alternative is to sign the lease for renting the large warehouse. The difference is $124{,}998 - \$122{,}032 = \$2966$.

# VALUE OF ADDITIONAL INFORMATION

The novelty company now has a quantitative base for making its decision. It may be satisfied with the information and proceed to sign the lease. It is also possible that some

| | COMPANY GROWTH PATTERNS | | | | |
| Alternatives | Constant 10 Years (0.15) | Constant 3 Years, Increase 7 Years (0.15) | Increase 3 Years, Constant 7 Years (0.14) | Increase 10 Years (0.56) | Expected Value (cost) |
|---|---|---|---|---|---|
| BSW | −$ 85,821 | −$132,007 | −$105,905 | −$138,389 | −$124,998 |
| RLW | −101,704 | −111,448 | −123,457 | −129,955 | −122,032 |

**FIGURE 18.11**  Payoff table for decision point 1.

segment of management may not agree on the indicated course of action. There may be a disagreement as to estimated growth patterns or cost figures. Assuming that the need for some kind of storage facility is unanimously recognized, there is still another alternative available: The decision can be postponed. This alternative would be procrastination unless it were coupled with a firm desire to obtain more information about the problem. Such

**Step 1:** Assume that a certain state is certain to occur.

**Step 2:** Select the preferred alternative for that future based on returns discounted to the primary decision point. This strategy may be a combination of alternatives from several decision points.

**Step 3:** Evaluate the alternatives for the remaining future states.

**Step 4:** Multiply the probability of each state by the value of the associated preferred alternative. Total the products to obtain the expected value of perfect information.

**Step 5:** Compare the value obtained in Step 4 to the expected value obtained using probable futures. The difference is the amount that could be paid for perfect information.

**FIGURE 18.12**
Flowchart for determining the value of perfect information.

information could be provided by further intensive investigation by company personnel or by a study conducted by an independent agency.

The first step in considering the advisability of further research is to determine the worth of additional information. Securing new data costs money, whether the investigation is conducted by company or outside investigators. This additional investment should be exceeded by the expected value of added profits or reduced costs realized from the information.

With *perfect* information the company would *know* which alternative would cost the least. Figure 18.11 revealed that the best alternative would be to build a small warehouse without an addition if it were *known* that the company would experience a constant growth pattern for 10 years. The cost of building ($85,821) is $15,883 less than leasing for this growth pattern. In a similar fashion the best alternative for each state assumed *known* can be determined. The expected value of such perfect foresight is calculated as shown in Figure 18.12.

Four future states were identified in the warehouse illustration. It was observed that a small warehouse should be built for a condition of constant growth for 10 years. The best alternative for 3 years of constant growth followed by 7 years of increasing activity is to lease. Figure 18.11 shows that the present worth of renting expense is $111,448 versus building costs of $132,007.

For the state of accelerated growth for 3 years followed by 7 years of level activity, Figure 18.11 shows that the present worth of renting expense is $123,457 versus building costs of $105,905. Thus, building is preferred to leasing. However, if it is known with certainty that 7 years of level activity will follow the 3 years of accelerated growth, then the warehouse expansion should *not* be built after three years. This reduces the building costs to $102,772. (Recall the cost for no change in the capacity of the small warehouse was determined to be $4564. Discounting this value to the present and including the initial cost, resale, and annual costs for the first 3 years give

$$PW(BSW{:}I_3C_7) = -\$110{,}000 + \$40{,}000(P/F,\ 12,\ 10) + -\$1000(P/A,\ 12,\ 3)$$
$$+ -\$4564(P/F,\ 12,\ 3)$$
$$= -\$102{,}772.)$$

For the state of accelerated growth for 10 years, Figure 18.11 reveals that the present worth of renting expense is $129,955 versus building costs of $138,389. (If the expansion were not built, building costs would be even higher.) Thus, leasing is preferred in this situation.

| State | Preferred Alternative | Cost | Probability | Product |
|---|---|---|---|---|
| Constant 10 years | *BSW* | −$85,821 | 0.15 | −$12,873 |
| Constant 3 years, increase 7 years | *RLW* | −111,448 | 0.15 | −16,717 |
| Increase 3 years, constant 7 years | *BSW-NC* | −102,772 | 0.14 | −14,388 |
| Increase 10 years | *RLW* | −129,955 | 0.56 | −72,775 |
|  |  |  | Expected value | −$116,753 |

**TABLE 18.2** Expected value of perfect information.

The expected value from the preferred alternatives for each state evaluated separately is shown in Table 18.2.

Comparison of the expected value of perfect information with the expected value of the best alternative obtained earlier (Figure 18.10) indicates that the novelty company could afford to pay up to $122,032 − $116,753 = $5279 for a perfect forecast. Securing perfect information is at best a wild hope, but these figures do suggest that significant savings could result from further study of the uncertainties in expected growth patterns.

### Example 18.2   Value of Perfect Information

An ambitious entrepreneur has signed a regionally well known rock band to give a concert on the First of July. The concert can be staged in a conveniently located pasture or in a school auditorium. If the weather is sunny, a concert in the pasture could be very profitable, but rain would ruin attendance and cause a loss due to the high fixed costs of preparing the site. Attendance at the auditorium would be largely unaffected by weather, but the maximum capacity is far less than the pasture. Weather records indicate that odds against rain on July 1 are 9 to 1. Using the probabilities given and the estimated returns shown for concerts held at the two locations, calculate the *expected value* and the amount of money that could be paid for *perfect information* about the weather, if it could be purchased.

|             | NET RETURNS IF THERE IS | |
| ----------- | --------- | --------- |
| *Alternative* | *Rain* | *No Rain* |
| Auditorium  | $24,000   | $30,000   |
| Pasture     | −27,000   | 90,000    |

### Solution 18.2

The payoff table indicates that holding the concert in the pasture has the greater expected value.

|             | *Rain* (P = 0.1) | *No Rain* (P = 0.9) | *Expected Value* |
| ----------- | ---------------- | ------------------- | ---------------- |
| *Auditorium* | $24,000         | $30,000             | $29,400          |
| *Pasture*    | −27,000          | 90,000              | 78,300 ←*Preferred* |

The shaded outcomes in the payoff table show the highest possible returns for each future state. If the entrepreneur *knew* that it was going to rain on the First of July, the concert would surely be scheduled in the auditorium to reap a $24,000 profit instead of a loss. Equivalently, assurance of dry weather would lead to a profit of $90,000 from the concert held in the pasture. Since it is dry 9 out of 10 July Firsts the *expected value* of perfect information is

$24,000(0.10) + $90,000(0.9) = $83,400

and the amount that could be paid for it is $83,400 - $78,300 = $5100$, the difference between the returns from a commitment to hold the concert in the pasture and the option to schedule it at the site best suited to the weather. This is the *value* of perfect information.

## APPLICATION OF DECISION TREES

Nonrepetitive decisions that involve risk and substantial outcomes are good candidates for decision-tree analysis. The tree structure forces an explicit recognition of risk and promotes the comprehensive organization of alternative strategies. The graphical representation of data and competing options improves communication between decision makers and analysts. It also helps in "selling" a decision.

Negative aspects of decision trees stem largely from difficulties in displaying very complex situations. A tree gets too "bushy" to comprehend when branches are proliferated to accommodate complicated relationships. Nonquantitative influences may be lost in the quest for data to complete all the branches, or ignored because they do not fit conveniently into the tree. While the formalized analysis procedure provides evaluation consistency, it may discourage consideration of interrelationships that cannot be definitively expressed. Decision-tree language does not lend itself to intuition.

Decision-tree concepts are adaptable to diverse managerial and engineering applications. Scratch-pad sketches can be used to "scope out" preliminary designs. Sketches may stimulate the generation of new alternatives through association with displayed strategy. Refinements can be made to the basic tree format to better represent certain problem situations. Extension 18A presents a tree modified to portray the origin of accidents and the data needed to decide whether safety investments are warranted.

## REVIEW EXERCISES AND DISCUSSIONS

**Exercise 1**    For several years, records were kept of the number of absentees in two offices of a firm. The average number of employees absent from work on each day of the work week at each office are summarized in the following table:

|                    | M  | T  | W  | Th | F  | Total |
|--------------------|----|----|----|----|----|-------|
| Dartmouth office   | 40 | 28 | 29 | 32 | 44 | 173   |
| Montreal office    | 26 | 21 | 20 | 22 | 28 | 117   |
|                    | 66 | 49 | 49 | 54 | 72 | 290   |

Knowing only that an employee was absent one day, how is the absence related to a day of the week (Friday) and the place of employment (Dartmouth)?

**Solution 1**    The probability that the employee was absent on Friday is $P(F) = 72/290 = 0.248$. The probability that the employee worked in Dartmouth is $P(D) = 173/290 = 0.6$.

The probability that an employee who works in Dartmouth was absent on Friday is $P(F|D) = 44/173 = 0.255$.

The probability that an employee was absent on Friday *and* worked in Dartmouth is

$$P(FD) = P(F|D) \times P(D) = 0.255 \times 0.6 = 0.15$$

or

$$P(DF) = P(D|F) \times P(F) = 44/72 \times 72/290 = 0.15$$

---

**Exercise 2**  A complaint was received by company $C$ from one of its wholesalers that a certain key part on appliances recently delivered by company $C$ had often failed to operate properly. The company immediately stopped shipment on the remaining appliances made in the same production run as those supplied to the wholesaler. An investigation of similar malfunctions revealed that 70 percent of the time the trouble was caused by poor assembly, and 30 percent of the time by inferior materials. It was also determined that the probability of failure from incorrectly assembled parts is 0.40, and the probability of failure from faulty materials is 0.90. If the material is bad, the whole part has to be replaced, but if the trouble was caused by improper assembling, the part may be adjusted to perform adequately. The only means of determining the cause of trouble is by destructive testing. A decision was made to test enough parts to determine with a probability of 0.95 that the trouble stemmed from one cause or the other.

If the first five parts tested all failed because of poor materials, what conclusion can be drawn?

**Solution 2**  As shown by the table below, enough parts have been tested to determine that the probability is 0.96 that the trouble is caused by faulty materials. Since the company planned to take action when it was 95 percent sure of the cause, the five tests provide adequate reason to begin replacement of the defective parts.

| *Cause* | *P(E1)* | *P(failure \| cause)* | *P(5 failures \| cause)* | *P(5 failures)* |
|---------|---------|------------------------|---------------------------|-----------------|
| Material | 0.3 | 0.90 | $(0.9)^5 = 0.59$ | 0.177 |
| Assembly | 0.7 | 0.40 | $(0.4)^5 = 0.01$ | 0.007 |
| | | | | 0.184 |

$$P(\text{poor material} \mid 5 \text{ failures}) = \frac{0.177}{0.184} = 0.96$$

---

**Exercise 3**  Compare the value of sampling information with the value of perfect information for the pick-a-box gamble portrayed in Figure 18.6.

**Solution 3**  The value of sampling information is the amount by which the expected value of the sampling alternative differs from the best expected value among other alternatives. Without sampling the best alternative is to refuse to gamble: EV(do not gamble) = 0. The previously calculated EV(sampling) = $1 gives a value of $1 − $0 = $1 to the information gained from sampling.

Perfect information for the pick-a-box choice presumes prior knowledge of the identity of each box. Knowing which box is which eliminates the gamble and is consequently an unlikely proposition. But if it did exist, the "gambler" would pay $100 with complete assurance of winning $180 each time, a net gain of $80 per play. The value of perfect information is then $80 − $0 = $80.

**Exercise 4**  A firm has identified three potential outcomes for an investment of $1 million. The total return from each investment plus the profit which will occur in less than a year, and the associated probabilities are: $A$ = $1,400,000 with $P(A)$ = 0.2; $B$ = $1,200,000 with $P(B)$ = 0.5; and $C$ = $500,000 with $P(C)$ = 0.3.

A consultant could be hired to provide additional information. The past record of the consultant in evaluating similar conditions is given in the table below, where $A_c$, $B_c$, and $C_c$ represent predictions by the consultant that, respectively, states $A$, $B$, and $C$ will occur.

| Consultant's Predictions | OCCURRENCE OF STATE | | | |
|---|---|---|---|---|
| | $A$ | $B$ | $C$ | |
| $A_c$ | 0.8 | 0.1 | 0.1 | Probability of the |
| $B_c$ | 0.1 | 0.9 | 0.2 | consultant's prediction |
| $C_c$ | 0.1 | 0.0 | 0.7 | given that the state occurs |

**a**  Construct a decision tree to represent the alternatives, outcomes, and associated probabilities.
**b**  What is the value of perfect information, if it could be obtained?
**c**  What is the amount that could be paid for additional information based on the consultant's record?

**Solution 4a**  The top branch of the decision tree in Figure 18.13 is the *no-consultant* alternative which leads to a decision between investing and not investing. From the probabilities and outcomes given in the problem statement for the investment option, the branches are labeled as

Outcome $A$ = $1,400,000 − $1,000,000 = $400,000     and     $P(A)$ = 0.2
Outcome $B$ = $1,200,000 − $1,000,000 = $200,000     and     $P(B)$ = 0.5
Outcome $C$ = $500,000 − $1,000,000 = −$500,000     and     $P(C)$ = 0.3

If a consultant is hired (the second alternative at decision point 1), outcome $A_c$, $B_c$, or $C_c$ could result. Each outcome leads to a second decision about investing. The probability of outcome $A$ *given* the consultant's prediction $(A_c)$ that $A$ will occur is calculated as

$$P(A|A_c) = \frac{P(A)\,P(A_c|A)}{P(A)\,P(A_c|A) + P(B)\,P(A_c|B) + P(C)\,P(A_c|C)}$$

$$= \frac{P(A)\,P(A_c|A)}{P(A_c)}$$

$$= \frac{(0.2)(0.8)}{(0.2)(0.8) + (0.5)(0.1) + (0.3)(0.1)}$$

$$= \frac{0.16}{0.24} = 0.667$$

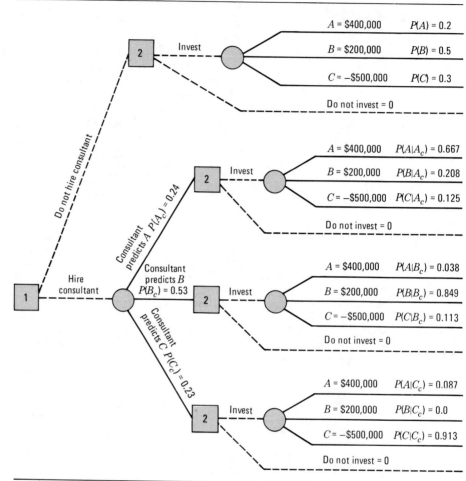

**FIGURE 18.13**

The other probabilities in the tree are calculated similarly, as shown below.

$$P(B|A_c) = \frac{(0.5)(0.1)}{0.24} = 0.208$$

$$P(C|A_c) = \frac{(0.3)(0.1)}{0.24} = 0.125$$

$$P(A|B_c) = \frac{(0.2)(0.1)}{(0.2)(0.1) + (0.5)(0.9) + (0.3)(0.2)} = \frac{0.02}{0.53} = 0.038$$

$$P(B|B_c) = \frac{(0.5)(0.9)}{0.53} = 0.849$$

$$P(C|B_c) = \frac{(0.3)(0.2)}{0.53} = 0.113$$

$$P(A|C_c) = \frac{(0.2)(0.1)}{(0.2)(0.1) + (0.5)(0.0) + (0.3)(0.7)} = \frac{0.02}{0.23} = 0.087$$

$$P(B|C_c) = \frac{(0.5)(0.0)}{0.23} = 0.0$$

$$P(C|C_c) = \frac{(0.3)(0.7)}{0.23} = 0.913$$

And, from the above, $P(A_c) = 0.24$, $P(B_c) = 0.53$, and $P(C_c) = 0.23$.

**Solution 4b**  The value of perfect information is determined from the payoff table below, which represents the top branch of the tree.

| | State A: $P(A) = 0.2$ | State B: $P(B) = 0.5$ | State C: $P(C) = 0.3$ | Expected Value |
|---|---|---|---|---|
| Invest | $400,000 | $200,000 | −$500,000 | $30,000 |
| Do not invest | 0 | 0 | 0 | 0 |

With perfect information the investment would be made when either state $A$ or state $B$ occurred, but no investment would be made when state $C$ occurred. Therefore,

EV(perfect information) = $400,000(0.2) + $200,000(0.5) + $0(0.3)
= $180,000

and the value of perfect information is $180,000 − $30,000 = $150,000.

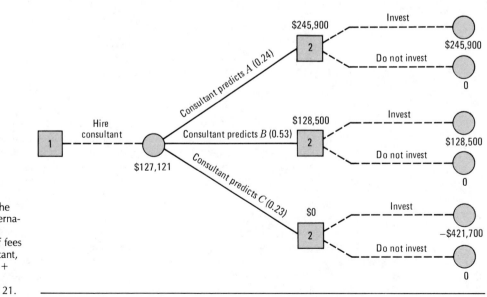

**FIGURE 18.14**
Decision tree for the hire-consultant alternative. The expected value, exclusive of fees paid to the consultant, is $245,900(0.24) + $128,500(0.53) + $0(0.23) = $127,121.

**Solution 4c** The expected value of additional information from the consultant is calculated by rolling back from decision points 2 to determine the outcome at the node where the three consultant predictions merge. A pruned version of the lower branch of the decision tree is given in Figure 18.14. It shows the expected value at each outcome node and the worth of the preferred alternative at decision points 2. Note that the outcomes do not have to be discounted because they occur within 1 year.

The expected value from using the consultant's prediction is $127,121, which leads to

Value of additional information = EV(with added information) − EV(with original data) = $127,121 − $30,000 = $97,121

The breakeven point for purchasing additional information is therefore $97,121, which is the maximum amount the consultant should be paid.

# PROBLEMS

**18.1a**  Given the probability that 1 out of every 1000 tire valves is defective, what is the probability that two of the four tires on a car will have defective valves?

*(5.98 × 10⁻⁶)*

**18.1b**  In super-safety tires which have a separate inner tire, the valves for the inner tire are defective 1 time in 500. What is the probability that a tire will have both valves defective? (See Problem 18.1a.)

*(2 × 10⁻⁶)*

**18.2**  When a machine is properly adjusted, it will produce an acceptable product 9 times in 10. When it is out of adjustment, the probability of an acceptable product is 0.4. The probability of the machine's being adjusted properly is 0.95.

**18.2a**  If the first part tested after an adjustment is not acceptable, what is the probability that the machine was correctly adjusted?

*(0.76)*

**18.2b**  If the first two parts were acceptable, what is the probability of a correctly adjusted machine?

*(0.99)*

**18.3**  A shipment of parts contains 20 items, 8 of which are defective. Two of the items are randomly selected from the shipment and inspected.

**18.3a**  What is the probability that the first one selected is good?

**18.3b**  What is the probability that both are good?

**18.3c**  What is the probability that one is good and one is bad?

**18.4**  A data processing firm mails 1000 bimonthly newsletters to present or potential clients. In one issue the firm announced a new service and asked that interested parties write for more information. The firm believed that one of every two replies would come from one of its present customers. From past experience, it is estimated that the probability of a reply from noncustomers is 0.40. On the assumption that the mailing list includes the names of 300 present customers, how many replies can be expected?

*(560 replies)*

**18.5**  New types of concrete mixes are tested in a laboratory by batching four test cylinders. The probability that a trial batch will yield the specified strength is 0.90 if the mix is properly prepared and tested. Occasionally, about once every 20 times, the trial batch will be improperly handled or the ingredients inaccurately measured. The probability that a poorly prepared mix will yield the specified strength is 0.20. If only one cylinder in a trial batch of four meets the specified strength, what is the probability that the mix was correctly prepared?

*(0.145)*

**18.6** An Alberta oil operator owns a $5-million oil rig. It costs $75,000 to pull the drills to safety and batten down the rig in anticipation of a bad storm. An uninsured average loss of $400,000 results from a bad storm when no precautionary measures are taken. A weather forecasting service provides an assessment of the probability of a severe storm. Four out of five times that a severe storm is predicted with a probability of 1.0, it does occur. Only 1 severe storm in 100 arrives unpredicted. Should the rig owner pull the drills when the forecasting service predicts a storm at 1.0?

**18.7** A manufacturer has three inspection plans: *A*, *B*, and *C*. The chance that a faulty unit will pass undetected is 2 percent in plan *A*, 5 percent in plan *B*, and 10 percent in plan *C*. The respective inspection costs per unit are $0.35, $0.10, and $0.01. A defective unit going undetected causes opportunity costs of $3.00. The manufacturing process averages 12 percent defectives.

    **18.7a** Which inspection plan should be used?

    **18.7b** Compare the plan selected in Problem 18.7a with a policy of no inspection.

**18.8** Ninety percent of the fruit received at a cannery comes from local growers. The fruit from local sources averages 80 percent grade 1 and 20 percent grade 2. The fruit obtained from other sources averages 40 percent grade 1 and 60 percent grade 2. The markings on a shipment of bins full of fruit were lost. One bin was sampled, and from five pieces of fruit inspected, four were of grade 1. What is the probability that the bin came from a local grower? *(0.98)*

**18.9** How much could be paid for perfect information for the investment decision described in Problem 17.9? *($240,000)*

**18.10** For the decision situation depicted in Figure 18.15, where capital is valued at 8 percent:

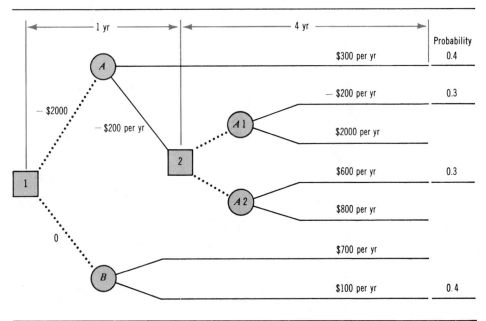

**FIGURE 18.15**

**18.10a**  What is the expected profit at decision point 2?    [*EV(A1)* = *$4438*]
**18.10b**  Which alternative should be selected at decision point 1, and what is its
expected value?    [*EV(B)* = *$1835*]
**18.10c**  How much could be paid for perfect information?    (*$0*)

**18.11**  Plans are being developed for the construction of a new school. The engineer now
feels that the probability of growth (*G*) in the school area is 0.6 as opposed to a stable (*S*)
census probability of 0.4. Two alternative designs are being considered. One is to build a
medium-size school (*M*) with provisions for adding (*A*) onto it if needed, and the other is to
construct a large (*L*) facility with the possibility of leasing part of the space to city and county
departments if the classroom space is not required.

The study period for the school question is 15 years. It is believed that after 5 years the
growth pattern will be evident. If the population is stable for 5 years, there is still a 50
percent chance it will remain stable for the rest of the 15-year period; there is no chance
the population will decrease. Given growth during the first 5 years, the probability of
continued growth is 0.8, with a corresponding probability of 0.2 for a stable census during
the next 10 years.

Additional data are as follows:

*Estimated construction costs*

| | |
|---|---|
| Medium-size school to accommodate stable census | $5,000,000 |
| Addition to medium-size school to accommodate growth | $4,000,000 |
| Large-size school to accommodate a growing census | $7,500,000 |
| Remodeling of large school to provide rental space if all the classrooms are not needed | $500,000 |

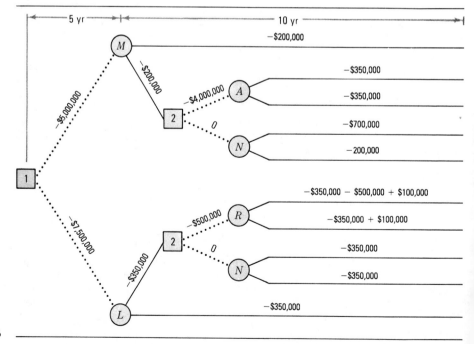

**FIGURE 18.16**

*Annual costs and income*

| | |
|---|---|
| Maintenance: Medium-size school | $200,000/year |
| Large or enlarged school | $350,000/year |
| Revenue expected from rental space in a large school if all the capacity is not needed for classrooms | $100,000/year |
| Busing and overcrowding costs if the school is not large enough to accommodate the population after the first 5 years | $500,000/year |

The outcomes for the various options are labeled on the partially completed discounted decision tree in Figure 18.16. Nodes are identified by the symbols above, and *N* means no change. The interest rate for the study is 7 percent.

**18.11a** Construct payoff tables for each decision point 2, and determine the preferred alternatives.

**18.11b** Develop a payoff table for decision point 1, and determine the preferred course of action for school construction.

**18.12** The editor of a publishing house is deciding whether or not to accept a book manuscript. She has already spent $1000 on the development of the manuscript and must now decide whether to

*A1* Reject the manuscript and forfeit the $1000

*A2* Accept the manuscript without obtaining an expert review

*A3* Obtain an expert review at a cost of $800

Data affecting the decision are given in the table below.

| Decision and Outcome if Published | *Editor-only Evaluation (10 cases)* | EVALUATION BY AN EXPERT (20 CASES) | | | *PW(net returns) per Manuscript if Published* |
|---|---|---|---|---|---|
| | | *Bad* | *Fair* | *Great* | |
| *M0* Do not publish | 4 | 9 | 0 | 0 | 0 |
| *M1* Low demand | 3 | 3 | 2 | 0 | −$10,000 |
| *M2* Good sales | 2 | 1 | 1 | 1 | $50,000 |
| *M3* Best seller | 1 | 0 | 2 | 1 | $200,000 |

There are three possible market outcomes if the book is published: M1, M2, and M3. Estimates for the present worth of revenues minus publishing costs are given for each market condition. Previous publishing decisions, made after reviewing, are indicated. The editor has accepted six out of the last ten manuscripts of a similar nature and has obtained one bestseller. The expert has rated 20 books as bad, fair, or great for a fee of $800 and has the indicated success.

**18.12a** Construct a decision tree that represents the editor's alternatives. Indicate outcomes and associated probabilities.

**18.12b** Calculate the value of sample information.

**18.13** A small foundry has had trouble with its old arc furnace. This furnace has been completely depreciated for accounting purposes, but it could currently be sold for $60,000. The immediate alternatives are to overhaul and modify the old machine or to buy a current model which has many desirable features that could not be incorporated in the modification of the old machine. The plans are complicated by the general opinion in the industry that a breakthrough could be made in furnace technology in the near future.

The best estimate the foundry owners can make is that there is a 40 percent chance that a radically improved furnace will be available in about 3 years. If it is developed, the probability that it will make present models noncompetitive is 0.90, and that it will be only a minor improvement is 0.10.

The cost of modifying the old machine is $80,000, and the cost of a new, current-model machine is $250,000. Expected savings and resale values are given in the accompanying table, based on the following three possible future states:

$S1$ = no technological breakthrough
$S2$ = furnace developed which provides significant savings
$S3$ = furnace developed which provides minor savings

| Possible Outcomes | BUY NEW | | MODIFY | |
| :---: | :---: | :---: | :---: | :---: |
| | Savings per Year | Resale at 8 Years | Savings per Year | Resale at 8 Years |
| $S1$ | $60,000 | $80,000 | $20,000 | $40,000 |
| $S2$ | 20,000 | 20,000 | 10,000 | 20,000 |
| $S3$ | 30,000 | 40,000 | 10,000 | 30,000 |

The table is based on a study period and life of 8 years for both furnaces. The sharp decreases in savings and salvage in states 2 and 3 occur because the development of a radically different or even improved furnace would probably cut into the foundry's demand and its general competitive position.

Another alternative exists for the foundry. If the new type of furnace is developed in 3 years, the modified furnace could be sold at that time for $90,000 and the new one purchased for an estimated $450,000. This new furnace would provide a saving of $130,000 per year with a probability of 0.90, and $80,000 per year with a probability of 0.10. It will be worth $200,000 or $150,000 after 5 years with respective probabilities of 0.90 and 0.10.

If a new machine is purchased now, it will be used for 8 years regardless of new developments.

Using a discounted decision tree, determine whether the old furnace should be modified or a new, current model should be purchased. Interest is 10 percent.

**18.14** A firm has produced a new product which was unusually successful, and in order to meet the unexpectedly high demand it will be necessary to add additional production facilities. The troubling question is whether the high demand will continue, increase, or decrease. Plan $A$ provides a permanent capacity increase and will be more profitable if the demand continues to increase. Plan $B$ is a stopgap measure which can be converted to permanent capacity by a supplementary investment $B'$ after 3 years, when the demand pattern is better known. For a steady or lower demand, plan $B$ is more profitable than plan $A$. The estimated future outcomes for an 8-year study period are as indicated in the table.

| First<br>3 Years | Last<br>5 Years | Proba-<br>bility |
|---|---|---|
| High | High | 0.40 |
| High | Low | 0.20 |
| Low | High | 0.30 |
| Low | Low | 0.10 |

Initial cost estimates are

| Plan *A* | $1,000,000 |
|---|---|
| Plan *B* | 700,000 |
| Plan *B'* | 450,000 |

*B'*, the supplementary investment in plan *B*, will take place after the demand is known for the first 3 years.

Annual income estimates are as follows:

Plan *A* with a high demand will yield a cash flow of $400,000 per year.

Plan *A* with a low demand will yield $50,000 per year.

Plan *B* with a high demand will yield $300,000 per year in the first 3 years and $200,000 annually in the last 5 years.

Plan *B* combined with *B'* will yield $400,000 per year with high demand.

Plan *B* combined with *B'* will yield $100,000 per year with low demand.

Plan *B* with a low demand will yield $300,000 per year.

With interest at an annual rate of 8 percent, determine which plan or combination of plans appears most attractive.

**18.15**  The owners of the novelty company described in the chapter disagree as to the solution of their storage problem. There is a minority feeling that more research should be given to the question. One member of the minority group is anxious to do such a study and estimates that it would cost about $5000 and take approximately 6 months to complete. The company could limp through this period with existing inventory facilities. Although the other owners have faith in the person who would make the study, they feel that she is overconservative. Because of this attitude they estimate (1) that if company activity in the next 6 months is very strong, the probability that the study will indicate a continuation of increasing growth will be 0.60, and (2) that if the next 6 months' activity is relatively constant, the chance of a forecast for increasing growth will be 0.10. On the basis of these estimates an engineer in the company is asked to calculate:

**18.15a**  The probability that the study will indicate increasing growth
$$[P(I_s) = 0.45]$$

**18.15b**  If the study indicates increasing growth, the probability of continued increase and the chance of leveling off      $$[P(I_a|I_s) = 0.933; P(C_a|I_s) = 0.067]$$

**18.15c**  If the study indicates no increase, the probability of increase and the chance of level activity      $$[P(I_a|C_s) = 0.509; P(C_a|C_s) = 0.491]$$

Carry out the engineer's assignment, and show the results in a decision-free format without costs. (*Hint:* You must use the original estimates disclosed in the chapter example in conjunction with those in the problem.)

**18.16** Engineering Service, a large consulting firm, is considering the acquisition of a computer to lower its project accounting and control costs. It can rent a large computer for $540,000 per year on a noncancellable but renewable 3-year lease. The other alternative is to buy a smaller computer at a cost of $600,000.

There is a probability of 0.70 for a high service demand in the next 3 years. If the demand is large the first 3 years, the probability that it will continue large is 0.60. Expected annual net savings during a period of high demand are $900,000 from a large computer and $510,000 from a smaller model. If demand is low, the large computer will permit a saving of $420,000 per year, and the smaller computer's net annual saving will be $330,000. The probability of a continuously low demand for the 6-year study period is 0.27.

After 3 years the lease on the large computer could be terminated and a smaller, used computer could be purchased for $360,000. Either purchased computer would have a negligible salvage value at the end of the 6-year period. Also, after 3 years the smaller computer could be sold for $360,000, and a large one could be leased for the remaining 3 years for $600,000 per year.

Assume that all receipts and disbursements are end-of-year payments and the acceptable interest rate is 8 percent before taxes. Using a decision tree, determine the most attractive alternative for Engineering Services.

# EXTENSION

*18A  Fault Trees*\*  Various "tree" forms have been developed to represent decision situations found in many disciplines. The shape naturally evolves because decisions typically stem from a central issue and branch out to encompass several contributing factors or alternative courses of action. A graphical display assists in the organization and evaluation of data. A *fault tree* is an example of such a structure for analyzing the reliability or other characteristics of a system. It has been applied to the design of spacecraft, quality control, and safety studies. It is illustrated in the following pages as a tool for accident analysis.

### STRUCTURE

A fault tree is a diagram of relationships or components within a system which collectively describe a specific operation or function. Construction of a tree may reveal the critical, though often hidden, faults of a system. As applied to a safety study, it traces an accident—a fault of a system—to its origins—faulty components within a subsystem. From a list of undesirable events, one is chosen for intense study. This becomes the *head event* for the fault tree.

From the head event, a top-down analysis is conducted by determining primary and secondary events that cause the head event. Factors that contribute to the head event are traced to the smallest subdivisions, called *basic events*. The cascade effect develops by progressively refining groups of causal events through *AND* and *OR*

---

\*Adapted from J. L. Riggs, *Production Systems: Planning, Analysis, and Control*, Wiley, New York, 1981.

relationships. Symbols are used to represent factors involved in the analysis, as follows:

1  *Rectangles* identify events that deserve further analysis.
2  *Solid circles* identify basic events that need no further development because sufficient information is known.
3  *Dashed circles* identify events that will not be developed further because of insufficient data or because they are relatively inconsequential.
4  A *half circle* identifies an AND gate that indicates two or more inputs to one output. In order for the output event to occur, *all* inputs must occur.
5  A *diamond* identifies an OR gate that indicates multiple possible inputs to one output. In order for the output event to occur, *at least one* of the input events must occur.

Additional symbols or explanatory notes can be used to show special conditions, such as a timing sequence for AND inputs.

An example of a fault-tree representation of one fault in a grinding and polishing operation is shown in Figure 18.17. The head event is eye injury from particles

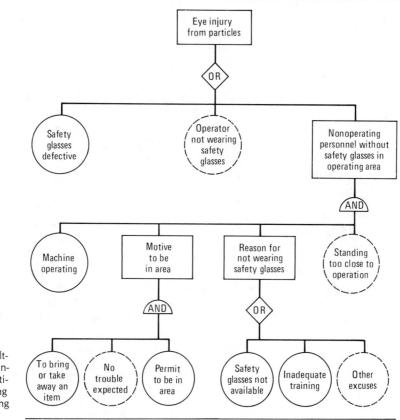

**FIGURE 18.17** Fault-tree analysis of eye injuries caused by particles thrown off during grinding and polishing operations.

thrown by machines. The first OR gate defines the ways the head event could occur. For the conditions shown it is assumed that safety records indicate most eye injuries occur to nonoperating personnel who fail to wear safety glasses; this fault then receives more intense study. Four conditions that must occur before an injury results are shown below the first AND gate. Two of these conditions are further defined by lower gates. Note that the AND gates indicate *what must happen,* whereas the OR gates show *what could be the cause.*

### ANALYSIS

Tracing an injury back to its constituent causes gives a safety analyst significant insight, but even more value is realized by determining the cost of the accident and the probabilities of contributing events. The fault-tree structure accommodates this quantitative evaluation. A cost is determined for the occurrence of the head event, and the probability of this occurrence is calculated from the events that lead to the head event. The cost of the head event is multiplied by its probability to provide a *criticality index.* The steps in the procedure are described below.

*1   Head-event cost (negative utility of an accident)*   The direct and indirect costs of an accident are included in a measure of the negative utility that results when a head event occurs. Units of measurement can be dollars, lost time, material wasted, or any dimension that indicates the magnitude of loss incurred. The loss should be stated in terms of an appropriate reference unit of production time, such as a million worker-hours. The reference unit is typically scaled to produce a head-event probability that falls between zero and 0.1.

*2   Head-event probabilities*   For some situations it is sufficient to directly measure the probability of the head event. For instance, the probability for the head event "break leg" on a particular ski trail at a resort could be measured by counting the number of broken legs and dividing it by the number of skiers who went down that trail over a period of time; if seven broken legs were recorded in a 2-week period when 19,420 skiers made the difficult run, the probability of a broken leg for that trail is

$$\frac{7 \text{ broken legs}}{19,420 \text{ ski runs}} = 0.00036 \quad \text{or} \quad 0.036 \text{ per } 100 \text{ runs}$$

A more revealing head-event probability is determined from the constituent events in the fault tree. By assigning probabilities to each cause and condition, and using these numbers to calculate the resulting head-event probability, a more complete study is assured. It is more difficult to collect all these probability factors, of course, but the effort is rewarded by more exact knowledge of the benefits that could result from safety improvements for specific causal events.

Once event probabilities have been assigned, computations proceed from the roots of the fault tree upward to the head event. The following Boolean relationships are utilized:

OR *relationship—any of the events cause the subsequent event to occur:*

Probability of subsequent event $= P_{OR} = 1 - \prod_{i=1}^{n} (1 - p_i)$

*where* $p_i$ = probability of $i$th causal event

$n$ = number of parallel events in OR relationship

AND *relationship—all the events must occur before the subsequent event occurs:*

Probability of subsequent event $= P_{AND} = \prod_{i=1}^{n} p_i$

where $n$ is the number of causal events in the AND series. Sample calculations are shown in Figure 18.18. Note that the probability of a subsequent event is always increased as more events are included in an OR relationship and is always decreased as more events are included in an AND series.

*3   Criticality index*   A measure of the significance of an event that incapacitates the system (human or machine) for normal operations is its *criticality index*—the head-event cost multiplied by its probability of occurrence. For instance, assume the accident represented by the head event in Figure 18.18 requires first-aid treatment 80 percent of the time and results in temporary disability in 15 percent of the cases and permanent partial disability on 5 percent of the occasions. Costs per incident (including indirect losses from production disruptions and administrative expenses) for the three classes of accident severity are, respectively, $352, $5014, and $24,480. Then the weighted cost for event A is $352(0.80) + $5014(0.15) + $24,480(0.05) = $2258. Further assuming that the probability of the head event is based on 100,000 worker-hours and that the total annual exposure of the work force to the hazard is 1.2 million hours, the criticality index (CI) has a value of

$$CI = \frac{\$2258}{100,000 \text{ worker-hours}} \frac{1,200,000 \text{ hours}}{\text{year}} P(\text{head event})$$

$$= \$27,096(0.1) = \$2710/\text{year}$$

*4   Evaluation of fault-correction alternatives*   When money is allocated to improve safety, one or more of the event probabilities in the fault tree should be reduced. Each of the events is a potential alternative for safety improvement. Reducing the probability of any basic event reduces the probability of the head event, which decreases its criticality index. The amount of reduction is a "saving." By comparing the *saving* with the investment required to produce it, a measure of preference is obtained for alternative safety improvements.

Given the accident structure in Figure 18.18 and the associated cost and exposure data, assume safety improvements have been identified that can reduce the probabilities of events $H$ and $F$ by 0.1. "Savings" resulting from either improvement are calculated in Table 18.3. It is apparent that an investment to reduce the probability of event $H$ causes a greater reduction in the criticality index than the improvement for event $F$. If the cost of capital is 12 percent and the study period for

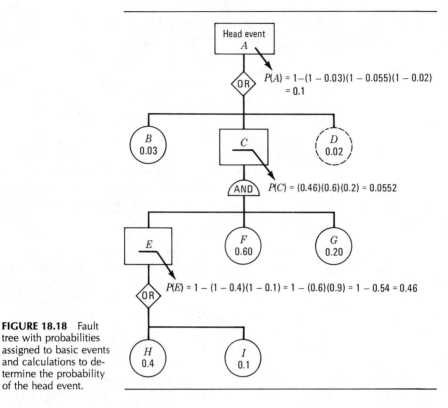

**FIGURE 18.18** Fault tree with probabilities assigned to basic events and calculations to determine the probability of the head event.

the safety proposal is 3 years, the maximum investment $P$ supportable from reduced accident costs due to improved conditions for event $H$ is

$$P = \$217(P/A, 12, 3) = \$217(2.4018) = \$521$$

Other factors that are difficult to quantify, such as improved morale resulting from a

**TABLE 18.3** Evaluation of safety improvements for events $H$ and $F$ in Figure 18.18. Effects of reducing the probabilities of events $H$ and $F$ by 0.1 are traced through events $E$ and $C$ to event $A$. The new criticality index of $A$ is compared to its former value to determine the "savings" provided by the investment.

| | | SAFETY IMPROVEMENT TO | |
|---|---|---|---|
| | *Calculation Procedure* | *Event H:* $P(H) = 0.4 - 0.1 = 0.3$ | *Event F:* $P(F) = 0.6 - 0.1 = 0.5$ |
| | Probability of event $E$ | $1 - (1 - 0.3)(1 - 0.1) =$ 0.37 | $1 - (1 - 0.4)(1 - 0.1) =$ 0.46 |
| | Probability of event $C$ | $0.37(0.6)(0.2) = 0.0444$ | $0.46(0.5)(0.2) = 0.046$ |
| | Probability of event $A$ | $1 - (1 - 0.03)$ $(1 - 0.0444)(1 - 0.02)$ $= 0.092$ | $1 - (1 - 0.03)$ $(1 - 0.046)(1 - 0.02)$ $= 0.093$ |
| | Criticality Index of $A$ | $\$27,096(0.092) = \$2493$ | $\$27,096(0.093) = \$2520$ |
| | Reduction in the criticality index from the proposed safety improvement | $\$2710 - \$2493 = \$217$ | $\$2710 - \$2520 = \$190$ |

safety-improvement expenditure, are likely to influence the investment decision. Intangible considerations of this nature are examined in the next chapter.

**QUESTIONS**

**18A.1** Construct a fault tree in which events $F$ and $G$ must occur prior to event $D$; $D$ *or* $E$ prior to $C$; and $B$ *and* $C$ prior to head event $A$. Probabilities for basic events $F$, $G$, $E$, and $B$ are, respectively, 0.4, 0.2, 0.05, and 0.1. These probabilities are based on 1 million operator-hours, and the 3-year production plan calls for 10 million operator-hours annually, during which the injury exposure will continue, unless safety improvements are made.

**18A.2** Although the injury rate is not unreasonably high, the severity of each injury is exceptionally great. Previous experience with event $A$ indicates that the average loss from each occurrence is $205,900, including both indirect and direct costs. How large an investment could be supported by the safety saving that results from reducing the probability of event $B$ from 0.1 to 0.05? Use a before-tax analysis with a required rate of return of 15 percent.                    *($29,614)*

# CHAPTER 19

## DECISION MATRICES

OVERVIEW

In all previous chapters we have assumed that the numbers needed for economic evaluation models were obtainable. In this chapter the assumption is relaxed. Conditions are examined in which decisions are made without complete data and where numbers are generated to account for intangible factors that affect decisions. In the first case, principles of choice are suggested for decisions under uncertainty—where outcomes are known for different future states, but the probabilities of occurrence for the states are unknown. In the second case, methods of assigning numbers to difficult-to-quantify factors are discussed, and a comparison model is presented that accommodates both tangible and intangible factors.

Several *principles of choice* have been developed to systematize choices made in a neutral decision environment. Once the outcomes of alternatives are arranged in a payoff matrix, attention to the best or worst outcomes leads to the *maximin* or *maximax* criterion. An intermediate outlook is defined by a coefficient of optimism in the *Hurwicz* criterion. Opportunity costs assigned to less favored alternatives guide decisions according to the *minimax-regret* criterion. The *equal-likelihood* criterion registers the belief that each state must have an equal chance to occur if there is insufficient reason to rate one more likely than another. Each criterion has certain unattractive properties, but they are still useful in directing attention to the attitudes and objectives of the decision makers.

Giving the proper weight to intangible factors is one of the toughest problems in making economic comparisons. Rating factors on an ordinal scale gives only the order of preference. An interval scale shows the relative positions of the factors rated. Three procedures designed to yield interval scaling are the Churchman-Ackoff method, standard gamble, and rating forms. Dimensionless numbers are developed in the *mixed-rating comparison* model by using fractions to convert ratio scale numbers to a 10-point scale. Importance factors are assigned to each criterion by which the alternatives are being evaluated. The sum of the 10-point scaled criteria ratings multiplied by their respective importance ratings gives a score for measuring alternatives.

# DECISION DIFFICULTIES

Discussions of decision processes usually start from the premise that the decision maker is *rational*. Beyond the flippant assertion that "You are rational if you agree with me," rationality implies a reasoned response to a problem. In economic decisions, reasoning involves delineation of alternatives, specification of outcomes, and adherence to selection criteria. Two major obstacles to rational decision making are confronted in this chapter. One is inclusion of difficult-to-measure outcomes in the decision process, and the other is adoption of an appropriate selection criterion when risk has to be considered but outcome probabilities are not available.

Both problems are major deterrents to consistent decision making because neither has a well-established solution. Several approaches are examined in this chapter. All of them attempt to compensate for insufficient data by providing a framework for reasoning through to a decision. The lack of probability figures for future states prevents the application of the expected-value criterion, necessitating another decision rule. Once data have been developed to represent intangibles (a significant achievement), it is then necessary to combine the generated outcome figures with economic data in dollar dimensions; consequently the preference among alternatives cannot be discerned from a single summary monetary value, so that a mixed-dimension decision model is required.

There should be no dismay that convenient, precise solution procedures are not available for all decision conditions. That is why decision making is a continuing challenge and why good decision makers are so valuable. The absence of established preference criteria is just a call for judgments that reflect the disposition of individual decision makers.

# COMPARISON OF DECISIONS UNDER CONDITIONS OF CERTAINTY, RISK, AND UNCERTAINTY

When outcomes are presumed to be known, a decision is said to be made under a condition of certainty. There is always some doubt, of course, that a given cash flow will materialize, but an assumption of certainty narrows consideration of the future to a single state and one set of data for that state. The data set may include numbers to represent intangible factors.

Decisions under risk and uncertainty are initially treated in the same way. Possible future states are identified, and outcomes are estimated for each alternative by assuming each state will indeed occur. The difference between risk and uncertainty depends on the capability of estimating the likelihood of future states. When state probabilities can legitimately be prescribed, it is a decision under risk, and the expected-value criterion is appropriate. When probabilities are unattainable, other criteria must be applied to select the preferred alternative. Similarities and differences among decisions under certainty, risk, and uncertainty are illustrated by their associated matrices in Figure 19.1.

|  |  | FUTURE STATES | | | STATE OF NATURE | |
|---|---|---|---|---|---|---|
|  | $P(1.0)$ | $P(0.7)$ | $P(0.3)$ | | $N1$ | $N2$ |
| $A$ | $O_i$ | $O_{ij}$ | $O_{ij}$ | $A$ | $O_{ij}$ | $O_{ij}$ |
| $B$ | $O_i$ | $O_{ij}$ | $O_{ij}$ | $B$ | $O_{ij}$ | $O_{ij}$ |

**FIGURE 19.1**
Decision matrices for conditions of certainty, risk, and uncertainty.

(A) *CERTAINTY.* SOLUTION: PREFERRED OUTCOME

(B) *RISK.* SOLUTION: HIGHEST EXPECTED VALUE

(C) *UNCERTAINTY.* SOLUTION: PREFERRED STRATEGY

## Payoff Matrix

As indicated in matrix (C) of Figure 19.1, no probabilities are available for states of nature $N1, N2, \ldots, Nn$ for the decision condition of *uncertainty*. Each state is assumed to be independent of other states and immune to manipulation by the decision maker; *the decision environment is neutral*. Because there are no probabilities associated with the states of nature—only payoffs for each option in each state—selection of an alternative depends on the evaluation strategy employed by the decision maker.

It is important to identify all the states pertinent to the decision situation. Omitting states of nature is equivalent to neglecting states of risk, but it is easier to detect an omission under risk, because the associated probabilities would sum to less than 1. Sometimes related states of nature are lumped together because their effect on alternatives is the same. The check for using composite states comes when estimating outcomes $O_{ij}$. If one payoff for each alternative accurately measures the effect of every condition implied by the composite state, the combination is valid.

## Dominance

After the payoff matrix has been developed, the next step is to check for dominance. The problem objective is to select the best-paying alternative. If one alternative produces a greater payoff than another alternative for *every* state of nature, then a rational decision maker would never select the lower-paying course of action. The higher-paying alternative is said to *dominate* the lower one.* In Figure 19.2, alternative $A$ dominates alternative $C$. Consequently, the dominated alternative $C$ may be dropped from the matrix. An early check for dominance avoids unnecessary calculations by reducing the size of the problem matrix.

---

*When *all* payoffs for one alternative are better than those of a second alternative, a condition called *strict dominance* exists. However, an alternative is still dominant when some of its payoffs are *equal to* and others are *greater than* the corresponding payoffs of another alternative.

STATE OF NATURE

|   | *N1* | *N2* | *N3* | *N4* |
|---|------|------|------|------|
| *A* | 10 | 1 | 3 | 6 |
| *B* | 6 | 2 | 5 | 3 |
| *C* | 7 | 0 | 2 | 4 |

**FIGURE 19.2**
Dominance relationship.

# CRITERIA FOR DECISIONS UNDER UNCERTAINTY

The most difficult aspect of noncompetitive problems under uncertainty is to decide what type of criteria to use for making a decision. In essence, we must determine the criteria for the criterion. The choice should be consistent with management philosophy. Is the current management outlook optimistic or pessimistic, conservative or adventurous? Certain criteria are compatible only with certain management views. Thus, it is necessary to understand both management policy and the principles of choice before selecting a decision criterion.

## Minimum-Maximum Criterion

A conservative approach to a decision is to look at the worst possible outcome for each alternative and select the course of action which assures the best results for the worst conditions. The underlying viewpoint is that nature is malicious. If things can go wrong, they will. This pessimistic philosophy dictates that attention be focused only on the most damaging outcomes in order to limit the damage as much as possible.

The words "minimax" and "maximin" are derived from the measures taken to identify the limiting loss or the guaranteed gain. A *minimax* decision minimizes the maximum loss. The *maximin* principle is associated with positive payoffs, where it maximizes the minimum gain or profit. For either criterion the smallest payoff (or greatest loss) for each alternative is noted. Then the alternative having the most favorable of the collected worst payoffs is selected.

## Maximax Criterion

A maximax philosophy is one of optimism and adventure. Nature is considered to be benevolent, so greatest gains are highlighted. The principle of choice is to identify the maximum gain possible for each alternative and then choose the course of action with the greatest maximum gain.

## Hurwicz Criterion

A moderate outlook between the extremes of optimism and pessimism is allowed by the Hurwicz criterion. The degree of optimism is established by a coefficient called alpha ($\alpha$), which may take any value between 0 and 1.0, with the following interpretation:

| Coefficient of optimism ($\alpha$): | 0.0 | | 1.0 |
|---|---|---|---|
| Decision maker's philosophy: | Pessimistic | $\longrightarrow$ | Optimistic |

After deciding the value of $\alpha$ which measures the decision maker's degree of optimism, maximum and minimum gains are identified for each alternative. Then the maximum payoffs are multiplied by $\alpha$, and the minimum payoffs by $1 - \alpha$. The two products for each alternative are added, and the alternative with the largest sum is chosen.

The minimax-maximin and maximax criteria are special cases of the Hurwicz criterion. When $\alpha = 1$ only the maximum payoffs are included in the final alternative selection, because the minimum payoffs have been eliminated by zero multiplication. The opposite is true for $\alpha = 0$, a completely pessimistic outlook. Any value of $\alpha$ other than 1 or 0 is a compromise opinion about the hostility or benevolence of nature.

### Example 19.1   Different Degrees of Optimism

Two sons and their mother own and operate an import shop in a medium-sized city. They have been successful enough to be in a position to expand their operations. Three courses of action are deemed most desirable: (1) expand their present operations by opening a store in a nearby city; (2) start a catalogue business from their present location; or (3) invest their extra money in real estate and rentals. Each alternative will utilize about the same amount of capital and will require equivalent management. They recognize that the returns from each of these investments depend on the national economy (inflation versus recession) and on the local economy (growth versus stagnation). However, they have no consensus of the probabilities of future conditions.

Outcomes for each of the alternatives have been developed for four possible levels of business activity: very high (VH), high (H), medium (M), and low (L). The payoffs shown are the estimated percentage returns on invested capital for expanding (E), starting a catalogue service (C), and investing in property (P):

STATE OF NATURE

| | VH | H | M | L |
|---|---|---|---|---|
| E | 20 | 12 | 8 | 4 |
| C | 26 | 10 | 4 | −4 |
| P | 10 | 8 | 7 | 5 |

The youngest son is an optimist and a risktaker. The mother is conservative, and the other son is midway between his mother and brother. Which alternative would probably appeal to each member of the family?

## Solution 19.1

The younger son, being an optimist, would use the maximax criterion. By doing so he would limit his selection area to the *VH* level of business activity, where the largest gains occur. From the possible gains of 20, 26, and 10 percent, he would naturally select the highest, which results from opening a catalogue store.

The conservative mother would lean toward the maximin criterion, where she could be assured a minimum gain of 5 percent (the maximum gain under the worst condition of low business activity) by choosing to invest in real estate and rentals.

The other son might use the Hurwicz criterion with a coefficient of optimism $\alpha$ of 0.5. The consequent calculations reveal that his choice would be to expand the import business to the nearby town.

| *Alternative* | *Max $O_i \times \alpha + min\ O_i(1 - \alpha)$ = total* | |
|---|---|---|
| E | $20 \times 0.5 + 4(1 - 0.5)$    = 12 | ←*Maximum* |
| C | $26 \times 0.5 + (-4)(1 - 0.5)$ = 11 | |
| P | $10 \times 0.5 + 5(1 - 0.5)$   = 7.5 | |

The relationship of the three philosophies can be better interpreted by plotting the maximum and minimum gains from each as a function of $\alpha$. As shown in Figure 19.3, the topmost lines indicate the alternative that would be selected for different levels of optimism. At $\alpha = 0$ the maximin criterion is in effect, and property appears to be the most attractive investment. Property continues to be favored until the less pessimistic attitude of $\alpha = 0.09$ is attained. The next switch point occurs at the intersection of the lines representing "expand" and "catalogue." Using the equation for the return expected from these two alternatives, the value of $\alpha$ at which a decision maker is indifferent to the choice between the two is calculated as

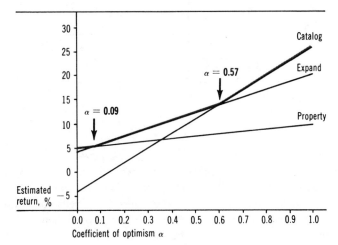

**FIGURE 19.3**
Sensitivity of alternatives to the decision maker's degree of optimism.

$$20\alpha + 4 \times (1 - \alpha) = 26\alpha + (-4)(1 - \alpha)$$
$$16\alpha + 4 = 30\alpha - 4$$
$$\alpha = 0.571$$

Mapping the alternatives gives an indication of their sensitivity with respect to the degree of optimism of the decision maker. The property alternative is quite sensitive because its selection requires a very pessimistic attitude. The remaining alternatives are relatively insensitive because each would be chosen over a considerable range of $\alpha$ values. The apparent range of attitudes which favor each alternative could aid the mother and sons in a search for a compromise solution.

## Minimax-Regret Criterion

Opportunity costs have been used in previous chapters to express the loss incurred by not selecting the best alternative. The minimax-regret criterion is based on similar costs. The opportunity costs are determined for each state of nature by subtracting the largest payoff in each column from all other payoffs in the column. The absolute value of each subtraction is the amount of "regret" that results from not selecting the best alternative for the occurrence of a given state. This procedure converts the original matrix to a regret matrix.

A rational decision maker attempts to minimize regret. By applying the minimax principle, the alternative with the minimum maximum (lowest value of the worst regret for each row) is selected. The minimax-regret procedure applied to the data from Example 19.1 is shown in Figure 19.4. The indicated preference is for the "expand" alternative. In general, the minimax-regret criterion tends toward a conservative viewpoint.

ORIGINAL PAYOFF MATRIX

|   | VH | H | M | L |
|---|---|---|---|---|
| E | 20 | 12 | 8 | 4 |
| C | 26 | 10 | 4 | −4 |
| P | 10 | 8 | 7 | 5 |

REGRET MATRIX

|   | VH | H | M | L | Worst Regret |
|---|---|---|---|---|---|
| E | 6 | 0 | 0 | 1 | 6 |
| C | 0 | 2 | 4 | 9 | 9 |
| P | 16 | 4 | 1 | 0 | 16 |

FIGURE 19.4   Original and regret matrix.

## Equal-Likelihood Criterion

When it is possible to assign probabilities to future states, we use the expected-value criterion to select a preferred alternative. An extension of this approach is the basis of the *equal-likelihood* criterion. Under uncertainty we admit that we cannot reasonably estimate outcome probabilities. Therefore, since we have no excuse to believe otherwise, why not treat each outcome as the same? The rationale behind this theory is that there is insufficient reason to believe one state of nature more probable than another, so each should be assigned an equal probability of occurrence.

The equal-likelihood criterion is certainly the simplest to apply. Under the assumption that each future is equally likely to occur, the expected value of an alternative becomes its average outcome. The alternative with the largest average payoff is preferred. As applied to the data from Example 19.1, we have

$$E(E) = 20 \times 1/4 + 12 \times 1/4 + 8 \times 1/4 + 4 \times 1/4 = 11$$

$$E(C) = 26 \times 1/4 + 10 \times 1/4 + 4 \times 1/4 - 4 \times 1/4 = 9$$

$$E(P) = 10 \times 1/4 + 8 \times 1/4 + 7 \times 1/4 + 5 \times 1/4 = 7.5$$

which again lead to the decision to expand.

# EVALUATION OF DECISION CRITERIA

Several different criteria for making noncompetitive decisions under uncertainty have been offered because no one criterion is unanimously preferred. Each one has certain weaknesses. Often one criterion is more intuitively appealing than the others. This appeal seems to vary among individuals and to vary with time or circumstances. As there is no universal preference, a sound recourse is to investigate the criteria limitations in order to select the principle which accommodates a given decision environment.

## Partial-Optimist Principle

The key factor in applying the Hurwicz criterion is the choice of a value for $\alpha$. An arbitrary choice defeats the intent of portraying an individual outlook. A deliberate choice is a forced judgment often based on slim evidence. However, the judgment does allow a measure of added knowledge, even though it is undefined, to be included in the decision. This additional knowledge could be described as "a feel for the problem" or an "educated guess." Until methods are developed to determine $\alpha$ objectively, its value will remain uniquely individual.

Pure optimism and pessimism are special cases of the Hurwicz criterion. Since these are extreme outlooks, they often leave a decision maker uncomfortable in applying them to special situations. For instance, the maximin criterion applied to

|   | *N1* | *N2* | *Minimum* |
|---|------|------|-----------|
| *A* | $0.01 | $0.01 | $0.01 ←Maximin |
| *B* | 0 | $100 | 0 |

would indicate that alternative $A$ should be selected, yet most people would be inclined to choose $B$. In the same vein, the maximax criterion applied to the next matrix would lead to the choice of $B$; most decision makers would express a decided preference for alternative $A$.

|   | N1 | N2 | Maximum |
|---|-----|-----|---------|
| A | $99 | $99 | $99 |
| B | 0 | $100 | $100 ←Maximax |

By selecting a value for α rather than 1 or 0, a more moderate outlook is achieved. However, the criterion still possesses some dissatisfying aspects. According to the criterion, the two alternatives in the following matrix are considered equivalent, because attention is given only to the best and worst outcomes:

|   | N1 | N2 | N3 | N4 | N5 | N6 |
|---|------|------|------|------|------|------|
| A | $100 | $100 | $100 | $100 | $100 | 0 |
| B | 0 | 0 | 0 | 0 | 0 | $100 |

Many people faced with this choice would cast a strong vote in favor of A over B.

There is also another difficulty. Some critics object to a decision criterion that changes preferences when a constant is added to all the outcomes in one column. Such a criterion is said to lack the property of "column linearity." To illustrate, the maximin criterion would indicate a preference for alternative B when applied to Figure 19.5(a). The outcomes in both matrices are the same, with the exception of 100 added to both alternatives under N1 in Figure 19.5(b). Such an exception could be caused by a discovery that a bonus payoff would result from the occurrence of state N1 regardless of which alternative were selected. The disturbing feature is that although the bonus has the same effect on both alternatives, it changes the preference from B to A.

|   | N1 | N2 |
|---|-----|-----|
| A | 0 | 100 |
| B | 50 | 50 |

(a)

|   | N1 | N2 |
|---|-----|-----|
| A | 100 | 100 |
| B | 150 | 50 |

(b)

**FIGURE 19.5** Column linearity.

## Opportunity-Loss Principle

The minimax-regret criterion is plagued by many of the same defects as the Hurwicz criterion. Attention is focused on only the largest opportunity costs, with a resultant disregard for other payoffs.

A further argument against the minimax-regret criterion is that the addition of irrelevant information to the matrix can switch the alternative preferences. From the payoff matrix

|     | *N1* | *N2* | *N3* |
| --- | --- | --- | --- |
| *A* | 100 | 125 | 25 |
| *B* | 25 | 125 | 75 |

the resulting regret matrix is

|     | *N1* | *N2* | *N3* | *Worst Regret* |
| --- | --- | --- | --- | --- |
| *A* | 0 | 0 | 50 | 50 ←Minimax |
| *B* | 75 | 0 | 0 | 75 |

which leads to the choice of alternative *A*. Now an additional, rather unattractive, course of action is included in the matrix as

|     | *N1* | *N2* | *N3* |
| --- | --- | --- | --- |
| *A* | 100 | 125 | 25 |
| *B* | 25 | 125 | 75 |
| *C* | 25 | 25 | 125 |

The addition, alternative *C*, changes the regret matrix to

|     | *N1* | *N2* | *N3* | *Worst Regret* |
| --- | --- | --- | --- | --- |
| *A* | 0 | 0 | 100 | 100 |
| *B* | 75 | 0 | 50 | 75 ←Minimax |
| *C* | 75 | 100 | 0 | 100 |

which indicates that alternative *B* rather than *A* should be selected. Although the switch caused by irrelevant information may seem disturbing, it can also be argued that the additional alternative is not necessarily "irrelevant," because it can reveal more information about the states of nature, such as the change in the maximum possible payoff for *N3*.

## Average-Outcome Principle

Most of the doubts raised for the other criteria are not applicable to the equal-likelihood criterion. It has column linearity, and includes all the outcomes in an evaluation, and the addition of an unattractive alternative cannot switch an earlier preference. However, it also has one serious defect: The selection is very sensitive to the number of future states identified for a problem.

Consider the problem faced by a company that is bidding on a contract. They can build special low-operating-cost equipment which will be ready if they get the contract, or they can buy higher-operating-cost equipment after they know they have won the bidding. The payoffs, in thousands of dollars, are shown in the accompanying matrix.

|  | *No Contract* | *Win Contract* | *Average Outcome* |
|---|---|---|---|
| *Build* | −50 | 125 | 37.5 |
| *Buy* | 0 | 100 | 50.0 ←Maximum |

When the future states are limited to winning or losing the one contract, the equal-likelihood criterion shows a preference for buying the equipment. If other future states, such as the possibilities of winning two more similar contracts, are included, the same criterion indicates a preference for building the equipment.

|  | *No Contract* | *Win Contract 1* | *Win Contract 2* | *Win Contract 3* | *Average Outcome* |
|---|---|---|---|---|---|
| *Build* | −50 | 125 | 125 | 125 | 81.25 ←Maximum |
| *Buy* | 0 | 100 | 100 | 100 | 75.0 |

Beginning with an exhaustive list of futures will eliminate the chance of a preference change. If one state is subdivided into substates such that the sum of the probabilities for the substates is equal to the probability of the original state, the problem is also avoided. However, each of these methods presumes some knowledge of the future that contradicts the assumption of uncertainty upon which the criterion is based.

## Application of Principles

None of the criteria is perfect. None can take the place of an accurate forecast. They should be considered guidelines which will help in the interpretation and consideration of possible choices.

It should be noted that most of the reservations about the criteria were more intuitive than deductive. Perhaps the adoption of a certain criterion must also rely to some degree upon intuition, because such insight is often a function of knowledge not yet formalized into distinct views. Nevertheless, the decision maker must understand the characteristics of each principle to be able to select the one which corresponds most closely to the uncertainties of a situation.

# DIMENSIONS FOR DECISIONS

Numbers have been called the "language of engineering." Every engineering student is well aware of the emphasis given to mathematics and the sometimes bewildering variety of number manipulations used in solving engineering problems. What tends to be overlooked is the difficulty of acquiring those numbers. "Hard" data, ratio scale numbers for receipts and disbursements, can usually be obtained, although diligent digging may be necessary. "Soft" data, composed of subjective opinions, are normally easy to obtain, but their reliability is questionable. Both hard and soft data are involved in most comparisons.

Many factors that affect a decision have no natural measures. How can you measure the relative *attractiveness* of two designs—by the number of beauty points they possess? If so, how do you define a "beaut"? The evaluation of intangibles is important because the final decision could hinge on the value placed on a factor such as attractiveness.

No ideal method has yet been devised to quantify intangibles. The choice is to use imperfect methods or ignore the intangible aspects in quantitatively evaluating economic decisions. Where intangibles have little influence, neglect is reasonable. When there are important subjective factors involved, imperfect methods are better than nothing because they at least expose the opinions to formal scrutiny.

## Ordinal Scaling

A simple order scale ranks every item in a list in order of preference. It works fine when there are just two alternatives to be subjectively rated for a single criterion. Then it is merely a choice of judging which alternative is more satisfying. However, an order scale does not measure the degree of preference; it is only a listing in preferential order. If three alternatives, $X$, $Y$, and $Z$, are respectively ranked in order 1, 2, and 3, the ranker expresses preference for $X$ over $Y$ and $Y$ over $Z$. But there is no clue as to how much $X$ is preferred to $Y$ and $Z$, or why it is preferred.

After narrowing the purpose of ranking a single merit such as more useful than, more convenient than, or easier to understand than, all methods of ordinal ranking are about the same. Whether starting from a "most preferred" level and working down the list or starting from the bottom up, ranking is essentially by pairs.

Assume there are five alternatives to be ranked for the same criterion: $V, W, X, Y$, and $Z$. As shown in Figure 19.6, all possible pairings are listed on the "steps." There will always be one step fewer than the number of items to be compared. The sequence in which the items are listed is purely arbitrary. In the first step, $V$ is paired with $W, X, Y$, and $Z$. In the second step, $V$ is dropped, and the next item, $W$, is compared in turn to the remaining items. The procedure is continued until a single pair remains.

Ranking is accomplished by circling the preferred item in each comparison. In the first step, if $V$ is preferred to $W$ and $Z$, it is circled for these pairs. Meanwhile, $X$ and $Y$ are circled to show their rank above $V$. The formal ordering results from a tabulation of the number of times each item is preferred in the complete pairwise comparison. In the example, item $Y$ was circled four times to receive the top rank, and the never preferred item $Z$ is relegated to the last position.

**FIGURE 19.6** Step-by-step comparison of alternatives to develop an ordinal-scale ranking. Circles indicate the preference among pairs at each step. The tabulation shows that the ordinal scale for the five alternatives is $Y$ over $X$ over $V$ over $W$ over $Z$.

Step 4: $Y$ paired with $Z$

Step 3: $X$ paired with $Y$ and $Z$

Step 2: $W$ paired with $X$, $Y$, and $Z$

Step 1: $V$ paired with $W$, $X$, $Y$, and $Z$

| $\dfrac{Y}{Z}$ | | | |
| $\dfrac{X}{Y}$ | $\dfrac{X}{Z}$ | | |
| $\dfrac{W}{X}$ | $\dfrac{W}{Y}$ | $\dfrac{W}{Z}$ | |
| $\dfrac{V}{W}$ | $\dfrac{V}{X}$ | $\dfrac{V}{Y}$ | $\dfrac{V}{Z}$ |

| Alternative | Number of Circles | Rank |
|---|---|---|
| $V$ | 2 | 3 |
| $W$ | 1 | 4 |
| $X$ | 3 | 2 |
| $Y$ | 4 | 1 |
| $Z$ | 0 | 5 |

The tempting violation of ordinal scaling is to read into an ordering a certain mathematical spacing between entries. The simple order of $X > Z > W > Y$ (where $>$ is read "is preferred to") could represent a number set of $100 > 99 > 98 > 2$ or $41 > 10 > 3 > 2$. The lack of specific intervals rules out any arithmetic operations.

## Interval Scaling

An interval scale is the next improvement from an order scale. This type of scale provides a relative measure of preference in the same way a thermometer measures relative warmth. An interval scale is a big improvement over ranking, but it still cannot be used like a ratio scale of distance or weight. This limitation stems from the lack of a natural zero. A zero in a ratio scale has a universal meaning; a zero distance or a zero weight means the same thing to everyone. A zero temperature can convey different meanings according to the type of interval scaling employed: Fahrenheit or Celsius. But once this zero value is understood, both temperature scales use standardized units of measurements which allow certain arithmetic operations, such as averaging, to be performed with the scaled values. Three methods for developing an interval scale are described in the following sections.

## 1 CHURCHMAN-ACKOFF METHOD*

Churchman and Ackoff offer a procedure for quantifying intangibles in which the developed values are assumed to be additive. The rater is asked first to rank the items and then to assign numbers between 1.0 and 0.0 to alternative outcomes according to the approximate intensity of preference. Thus, a rating for outcomes from alternatives $W$, $X$, $Y$, and $Z$ might appear as

| $X$ | $Z$ | $W$ | $Y$ |
|---|---|---|---|
| 1.0 | 0.8 | 0.4 | 0.3 |

Now the sum of the values for $Z$, $W$, and $Y$ ($0.8 + 0.4 + 0.3 = 1.5$) is compared with the rating for $X$ (1.0). In order to show a distinct preference for $X$, its rating must exceed the

*Discussed in R. L. Ackoff and M. W. Sasieni, *Fundamentals of Operations Research*, Wiley, New York, 1968.

sum of all lower-ranked ratings ($X > Z + W + Y$).* If the ratings do not conform to the rule, they are changed as little as possible in making them conform. The new value assignment might be

| X | Z | W | Y |
|---|---|---|---|
| 1.0 | 0.6 | 0.2 | 0.1 |

where $1.0 > 0.6 + 0.2 + 0.1$. Next the value for $Z$ is compared to the sum of $W$ and $Y$. The values above confirm a preference for $Z$, since $0.6 > 0.2 + 0.1$. The sequence ends with a preference shown for $W$ over $Y$, with $0.2 > 0.1$.

There are many sets of numbers that conform to the procedure and show the same order of preference but different intervals:

| X | Z | W | Y |
|---|---|---|---|
| 1.00 | 0.97 | 0.02 | 0.01 |
| 1.00 | 0.34 | 0.32 | 0.01 |
| 1.00 | 0.04 | 0.02 | 0.01 |

The procedure by itself does not assure that a legitimate interval scale has been developed. It systematizes the judgment process, but accuracy is still a function of the rater's conscientiousness.

## 2  RATING FORMS

A standardized rating form which has written descriptions of each level of desirability is the most commonly used method for rating intangibles. The scales typically run from 0 to 10 with explanations of the attributes expected at each interval. Well-composed rating forms define, in easily understood language, the outcome that qualifies an alternative for each numbered rating.

Personnel ratings are often made on standardized appraisal forms. A satirical form is innocently offered in Figure 19.7. More serious versions are widely used. A rater is asked to assign a number or choose a proficiency level that describes the person being rated. The selection of a fitting description fixes a number to a particular criterion of performance. Resulting numbers are collectively taken as a representative measure of stature for the person being ranked.

Rating forms with similar characteristics have been developed to evaluate recurring decision situations. For example, government agencies engaged in research solicit bids from internal and outside investigators for conducting studies. A request for proposals (RFP) contains a statement of the technical requirements of the work and requests bidders to

*> is used here in its usual mathematical sense, to indicate a quantity relationship.

| Ranking | Phenomenal 4 | Marvelous 3 | Good 2 | Not so Good 1 | Pathetic 0 |
|---|---|---|---|---|---|
| Competitiveness | Slays giants | Holds his own against giants | Holds his own against equals | Runs from midgets | Gets caught by midgets |
| Personal appearance | Could be a professional model | Could model but wouldn't be paid much | Could model as the "before" | Goes unnoticed in a crowd | Panics a crowd if noticed |
| Leadership | Walks on water consistently | Walks on water in emergencies | Wades through water | Gets caught in hot water | Passes water in emergencies |
| Intelligence | Knows everything | Knows a lot | Knows enough | Knows nothing | Forgets what he never knew |
| Communication | Talks to big shots | Talks to little shots | Talks to himself | Argues with himself | Loses those arguments |

EMPLOYEE APPRAISAL GUIDE

**FIGURE 19.7** A spoof of an employee-ranking system that makes just enough sense to be frightening.

provide cost estimates, time schedules, and proof of competence. The replies are then evaluated by a board according to how well they meet the criteria of acceptance. A typical guideline for assigning numerical ratings for each criterion is given below.

| Score | | | | Description |
|---|---|---|---|---|
| 10 | 9 | | Very good | Has a high probability of exceeding all the requirements expressed in the RFP for the criterion |
| 8 | 7 | 6 | Normal | Will most likely meet the minimum requirements and scope of work established in the RFP |
| 5 | 4 | 3 | Below normal | May fail to meet the stated minimum requirements but is of such a nature that it has correction potential |
| 2 | 1 | | Unacceptable | Cannot be expected to meet the stated minimum requirements and is of such a nature that drastic revision is necessary for correction |

While using an appraisal form, it is important to keep referring to a mental standard that conforms to each level. In the RFP evaluation, the standards are defined in writing. In personnel rating forms the standards result from experiences with the performance of people who were previously rated in each category. Each rater likely has a different interpretation of what constitutes perfection, based on personal views and past exposures. It is not vital that all raters have the same absolute limits for their interval scale; it is vital that they are consistent in applying their own scale among alternatives. Some raters believe their consistency is improved by initially giving each criterion a rating of 10 and then subtracting points as the alternatives are compared.

A review of past ratings can improve future ratings. A numerical rating system is only as good as the rationale exercised in its use. A rater should be prepared to convince a questioner that the judgment was correct. Since intangible judgments are necessarily fragile, they deserve to be handled with care.

## Example 19.2   Standardized Scoring

Alternatives are often evaluated by a team of appraisers. Each person evaluates all alternatives using the same scaling technique, and the resulting scores for each alternative are summed to provide a ranking among alternatives. Unless all appraisers have about the same range of scores, bias is introduced. A single score for an alternative that is far outside the range used by the rest of the appraisers can bias the selection toward the alternative favored by one enthusiastic backer. A simple procedure for standardizing the scores reduces this type of biasing.

The procedure described below is used by several organizations to convert each appraiser's ratings to an average value of 500 with a standard deviation of 100. After the scores are standardized, they are averaged for a final evaluation.

To standardize the scores given by each evaluator, calculate:

$$\text{Mean} = \bar{x} = \frac{\Sigma x_i}{N}$$

$$\text{Standard deviation} = s = \sqrt{\frac{\Sigma(x_i - \bar{x})^2}{N - 1}}$$

*where* $x_i$ = rating for alternative $i$
$N$ = number of alternatives

$$\text{Standardized score} = 500 + 100\frac{x_i - \bar{x}}{s}$$

To illustrate the procedure, assume four people have rated six alternatives, *A* through *F*. The raw scores for the alternatives (sum of the criteria ratings multiplied by importance ratings) given by each appraiser are shown below.

|  | APPRAISER | | | |
| --- | --- | --- | --- | --- |
| *Alternative* | *1* | *2* | *3* | *4* |
| *A* | 490 | 680 | 610 | 730 |
| *B* | 515 | 625 | 530 | 610 |
| *C* | 480 | 640 | 560 | 760 |
| *D* | 505 | 670 | 500 | 685 |
| *E* | 460 | 700 | 590 | 750 |
| *F* | 800 | 600 | 480 | 660 |

The mean score for appraiser 1 is $(490 + 515 + 480 + 505 + 460 + 800)/6 = 542$. The sum of the squares of the differences between each score and the mean is $(490 -$

$542)^2 + (515 - 542)^2 + (480 - 542)^2 + (505 - 542)^2 + (460 - 542)^2 + (800 - 542)^2 = 81{,}934$. Then the standard deviation is

$$s = \sqrt{\frac{81{,}934}{6 - 1}} = 128$$

which makes the standardized score given alternative $A$ by appraiser 1 equal to

$$500 + 100\frac{490 - 542}{128} = 459$$

Standardized scores for the rest of appraiser 1's ratings are $B = 479$, $C = 452$, $D = 471$, $E = 436$, and $F = 702$.

## 3 STANDARD GAMBLE METHOD

Another procedure designed to yield an interval scale is called the *standard gamble method.* The top and bottom levels of the scale are mentally fixed by visualizing the perfect outcome of the criterion for a 1.0 rating, and the worst possible outcome for a 0.0 rating. Then the alternative being rated is compared to the extreme examples. The comparison is made like a lottery: The rater selects acceptable odds for a gamble between having a perfect outcome (1.0) against the worst outcome (0.0) *or* having the certain outcome of the alternative. The mental gymnastics required to conduct this mental lottery are difficult to master, but the scale boundaries for the best and worst outcomes make the ratings comparable for all alternatives.

To further describe the standard gamble method, assume graduate schools are being compared. One of the criteria is *prestige,* an attribute with no natural measurements. The first step is to select the most prestigious school imaginable, and give it a rating of 1.0. Next select a school with the least possible prestige for the 0.0 rated outcome. The best and worst limits do not have to be practical outcomes; that is, it might be impossible to attend the most prestigious institution but it still sets the upper limit. Then a theoretical lottery matches the preference for the top school (1.0) over the lowest (0.0) against surely attending the school being rated.

The lottery takes the form of a specific query aimed at each school being rated: "What probabilities of going to the 1.0 rated school instead of the 0.0 school would I accept to make the gamble equivalent to surely going to school $X$ ($X$ is the school being rated)." An answer of 0.4 indicates indifference between attending school $X$ and having 4 chances in 10 of attending the top school (which means there are 6 chances in 10 of attending the worst school). A rating of 0.5 shows no preference between school $X$ and a 50 percent chance of going to either the top or bottom school. The selected probabilities become the ratings for each alternative. As shown in Figure 19.8, Multiversity, with a rating of 0.9, is preferred over the other two alternatives by the intervals given by the lotteries.

Variations of the standard gamble method have been suggested where ratings range from 1 to 10 and graphic scales are used to assist in the assessment of the relative significance of

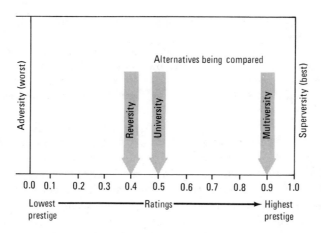

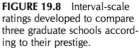

**FIGURE 19.8** Interval-scale ratings developed to compare three graduate schools according to their prestige.

outcomes. For instance, *importance ratings* are often sought for criteria upon which a decision is based. A vertical 1-to-10 scale may be drawn and descriptive phrases written at the top and bottom to define the most- and least-important conditions. Then ordered criteria are entered on the scale, starting with the criterion considered more important than the others (quite often it earns a 10 rating). As each criterion is physically entered on the scale, it is mentally compared to both the scale descriptions of importance and to the significance of other criteria already positioned on the scale. The end result is a ladder arrangement of importance, with irregular steps, that closely measures the relative stature of the decision criteria. The scale assigns a number to each criterion for use in decision models that recognize priority among influencing factors, as in the matrix described in the next section.

# MIXED-RATING COMPARISON MODEL

Just as there are several ways to make criterion ratings, there are different opinions concerning the best method for including the ratings in a comparison model. The model must be able to accommodate all dimensions for the various qualities considered; each alternative could be evaluated with respect to dollars of cost, weight in kg, length in m, efficiency in percentages, and attractiveness estimated on a subjective scale. In this section, we consider the popular additive model. Multiplicative and exponential models are also available, but the additive model with minor variations is apparently the most widely used.

The five steps listed below provide a procedure for combining different outcome dimensions into a single number that represents each alternative course of action.

1   Select independent criteria by which to compare all alternatives.
2   Rate the relative importance of the criteria.
3   Determine whether there is a cutoff score for any criterion that makes an alternative

unacceptable, regardless of the scores on the rest of the criteria. If so, state the cutoff ratings.

4   Assign values to the extent each alternative satisfies each criterion. An alternative is eliminated if any value falls below a criterion cutoff score.

5   For each alternative, multiply its criteria ratings by the respective importance factors, and add all the resulting products. The total scores thus obtained can be compared to determine the most attractive alternative.

Consider the comparison of three prototypes for a new bumper-jack design. Five independent criteria have been selected for evaluation: safety, cost, appearance, weight, and reliability. The relative importance of each criterion is determined as an interval scale rating. With 10 representing the utmost importance, the criteria have the ratings shown in Table 19.1. While rating the importance, a cutoff score may be recognized that makes an alternative unacceptable. For example, $20 is considered the top limit for a jack's cost, and any alternative that exceeds this cutoff level is eliminated regardless of how well it scores on the other criteria.

|  | Safety | Appearance | Cost | Weight, kg | Reliability |
|---|---|---|---|---|---|
| Jack 1 | 8 | 4 | $17.56 | 5.00 | 0.96 |
| Jack 2 | 7 | 9 | $ 9.95 | 3.13 | 0.81 |
| Jack 3 | 7 | 7 | $14.47 | 3.10 | 0.90 |
| Importance | 9 | 4 | 8 | 3 | 6 |
| Cutoff |  |  | <$20 |  |  |

**TABLE 19.1**   Criteria and comparison values for evaluating two bumper-jack designs.

Cost, weight, and reliability are ratio scale measurements. Lower cost and weight are preferred, while a higher reliability is desired. All criteria measurements are converted to dimensionless numbers by taking a ratio of each criterion value to the best value available among the alternatives for that criterion. The best value is assumed to have a 10 rating. Ratios used to convert the reliability figures to a 10-point scale are

| Jack 1 | Jack 2 | Jack 3 |
|---|---|---|
| $\frac{0.96}{0.96} 10 = 10$ | $\frac{0.81}{0.96} 10 = 8.4$ | $\frac{0.90}{0.96} 10 = 9.4$ |

since 0.96 is the highest reliability rating among the alternatives.

The converted cost scores are calculated as

| Jack 1 | Jack 2 | Jack 3 |
|---|---|---|
| $\frac{\$9.95}{\$17.56} 10 = 5.7$ | $\frac{\$9.95}{\$9.95} 10 = 10$ | $\frac{\$9.95}{\$14.47} 10 = 6.9$ |

since $9.95 is the lowest cost for any alternative. Note that none of the costs exceeded the $20 cutoff level which would have eliminated an alternative from further consideration. Safety and appearance need no conversion because they are already rated on an interval scale with a top score of 10.

The final step is to multiply the criteria ratings by their respective importance factors and add the resulting products for each alternative. The alternative with the highest total score is the winner. As shown in Table 19.2, jack 2, with a score of 258, is preferred over the other two prototypes.

| ALTERNATIVES | | JACK 1 | | | JACK 2 | | | JACK 3 | | |
|---|---|---|---|---|---|---|---|---|---|---|
| *Criteria* | *I* | *Observation* | *Rate* | *R × I* | *Observation* | *Rate* | *R × I* | *Observation* | *Rate* | *R × I* |
| Safety | 9 | | 8 | 72 | | 7 | 63 | | 7 | 63 |
| Appearance | 4 | | 4 | 16 | | 9 | 36 | | 7 | 28 |
| Cost (<$20) | 8 | $17.56 | 5.7 | 46 | $9.95 | 10 | 80 | $14.47 | 6.9 | 55 |
| Weight, kg | 3 | 5.00 | 6.2 | 19 | 3.13 | 9.7 | 29 | 3.10 | 10 | 30 |
| Reliability | 6 | 0.96 | 10 | 60 | 0.81 | 8.4 | 50 | 0.90 | 9.4 | 56 |
| *Totals* | | *Jack 1* | | 213 | *Jack 2* | | 258 | *Jack 3* | | 232 |

**TABLE 19.2**   Typical format by which alternatives are scored according to the sum of the products from dimensionless criterion ratings $R$ multiplied by their relative importance $I$.

**FIGURE 19.9**

# REVIEW EXERCISES AND DISCUSSIONS

**Exercise 1**   Given the payoff matrix below, which alternative would be selected under each of the described decision criteria? Assume that the coefficient of optimism is 0.375 ($\alpha = 3/8$) for the Hurwicz criterion.

|   | N1 | N2 | N3 | N4 |
|---|----|----|----|----|
| A | 2 | 2 | 2 | 2 |
| B | 1 | 5 | 1 | 0 |
| C | 1 | 4 | 1 | 1 |
| D | 1 | 3 | 1 | 4 |
| E | 3 | 4 | 3 | 0 |

**Solution 1**   The procedures followed for each criterion reduce the original matrix to a single column of outcomes from which the desired value is selected. The results and preferences indicated by applying all the criteria are as shown:

| Alternative | Maximin (pessimist) | Maximax (optimist) | Hurwicz ($\alpha = 3/8$) | Minimax Regret | Equal Likelihood |
|---|---|---|---|---|---|
| A | **2** | 2 | 2 | 3 | 2.0 |
| B | 0 | **5** | 15/8 | 4 | 1.75 |
| C | 1 | 4 | **17/8** | 3 | 1.75 |
| D | 1 | 4 | 17/8 | **2** | 2.25 |
| E | 0 | 4 | 12/8 | 4 | **2.5** |

It should not be too surprising that each criterion indicates a different preferred alternative. Each criterion has a slightly distinctive underlying principle. The key is to decide which criterion best fits the decision environment for each specific application.

**Exercise 2**   Try ranking your three favorite sports. Then stop and ask yourself why you ranked them as you did. For the sake of argument, say the ranking came out skiing, tennis, and jogging. You reason that skiing is more thrilling than tennis, tennis is more fun than jogging, but jogging is handier and cheaper than skiing. How do you get out of this circular reasoning, called *intransitivity*, where $X$ is preferred to $Y$ which is preferred to $Z$, and $Z$ is preferred to $X$?

**Solution 2**   The exit from circular reasoning is found in more precise objectives. The intangible values of sports could be ranked according to fun per minute of activity, thrills per outing, fellowship enjoyed, satisfaction obtained, etc. Each of these qualities could be the basis for a different ranking episode. They cannot be mixed effectively within one rank. Only one dimension is implicit in a ranking episode. Each quality deserves its own trial.

**Exercise 3**   Ipso Facto, a thriving, independent data-processing company is planning an image-improvement and business-expansion campaign. Three courses of action have been proposed:

**1** *Tell-Sell*   Develop a staff to increase personal contacts with old and proposed clients; offer short courses and educational programs on the benefits of modern data-processing methods.
**2** *Soft-Sell*   Hire a staff to put out a professional newsletter about data-processing activities; volunteer data-processing services for community and charity projects.
**3** *Jell-Sell*   Hire personnel to develop new service areas and offer customized service to potential customers; donate consulting time to charitable organizations.

Only one of the three alternatives can be implemented, owing to budgetary limitations.
The outcomes or returns for each alternative are rated according to desired characteristics, and the importance of each criterion is ranked as shown below, where effectiveness and importance are rated on a 0-to-10 scale; 10 is the top rating.

|  | *Annual Cost* | *Immediate Effectiveness* | *Long-Range Effectiveness* |
|---|---|---|---|
| Tell-Sell | $250,000 | 9 | 7 |
| Soft-Sell | 150,000 | 8 | 6 |
| Jell-Sell | 180,000 | 6 | 9 |
| *Importance* | 3 | 10 | 6 |

Using a mixed-rating, additive model, determine the overall rankings for the three alternatives.

**Solution 3**   Since the amount of data is small, it is more convenient to calculate the ratings from an equation than a matrix. The first expression in each of the following equations converts the annual cost to a dimensionless number; the least expensive alternative is, in effect, given the top rating of 10 by using it as the numerator in each of the cost-criterion ratios. The other criteria already have interval-scale ratings and are consequently multiplied directly by their importance ratings to give them the desired weighting.

$$\textit{Tell-Sell:}\quad \frac{\$150,000}{\$250,000}(10)(3) + (9)(10) + (7)(6) = 150$$

$$\textit{Soft-Sell:}\quad \frac{\$150,000}{\$150,000}(10)(3) + (8)(10) + (6)(6) = 146$$

$$\textit{Jell-Sell:}\quad \frac{\$150,000}{\$180,000}(10)(3) + (6)(10) + (9)(6) = 139$$

The narrow edge given to Tell-Sell over Soft-Sell suggests that the subjective values used in the comparison model be appraised carefully. For instance, increasing the importance rating for cost from 3 to 4, with all other figures unchanged, creates the same overall rating for the top two alternatives, 156. Such tests of sensitivity reveal how large a shift in a factor is required to alter the preference from one option to another.

# PROBLEMS

**19.1**   The profit expected from four alternative courses of action, $A, B, C,$ and $D,$ under four states of nature, are given in the matrix below.

|   | 1 | 2 | 3 | 4 |
|---|---|---|----|---|
| A | 7 | 9 | 5  | 2 |
| B | 8 | 1 | 10 | 4 |
| C | 6 | 6 | 6  | 6 |
| D | 5 | 7 | 9  | 8 |

**19.1a**   Which alternative would be selected by applying each of the following criteria: maximax, maximin, regret, and equal likelihood?

**19.1b**   Subtract 12 from each number in the matrix, and multiply the resulting difference by 3. Apply the criteria from Problem 19.1a to the modified payoffs. What do the results indicate?

**19.1c**   Suppose the states of nature are hair colors: brown, black, blonde, and red. A payoff will be made according to the color of hair of the next person that passes. You do not know which state applies to each hair color. Which alternative would you choose if the numbers in the matrix represented $1000 bills? If the numbers in the matrix represented $1 bills? Which criterion do the above choices resemble?

**19.1d**   Add 10 to each number in the first column of the original matrix. Apply the same criteria as in Problem 19.1a. What do the results indicate?

**19.2**   Apply the Hurwicz criterion to the matrix below, and show how different degrees of optimism will affect the selection of a preferred alternative:

|   | V  | W  | X   | Y  | Z  |
|---|----|----|-----|----|----|
| A | −8 | 6  | 2   | −5 | 4  |
| B | 4  | −2 | −3  | 3  | 2  |
| C | 0  | 1  | 2   | 1  | 0  |
| D | 6  | 11 | −10 | 4  | −7 |

If each payoff represented years added to or subtracted from your life expectancy, which alternative would you choose?

**19.3**   An enterprising young man read about a national Nature Club meeting to be held in a remote desert setting. He visualizes a great potential for the sale of ice-cream products during their meeting in the hot desert. He can carry up to 3000 ice-cream bars in a rented refrigeration truck. The bars will be sold for $1.50 each and cost only $0.15. Any bars he fails to sell will have no salvage value because of melting and refreezing. His only problem is that he does not know how many will attend the meeting or how many of those that do attend will buy his products. A rough guess is that 750 people will attend, and his expenses, exclusive of the cost of ice-cream bars, would be $375 to make the trip. What criterion would you suggest he use to help decide whether or not to go and how many bars to take? Why? What perference is indicated? Assume that his alternatives are increments of 500 bars.

**19.4**   The expected rates of return for investment in securities and investment in expanded plant facilities are estimated for two levels of future business activity:

|            | *Recession* | *Inflation* |
|------------|:-----------:|:-----------:|
| Securities | 5           | 7           |
| Expansion  | 1           | 15          |

The company is undecided as to the likelihood of each of the future conditions. It has been suggested that each future be considered equally likely. Then the probability of each future at which the two alternatives are equivalent can be calculated. These are "indifference probabilities." The decision rule would be to select the alternative which has the highest return for the future state that has the greatest difference between the equal-likelihood probability and the indifference probability. Apply this decision rule, and comment on the results.

**19.5**   Fancyfree Products has received a low-interest industrial loan to enable it to build a manufacturing plant in an economically depressed area. Effects of future economic and political conditions influence the site selection. As a preliminary study of the situation, ratings have been assigned as outcomes for operating the plant at each site under each of the more likely future conditions.

|        |     | POSSIBLE CONDITIONS | | |
|--------|:---:|:---:|:---:|:---:|
| *Site* | *1* | *2* | *3* | *4* |
| NW     | 0   | 2   | 8   | 20  |
| NE     | 4   | 14  | 12  | 10  |
| SW     | 16  | 6   | 6   | 8   |
| SE     | 4   | 4   | 18  | 6   |
| C      | 4   | 14  | 10  | 9   |

**19.5a**   Which site is dominated?                                                         *(C)*
**19.5b**   Which site is preferred according to the maximin principle?          *(SW)*
**19.5c**   Which site is preferred according to the maximax principle?          *(NW)*
**19.5d**   Which site gets a preference when the equal-likelihood principle is applied?          *(NE)*

**19.5e**  When $\alpha = 0.75$, which site has the highest rating by the partial-optimist principle?                                                                            *(SE)*

**19.5f**  Which site is preferred according to the regret principle?         *(NE or SW)*

**19.6**  Venture Capitalists, Inc. has $500,000 to invest in any one of the mutually exclusive projects shown below. Each of the projects has a life of 4 years, and the outcomes shown are annual returns in thousands of dollars of after-tax cash flow. Since each of the proposals depends upon public acceptance of an untested new product, there is considerable doubt about the state of each return. Apply the five principles of choice listed in Problem 19.5, and comment on the diversification of preference. (Let $\alpha = 0.6$.)

|         | POTENTIAL MARKET CONDITIONS | | | |
|---------|-----|-----|-----|-----|
| *Project* | *W* | *X* | *Y* | *Z* |
| *A* | 200 | 200 | 200 | 200 |
| *B* | 50 | 150 | 500 | 0 |
| *C* | 100 | 300 | 200 | 100 |
| *D* | 400 | 350 | 200 | 50 |
| *E* | 300 | 200 | 100 | 0 |

**19.7**  Based on the payoffs in the matrix

|     | *S1* | *S2* | *S3* |
|-----|------|------|------|
| *A1* | 20 | 10 | 0 |
| *A2* | 40 | 0 | -20 |
| *A3* | 5 | 25 | -5 |

determine the following:

**19.7a**  If $S1$, $S2$, and $S3$ have respective probabilities of occurrence of 0.3, 0.4, and 0.3, which alternative is preferred according to the expected-value criterion?*(A1 or A3)*

**19.7b**  What is the value of perfect information?                               *(12)*

**19.7c**  If the probabilities of $S$, $S2$, and $S3$ are unknown, at what values of $\alpha$ in the Hurwicz criterion would different alternatives be preferred?

*(A1, from $\alpha = 0$ to $\alpha = 0.5$; A3, from $\alpha = 0.5$ to $\alpha = 1$)*

**19.7d**  For unknown future states, determine the preferred alternative using a regret matrix.                                                                            *(A1)*

**19.8**  Based on the raw scores for six alternatives made by four appraisers in Example 19.2:

**19.8a**  Calculate the standardized scores for appraisers 2, 3, and 4 and sum the scores for the six alternatives to determine their ranking.         *(E > A > C > D > F > B)*

**19.8b**  Alternative $F$ would have had the top ranking based on raw scores, but it ranks fifth after the scores have been standardized. How do you account for this switch?

**19.9**  The most widely used mousetrap is the spring-operated type that uses impact to kill the mouse. This kind has been used for many years and is quite efficient. Both the spring and triggering systems are almost the ultimate in simplicity and economy. However, there are certain disadvantages to this type of trap. It is dangerous because it is not selective. It can kill kittens and puppies, and it can hurt babies or adults who happen to touch the sensitive bait trigger. It can make quite a mess if the mouse bleeds or is cut in half. Setting the trap and removing the dead victim is not to the liking of many sensitive people.

In an attempt to have the world beat a path to your door by inventing a better mousetrap, assume the three designs shown below are your best creations and you want to select one for a market trial.

**19.9a**  List the criteria for evaluating the designs.

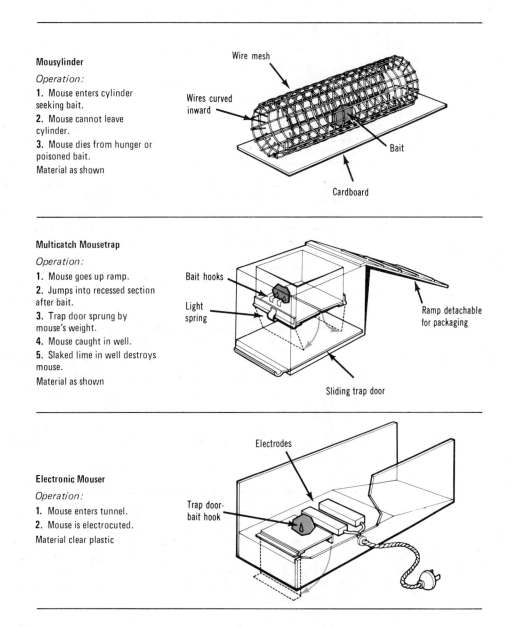

**Mousylinder**

*Operation:*

**1.** Mouse enters cylinder seeking bait.
**2.** Mouse cannot leave cylinder.
**3.** Mouse dies from hunger or poisoned bait.
Material as shown

**Multicatch Mousetrap**

*Operation:*

**1.** Mouse goes up ramp.
**2.** Jumps into recessed section after bait.
**3.** Trap door sprung by mouse's weight.
**4.** Mouse caught in well.
**5.** Slaked lime in well destroys mouse.
Material as shown

**Electronic Mouser**

*Operation:*

**1.** Mouse enters tunnel.
**2.** Mouse is electrocuted.
Material clear plastic

**19.9b** Weight the importance of the criteria, using either the Churchmann-Ackoff or standard gamble method.

**19.9c** Determine a rating for each outcome of the criteria.

**19.9d** Decide which design is the most promising. Comment on the results of your calculations (sensitivity, confidence, etc.).

**19.10** Three designs have been proposed for a new type of can opener. Careful studies have been conducted to evaluate the degree to which each design meets the desired criteria. The characteristics with familiar measurements were determined by design engineers. Opinions of many people were collected to obtain interval-scaled ratings for intangible characteristics. The results are shown below.

| Criteria | Design A | Design B | Design C |
|---|---|---|---|
| Cost (minimize) | $3.42 | $5.84 | $9.88 |
| Cleanability (minimize time) | 3.3 min | 1.8 min | 3.0 min |
| Reliability (maximize) | 0.78 | 0.91 | 0.99 |
| Size (minimize) | 1020 cm³ | 1020 cm³ | 3200 cm³ |
| Appearance (maximize) | 6 | 7 | 9 |
| Safety (maximize) | 7 | 9 | 9 |

**19.10a** Assuming all criteria are rated equally important, use the dimensionless comparison model to determine the preferred design.

**19.10b** Select importance ratings for the criteria using a scale of 1 to 10, and apply the additive, mixed-rating model to determine the preferred design. Compare the results from Problem 19.10a with calculations based on your importance ratings.

**19.11** Prospective sites for a new chemical plant have been narrowed to three locations. The criteria for each alternative and the importance of the criteria are shown below. Higher interval-scaled ratings show a preference. Which site is apparently more attractive? Comment on the sensitivity of the choice.

| Criteria | ALTERNATIVE Site 1 | Site 2 | Site 3 | Importance |
|---|---|---|---|---|
| Labor supply | 2 | 8 | 9 | 9 |
| Raw materials | 3 | 10 | 5 | 8 |
| Transportation | 8 | 7 | 9 | 7 |
| Cost of land | $200,000 | $700,000 | $400,000 | 5 |
| Building costs | $2,000,000 | $3,800,000 | $1,800,000 | 6 |
| Annual taxes and utility costs | $60,000 | $120,000 | $80,000 | 7 |
| Climate | 7 | 6 | 4 | 5 |

**19.12** Contestants in the "Miss All" competition are judged on beauty, personality, and talent. Beauty is considered twice as important as personality and four times as important as talent. Girls are rated on a simple order scale (1, 2, 3, . . . , $n$) with 1 being the highest rating. One girl has been judged first in beauty but tenth in talent. She knows the girl rated second in beauty is sixth in talent.

**19.12a** What is the minimum rating in personality the girl first in beauty needs to assure being selected as "Miss All"?

**19.12b** How could the beauty judging system be improved?

**19.13** After a recent visit by provincial inspectors, a company must install better ventilation and filtering equipment or replace existing machines with newer versions having built-in controls. Costs of two alternatives that will satisfy safety codes are listed below.

|  | Add Ventilation Equipment to Existing Plant | Install New, Improved Machines |
|---|---|---|
| First cost | $80,000 | $420,000 |
| Present value of old machines | $150,000 |  |
| Economic life, years remaining | 4 years | 9 years |
| Salvage value at end of life |  | $70,000 |
| Added maintenance cost/year | $7,000 |  |
| Total annual operating costs | $36,000 | $25,000 |

The company desires a rate of return of 9 percent on investments to improve operations and, owing to current cash-availability problems, seeks to minimize major capital allocations. Therefore, a temporary priority system has been established to rate the desirability of alternative investments based on need, immediate cash outlays (net first cost), and total present worth, with relative-importance ratings of 10, 10, and 5, respectively. Both alternatives have the same score for need, 10.

**19.13a** Under the assumption of a before-tax economic evaluation for a 9-year study period and using the mixed-rating comparison model, which alternative is preferred? *(Add equipment: rating = 244)*

**19.13b** Discuss the dangers of temporal suboptimization involved in the given importance ratings. What other method can you suggest to include consideration of the conservation of capital in economic evaluations?

**19.14** Sites for a new research lab have been narrowed to three localities. The construction cost of the plant will be approximately the same regardless of the location chosen. However, the costs of land and intangible factors largely applicable to personnel recruitment vary considerably from one location to another. Based on the following figures, which site should be selected? *(Site 1)*

| Characteristics | Site 1 | Site 2 | Site 3 | Importance |
|---|---|---|---|---|
| Availability of technicians | 7 | 10 | 2 | 10 |
| Adequacy of subcontractors | 5 | 9 | 5 | 8 |
| Proximity to a university | 10 km | 40 km | 30 km | 8 |
| Cost of land | $300,000 | $400,000 | $50,000 | 6 |
| Recreational potential | 7 | 2 | 10 | 4 |
| Climate | 6 | 1 | 9 | 2 |
| Transportation | 9 | 10 | 5 | 2 |

**19.15** An engineer and an accountant had two things in common. Both saw the potential for computers in production enterprises, and their favorite meal was a prime rib dinner. The outgrowth of these shared interests was a computer service named Prime Rib Inc. (PRI) that provided customized software for production costing and scheduling. They started the company 3 years ago and now employ 35 people. Business is good and promises to get even better.

At a dinner to commemorate their first 3 years together (serving prime rib, naturally), Ed, the engineer, and Al, the accountant, became engaged in a heated discussion about purchasing a company car. They seldom disagreed on directions PRI should take to serve customers, but delicate questions about perquisites caused them trouble. In this instance, the question was what type of vehicle the company should buy for their use. They both agreed a vehicle was needed. They disagreed on the type it should be.

*Ed:*  You're thinking too big, Al. We need a limo like a beggar needs a tux. All we require is a nice little economical pickup truck to run errands.

*Al:*  We gotta think big. We're on our way and should let other people know it. A flashy set of wheels will do it. Do you want to meet a customer at the airport in a pickup?

*Ed:*  Maybe that's all we can afford. I figure the price of a fancy sedan is three times that of a pickup. Upkeep and gas will at least be double. That's expensive prestige you want to buy.

*Al:*  It's all a matter of priorities, old buddy. We may have to stretch a bit to meet the sticker price, but we can surely afford the upkeep as we get more accounts. And that "fancy sedan," as you call it, will help us get those accounts. I say prestige should be our top priority in the decision, and my type of car would have at least five times the prestige of yours. You gotta' look successful to be successful.

*Ed:*  Okay. I can go along with your rating for prestige, reluctantly. On the same scale, I'd rate cost 8 and upkeep 5, if prestige is 10. I'd also rate utility right next to prestige. We need something versatile, not just a gas hog that impresses people.

*Al:*  I'll accept your numbers, and your argument for utility too, but I also think my big, impressive, luxurious chariot would be great to run errands in. It'll have a trunk big enough to carry our stuff in. I'd rate its utility umteen times a pickup's.

*Ed:*  No way! We're going in circles. Let's pretend its someone else's problem and solve it the Prime Rib way. I'll set up the decision matrix.

He then pulled out a pencil, grabbed a napkin, and started scribbling. Assuming Prime Rib Inc. uses a mixed-rating comparison model for decision analysis, complete the matrix Ed started. Using the figures given in the dialogue, analyze the situation, giving particular attention to the ratings for utility. Suggest how an interval scale could be set up (describe the 0 and 10 extremes) to determine a rating for utility. Discuss the sensitivity of the decision.

# EXTENSION

*19A*  *Value of a Human Life*  Perhaps the consummate challenge for quantification of intangibles is to assign a number for the value of a human life. Although the challenge may be spiritually repugnant, it exists because many economic decisions unavoidably hinge on the monetary worth placed on human lives: How much can be spent to reduce fatalities associated with a certain stretch of highway, a dangerous occupation, or a particular disease? How large should damages be for a defective design or an irresponsible act that causes a death?

Sir William Petty attempted to place a value on human life in the seventeenth century. His estimate was based on the total earnings of the population and the equivalent total earnings yielded by a capital sum invested at a given interest rate. He divided the capital sum by the total population to obtain a value of 80£ per individual. Since that time many investigators have addressed the question and proposed a variety of answers.*

According to Dr. Solomon Huebner, the valuation should be "the capitalization of the value of a human life for the benefit of the dependent household." He suggested the following considerations for determining a numerical value:

1  Individual working capacity should be capitalized in the same way as business property.
2  Life value is an economic asset that is subject to depreciation of its earning capacity in a manner similar to tangible assets.
3  Life has a societal trade-off value that encompasses old-age support, aid to dependents, income taxes, and many other give-and-take relationships.
4  Preservation of life embodies the same principles that apply to the preservation of property; e.g., health care is comparable to periodic maintenance of machines, since both are designed to avoid economic losses.

The premises proposed by Dr. Huebner have led to four general approaches to human-life valuation: (1) money value of a person as a wage earner, (2) life insurance as protection for dependents, (3) damage to society resulting from a preventable death, and (4) loss in capital value caused by a person's death. The first two view a person as a "money-making machine," and tabular procedures have been developed that account for the age of the machine with respect to its service life, earnings less consumption, related receivables and payables, and dependencies. The third perspective is often used in benefit-cost analyses and includes the cost to society of losing one of its members who pays taxes, supports dependents, and contributes to the social structure of a nation. The fourth view is sometimes called "human-resources accounting" and is associated with the value of a person to an organization in terms of ongoing activities and replacement cost.

Actual dollar values placed on human life by the valuation methods vary widely, as expected. Amounts are influenced by occupation, productivity record, national standard of living, family relationships, age, discount rate used, socioeconomic factors, and a host of other considerations. Consequently, monetary sums assignable to life values among individuals range from a few hundred to millions of dollars, depending on which factors are included, and the amount for one individual may vary by many thousands of dollars according to which valuation philosophy is followed.

In a major liability suit brought against an automobile manufacturer, the defendant sought to prove that the cost of providing special safety features (an additional expense to the public for transportation) would be greater than the cost of fatalities and injuries circumvented by the safety features. The value of a human life used in the case, as a set of losses assignable to specific factors in 1971 dollars, is shown in Table 19.3.

*See references at the end of Extension 19A.

| Factors | 1971 Costs |
|---|---|
| *Future productivity losses* | |
| Direct | $132,000 |
| Indirect | 41,300 |
| *Medical costs* | |
| Hospital | 700 |
| Other | 425 |
| Property damage | 1,500 |
| Insurance administration | 4,700 |
| Legal and court | 3,000 |
| Employer losses | 1,000 |
| Victim's pain and suffering | 10,000 |
| Funeral | 900 |
| Assets (lost consumption) | 5,000 |
| Miscellaneous accident cost | 200 |
| *Total* | $200,725 |

**TABLE 19.3**  Human-life value determined as the summation of fatality costs.

The value of a human life is also implied by previous actions taken to avoid fatalities. This surrogate approach makes no attempt to classify the individual factors that contribute to the total value. Instead, it relies on historical perspective to obtain surrogate measures that can be applied to current situations under similar circumstances. For example, assume that $100,000 has been spent previously in a given area to reduce the probability of a fatal accident from 0.001 to 0.0001. The consequent value implied for a life is

$$\frac{\$100,000}{0.001 - 0.0001} = \$111,111,111$$

Although this method is not too precise in that it recognizes no other contributory factors, it does provide a justifiable reference level from which to estimate or negotiate.

There is obviously no agreement about what value should be placed on a human life, and there probably never will be. Nevertheless, such values will continue to be generated and used in economic justifications because life and death considerations are integral to many economic decisions. Including even dabatable figures is preferable to ignoring the value of life. The figures at least mitigate the emotional overtones of the subject and encourage objective assessments. That is why the quantification of intangibles is essential to engineering economics.

Here are some references pertaining to the value of a human life:

Dublin, L. I., and A. J. Lotka, *The Money Value of a Man,* Ronald, New York, 1946.

Edwards, N. F., "Selecting the Discount Rate in Personal Injury and Wrongful Death Cases," *The Journal of Risk and Insurance,* June 1975.

Flamholtz, E. C., "A Model for Human Resource Valuation: A Stochastic Process with Service Rewards," *The Accounting Review,* April 1971.

Frantzreb, R. B., L. T. Landeau, and D. P. Lunberg, "The Valuation of Human Resources," *Business Horizons*, March 1974.

Huebner, S. S., *The Economics of Life Insurance*, Appleton, New York, 1927.

Jones-Lee, M. W., *The Value of Life; an Economic Analysis*, University of Chicago Press, Chicago, 1976.

Lave, L. B., and W. E. Weber, "A Benefit-Cost Analysis of Auto Safety Features," *Applied Economics*, vol. 2, 1970.

**19B  Utility Theory**  Utility theory provides a structure for personalizing the value of money in terms of risk—its utility to the decision maker. When investors struggle to avoid risk (or, conversely, relish gambling), the attractiveness of a risky investment to them is not adequately measured by the expected monetary value of possible returns. For these cases, a more rational decision should result from comparing the *expected utility*, rather than expected monetary value, of the alternatives. It is supposedly possible to construct a *utility function*, or reference contract, that specifies on a scale of 0.0 to 1.0 the relative worth that a given individual places on gains and losses over a given range. The resulting numbers from the utility scale replace the dollar value of outcomes in a payoff matrix. The alternative with the highest expected utility is preferred.

The idea of assigning a number to human feelings, such as pain and pleasure, has been around a long time. Blaise Pascal, the seventeenth century French mathematician, and Jeremy Bentham, the eighteenth century English philosopher, explored mathematical proofs for the value of being virtuous. Alfred Marshall* expounded the concept of *cardinal* utility in which psychic properties are believed to be measurable and quantifiable; thus a person is assumed to get $x$ units of satisfaction from a hedonistic activity, and each additional unit of that activity provides successively fewer units of satisfaction. A theory of *ordinal* utility[†] was later proposed that assumed consumers could rank the desirability of goods without measuring the exact utility of each good.

The most celebrated concept of utility theory is owed to John von Neurmann and Oskar Morgenstern.[‡] Their dealings with decision making under conditions of uncertainty led to a numerical method of evaluating the riskiness of outcomes.

A von Neumann-Morgenstern utility index is the certainty equivalent of a risky transaction. It is obtained by measuring the relative worth of monetary returns to the decision maker by varying the probabilities of getting those returns. Depending on the attitude toward risk, a utility rating is assigned to a certain-to-be-received sum that is considered equivalent to a gamble at given probabilities of a certain gain or loss. Under plausible conditions an individual is assumed to have a utility function with the following key properties:

---

*A. Marshall, *Principles of Economics*, Macmillan, London, 1920.
†J. R. Hicks, and R. G. D. Allen, "A Reconsideration of the Theory of Value," *Econometrica*, February, 1934.
‡J. von Neurmann and O. Morgenstern, *Theory of Games and Economic Behavior*, Princeton University Press, Princeton, N.J., 1947.

1   If outcome $A$ is preferred to outcome $B$, the utility of $A$ is greater than the utility of $B$, and the converse is true.
2   If an individual has a contract that carries a payoff of $A$ with a probability of $p$ and a payoff of $B$ with a probability of $1 - p$, the utility of the contract is the expected value of the utilities of the payoffs.

The first statement confirms that utility values move in the same direction as payoffs, rising and falling as outcomes become more or less favorable. The second statement allows the utility of a contract, $u(C)$, to be calculated from the utilities of the payoffs, $u(A)$ and $u(B)$, and their respective probabilities, $p$ and $1 - p$:

$$u(C) = u(A)p + u(B)(1 - p)$$

This relationship underlies the *standard-gamble method* of assigning numbers to intangibles, as discussed in Chapter 19. It is also the basis for *reference contracts* as an approach to the development of a utility scale, and *expected utility* as a measure of merit for evaluating proposals.

---

### Example 19B.1   Reaction to Risk

Suppose each of two university students was offered a proposition of putting up $100 for a double-or-nothing return on the throw of a single die. Each would win $100 if a 3, 4, 5, or 6 showed, or would lose the ante if a 1 or a 2 turned up. Assume that both students have the same gambling instincts, but one is working for school fees and the other is the recent recipient of a large inheritance. The alternatives for acceptance or rejection of the proposition are expressed in the payoff table:

|          | Win (2/3) | Lose (1/3) |
|----------|-----------|------------|
| Accept   | $100      | −$100      |
| Reject   | 0         | 0          |

The two students would undoubtedly consider the proposition with different feelings. The lucky student with ample resources would probably consider it a "good" bet. This student might question the reason behind the odds or the fairness of the die, but if the probabilities appeared true, would likely accept the proposition because of the adventure aspects and because the consequence of a $100 loss would not be disastrous. On the other hand, the working student would quite possibly reject the proposition because the loss of $100 would be a painful experience. The working student would appreciate the gain, but even with favorable odds, the potential reverse in fortunes would outweigh the opportunity of winning. This student might accept the proposition if the odds of winning were upped to 10 to 1, or if the original odds could be applied to a smaller sum, such as $10. The reaction to risk is a function of the degree of that risk relative to the importance of the gain or loss.

The concept of a reference contract is a means of taking into account the unique value that individual parties place on different alternatives. To develop this reference contract, we must determine the amount of money a party would demand or be willing to pay to be relieved of the obligation stated in a proposition. The fact that individuals are often inconsistent in stating their preferences for specified combinations of risk and the associated consequences necessitates a measure of caution in the analysis.

Returning to the two students described in Example 19B.1, consider their reactions to the opportunity of investing the money instead in campus services. The three alternatives are to invest in a food catering service $C$, or a tutoring service $T$, or to do nothing $N$. Figure 19B.1 shows the returns to be expected. The probability of success $S$ in the ventures is based on enrollment in the university and the general state of the economy. We assume the stated probabilities and the expected rewards are realistic. The outcomes are the profits from an investment of $100 over a year's period.

| | $S1$ (0.5) | $S2$ (0.3) | $S3$ (0.2) |
|---|---|---|---|
| $C$ | $80 | 0 | −$40 |
| $T$ | $100 | $40 | −$100 |
| $N$ | 0 | 0 | 0 |

**FIGURE 19B.1** Payoff table for three alternatives.

Let us look first at the preferences of the wealthy student, whom we shall call Mr. Loaded. He is, at the time of the proposition, inclined to be a risk taker. He feels that he will not be hurt by the consequences of a poor investment of this magnitude but will receive disproportionately high satisfaction from a success.

By asking him to relate the value he attaches to wins or losses associated with various probabilities, we hope to establish the cash equivalence of his preferences. We shall consider a range of values from a gain of $100 to a loss of $100, although we could use any scale. The starting question could be, "What amount of cash would you be willing to accept in lieu of a contract that assures you (probability of 1.0) a gain of $100?" Any sensible person would ask at least $100, even though hoping to receive more for it. Next we could ask what amount he would take in place of a contract that gave him an 80 percent chance of winning $100 and a 20 percent chance of losing $100. Since he is a risk taker, he would probably ask for at least $80. This means he places an $80 value on the opportunity to win $100 at a probability of 0.8 with the associated 20 percent chance of losing $100. We could say he is indifferent to the two alternatives. By continuing this procedure through a selected range of discrete probabilities, we would obtain his reference contract or *utility function* as depicted in Figure 19B.2.

The preferences for the working student, denoted as Ms. Broke in the table, could be determined by the same procedure. Because of her tight financial condition, we would expect her to try to avoid risk. Her cautious nature is evident in her response to the offer of an 80 percent chance of a $100 gain versus a 20 percent chance of a $100 loss. She would be willing to accept $40 in place of the alternative. That is, she is indifferent to a sure gain of $40 in place of winning $100 with a probability of 0.8 or losing $100 with a probability

|  |  | REFERENCE CONTRACT | |
|---|---|---|---|
| *P($100 loss)* | *P($100 gain)* | *Mr. Loaded* | *Ms. Broke* |
| 0.0 | 1.0 | $100 | $100 |
| 0.2 | 0.8 | 80 | 40 |
| 0.4 | 0.6 | 40 | 0 |
| 0.6 | 0.4 | 0 | −40 |
| 0.8 | 0.2 | −40 | −70 |
| 1.0 | 0.0 | −100 | −100 |

**FIGURE 19B.2**
Reference contracts for a risk taker and a risk avoider.

of 0.2. The table continues to reflect her reluctance to incur a large debt. She would pay $40 to be relieved of a proposition that gave her only a 40 percent chance of winning and a 60 percent chance of losing $100.

Now that we have a utility index for each of the two students, we can personalise the original contract to indicate individual preferences. In the first statement of the payoffs the expected values of the alternatives were

$$EV(C) = \$80 \times 0.5 + 0 \times 0.3 + (-\$40) \times 0.2 = \$32$$
$$EV(T) = \$100 \times 0.5 + \$40 \times 0.3 + (-\$100) \times 0.2 = \$42$$
$$EV(N) = 0 + 0 + 0 = \$0$$

An immediate assumption is that a reasonable person would always choose the tutoring investment. However, by expressing the outcome in terms of the utility of each investment as expressed in the reference contract, we can see how conclusions would vary according to individual preferences. This is done by substituting the equivalent probability, or utility rating, of each return for the monetary outcome. Thus, the dollar payoff table is translated to a utility payoff table.

Mr. Loaded, for instance, is indifferent to a sure reward of $80 and the probability of 0.8 of a $100 gain. Therefore we can substitute 0.8 for the $80 in his payoff table. This procedure is repeated for all the outcomes for each student and is shown in Figure 19B.3 along with the original payoff table.

Then the expectation for the utility EU of each alternative is

*Mr. Loaded*
$$EU(C) = 0.5 \times 0.8 + 0.3 \times 0.4 + 0.2 \times 0.2 = 0.56$$
$$EU(T) = 0.5 \times 1.0 + 0.3 \times 0.6 + 0.2 \times 0.0 = 0.68$$
$$EU(N) = 0.40$$

*Ms. Broke*
$$EU(C) = 0.5 \times 0.96 + 0.3 \times 0.6 + 0.2 \times 0.4 = 0.74$$
$$EU(T) = 0.5 \times 1.0 + 0.3 \times 0.8 + 0.2 \times 0.0 = 0.74$$
$$EU(N) = 0.60$$

If the goal is to maximize the expected utility, Mr. Loaded would reasonably select an investment in the tutoring service, but Ms. Broke would be highly uncertain. Both investments appear to be equal if we assume that Ms. Broke has been consistent in her

|   | S1 (0.5) | S2 (0.3) | S3 (0.2) |
|---|---|---|---|
| C | $80 | 0 | −$40 |
| T | $100 | $40 | −$100 |
| N | 0 | 0 | 0 |

(a) ORIGINAL PAYOFF

|   | S1 | S2 | S3 |
|---|---|---|---|
| C | 0.8 | 0.4 | 0.2 |
| T | 1.0 | 0.6 | 0.0 |
| N | 0.4 | 0.4 | 0.4 |

(b) MR. LOADED'S UTILITY PAYOFF

|   | S1 | S2 | S3 |
|---|---|---|---|
| C | 0.96 | 0.6 | 0.4 |
| T | 1.0 | 0.8 | 0.0 |
| N | 0.6 | 0.6 | 0.6 |

**FIGURE 19B. 3** (c) MS. BROKE'S UTILITY PAYOFF

stated preferences and that neither investment is too much larger than the utility she places on doing nothing. She should obviously investigate the investment potentials further and assess the value of any other influencing factors.

## Example 19B.2 Using Utility Functions to Assist Decision Making

A small company is faced with the prospect that one of its products will shortly be outmoded by new developments achieved by a competitor. It would be possible to launch a crash program to develop a new version of the product that would be equal to or better than the competition. However, there is a better than even chance that neither the company's own new version nor the competitor's will receive significantly greater acceptance than the current model. A suggested compromise between doing nothing and developing a new model is to retain the present model but increase the sales budget. From a market survey on the likelihood of acceptance of the new product and the plant engineers' estimates of anticipated developmental costs, the following payoff table was obtained:

| | NEW MODEL | | |
|---|---|---|---|
| *Alternative* | *Acceptance (0.4)* | *Rejection (0.6)* | *Expected Value* |
| Develop new model (A) | $300,000 | −$200,000 | $ 0 |
| Increase sales budget (B) | −50,000 | 100,000 | 40,000 |
| Retain present model (C) | −100,000 | 0 | −40,000 |

Regardless of the reaction to risk, it is apparent that alternative C can be eliminated, because B is a more attractive choice in both possible futures. If the new

| Utility | Dollars |
|---------|---------|
| 0.00 | −400,000 |
| 0.06 | −200,000 |
| 0.12 | −100,000 |
| 0.16 | −50,000 |
| 0.20 | 0 |
| 0.30 | 100,000 |
| 0.45 | 200,000 |
| 0.65 | 300,000 |
| 0.95 | 400,000 |

product fails, $B$ earns a reward of $100,000, compared with no gain for $C$; and if the new version succeeds, the expected loss from $B$ will be $50,000 less than that from $C$. We can say that $B$ *dominates* $C$. An alternative that is dominated by another can be eliminated from the decision process.

The next step is to consider the utility function of the company. It is a small but ambitious firm. It has made rapid growth, and its products are well diversified. A loss of $200,000 would certainly be serious, but other successful products could carry the company without too much hardship. The management feels that it needs a major accomplishment to build its reputation. A significant success would improve prestige and enlarge the horizons of the whole organization. The company has a proven engineering staff and is willing to gamble. The accompanying utility index describes its current attitude.

Judging just from the described attitude, we might guess that the company would decide to choose alternative $A$, even though the expected dollar value is zero. This is confirmed by converting the payoffs to utilities and calculating the expected value.

| | NEW MODEL | | |
|---|---|---|---|
| Alternative | P(A) (0.4) | P(R) (0.6) | Expected Value (utility) |
| A | 0.65 | 0.06 | 0.296 |
| B | 0.16 | 0.30 | 0.244 |
| C | 0.12 | 0.20 | 0.168 |

We can make additional insights about utility functions by plotting the utilities of the money values involved in the decision. The shape of the curve in Figure 19B.4 typifies a risk taker; it shows an increasing *marginal utility* for money. This means that as the rewards become higher, more value is placed on each additional dollar.

The alternatives can be shown by lines connecting the points on the utility curve which represent the outcomes. The dotted line to each chord shows the expected dollar value of each alternative. For $A$, the expected dollar value is zero and the expected utility is about 0.3. Alternative $C$ is shown in a similar manner and can be seen to have an expected loss of $40,000, with the corresponding utility rating of 0.17. The dollar expectation of $B$ is greatest, but its utility is exceeded by that for $A$.

If the utility function for the company had been linear over its entire range, it would have appeared as the straight dotted line in the figure. Such a function shows the utility in proportion to the monetary value. In this case the expected value calculated from the dollar-payoff table would directly indicate the utility of each alternative.

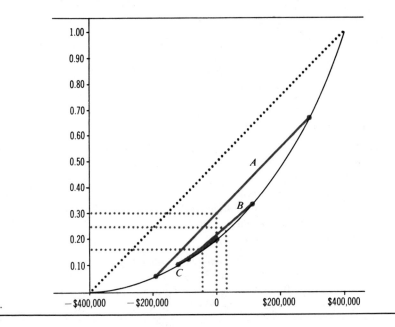

**Figure 19B.4**
Utility function.

It is easier to manipulate utilities that it is to obtain them. Determining an individual's utility index is often a tedious and time-consuming task, but it can be even more difficult to obtain one that represents an organization's policy. While asking the series of questions necessary to establish a utility scale, side issues arising from the wording of the questions may cause distractions that show up as inconsistent responses. Then there is always the possibility that different responses would have been obtained on another day because of a change in mood or the temporary outlook of the person being questioned.

It should also be apparent that a utility function for a particular set of alternatives is not necessarily valid for another set of alternatives. Many intangible considerations fringe the choice of any specific rating. A manager might indicate a utility function which clearly shows conservative attitudes toward industrial actions, but he or she might have an entirely different set of attitudes for gambling at a gaming table or in the stock market.*

Under some conditions it is expedient to employ methods that retain the concepts of utility functions without the requirement of actually enumerating the full range of utilities.

## PROBLEMS

**19B.1** An individual decides that his utility rating for a loss of $20 is 0.10, and for a gain of $100 is 0.60. In addition, he finds himself indifferent to the two alternatives in the payoff table below.

*R. O. Swalm, "Utility Theory—Insights into Risk Taking," *Harvard Business Review*, no. 6, 1966.

|     | P<br>(0.3) | P<br>(0.7) |
|-----|------------|------------|
| A1  | $50        | 50         |
| A2  | −20        | 100        |

What is his utility rating for $50?                                        *[U($50) = 0.45]*

| Utility | Dollars  |
|---------|----------|
| 0.00    | −400,000 |
| 0.40    | −200,000 |
| 0.58    | −100,000 |
| 0.65    | −50,000  |
| 0.71    | 0        |
| 0.82    | 100,000  |
| 0.90    | 200,000  |
| 0.95    | 300,000  |
| 0.98    | 400,000  |

**19B.2** The company described in Example 19B.2 has determined a new utility index since its decision to develop a refined version of its product.

**19B.2a** If this index had been applied to the decision to develop a refined product, what would the decision have been?                                        *(Option B)*

**19B.2b** What are some possibilities that could have influenced the altered utility index?

**19B.2c** At what probability would the expected utility of alternatives A and B be equal under the new utility scale?                                        *[P(acceptance) = 0.584]*

**19B.3** An investor is deciding whether to buy bonds or stocks. She estimates that the probabilities of inflation and recession are, respectively, 0.7 and 0.3. For her anticipated investment of $10,000, she believes her choice of stocks would gain 10 percent per year during a period of inflation and would lose 5 percent of their value in a recession. Her selection of bonds would show a gain of 4 percent regardless of inflation or recession.

**19B.3a** Which alternative would she choose if her utility scale were −$1000 = 0.0; −$500 = 0.2; $0 = 0.4; $400 = 0.6; $800 = 0.8; and $1000 = 1.0? The scale shows the dollar values equated to an equivalent utility, and intermediate values can be obtained by straight-line interpolation.                                        *(Stocks)*

**19B.3b** Which alternative would the investor choose if her utility scale were directly proportional to dollar values?                                        *(Stocks)*

**19B.3C** At what probability of recession would she be indifferent to the two alternatives?                                        *[P(recession) = 0.4]*

# SECTION FIVE

# FORECASTING To make all of the techniques and concepts of the first nineteen chapters operational, the engineering economist must make estimates and forecasts. Chapter 20 deals with anticipating needs and predicting cash flows.

# CHAPTER 20

## ESTIMATING AND FORECASTING

OVERVIEW

Economic decision models bereft of numbers are like empty cups; they have to be filled before they are useful. Ways to generate numbers to represent intangible considerations were examined in the last chapter. This chapter continues the quest for data by presenting estimating practices and forecasting methods.

All future cash flows are necessarily estimations. Some can be made with more confidence than others. Flows that originate from controllable conditions, such as savings yielded by a new machine, are much easier to estimate and are usually quite reliable. When flows depend on external factors that are largely beyond control of the decision maker, such as market acceptance of a new product, trend predictions of future influences are often necessary. A few of the more prominent forecasting methods are presented in the following pages to illustrate general concepts.

Most cash flow data can be secured from familiar sources: competitive bids, price quotes, accounting records, standard times and costs, cost indexes, etc. Two estimates to watch closely are first cost and overhead cost.

Forecasting methods are used to predict future business conditions and technical developments. *Subjective* methods, which rely on personal opinions, are comparatively inexpensive to obtain but may be biased. Historical data are the bases for *line-fitting* and *smoothing techniques* that extrapolate past trends to predict the future. The *least-squares method* fits a straight line to data to form a simple regression model. The choice of alpha in *exponential smoothing* and the number of periods used in a *moving average* determine how sensitive the forecasts are to recent data. *Causal models* attempt to predict future happenings from changes in the causes of events. A *leading indicator* is a statistic that behaves the same but precedes the behavior of the data sought. A *correlation* model examines the closeness of the relationship.

# DATA DIFFICULTIES

Economic analyses are built from data as a house is built of bricks, but an accumulation of data is no more an analysis than a pile of bricks is a house. There are piles of data everywhere. They fill the shelves of libraries and accumulate limitlessly from the unending parade of statistics and information issued by all kinds of agencies, public and private. Yet, when a particular fact is crucial to an analysis, it may be elusive or impossible to procure. Data difficulties range from an overabundance, when the problem is to digest information into a usable form, to a scarcity that may force guesses to substitute for facts.

Information is both the raw material and the finished product of an engineering economic evaluation. The evaluation process is similar to familiar production processes. Bits of data, the raw materials, are received from many sources and inspected for accuracy before being accepted. They are fed into the engineering economics "machinery," where they are translated and transformed into the desired product: an economic comparison. As in any product process, it is necessary to know what raw materials are needed, the best sources, and ways to determine whether they are adequate.

# ESTIMATING TECHNIQUES

A new project may be identical in design and mission to one just completed, but the cash flows for the two will probably differ considerably. This variation from one study to the next is characteristic of economic analyses. Unlike physical laws which consistently follow an orderly cause-and-effect relationship, economic laws depend on the behavior of people, and they are erratic. However, past behavior is still a respectable clue to future behavior.

Engineers are well prepared to judge the future performance of materials and machines. Past performance can be extrapolated, and modified if necessary, to predict performance on the next project. The monetary values for the future conditions are less reliably predicted. Strikes, shortages, competition, inflation, and other factors that affect unit costs cannot always be anticipated. Therefore, estimating starts with the calculation of design amounts based on known physical relationships and concludes with the assignment of comparatively less known monetary measures for the design conditions.

## Sources of Cost Data

Figure 20.1 shows the traditional cost and price structure for a manufactured product. Most of the categories are also appropriate for service functions. The principal variation occurs in the relative sizes of the cost categories; manufacturing usually has a higher material-to-

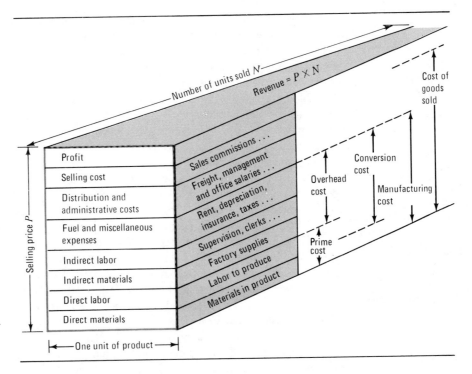

**FIGURE 20.1**
Composition of costs traditionally used in accounting for the price of a manufactured product.

labor ratio than service. Public services would be represented by the model by eliminating the top two tiers. Many of the components within the categories were discussed in Chapter 16.

The quantities and types of materials required can be determined quite accurately from past records and engineering design documents (e.g., the bill of materials and parts list that accompany blueprints). Current prices are also readily assessable. Difficulties creep in as the price quotes are pushed further into the future. Experts from the purchasing department in a large firm can assist with predictions through their experience with commodity futures and knowledge of the firm's policies toward speculating (buying in large quantities to take advantage of price fluctuations, or buying contracts for future deliveries at prices set now, called *hedging*). A vital part of any estimating process is to be aware of the organization's economic policies and practices.

When purchasing experts are not available, many types of *cost indexes* can furnish information. A cost index provides a comparison of cost or price changes from year to year for a fixed quantity of goods or services at particular locations. For building construction alone, there are indexes compiled for different parts of the country and different types of construction. Statistics Canada is the primary source of national data.

*Labor costs* are a function of skill level, labor supply, and time required. The saying that "time is money" is especially true in estimating the cost of work. Standards for the amount of output per labor hour have been developed for many classes of work. The standards are based on a "normal" pace for an activity, with allowances included for personal relief and unusually severe working conditions. Standard times combined with expected wage rates provide a reasonable estimate of labor costs for repetitive jobs. Labor costs for specialized work can be predicted from bid estimates or quotes by professionals and agencies offering the service. A project involving a new type of work will likely have higher labor costs at first, while experience is gained.

It should be remembered that the cost of labor includes more than direct wages. Fringe benefits may amount to more than half the base wage in accounting for accident, health, and unemployment insurance; vacation and retirement pay; and special agreements such as guaranteed annual wages or sabbatical leaves. Extra costs due to relocation allowances, accidents, and sickness should also be considered.

*Maintenance costs* are the ordinary costs required for the upkeep of property and the restoration required when assets are damaged but not replaced. Items under maintenance include the costs of inspecting and locating trouble areas, replacement of minor parts, power, labor, materials, and minor changes in or rearrangements of existing facilities for more efficient use. Maintenance costs tend to increase with the age of an asset because more upkeep is required later in life and the trend of wages and material prices is upward.

*Property taxes and insurance* are usually expressed as a percentage of first cost in economic comparisons. Although the value of property decreases with age, taxes and insurance seldom show a corresponding decrease. Therefore, a constant annual charge is a realistic appraisal of future expense.

The *first cost* of acquiring a major asset may rise well above expectation, especially if the asset originates from a new design or untried process. Cost "overruns" are legendary in government projects, and they haunt the private sector too. After a design is set, direct acquisition costs are readily determined from manufacturers' quotes or competitive bidding. When errors occur, they are typically on the low side, as a result of incomplete listings of desired features and neglecting less obvious costs such as the following:

Materials (freight, sales tax, storage costs, damage)

Installation (extra costs for special arrangements and unconventional designs)

Interest, taxes, salaries, and insurance during a design or construction phase

Change orders during construction (installation costs for additions to or deletions from the original plans)

Investigation, exploratory, and legal fees

Promotional costs

Engineering and associated fees

Debugging and start-up costs

Most construction projects include a "contingency cost" category to account for undefined costs that will assuredly crop up. Although such expenses are ticklish to tally, they can drain capital as thoroughly as design changes for physical assets.

Current levels of costs used in estimating investments may not be applicable to future conditions. Generally this is not a serious problem, but two situations bear watching. One is when an old alternative is resurrected for reconsideration. Old cost estimates may be outdated by new methods or different price levels. The other situation is when current levels reflect abnormal or temporary prices. If prices are adjusted for first costs, similar adjustments should be investigated for other costs.

First costs can immediately eliminate some alternatives. Insufficient capital is a genuine reason to turn down an investment proposal even though it has a handsome rate of return. An investment that would be wise for a firm with adequate capital could be a futile or even disastrous course of action for a firm with limited finances and big ambitions.

*Overhead cost* is by definition that portion of the cost which cannot be clearly associated with particular operations or products and must be prorated among all the cost units on some arbitrary basis. The reason for this catchall category is the prohibitive expense of assigning and charging to each product a specific proportion of such costs as wages of supervisors, factory heat and light, janitorial services, secretarial help, and incidental supplies.

Several methods are used to allocate the composite overhead expense to a product or operation. The versions differ among companies because of differences in the nature of production; it is not uncommon to find different overhead rates used within one firm. Overhead costs may be applied on the basis of

1   Direct labor, direct materials, or prime costs
2   Machine hours or direct labor time
3   Fixed and variable cost classifications (for instance, overhead such as indirect material and power costs would be treated as varying with output, whereas property taxes, depreciation, and indirect labor would be considered as fixed costs)

Once a base is selected, annual overhead as determined from accounting records is divided by the annual cost or usage time of the base category. The resulting ratio is multiplied by the base cost for the alternative being evaluated. For instance, if overhead is charged on the basis of direct labor,

$$\text{Direct labor ratio} = \frac{\text{total annual overhead cost}}{\text{total annual direct labor}}$$

and the overhead charge for one unit of product $X$ is

$$\frac{\text{Overhead charge}}{\text{Unit of product } X} = \text{direct labor ratio} \times \frac{\text{direct labor cost}}{\text{unit of product } X}$$

which is included as a cost in determining the selling price of product $X$. By the same reasoning, a machine used in the production of product $X$ could be assigned an overhead burden based on the operator's wages:

$$\frac{\text{Annual overhead charges}}{\text{Machine } A \text{ producing } X} = \text{direct labor ratio} \times \frac{\text{annual wages of operator}}{\text{machine } A \text{ producing } X}$$

An important condition to recognize in economic comparisons is that *overhead costs are associated with a certain level of output.* This can be a critical factor in a comparison such as the purchase of either a $200,000 numerically controlled milling machine or a standard $20,000 general-purpose milling machine. If the labor rate of operators of both machines is $9 per hour and the burden rate is based on a direct labor ratio of 300 percent, the machine-hour costs of both machines would be $27 per hour. This figure has to be an incorrect machine-hour costing because the investment in the numerically controlled machine is 10 times that in the standard model. Fortunately, overhead costs often have an identical effect on several alternatives. That is, the same value for overhead costs would apply for different alternatives being compared, making their inclusion redundant in the comparison.

## Sources of Income Data

In an industrial setting, revenue is the money received from customers for the services or products sold to them. There are many patterns of revenue flow. A retail store has an essentially continuous influx of revenue during working hours. Plumbers are often paid after each service call. Utility services are paid for by the month. Farmers usually get their money after a crop is harvested. A homebuilder has to wait until a house is sold before receiving revenue. The timing of the revenues associated with an alternative may have a significant bearing on its acceptability. One of the main reasons that new businesses often fail is the time lag between incurred first costs and the establishment of an expected level of revenue.

Revenue is somewhat harder to estimate than costs for many industrial projects. If a new investment is to serve the same purpose as an existing asset, historical data provide a reliable estimate of future revenue. When the investment is destined to satisfy a new function, revenue estimates are less certain. What looks like a sure bet on the drawing board may end as a miserable flop in the market, where it is exposed to the buying whims of the public.

Occasionally, a precise measure of revenue contribution is impossible. Sums spent on customer goodwill and improved employer-employee relationships are at best extremely difficult to measure in terms of revenue increments. This situation often results in the setting aside of a certain sum for "public relations" or investment in intangible returns. Then the sum is divided among projects rated according to a nonmonetary scale of attractiveness as described in Chapter 19.

Funds for government or public activities result from various types of taxes, charges for specific services, and borrowing. Everyone is familiar with income taxes and charges for services such as mail delivery. Both are revenue sources secured from the public for benefits expected from governing agencies. Because of their mandatory nature and long history, they can be estimated quite accurately. And as a supplement, when the perceived demand for public expenditures exceeds public revenue, governments at all levels tend to engage in deficit financing. The money so borrowed is a pledge that future members of society will pay for projects undertaken by the present society. (The economics of public projects was examined in Chapter 10.) Although the base for public revenues is broad and solid, the portion justified for a specific public project is difficult to determine.

Privately owned public utility companies occupy a position midway between government and industry. This position results from the great amount of invested capital required to provide public services such as electricity and telephone communications. Only by developing a high usage factor can an acceptable return on invested capital be obtained from low service rates. In order to assure both reasonable returns and reasonable rates, an exclusive geographical franchise is allotted to a utility company. Coupled with the grant of a monopolistic position are regulations controlling rates and standards of service. A regulatory body seeks to set a quality of service which satisfies the customers while permitting rates that allow the utility to earn an acceptable rate of return.

# FORECASTING

Estimating is more of a science than an art when conditions are stable; then standard costs and catalog prices are satisfactory data. But nothing is static for long. Changes in the economic environment may be as gradual as wind erosion in the desert or as sudden as a tornado. Economic estimators are particularly sensitive to a sudden shift, for it may mean the difference between fortune and fiasco. The prediction of a shift is a work of art.

The function of forecasting is to predict future events by the best means possible. The simplest form of forecasting is a mental voyage into the future to guess what might occur. Experienced estimators can do amazingly well, but "seat of the pants" forecasting promises a rude jolt to the inexperienced. More disciplined forecasting methods utilize statistical analysis and other formal procedures to draw conclusions about future events from past events. Regardless of the methods used (see Figure 20.2), the basic issues to predict for economic comparisons are the amount and timing of resource requirements and the associated cash flow streams.

Forecasting is predominately concerned with future economic conditions. *Business forecasting* comprises the prediction of market demands, conversion costs, availability of

**FIGURE 20.2**
Forecasting methods.

labor, and the like. Nearly every major engineering decision is affected by business forecasts because engineering projects inevitably are launched to satisfy future demands. Both the pace and the magnitude of engineering expenditures are linked to economic conditions, and business activity is the barometer of these conditions.

Prediction of new engineering developments and scientific advances, assumed to be independent of business activity, is called *technological forecasting*. It is concerned with activities that are largely under the control of an organization or an association sharing common interests. For example, technological forecasts have been developed for advances in nuclear-power technology and laser developments. These forecasts could be used by engineering economists to estimate the economic life and usage of assets in investment proposals for nuclear reactors and laser applications.

Attempts to seek a competitive edge from a glimpse into the future are nothing new. Rulers in the Middle Ages had their favorite crystal gazers and fortune tellers. Today astrologers and palm readers have believers, including some business people and engineers. Other organizational leaders rely on market surveys, product questionnaires, and quantitatively trained forecasting experts to anticipate levels of future activity. Yet no forecasting technique is infallible. Even the overwhelming amount of timely data about current conditions and advanced computer analyses now available cannot ensure accurate forecasts. Just ask any weather forecaster.

There are many ways to develop predictions. For convenience in getting an overview of the methods utilized, they can be grouped into the following three categories:

*Subjective methods*, based on opinions
*Historical methods*, based on past performance
*Causal methods*, based on underlying causes of events

Since more precise predictions are customarily more expensive to develop, it would be financial foolishness to allocate the same estimating time and cost to small and large investment evaluations. Similarly, only limited forecasting effort need be devoted to comparisons of alternatives that are identically affected by future conditions, and many comparisons do fit this category. An indication of the relationship between forecasting methods and costs is given in Figure 20.3.

## FORECASTS BASED ON OPINIONS

When an estimator does not have access to a staff of forecasting specialists, subjective predictions may be the most feasible forecasting method. A prime source is the opinion of the forecaster. This judgment has a better chance for accuracy if it is grounded in facts. An abundance of free information is available to aid estimators. General data about national economic health, pricing indexes, consumer spending trends, etc., are offered in magazines, newspapers, and publications from trade associations and government agencies. Even specific data and item-by-item forecasts about particular industries are available from various publishers and consultants.

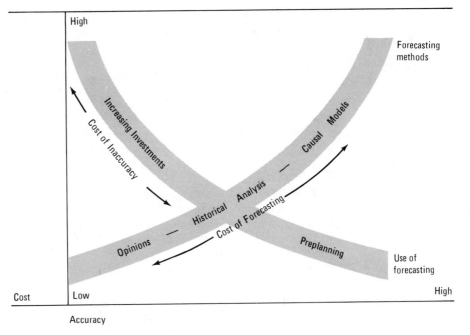

**FIGURE 20.3** The method of forecasting must be justified by its economic feasibility. More sophisticated techniques should produce more accurate predictions. Since the total cost includes both the expense of making a forecast and the cost of damage resulting from inaccurate forecasts, more funds should be allowed for predictions upon which larger investments will be judged.

The danger in basing forecasts on opinions is that individuals may let their personal feelings take command over what they know are facts. As an example of well meant but biased advice, consider the case of a young entrepreneur who went to an unfamiliar area some years ago to invest in a coin-operated car wash. He sought advice on the investment and was put in touch with a person who had considerable experience in the automotive field; he had been a mechanic, an automotive service manager, and the operator of a taxi company. The entrepreneur asked him, "What do you think of the possibilities for success of coin-operated car washes in this area?" Now this person had a particular aversion to any mechanical device for cleaning the finish of a car. He simply did not believe that it was good for the finish to use pressure hoses, mechanical scrubbers, spray waxes, etc. He did believe in hand washing with sponge and chamois and in hand waxing and polishing. As a result, his answer was, "Those coin-op car laundries are a flash in the pan. They'll never have any success around here."

It so happened that the facts indicated the opposite. Sales of new cars, personal incomes, traffic counts, and population growth curves all would have said yes to our entrepreneur's question. That area was one in which salt was used on the roads in winter. This fact alone leads many people to wash their cars frequently in coin operated washes. Now there are several hundred of these car-wash units in the area. The sad part of the tale is that all these coin-ops are now operated by other people. The prediction our entrepreneur got was based upon subjective rather than objective data.

Personal opinions are not necessarily bad sources of advice. In many instances they are the only source of advice. Even when more objective sources can be called upon, opinions may offer valuable insights or provide extra assurance about a prediction. Many companies routinely seek opinions from people who buy or sell their products. Five formal methods of obtaining subjective information are described below.

1   *Consumer survey*   A person who has actually bought a product is the most logical source of information about that product's sales appeal. Questions to the buyers are often part of the product's guarantee. Follow-up questionnaires are frequently mailed to the purchasers of a large item, such as an automobile. Sometimes surveys are made of potential rather than actual consumers. Replies from this audience have to be interpreted carefully because consumers' tastes change very rapidly, and what a customer intends or hopes to do in the future may be far removed from what he or she actually does.

2   *Opinions of sales representatives and distributors*   An experienced sales force is in a position to observe both the actions of suppliers and the behavior of consumers. They can give warnings about changes in buying trends and the activities of competitors. Sales engineers are particularly well qualified to suggest design changes to improve a product's acceptance. The optimism or pessimism of individuals in the sales force can be balanced by averaging the predictions made by several sales representatives and sales managers.

3   *Executive views*   Many forecasts used by executives are made by executives. The effect of individual biases is reduced by generating forecasts as a group effort. The mixture of interests and experience that ensures a good cross section of estimates makes a consensus difficult to obtain.

4   *Market trials*   The most elaborate means of gathering consumer opinions is to sell a new product on a trial basis. The trial is designed to be a carefully controlled experiment. A small market area is selected to represent, as realistically as possible, the whole market that the product will compete in. Care is taken to avoid obstructing the competition and to be sure the results are timely. Since the cost of these experiments is high, market trials are limited to significant product promotions.

5   *Delphi method*   A systematic routine for combining opinions into a reasoned consensus has the prophetic name *Delphi*. The technique was developed at the Rand Corporation and has gained fame in technological forecasting of future scientific developments. The procedure followed is to solicit and collate opinions about a certain subject from experts, and feed back digested appraisals to narrow the differences among opinions until a near agreement is obtained.

A carefully prepared questionnaire is delivered to a panel composed of experts from professional specialties that pertain to the forecasting problem. The survey can be conducted in a group meeting or by mail. Each questionnaire solicits written opinions about specific topics and requests supporting reasons for the opinions. These reasons are summarized by the Delphi moderator to assure anonymity of responses and then returned for consideration by the whole panel. The process is continued until the exchanged arguments and transfer of knowledge forges a consensus prediction. The end product may be a time-scaled "map" charting the nature of future technological developments. Advocates of the Delphi method claim the anonymity of written responses preserves the desirable features of a committee of specialists while reducing the "bandwagon" and dominant-personality effects that unduly sway group opinions.

# FORECASTS BASED ON HISTORICAL RECORDS

Basing forecasts on historical evidence relieves most of the uneasiness connected with relying on personal opinions. Historical data are simply facts. It is up to the forecaster to make interpretations from them. A forecaster can, of course, introduce personal bias into the interpretation, but this bias is open to exposure because the facts from which the forecast was drawn are still available for reexamination. In addition to the factual attractiveness of historical data, two adages bear out the value of past performance in estimating future performance: "History repeats itself," and "We learn from experience."

## Line Fitting

The most direct way to observe historical patterns is by plotting data on a time scale, a natural approach for engineering-minded analysts. A quarterly sales record for 10 years is plotted in Figure 20.4. The purpose of graphing is to expose a recurring shape or pattern that gives a clue as to where the next point or series of points should fall. The assumption that existing patterns will continue into the future is more likely to be correct over a short than a long estimating horizon, unless the patterns are unusually stable.

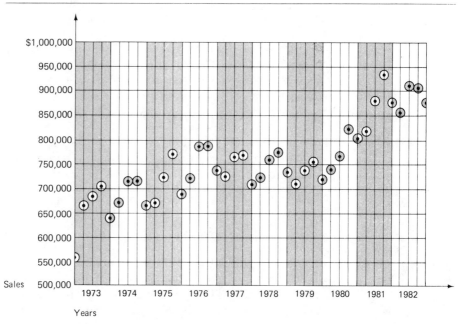

**FIGURE 20.4** Ten-year record of sales, where each dot represents quarterly sales.

The scattered sales-level dots from Figure 20.4 are repeated in Figure 20.5, with the addition of a *trend line*. This straight line is constructed to show the *long-term trend* in sales. It can be sketched freehand or fitted mathematically by use of regression techniques. By either method, roughly half the dots should be above the line, and half below. A good fit

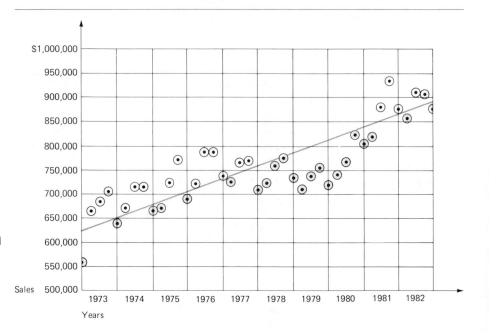

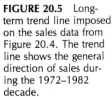

**FIGURE 20.5** Long-term trend line imposed on the sales data from Figure 20.4. The trend line shows the general direction of sales during the 1972–1982 decade.

exists when the sum of the squared vertical distances from each dot to the line is smaller than the sum for any other line that might be drawn. A routine to quantify this condition is appropriately called the *least-squares method* and is explained in Example 20.1. By this method, the formula for the trend line shown is

Sales = $625,000 + $26,500X

where $X$ is the number of years in the future from the end of the base year 1972 for which an estimate is sought. For instance, the sales level indicated by the trend line for year 1982 ($X = 1982 - 1972 = 10$) is

$$Sales_{1982} = 625,000 + (26,500)(10)$$
$$= 625,000 + 265,000 = \$890,000$$

Similarly, the forecast for 1983 would be

$$Sales_{1983} = 625,000 + (26,500)(11) = \$916,500$$

### Example 20.1   Line Fitting with the Least-Squares Method

Whenever plotted data points appear to follow a straight line, the least-squares method can be used to determine a line of good fit. Calculations provide the equation of the line for which the sum of the squares of the vertical distances between the actual values and the line is at a minimum. A further property of the line is that the sum of the same vertical distances equals zero.

A straight line is defined by the equation $Y = a + bX$. For our purposes, $Y$ is a forecast value at a point in time, and $X$ is measured in increments such as years from a base point. The objective is to determine $a$, which is the value of $Y$ at the base point, and $b$, which is the slope of the line.

Two equations are employed to determine $a$ and $b$. The first is obtained by multiplying the straight-line equation by the coefficient of $a$ and then summing the terms. With the coefficient of $a$ equal to 1 and $N$ as the number of data points, the equation becomes

$$\Sigma Y = Na + b\Sigma X$$

The second equation is developed in a similar manner. The coefficient of $b$ is $X$. After multiplying each term by $X$ and summing all the terms,

$$\Sigma XY = a\Sigma X + b\Sigma X^2$$

The two equations thus obtained are called *normal equations*.*

The four sums required to solve the normal equations ($\Sigma Y$, $\Sigma X$, $\Sigma XY$, and $\Sigma X^2$) are obtained from a tabular approach. The calculations can be simplified by carefully selecting the base point. Because $X$ equals the number of periods from the base point, selecting a midpoint in the time series as the base makes $\Sigma X$ equal to zero. The smaller numbers resulting from a centered base point also make other required products and sums easier to handle. After the four sums are obtained, they are substituted in the normal equations, and the values of $a$ and $b$ are calculated. Then these values are substituted into the straight-line equation to complete the simple regression forecasting model:

$$Y_F = a + bX \qquad where\ Y_F = \text{the forecast value } X \text{ periods in the future}$$

To illustrate simple linear regression, the linear relationship between an independent and dependent variable, the least-squares method will be applied to the data in Figure 20.6. A forecasting equation is sought to relate demand to time.

A straight, sloping line appears to be a reasonable fit for the data in Figure 20.6. To make the calculations easier, a centered base point is used; 1980 is the midpoint

*For more details, see Thomas H. Wonnacott and Ronald J. Wonnacott, *Regression: A Second Course in Statistics*, pp. 18-22, Wiley, New York, 1981.

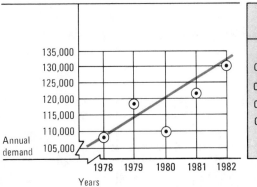

| QUARTERLY AND ANNUAL DEMAND | | | | | |
|---|---|---|---|---|---|
| *Year* | *1978* | *1979* | *1980* | *1981* | *1982* |
| Quarter 1 | 19,000 | 28,000 | 27,000 | 30,000 | 32,000 |
| Quarter 2 | 37,000 | 42,000 | 36,000 | 43,000 | 44,000 |
| Quarter 3 | 30,000 | 31,000 | 28,000 | 29,000 | 32,000 |
| Quarter 4 | 22,000 | 18,000 | 19,000 | 20,000 | 22,000 |
| Annual demand | 108,000 | 119,000 | 110,000 | 122,000 | 130,000 |

**FIGURE 20.6** Sample data for forecasting examples.

of the historical data and the date selected for $X = 0$. A tabular format with $Y$ as demand in 1000-unit increments is set up to obtain the sums required to solve the normal equations:

| Year | $Y$ | $X$ | $X^2$ | $XY$ | |
|------|-----|-----|-------|------|--|
| 1978 | 108 | −2 | 4 | −216 | |
| 1979 | 119 | −1 | 1 | −119 | |
| 1980 | 110 | 0 | 0 | 0 | ←—Base point |
| 1981 | 122 | +1 | 1 | 122 | |
| 1982 | 130 | +2 | 4 | 260 | |
| Sums | 589 | 0 | 10 | 47 | |

The sums are substituted into the normal equations, with $N = 5$, as

$$589 = 5a + b(0)$$
$$47 = a(0) + b(10)$$

and solved to yield $a = 589/5 = 117.8$ or 117,800 units, and $b = 47/10 = 4.7$ or 4700 units.

A forecasting equation is developed by substituting values of $a$ and $b$ into the straight-line equation:

$$Y_F = 117,800 + 4700X$$

The forecast for 1983, which is 3 years away from the 1980 base point for $X$, is given by substituting 3 for $X$ in the forecasting equation:

$$\text{Demand}_{1983} = 117,800 + 4700(3) = 131,900 \text{ units}$$

Historical data may also reveal *cyclic patterns* within the long-term trend. Two types of wavelike variations are noticeable in Figure 20.7. The large wave shows a business cycle. It may represent repeating fluctuations in local economic conditions, repeating changes in styles or consumer tastes, recurring fads and buying habits, or a combination of these and other factors.

The other cyclic pattern is attributable to seasonal variation. The insert in Figure 20.7 displays the data collected in respective quarters of a year. It is evident that higher sales can be expected in the middle two quarters of each year. Many products that depend on a particular season (ski equipment, swimming wear, gardening supplies, holiday treats, etc.) exhibit a repetitive sales pattern each year.

The purpose of distilling different patterns from a collection of data is to improve the forecast. A long-term trend gives a valid prediction of the general region in which future sales should fall. (This trend is modified by cyclic influences when they appear.) The longer-term cycles are difficult to identify, but seasonal cycles are quite apparent and predictable. The forecast for 1983 from the given sales data would probably be just slightly higher than the current (1982) sales, with the highest demand concentrated in the middle two quarters. A forecast for 1984 and 1985 would likely predict a sales pattern about the same as 1983, owing to the long-run cyclic influence. Less confidence can be placed in the

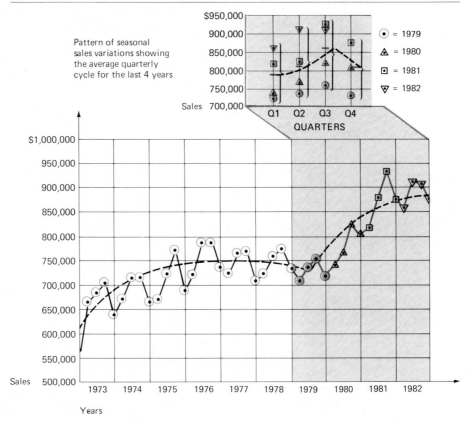

**FIGURE.20.7** Business cycle and seasonal variation patterns imposed on the sales data from Figure 20.5.

forecasts as they are pushed further into the future, because new factors could enter to disrupt the traditional patterns.

## Exponential Smoothing

A line-fit forecast gives equal weight to all the historical data included in the regression model. It may be advisable to give more weight to recent occurrences. This is accomplished in the exponential-smoothing model by selecting a weighting factor $\alpha$ that gives more or less prominence to recent happenings. The exponential-smoothing formula is very convenient to apply since it has only three inputs:

1 LD = latest demand, the most recent data on actual accomplishments of the subject being forecast. LD for a sales forecast would be the sales made during the current period.
2 PF = previous forecast, the forecast produced for the current period by applying the exponential-smoothing formula. The forecast made with the LD for the current period will be the PF for the next forecasting period.

**3** $\alpha$ = alpha, the smoothing constant, with a value between 0.0 and 1.0. The value selected for $\alpha$ determines how much emphasis is put on the most recent data.

The above factors are combined as shown below to yield a forecast NF for the next period:

Next forecast = NF = $\alpha$(LD) + (1 − $\alpha$)(PF)

This expression can be rewritten to show that the new forecast is simply the previous forecast corrected by adding a percentage $\alpha$ reflecting how much the old forecast missed the actual demand:

NF = PF + $\alpha$(LD − PF)

As an example, let alpha have a value of 0.4, sales for June be 4200 units, and the forecast made in May for the sales expected in June be 4500 units. Applying the two versions of the exponential-smoothing formula shows

$$NF_{July} = \alpha(LD_{June}) + (1 - \alpha)(PF_{June})$$
$$= 0.4(4200) + (1 - 0.4)(4500)$$
$$= 1680 + 2700 = 4380 \text{ units}$$

and

$$NF_{July} = PF_{June} + \alpha(LD_{June} - PF_{June})$$
$$= 4500 + 0.4(4200 - 4500)$$
$$= 4500 - 120 = 4380 \text{ units}$$

It is apparent from the above equations that the value used for alpha significantly affects the forecast. If alpha is set equal to zero, the original forecast never changes, no matter how much the actual demand varies from it. At the other extreme, when $\alpha$ = 1.0, the next forecast always equals the last demand experienced. A projection that the next period will be the same as the last period is extensively used for short-term scheduling and is known as *persistence forecasting* (in sporting circles it is called "sticking with a winner"). Between the extremes, $\alpha$ values closer to zero produce more stable predictions that may not detect current trends, and values closer to 1.0 closely track actual demands with forecasts that may fluctuate erratically.

The best way to choose alpha is to apply different values to historical data to see which one would have provided the most useful forecasts in the past. A simulation exercise to evaluate alpha values is shown in Figure 20.8. As expected, forecasts made with higher alphas are more responsive to current demand and consequently follow the actual demand pattern more closely. Other formulas using more involved smoothing functions can yield even better tracking,* but the simplicity of record-keeping, the easy computations, and the often commendable accuracy of the basic exponential-smoothing formula make it attractive for tactical planning.

## Moving Average

Another popular forecasting method predicts the demand for the next period from the average demand experienced during several recent periods. This method is appropriately

---

*More elaborate versions are incorporated in the Box-Jenkins technique; see G. E. P. Box and G. M. Jenkins, *Time Series Analysis, Forecasting, and Control*, Holden-Day, San Francisco, 1970.

| | | FORECASTS DEVELOPED FROM IDENTICAL DATA WITH ALPHA VALUES OF 0.2, 0.4, AND 0.6 | | | | | | |
|---|---|---|---|---|---|---|---|
| Date | Actual Demand | Forecast at $\alpha = 0.2$ | Absolute error | Forecast at $\alpha = 0.4$ | Absolute error | Forecast at $\alpha = 0.6$ | Absolute error |
| Oct. 8 | 180 | | | | | | |
| 15 | 164 | | | | | | |
| 22 | 162 | 177 | 15 | 174 | 12 | 170 | 8 |
| 29 | 151 | 174 | 23 | 169 | 18 | 165 | 14 |
| Nov. 5 | 143 | 169 | 26 | 162 | 19 | 157 | 14 |
| 12 | 158 | 164 | 8 | 154 | 10 | 148 | 10 |
| 19 | 154 | 163 | 9 | 156 | 2 | 154 | 0 |
| 26 | 160 | 161 | 1 | 158 | 7 | 154 | 6 |
| Dec. 3 | 172 | 161 | 11 | 159 | 16 | 158 | 14 |
| 10 | 178 | 163 | 15 | 164 | 16 | 166 | 12 |
| 17 | 188 | 166 | 22 | 170 | 18 | 173 | 15 |
| 24 | 174 | 170 | 4 | 177 | 4 | 182 | 8 |
| 31 | 172 | 171 | 1 | 175 | 4 | 177 | 5 |
| Jan. 7 | | 171 | — | 174 | — | 174 | — |
| Average error: | | | 12.3 | | 11.5 | | 9.6 |

**FIGURE 20.8**
Comparison of forecasts provided by the exponential-smoothing method using different alphas. To start the forecasting process, the first prediction is approximated by letting it equal the first demand. Thus, the forecast for Oct. 22, when $\alpha = 0.2$, was calculated as $NF_{Oct.\ 22} = 0.2(164) + 0.8(180) = 177$. Subsequent forecasts then include the estimate for the actual demand in each weekly period. The graph demonstrates how the lag between forecast and actual demand fluctuations is decreased by larger alpha values.

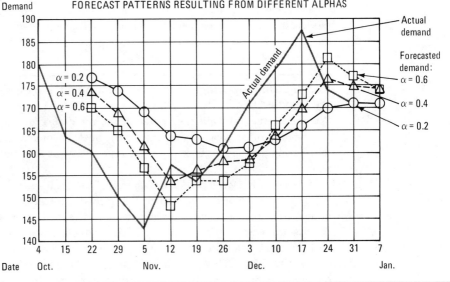

called the *moving average.* It is quite similar to exponential smoothing in that both methods "smooth" or "average out" the fluctuations in past demands to produce a forecast. The main difference between the two methods is that the choice of alpha in exponential smoothing determines how sensitive this forecast is to the most recent demands, while a moving-average forecast gives equal weight to each demand period included in the forecast.

A 3-month moving-average forecast for the next month would simply be the average demand experienced for the last 3 months. For example, the 3-month moving-average forecast for June would be calculated as

$$NF_{June} = \frac{March\ demand\ +\ April\ demand\ +\ May\ demand}{3}$$

In the same pattern, the forecast for July would result from averaging the demands for June, May, and April. The most recent block of actual demands is used in each successive forecast.

The choice of how many periods to include in the moving average involves the same considerations used to select an alpha value for exponential smoothing. A forecast based on very few periods is more sensitive to the latest events, as is an alpha value near 1.0. An average derived from data taken over several periods will better reduce fluctuations caused by random events, but it may be too stable to detect current trends. As was the case for exponential smoothing, the best way to decide how much smoothing is desirable is to experiment with past demands, trying different spans for the moving average and selecting the one that would have predicted previous demands most accurately.

A *seasonal index* referenced to a moving average improves the forecast unless the demand pattern is relatively constant. An index value is calculated by dividing the actual demand by the centered moving average for that period. A more reliable index is obtained by averaging several index values for common time periods. The forecast is thereby the product of the most recent centered moving average for a period and the index value for that period. The procedure for developing and using a seasonal index is demonstrated in Example 20.2.

---

### Example 20.2 Moving-Average Forecast Applied to the Quarterly Demand for the Sample Data in Figure 20.6

With the demand by quarters given in Figure 20.6, a four-quarter moving average will be used to forecast the demand for the next two quarters, $Q1_{1983}$ and $Q2_{1983}$. The four-period average is chosen because it smooths out seasonal variations over a full year.

The first moving average is one-fourth of the total sales for 1978; it represents a point in time between the end of the second quarter and the start of the third quarter. The second moving average is the sum of the last three quarters of 1978 and the first quarter of 1979 divided by 4. This value is associated with the end of $Q3_{1978}$ and the start of $Q4_{1978}$. An average of these two numbers gives a moving average *centered* at $Q3_{1978}$. This procedure for finding the midpoint value for all quarters is continued to obtain the four-period and centered moving averages in Table 20.1.

The last column in Table 20.1 is the seasonal index for each quarter. It is obtained by dividing the actual sales for a quarter by the centered moving average for that quarter. A better estimate of a quarter's index is obtained by averaging all the values available (see Table 20.2).

Before the average seasonal index is applied, two checks should be made:

1  The average of the periodic indexes should total to 1.0. In the example, the average is

$$\frac{0.9750\ +\ 1.3750\ +\ 1.0125\ +\ 0.6675}{4} = \frac{4.03}{4} = 1.0075$$

| Year | Quarter | Sales; 1000s of Units | Four-Period Moving Average | Centered Moving Average | Seasonal Index |
|------|---------|------------------------|-----------------------------|--------------------------|-----------------|
| 1978 | Q1 | 19.0 | | | |
| | Q2 | 37.0 | | | |
| | Q3 | 30.0 | 27.0 | 28.1 | 1.07 |
| | Q4 | 22.0 | 29.2 | 29.8 | 0.74 |
| 1979 | Q1 | 28.0 | 30.5 | 30.6 | 0.91 |
| | Q2 | 42.0 | 30.7 | 30.2 | 1.39 |
| | Q3 | 31.0 | 29.7 | 29.6 | 1.04 |
| | Q4 | 18.0 | 29.5 | 28.7 | 0.63 |
| 1980 | Q1 | 27.0 | 28.0 | 27.6 | 0.98 |
| | Q2 | 36.0 | 27.3 | 27.4 | 1.32 |
| | Q3 | 28.0 | 27.5 | 27.9 | 1.00 |
| | Q4 | 19.0 | 28.3 | 29.2 | 0.66 |
| 1981 | Q1 | 30.0 | 30.0 | 30.1 | 1.00 |
| | Q2 | 43.0 | 30.3 | 30.4 | 1.42 |
| | Q3 | 29.0 | 30.5 | 30.7 | 0.94 |
| | Q4 | 20.0 | 31.0 | 31.1 | 0.64 |
| 1982 | Q1 | 32.0 | 31.2 | 31.6 | 1.01 |
| | Q2 | 44.0 | 32.0 | 32.2 | 1.37 |
| | Q3 | 32.0 | 32.5 | | |
| | Q4 | 22.0 | | | |

**TABLE 20.1** Computation of four-period moving averages, centered moving averages, and quarterly seasonal index for the sample data from Figure 20.6.

Therefore, the indexes must be adjusted or else the quarterly forecasts will exceed the implied annual forecast by 0.75 percent.

2  Attention should be given to any obvious trends in a quarterly index. In Table 20.2, Q1 appears to be increasing and Q3 has a distinct downward trend.

The adjusted index reflects the above considerations. A fraction (4.00/4.03) of each average index was taken, and the results were rounded off with respect to the trend in Q3. Thus, calculations provide the forecasting framework, but finishing touches are supplied by judgment.

| Year | Q1 | Q2 | Q3 | Q4 |
|------|------|-------|--------|--------|
| 1978 | | | 1.07 | 0.74 |
| 1979 | 0.91 | 1.39 | 1.04 | 0.63 |
| 1980 | 0.98 | 1.32 | 1.00 | 0.66 |
| 1981 | 1.00 | 1.42 | 0.94 | 0.64 |
| 1982 | 1.01 | 1.37 | | |
| Totals | 3.90 | 5.50 | 4.05 | 2.67 |
| Average seasonal index | 0.975 | 1.375 | 1.0125 | 0.6675 |
| *Adjusted seasonal index* | *0.97* | *1.37* | *1.00* | *0.66* |

**TABLE 20.2** Calculation of an adjusted seasonal index.

The final step is to make the forecast. It results from taking the product of the most recent centered moving average and its respective seasonal index. Forecasts for the first two quarters of 1983 are

$$Q1_{1983} = 31.6 \times 0.97 = 30.7 \quad \text{or} \quad 30{,}700 \text{ units}$$
$$Q2_{1983} = 32.2 \times 1.37 = 44.1 \quad \text{or} \quad 44{,}100 \text{ units}$$

## Extensions of Historical-Basis Forecasting Methods

Only the perimeter has been explored in this survey of methods of forecasting from historical data. Simple regression, a model relating a dependent to an independent variable, can yield fits of many shapes besides straight lines. Curvilinear regression based on the equation $Y_F = aX^b$ could be used to develop certain curve-shaped fits. Hyperbolic and polynomial fits are also possible. Multiple regression, either linear or nonlinear, is used when the forecast depends on the relationship of several variables.

An indication of how much faith can be put on a forecast results from calculating statistical control limits for regression lines. Such calculations can also provide prediction limits. For instance, a statement could be made that there are only 5 chances in 100 that the accumulated demand will exceed a certain value at a certain time in the future.

The main value of regression models as compared with weighted-average techniques (exponential smoothing and moving average) is that the regression line can be extended several periods beyond the present. This advantage is gained at the expense of extra computational effort. But this burden can be shifted to computers; canned programs that handle huge regression models are widely available.

# FORECASTS BASED ON CAUSE

Very reliable predictions are possible if the causes for future demand can be identified and measured. The causal approach to forecasting has produced sophisticated models that attempt to include all the relevant causal relationships; in the most elaborate models there may be hundreds of quantified relationships. But causal models can also be quite simple. Perhaps knowledge of a single cause is sufficient for predicting, as in the case of a college bookstore which orders books based on knowledge of the number of students admitted to the school for next year. The manager of the bookstore could apply a factor based on past history to the number admitted, to forecast the demand by courses in the forthcoming terms.

*Leading indicators* are frequently used in business forecasting. These indicators are statistics compiled and published by many sources: *The Financial Post, The Financial Times*, government reports on almost everything, university publications, etc. If an indicator can be found that consistently predicts what demand to expect in, say, 6 months, current activites can be planned accordingly. It is even more comfortable to have two or three leading indicators pointing in the same direction. The problem is to find the accurate indicators.

## Correlation Model

A search for a leading indicator starts with assumptions as to the causes of demand. A house builder could hypothesize that housing demand depends on population growth, prices for houses, personal incomes, demolition of old homes, housing starts by

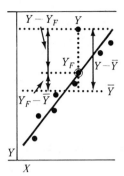

**FIGURE 20.9**
Deviations of a data
point.

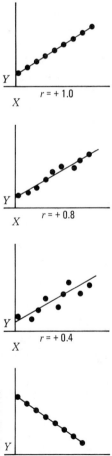

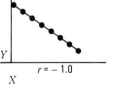

**FIGURE 20.10**
Correlation patterns.

competitors, and availability of financing. After data about the possible indicators have been collected, correlation studies are conducted to see if they are indeed related to housing demand. Ideally, an indicator will be identified that has a pattern similar to the historical demand, but that leads it by several periods. For example, it might be discovered that housing demand is correlated with interest rates: As rates climb, demand declines; but the change in demand follows a change in interest rates by 6 months. In this case, a builder could observe today what is happening to interest rates and use the observation as a leading indicator to predict with some confidence what the demand for houses will be in 6 months.

A correlation study examines the degree of linear relationship between variables. The variables are represented in mathematical expressions, such as the forecasting formula developed by the least-squares method in Example 20.1. Because not all the data points coincide with the fitted line, part of the relationship among variables remains unexplained. This dispersion of data points about regression lines is characterized by three sums-of-squares:

$$\Sigma(Y - \overline{Y})^2 = \Sigma(Y_F - \overline{Y})^2 + \Sigma(Y - Y_F)^2$$

| Total variation | Explained variation | Unexplained variation |

1   *Total variation*   The deviation $Y - \overline{Y}$, as shown in Figure 20.9, is the vertical distance between a data point and the mean of all observations, $\overline{Y} = \Sigma Y/N$. This term is a measure of the total variation of the dependent variable (in simple regression) and is divided into two parts: the explained and unexplained variations.
2   *Explained variation*   The variation explained by the regression line is represented by $Y_F - \overline{Y}$. In Figure 20.9, this deviation appears as the vertical distance between the line of regression and a horizontal line at $\overline{Y}$.
3   *Unexplained variation*   The sum-of-squares of the unexplained variation expresses the error between the forecast and actual values, $Y - Y_F$. Each deviation appears as the vertical distance from a data point $Y$ to the regression line.

The ratio of the sum-of-squares of the unexplained variation to the sum-of-squares of the total variation, $\Sigma(Y - Y_F)^2/\Sigma(Y - \overline{Y})^2$, measures the proportion of the total variation that is not explained by the regression. Therefore,

$$1 - \frac{\Sigma(Y - Y_F)^2}{\Sigma(Y - \overline{Y})^2}$$

measures the proportion of the total variation explained by the regression line, and the square root of this expression is the *coefficient of correlation, r*:

$$r = \sqrt{1 - \frac{\Sigma(Y - Y_F)^2}{\Sigma(Y - \overline{Y})^2}}$$

The value under the radical can never be greater than 1 nor less than 0. However, because the radical has both positive and negative roots, the value of $r$ is between $+1$ and $-1$. The plus or minus is indicative only of the slope of the regression line as depicted in Figure 20.10. When $r = +1$, all the data points fall on an upward-sloping regression line. When

$r$ is between $+1$ and $0$, the regression line still slopes upward, but data points fall on either side of the line. The closer they cluster around the line, the closer $r$ approaches 1.

When sufficient data are available, $r$ is calculated from the sum-of-squares expression or, more directly, from the formula

$$r = \frac{N\Sigma XY - (\Sigma X)(\Sigma Y)}{\sqrt{N\Sigma X^2 - (\Sigma X)^2}\,\sqrt{N\Sigma Y^2 - (\Sigma Y)^2}}$$

## Example 20.3    Development of a Leading-Indicator Forecast by Regression and Correlation Models

The Slam-Bang Company manufactures automatic nail drivers as modern replacements for the conventional hammer. The company sensibly reasoned that the sales of nail drivers should be related to the total amount spent on building construction. If a relationship does exist, published government and construction-industry forecasts of anticipated building levels can be used as a sales indicator. First a check was made to see that the building-level forecasts were relatively accurate. Next the national figures were broken down to conform to the Slam-Bang marketing areas. Then the records of monthly building volume and nail-driver sales for corresponding months were collected. The resulting data are tabulated in Table 20.3, where the construction volume is in $1 million units and product sales are in $1,000 units. The column headings correspond to the values needed for the calculation of $r$ and a linear-regression equation.

| Nail-Driver Sales $\times$ $10^{-3}$, $Y$ | Construction Volume $\times$ $10^{-6}$, $X$ | $Y^2$ | $X^2$ | $XY$ |
|---|---|---|---|---|
| 7.1 | 1.8 | 50.51 | 3.24 | 12.78 |
| 9.9 | 2.3 | 89.01 | 5.29 | 22.78 |
| 9.0 | 1.9 | 81.00 | 3.61 | 17.10 |
| 10.4 | 2.6 | 108.16 | 6.76 | 27.04 |
| 11.1 | 3.1 | 123.21 | 9.61 | 34.41 |
| 10.9 | 2.8 | 118.81 | 7.84 | 30.52 |
| 10.5 | 2.9 | 110.25 | 8.41 | 30.45 |
| 9.8 | 2.4 | 96.04 | 5.76 | 23.52 |
| 11.1 | 2.8 | 123.21 | 7.84 | 31.08 |
| 10.2 | 2.5 | 104.04 | 6.25 | 25.50 |
| 9.7 | 2.3 | 94.09 | 5.29 | 22.31 |
| 10.9 | 2.8 | 118.81 | 7.84 | 30.52 |
| 8.8 | 2.1 | 77.44 | 4.41 | 18.48 |
| 8.6 | 1.9 | 73.98 | 3.61 | 16.34 |
| 12.3 | 3.2 | 151.29 | 10.24 | 39.36 |
| 11.4 | 3.0 | 129.96 | 9.00 | 34.20 |
| 11.2 | 2.8 | 125.44 | 7.84 | 31.36 |
| 10.2 | 2.6 | 104.04 | 6.76 | 26.52 |
| 10.7 | 2.7 | 114.49 | 7.29 | 28.89 |
| 8.6 | 1.9 | 73.96 | 3.61 | 16.34 |
| 202.4 | 50.4 | 2076.62 | 130.50 | 519.50 |

TABLE 20.3   Correlation data for sales of Slam-Bang nail drivers and construction volume. The last three columns are the computations required to calculate $r$ and $Y_F$.

From this reasonably large sample, the coefficient of correlation was calculated as

$$r = \frac{N\Sigma XY - (\Sigma X)(\Sigma Y)}{\sqrt{N\Sigma X^2 - (\Sigma X)^2}\sqrt{N\Sigma Y^2 - (\Sigma Y)^2}}$$

$$= \frac{20(519.5) - (50.4)(202.4)}{\sqrt{20(130.5) - (50.4)^2}\sqrt{20(2076.62) - (202.4)^2}}$$

$$= \frac{10{,}390 - 10{,}201}{\sqrt{2610 - 2540.16}\sqrt{41{,}532.4 - 40{,}965.7}}$$

$$= \frac{189}{(8.36)(23.81)} = 0.95$$

Although the correlation is not exact, it is definitely worthy of consideration for prediction purposes. With the sums developed in Table 20.3, the least-squares method is applied to obtain a forecasting equation. The normal equations are

$$\Sigma Y = Na + b\Sigma X \qquad 202.4 = 20a + b(50.4)$$
$$\Sigma XY = a\Sigma X + b\Sigma X^2 \qquad 519.5 = a(50.4) + b(130.5)$$

They are solved for $a$ and $b$ to obtain

$$a = 3.37 \text{ or } \$3{,}370 \qquad b = 2.68 \text{ or } \$2{,}680$$

The forecasting equation is then

$$Y_F = \$3{,}370 + \$2{,}680X$$

Thus, a projected construction volume of $2,750,000 for the next month would suggest a nail-driver sales volume of

$$Y_F = \$3{,}370 + \$2{,}680(2.75) = \$10{,}740$$

## Econometric Models

Econometrics is a discipline concerned with the measurement and definition of economic systems. It utilizes statistical and programming methods to develop models based on the quantitative aspects of system behavior. The models vary from the simple regression methods previously described to very elegant and rich representations of large systems involving hundreds of variables.

The more sophisticated economic models are based on causal relationships. They have been developed for different engineering systems, most notably for transportation. The initial effort in developing a causal model is considerable, and after the causal forecast is accepted, *the model must be continually monitored to confirm that the modeled relationships are still valid.* Causes of demand can change, and the cause of the causes can change.

Causal models are hardly ever constructed just to generate better data for specific economic comparisons. When the models are already available, they should certainly be utilized in the comparisons, but a decision would have to be of "make or break" proportions to provoke the development of an original model. However, causal forecasting is more apt than historical forecasting to predict a turning point in demand, a point at which growth switches to decay or the reverse, and even a hint of a turning point is vital information to the estimator. Reputations and fortunes are made or lost by alternatives selected in anticipation of a shift from the existing trend.*

# Review Exercises and Discussions

**Exercise 1**   An equipment sales representative claims that the installation of a new machine will allow equal quality and quantity of output with one fewer worker. Using the firm's required rate of return (15 percent) and direct labor ratio (0.6), the representative substantiates the claim with the following figures:

*Annual savings for the elimination of one worker*

| | |
|---|---|
| Direct labor: 1 worker × $10,000/worker-year | $10,000 |
| Overhead: $10,000 × 0.60 | 6,000 |
| Total saving | $16,000 |

*Annual cost of new machine (P = $20,000, S = 0, N = 10)*

| | |
|---|---|
| Capital recovery: ($20,000 − 0)(A/P, 15, 10) = $20,000(0.19925) | $ 3,985 |
| Operation | 9,000 |
| Maintenance | 600 |
| Taxes and insurance | 400 |
| Total cost | $13,985 |
| *Net saving* | $2,015 |

Does the sales representative's evaluation appear valid?

**Solution 1**   Is the sales representative's evaluation valid? Maybe. If the estimated life of the machine and its operating costs are accurate, there is still a question of whether overhead costs will be reduced by $6000. A one-worker reduction in the work force would probably have little effect on total overhead costs. Since the main purpose of an overhead ratio is to allocate indirect costs to products, it is not an exact measure of indirect wages. Therefore, the quoted savings in overhead should be investigated.

**Exercise 2**   A rough indication is needed to determine whether additional trucks will be required to transport raw materials during the coming year. If the preliminary indication is positive, an economic study will be made to see how many and what kinds of trucks should be added to the company fleet.

---

*For more information on the topics covered in this chapter, see C.W.J. Granger, *Forecasting in Business and Economics*, Academic Press, New York, 1980.

Annual demands for the past 5 years have been plotted, and free-hand trend lines drawn as shown in Figure 20.11(a). The "eyeballed" trend line appears to start at 60,000 units and increase by 12,500 units per year.

A breakdown of annual demand by percentage per quarter is shown in Figure 20.11(b). A simple forecast by quarters would result from an arithmetic average of all the data. This average value would be of little use for the trucking problem because fleet size is a function of the *maximum* transportation needs any time during the year. A visual inspection is made to reveal that second-quarter demand accounts for about 41 percent of the year's total and is therefore the critical figure.

Statistics on national demand over the past 30 years suggest that the current business cycle is on an upswing. Therefore, a judgment value of +8 percent, or 1.08 times the trend-line forecast, is selected to represent the effect of this cycle.

Based on these unsophisticated forecasting methods, what forecast seems reasonable for the maximum demand that will occur during the next year?

**Solution 2** "Unsophisticated" is not a synonym for worthless. The "eyeball" approach delivers a reasonably close forecast at a minimum cost. Since a "guesstimate" does not depend on a formal procedure, it can put more weight on recent data or other factors that the forecaster feels are especially pertinent. From the given data, maximum demand should occur during the second quarter. The forecast results from multiplying the trend value by the cyclic correction and the quarterly percentage:

$$\text{Demand}_{\text{2d quarter}} = [60{,}000 + 12{,}500(5)](1.08)(0.41) = 54{,}243$$

---

**Exercise 3** Develop a forecast by the exponential-smoothing method for the demand in 1983 based on the sample data in Figure 20.6. Let $\alpha = 0.3$. To develop the PF value, start the process with a forecast for 1980 based on the demand in 1978 as PF, and the demand in 1979 as LD:

$$\text{NF}_{1980} = 108 + 0.3(119 - 108) = 111.3 \quad \text{or} \quad 111{,}300 \text{ units}$$

---

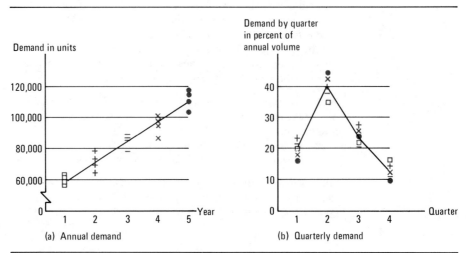

**FIGURE 20.11.**
Demand data with forecasting trends made by inspection.

and

$$NF_{1981} = 111.3 + 0.3(110 - 111.3) = 110.9 \quad \text{or} \quad 110,900 \text{ units}$$

Continue the procedure to obtain $NF_{1983}$. Compare this forecast with the one obtained using the least-squares regression model in Example 20.1.

**Solution 3** The sequence of calculations leading to the 1983 forecast is

$$NF_{1982} = 110.9 + 0.3(122 - 110.9) = 114.2 \quad \text{or} \quad 114,200 \text{ units}$$

$$NF_{1983} = 114.2 + 0.3(130 - 114.2) = 118.9 \quad \text{or} \quad 118,900 \text{ units}$$

Compared with the simple regression model in which $NF_{1983} = 131,900$ units, the exponential-smoothing model is more pessimistic. This is due to the selection of 0.3 for the value of $\alpha$, which puts more weight on the older data. Changing $\alpha$ to 0.8 increases the forecast for 1983 to 128,000.

# PROBLEMS

**20.1** A cost index is a dimensionless number that relates a certain type of cost at a given time to that cost during a reference year. That is,

$$C_p = C_r \frac{I_p}{I_r}$$

where $C_p$ = current cost, dollars
$\quad\quad C_r$ = cost during reference period
$\quad\quad I_p$ = current value of the cost index
$\quad\quad I_r$ = index value during reference period

**20.1a** Cost estimates are being developed to justify the construction of a warehouse. A structure of similar lay-up design was built 6 years ago at a unit price of $155 per m² of wall when the cost index was 116. The index now is 170. What would the construction cost be today for a warehouse with 5575 m² of wall? *($1,266,390)*
**20.1b** According to present plans, the warehouse construction will not get underway until 3 years from now. If the cost index continues to increase at its present rate, what construction bid can be expected for the warehouse?

**20.2** Persistence predictions may seem too naïve to be classified as a forecasting method, but they can be surprisingly successful under some conditions. Comment on the following observations:
**20.2a** In sporting events the usual forecast is for the current champion to win again.
**20.2b** A decision not to make a decision is a persistence prediction.

**20.3** What approximate mathematical relationship between the $\alpha$ used in exponential smoothing and the number of periods used in a moving average makes both methods equally responsive to changes in historical data?

**20.4** Sales figures for two products first marketed 6 months ago are shown:

| Month | Product 1 | Product 2 |
|-------|-----------|-----------|
| January | $110,000 | $ 54,000 |
| February | 102,000 | 63,000 |
| March | 95,000 | 80,000 |
| April | 85,000 | 98,000 |
| May | 78,000 | 112,000 |
| June | 70,000 | 133,000 |

**20.4a** What July forecast for each product is obtained by using a 6-month moving average? How do you explain these forecasts with respect to the dissimilar sales patterns?

**20.4b** What forecast would you make for each product for July?

**20.5** The least-squares method can be applied to fit a curve to data when the forecasting equation is $Y_F = ab^X$, in which $Y$ changes at a constant rate $b$ each period for $X$ periods. When this equation is translated from the exponential form to its logarithmic form,

$$\log Y = \log a + X \log b$$

normal equations can be set up as

$$\Sigma \log Y = N \log a + \Sigma X (\log b)$$
$$\Sigma (X \log Y) = \Sigma X (\log a) + \Sigma X^2 (\log b)$$

to allow the tabular approach of the least-squares method in determining the values of $a$ and $b$. When the base point is selected to make $\Sigma X = 0$, the solution reduces to

$$\log a = \frac{\Sigma \log Y}{N} \quad \text{and} \quad \log b = \frac{\Sigma (X \log Y)}{\Sigma X^2}$$

Set up a table with column headings for $Y$, $X$, $X^2$, $\log Y$, and $X \log Y$, and use the annual-demand data from Figure 20.6 to determine a curve-fitting forecasting formula. Compare the forecast for 1983 with the straight-line forecast.

$$[Y_F = 117{,}500(1.0404)^X; \ Y_{1983} = 132{,}324 \ units]$$

**20.6** Given the following data:

| Year | 1 | 2 | 3 | 4 | 5 | 6 | 7 | 8 |
|------|---|---|---|---|---|---|---|---|
| Demand | 90 | 100 | 107 | 113 | 123 | 136 | 144 | 155 |

**20.6a** Plot the data, and establish a forecast for year 9 by observation.

**20.6b** Use the least-squares method to develop a forecasting formula. What is the forecast for year 9?

**20.6c** What is the forecast for year 9 by the exponential-smoothing method when $\alpha = 0.25$?

**20.7** Quarterly unit demands for a product are:

| Year | Winter | Spring | Summer | Fall |
|------|--------|--------|--------|------|
| 1 | 81 | 64 | 73 | 83 |
| 2 | 80 | 70 | 84 | 74 |
| 3 | 86 | 59 | 71 | 73 |
| 4 | 98 | 72 | 74 | 64 |
| 5 | 106 | 68 | 75 | 60 |

**20.7a** Using a four-period moving average, determine a seasonal adjusted index, and establish a forecast for each quarter of next year.  $(F_{winter} = 114.5; F_{spring} = 67.9)$
**20.7b** Use line-fitting methods to determine a forecast for each period of next year.
$(F_{winter} = 110.6; F_{spring} = 69.7)$

**20.8** Assume you have the franchise to sell refreshments for theatrical performances given at a local playhouse. Besides the usual soft drinks and popcorn, you offer homemade tarts. Since the tarts have to be baked within a day of when they are to be sold and the market for stale tarts is quite limited, predicting sales is very important. The sales record for the first 10 performances is tabulated below. Each performance was a sellout, and all future performances are expected to play to capacity crowds.

| Date | Jan. 5 | 6 | 12 | 13 | 26 | 27 | Feb. 2 | 3 | 16 | 17 |
|------|--------|---|----|----|----|----|--------|---|----|----|
| Tarts sold | 120 | 120 | 120 | 144 | 191 | 171 | 172 | 186 | 153 | 145 |

In reviewing the sales, you recall that you sold all the tarts you baked for the first four performances. Then you increased production for the remaining performances to 16 dozen (192) and started having leftovers. For the last two performances you barely covered costs because so many tarts remained unsold. Now the question is how many to bake for the next performance.
**20.8a** What forecasts for tart demand would have been made for the last four performances by the exponential-smoothing formula with $\alpha = 0.4$? What is the forecast for the next performance? *(NF = 160)*
**20.8b** Repeat Problem 10.10a using a 3-month moving average.  *(NF = 161)*
**20.8c** What are the forecast tart sales for the next performance when both alpha and the number of moving-average periods are doubled ($\alpha = 0.8$ and $N = 6$)?
$[NF(\alpha = 0.8) = 148; NF(N = 6) = 170]$
**20.8d** What forecast do you recommend? What additional information might improve your prediction?

**20.9** A patented new product was introduced 9 years ago. Sales since its introduction are:

| Years since introduction | 1 | 2 | 3 | 4 | 5 | 6 | 7 | 8 | 9 |
|--------------------------|---|---|---|---|---|---|---|---|---|
| Annual unit sales | 2023 | 2102 | 2009 | 2768 | 3291 | 3881 | 4622 | 5494 | 5557 |

The original plant that produces the product is now operating at 100 percent capacity. A second plant, to be built immediately, must have the capacity to meet the additional demand expected for the next 5 years. What should be the design capacity of the new plant?

**20.10** Suggest possible leading indicators of readily available data for the following products and services:

   **20.10a** Industrial production in a developing country

   **20.10b** Enrolment in a private business school specializing in data-processing training.

   **20.10c** Demand for prepared baby foods.

**20.11** Private-aircraft sales in a three-province marketing area and the number of students enroling each year to take flying lessons are shown in the table.

| Year | Aircraft Sales | Student Starts |
|------|---------------|----------------|
| 1 | 300 | 4100 |
| 2 | 400 | 4600 |
| 3 | 350 | 4800 |
| 4 | 450 | 4300 |
| 5 | 500 | 5800 |
| 6 | 400 | 5600 |
| 7 | 600 | 6000 |
| 8 | 550 | 6300 |
| 9 | 600 | 6800 |
| 10 | 650 | 7200 |

**20.11a** Using just the past history of aircraft sales, estimate the number of sales to expect in year 11 and year 12.          *($Y_{11} = 677; Y_{12} = 712$)*

**20.11b** Calculate the coefficient of correlation to determine if student starts are a leading indicator for aircraft sales. Assume the sales pattern lags the starts pattern by 2 years.          *($r = 0.983$)*

**20.11c** Develop a forecasting formula for sales based on student starts. Develop the equation

$$\text{Sales}_{\text{year } t} = a + b(\text{starts}_{\text{year } t-2})$$

and use it to find the expected sales in years 11 and 12 ($t = 11, 12$) from the student starts in years 9 and 10 ($t - 2$).

# APPENDIX A

## SELECTED REFERENCES

BOOKS

American Telephone and Telegraph Company: *Engineering Economy*, 3rd ed., McGraw-Hill, New York, 1977.

Archer, M.: *An Introduction to Canadian Business*, 4th ed., McGraw-Hill Ryerson, Toronto, 1982.

Barish, N.N., and S. Kaplan: *Economic Analysis for Engineering and Managerial Decision Making*, 2nd ed., McGraw-Hill, New York, 1978.

Bierman, H., and S. Smidt: *The Capital Budgeting Decision*, 5th ed., Macmillan, New York, 1980.

Blanchard, B.S.: *Life Cycle Cost*, M/A Press, Portland, Oregon, 1978.

Box, G.E.P., and G.M. Jenkins: *Time Series Analysis, Forecasting, and Control*, 2nd ed., Holden-Day, San Francisco, 1976.

Brigham, E.F., A.L. Kahl, and W.F. Rentz: *Canadian Financial Management: Theory and Practice*, Holt, Rinehart and Winston of Canada, Toronto, 1983.

Briston, R.J., and J. Liversidge: *A Practical Approach to Business Investment Decisions*, Prentice-Hall, Englewood Cliffs, N.J., 1981.

Bussey, L.E.: *The Economic Analysis of Industrial Projects*, Prentice-Hall, Englewood Cliffs, N.J., 1980.

*515*

Butler, W.F., R.A. Kavesh and R.B. Platt: *Methods and Techniques of Business Forecasting*, Prentice-Hall, Englewood Cliffs, N.J., 1974.

Canada, J.R., and J.A. White: *Capital Investment Decision Analysis for Management and Engineering*, Prentice-Hall, Englewood Cliffs, N.J., 1980.

Clark, J.J., T.J. Hindelang, and R.E. Pritchard: *Capital Budgeting*, Prentice-Hall, Englewood Cliffs, N.J., 1979.

Clifton, D.S., and L.E. Fyffe: *Project Feasibility Analysis*, Wiley, New York, 1977.

Cornell, A.H.: *The Decision-Maker's Handbook*, Prentice-Hall, Englewood Cliffs, N.J., 1980.

Dasgupta, A.S., and S. Marglin: *Guidelines for Project Evaluation*, United Nations, 1972.

Davidson, S., C.L. Mitchell, C.P. Stickney, and R.L. Weil: *Intermediate Accounting*, First Canadian Edition, Holt, Rinehart and Winston of Canada, Toronto, 1982.

DeGarmo, E.P., J.R. Canada, and W.G. Sullivan: *Engineering Economy*, 6th ed., Macmillan, New York, 1979.

Edge, C.G., and V.B. Irvine: *A Practical Approach to the Appraisal of Capital Expenditures*, The Society of Management Accountants of Canada, Hamilton, Ont., 1981.

Fabrycky, W.J., and G.J. Thuesen: *Economic Decision Analysis*, 2nd ed., Prentice-Hall, Englewood Cliffs, N.J., 1980.

Fleischer, G.A. (ed.): *Risk and Uncertainty: Non-deterministic Decision Making in Engineering Economy*, American Institute of Industrial Engineers, Norcross, Ga., 1975.

Freidenfelds, J.: *Capacity Expansion*, North Holland, New York, 1981.

Godfrey, D.W.H.: *Modern Technical Communication*, McGraw-Hill Ryerson, Toronto, 1983.

Granger, C.W.J.: *Forecasting in Business and Economics*, Academic Press, New York, 1980.

Grant, E.L., W.G. Ireson, and R.S. Leavenworth: *Principles of Engineering Economy*, 7th ed., Wiley, New York, 1982.

Harris, E.C.: *Canadian Income Taxation*, 2nd ed., Butterworths, Toronto, 1981.

Herbst, A.F.: *Capital Budgeting*, Harper and Row, New York, 1982.

Holloway, C.A.: *Decision Making under Uncertainty*, Prentice-Hall, Englewood Cliffs, N.J., 1979.

Johnson, J.P.: *Government Financial Assistance Programs in Canada*, 2nd ed., Butterworths, Toronto, 1982.

Kim, S.H., and H.J. Guithues: *Capital Expenditure Analysis*, University Press of America, Washington, D.C., 1980.

Kuiper, E.: *Water Resources Project Economics*, Butterworths, London, 1971.

Kurtz, M.: *Engineering Economics for Professional Engineer's Examinations*, 2nd ed., McGraw-Hill, New York, 1975.

Levy, H., and M. Sarnat: *Capital Investment and Financial Decisions*, 2nd ed., Prentice-Hall, Englewood Cliffs, N.J., 1982.

Lin, S.A.Y.: *Theory and Measurement of Economic Externalities*, Academic Press, New York, 1976.

Linsley, R.K., and J.B. Franzini: *Water Resources Engineering*, 3rd ed., McGraw-Hill, New York, 1979.

Makridakis, S., and S.C. Wheelwright: *The Handbook of Forecasting*, Wiley, New York,

1982.

Mallik, A.K.: *Engineering Economy With Computer Applications*, Engineering Technology, Mahomet, Ill., 1979.

Mao, J.C.T.: *Quantitative Analysis of Financial Decisions*, Macmillan, New York, 1969.

Marston, D.L.: *Law for Professional Engineers*, McGraw-Hill Ryerson, Toronto, 1981.

Mayer, R.R.: *Capital Expenditure Analysis*, Waveland, Prospect Heights, Ill., 1978.

McConnell, C.R., and W.H. Pope: *Economics: Principles, Problems and Policies*, 2nd Canadian Edition, McGraw-Hill Ryerson, Toronto, 1983.

Merrett, A.J., and A. Sykes: *The Finance and Analysis of Capital Projects*, 2nd ed., Wiley, New York, 1973.

Mishan, E.J.: *Cost-Benefit Analysis*, Praeger, New York, 1976.

Morris, W.T.: *Engineering Economic Analysis*, Reston, Reston, Va., 1976.

Morrison, C., and P. Hughes: *Professional Engineering Practice: Ethical Aspects*, McGraw-Hill Ryerson, Toronto, 1982.

Newman, D.G.: *Engineering Economic Analysis*, Engineering Press, San Jose, Ca., 1976.

Newman, D.G.: *Economic Analysis for the Professional Engineer's Examination*, Engineering Press, San Jose, Ca., 1978.

Oakford, R.V.: *Capital Budgeting*, Ronald Press, New York, 1970.

Oglesby, C.H., and R.G. Hicks: *Highway Engineering*, 4th ed., Wiley, New York, 1982.

Osteryoung, J.S.: *Capital Budgeting*, 2nd ed., Grid, Columbus, Ohio, 1979.

Ostwald, P.F.: *Cost Estimating for Engineering and Management*, Prentice-Hall, Englewood Cliffs, N.J., 1974.

Pappas, J.L., and E.F. Brigham, and M. Hirschey: *Managerial Economics*, 4th ed., Dryden Press, Hinsdale, Ill., 1983.

Quirin, G.D., and J.C. Wiginton: *Analyzing Capital Expenditures: Private and Public Perspectives*, Irwin, Homewood, Ill., 1981.

Radford, K.J.: *Managerial Decision Making*, Reston, Reston, Va., 1975.

Reisman, A.: *Managerial and Engineering Economics*, Allyn and Bacon, Boston, 1971.

Rose. L.M.: *Engineering Investment Decisions: Planning Under Uncertainty*, Elsevier, New York, 1976.

Rosen, L.S., and M.H. Granof: *Canadian Financial Accounting: Principles and Issues*, Prentice-Hall of Canada, Scarborough, Ontario, 1980.

Samuelson, P., and A. Scott: *Economics*, 5th Canadian Edition, McGraw-Hill Ryerson, Toronto, 1980.

Smith, G.W.: *Engineering Economy*, 2nd ed., Iowa State University Press, Ames, Iowa, 1973.

Steiner, H.M.: *Public and Private Investments – Socioeconomic Analysis*, Wiley, New York, 1980.

Stevens, G.T.: *Economics and Financial Analysis of Capital Investments*, Wiley, New York, 1979.

Szonyi, A.J., R.G. Fenton, J.A. White, M.H. Agee, and K.E. Case: *Principles of Engineering Economic Analysis*, Canadian Edition, Wiley, Toronto, 1982.

Tarquin, A.J., and L.T. Blank: *Engineering Economy: A Behavioral Approach*, McGraw-Hill, New York 1976.

Taylor, G.A.: *Managerial and Engineering Economy*, 3rd ed., D. Van Nostrand, New

York, 1980.

Theusen, H.G., W.J. Fabrycky, and G.J. Theusen: *Engineering Economy*, 5th ed., Prentice-Hall, Englewood Cliffs, N.J., 1977.

Weingartner, H.M.: *Mathematical Programming and the Analysis of Capital Budgeting Problems*, Prentice-Hall, Englewood Cliffs, N.J., 1963.

Wilkes, F.M.: *Capital Budgeting Techniques*, Wiley, New York, 1977.

Wonnacott, T.H., and R.J. Wonnacott: *Regression: A Second Course in Statistics*, Wiley, New York, 1981.

## ARTICLES

Pertinent articles are named throughout the text. The most frequently cited sources for subjects associated with engineering economics are listed below.

*AIIE Transactions*

American Institute of Industrial Engineers *Conference Proceedings*

*Engineering Digest*

*Engineering Economy Abstracts*

*Harvard Business Review*

*Industrial Engineering* (called *The Journal of Industrial Engineering* prior to January, 1969)

*Journal of Business*

*Journal of Finance*

*Journal of Financial and Quantitative Analysis*

*Management Science*

*The Economic Journal*

*The Engineering Economist*

# APPENDIX B

## DISCRETE-COMPOUNDING INTEREST FACTORS

## ½% Interest Factors for Discrete Compounding Periods

| | SINGLE PAYMENT | | UNIFORM SERIES | | | | | |
|---|---|---|---|---|---|---|---|---|
| | Compound Amount Factor | Present Worth Factor | Capital Recovery Factor | Present Worth Factor | Sinking Fund Factor | Compound Amount Factor | Gradient Factor | |
| N | (F/P, ½, N) | (P/F, ½, N) | (A/P, ½, N) | (P/A, ½, N) | (A/F, ½, N) | (F/A, ½, N) | (A/G, ½, N) | N |
| 1 | 1.0050 | .99503 | 1.0051 | .9949 | 1.0001 | .9998 | .0000 | 1 |
| 2 | 1.0100 | .99008 | .50385 | 1.9847 | .49885 | 2.0046 | .4613 | 2 |
| 3 | 1.0150 | .98515 | .33674 | 2.9696 | .33174 | 3.0143 | .9537 | 3 |
| 4 | 1.0201 | .98025 | .25318 | 3.9497 | .24818 | 4.0292 | 1.4531 | 4 |
| 5 | 1.0252 | .97538 | .20305 | 4.9248 | .19805 | 5.0491 | 1.9462 | 5 |
| 6 | 1.0303 | .97052 | .16963 | 5.8951 | .16463 | 6.0741 | 2.4413 | 6 |
| 7 | 1.0355 | .96570 | .14576 | 6.8606 | .14076 | 7.1043 | 2.9364 | 7 |
| 8 | 1.0407 | .96089 | .12786 | 7.8213 | .12286 | 8.1396 | 3.4304 | 8 |
| 9 | 1.0459 | .95611 | .11393 | 8.7772 | .10893 | 9.1800 | 3.9231 | 9 |
| 10 | 1.0511 | .95136 | .10279 | 9.7282 | .09779 | 10.225 | 4.4140 | 10 |
| 11 | 1.0563 | .94663 | .09368 | 10.674 | .08868 | 11.276 | 4.9063 | 11 |
| 12 | 1.0616 | .94192 | .08609 | 11.616 | .08109 | 12.332 | 5.3959 | 12 |
| 13 | 1.0669 | .93723 | .07966 | 12.553 | .07466 | 13.394 | 5.8857 | 13 |
| 14 | 1.0723 | .93257 | .07415 | 13.485 | .06915 | 14.460 | 6.3752 | 14 |
| 15 | 1.0776 | .92793 | .06938 | 14.413 | .06438 | 15.532 | 6.8614 | 15 |
| 16 | 1.0830 | .92332 | .06520 | 15.336 | .06020 | 16.610 | 7.3489 | 16 |
| 17 | 1.0884 | .91872 | .06152 | 16.255 | .05652 | 17.693 | 7.8351 | 17 |
| 18 | 1.0939 | .91415 | .05824 | 17.168 | .05324 | 18.781 | 8.3198 | 18 |
| 19 | 1.0993 | .90961 | .05531 | 18.078 | .05031 | 19.874 | 8.8046 | 19 |
| 20 | 1.1048 | .90508 | .05268 | 18.983 | .04768 | 20.974 | 9.2892 | 20 |
| 21 | 1.1103 | .90058 | .05029 | 19.883 | .04529 | 22.078 | 9.7715 | 21 |
| 22 | 1.1159 | .89610 | .04812 | 20.779 | .04312 | 23.183 | 10.253 | 22 |
| 23 | 1.1215 | .89164 | .04614 | 21.671 | .04114 | 24.304 | 10.735 | 23 |
| 24 | 1.1271 | .88721 | .04433 | 22.558 | .03933 | 25.425 | 11.216 | 24 |
| 25 | 1.1327 | .88280 | .04266 | 23.440 | .03766 | 26.552 | 11.695 | 25 |
| 26 | 1.1384 | .87841 | .04112 | 24.318 | .03612 | 27.685 | 12.173 | 26 |
| 27 | 1.1441 | .87404 | .03969 | 25.192 | .03469 | 28.823 | 12.652 | 27 |
| 28 | 1.1498 | .86969 | .03837 | 26.062 | .03337 | 29.967 | 13.129 | 28 |
| 29 | 1.1555 | .86536 | .03714 | 26.927 | .03214 | 31.116 | 13.605 | 29 |
| 30 | 1.1613 | .86106 | .03599 | 27.788 | .03099 | 32.272 | 14.081 | 30 |
| 31 | 1.1671 | .85678 | .03491 | 28.644 | .02991 | 33.433 | 14.555 | 31 |
| 32 | 1.1730 | .85251 | .03390 | 29.497 | .02890 | 34.600 | 15.029 | 32 |
| 33 | 1.1788 | .84827 | .03295 | 30.345 | .02795 | 35.772 | 15.501 | 33 |
| 34 | 1.1847 | .84405 | .03206 | 31.189 | .02706 | 36.951 | 15.974 | 34 |
| 35 | 1.1906 | .83986 | .03122 | 32.028 | .02622 | 38.135 | 16.446 | 35 |
| 40 | 1.2207 | .81918 | .02765 | 36.164 | .02265 | 44.147 | 18.790 | 40 |
| 45 | 1.2515 | .79901 | .02488 | 40.198 | .01988 | 50.311 | 21.113 | 45 |
| 50 | 1.2831 | .77933 | .02266 | 44.133 | .01766 | 56.630 | 23.416 | 50 |
| 55 | 1.3155 | .76014 | .02085 | 47.971 | .01585 | 63.109 | 25.699 | 55 |
| 60 | 1.3487 | .74142 | .01934 | 51.715 | .01434 | 69.751 | 27.960 | 60 |
| 65 | 1.3828 | .72317 | .01806 | 55.366 | .01306 | 76.561 | 30.201 | 65 |
| 70 | 1.4177 | .70536 | .01697 | 58.928 | .01197 | 83.543 | 32.422 | 70 |
| 75 | 1.4535 | .68799 | .01603 | 62.401 | .01103 | 90.701 | 34.622 | 75 |
| 80 | 1.4902 | .67105 | .01520 | 65.790 | .01020 | 98.040 | 36.802 | 80 |
| 85 | 1.5278 | .65453 | .01447 | 69.094 | .00947 | 105.56 | 38.961 | 85 |
| 90 | 1.5663 | .63841 | .01383 | 72.318 | .00883 | 113.27 | 41.099 | 90 |
| 95 | 1.6059 | .62269 | .01325 | 75.462 | .00825 | 121.18 | 43.218 | 95 |
| 100 | 1.6464 | .60736 | .01273 | 78.528 | .00773 | 129.29 | 45.316 | 100 |

**1% Interest Factors for Discrete Compounding Periods**

| | SINGLE PAYMENT | | UNIFORM SERIES | | | | | |
|---|---|---|---|---|---|---|---|---|
| | Compound Amount Factor | Present Worth Factor | Capital Recovery Factor | Present Worth Factor | Sinking Fund Factor | Compound Amount Factor | Gradient Factor | |
| *N* | (F/P, 1, N) | (P/F, 1, N) | (A/P, 1, N) | (P/A, 1, N) | (A/F, 1, N) | (F/A, 1, N) | (A/G, 1, N) | *N* |
| 1 | 1.0100 | .99010 | 1.0100 | .9900 | 1.0000 | .9999 | .0000 | 1 |
| 2 | 1.0201 | .98030 | .50757 | 1.9701 | .49757 | 2.0097 | .4864 | 2 |
| 3 | 1.0303 | .97059 | .34006 | 2.9406 | .33006 | 3.0297 | .9813 | 3 |
| 4 | 1.0406 | .96099 | .25631 | 3.9014 | .24631 | 4.0598 | 1.4751 | 4 |
| 5 | 1.0510 | .95147 | .20606 | 4.8528 | .19607 | 5.1003 | 1.9675 | 5 |
| 6 | 1.0615 | .94205 | .17257 | 5.7947 | .16257 | 6.1512 | 2.4581 | 6 |
| 7 | 1.0721 | .93273 | .14865 | 6.7273 | .13865 | 7.2125 | 2.9469 | 7 |
| 8 | 1.0828 | .92349 | .13071 | 7.6507 | .12071 | 8.2845 | 3.4349 | 8 |
| 9 | 1.0936 | .91435 | .11675 | 8.5649 | .10675 | 9.3672 | 3.9209 | 9 |
| 10 | 1.1046 | .90530 | .10560 | 9.4701 | .09560 | 10.460 | 4.4047 | 10 |
| 11 | 1.1156 | .89634 | .09647 | 10.366 | .08647 | 11.565 | 4.8872 | 11 |
| 12 | 1.1268 | .88746 | .08886 | 11.253 | .07886 | 12.680 | 5.3682 | 12 |
| 13 | 1.1380 | .87868 | .08242 | 12.132 | .07242 | 13.807 | 5.8476 | 13 |
| 14 | 1.1494 | .86998 | .07691 | 13.002 | .06691 | 14.945 | 6.3253 | 14 |
| 15 | 1.1609 | .86137 | .07213 | 13.863 | .06213 | 16.094 | 6.8010 | 15 |
| 16 | 1.1725 | .85284 | .06795 | 14.716 | .05795 | 17.255 | 7.2754 | 16 |
| 17 | 1.1842 | .84440 | .06427 | 15.560 | .05427 | 18.427 | 7.7483 | 17 |
| 18 | 1.1961 | .83604 | .06099 | 16.396 | .05099 | 19.611 | 8.2192 | 18 |
| 19 | 1.2080 | .82776 | .05806 | 17.223 | .04806 | 20.807 | 8.6883 | 19 |
| 20 | 1.2201 | .81957 | .05542 | 18.043 | .04542 | 22.015 | 9.1560 | 20 |
| 21 | 1.2323 | .81145 | .05304 | 18.854 | .04304 | 23.235 | 9.6222 | 21 |
| 22 | 1.2446 | .80342 | .05087 | 19.658 | .04087 | 24.467 | 10.086 | 22 |
| 23 | 1.2571 | .79547 | .04889 | 20.453 | .03889 | 25.712 | 10.549 | 23 |
| 24 | 1.2696 | .78759 | .04708 | 21.240 | .03708 | 26.969 | 11.010 | 24 |
| 25 | 1.2823 | .77979 | .04541 | 22.020 | .03541 | 28.238 | 11.469 | 25 |
| 26 | 1.2952 | .77207 | .04387 | 22.792 | .03387 | 29.521 | 11.927 | 26 |
| 27 | 1.3081 | .76443 | .04245 | 23.556 | .03245 | 30.816 | 12.383 | 27 |
| 28 | 1.3212 | .75686 | .04113 | 24.313 | .03113 | 32.124 | 12.838 | 28 |
| 29 | 1.3344 | .74937 | .03990 | 25.062 | .02990 | 33.445 | 13.291 | 29 |
| 30 | 1.3478 | .74195 | .03875 | 25.804 | .02875 | 34.779 | 13.742 | 30 |
| 31 | 1.3612 | .73461 | .03768 | 26.539 | .02768 | 36.127 | 14.191 | 31 |
| 32 | 1.3748 | .72733 | .03667 | 27.266 | .02667 | 37.488 | 14.640 | 32 |
| 33 | 1.3886 | .72013 | .03573 | 27.986 | .02573 | 38.863 | 15.086 | 33 |
| 34 | 1.4025 | .71301 | .03484 | 28.699 | .02484 | 40.251 | 15.531 | 34 |
| 35 | 1.4165 | .70595 | .03401 | 29.405 | .02401 | 41.653 | 15.973 | 35 |
| 40 | 1.4887 | .67169 | .03046 | 32.831 | .02046 | 48.878 | 18.164 | 40 |
| 45 | 1.5647 | .63909 | .02771 | 36.090 | .01771 | 56.471 | 20.314 | 45 |
| 50 | 1.6445 | .60808 | .02552 | 39.192 | .01552 | 64.452 | 22.423 | 50 |
| 55 | 1.7284 | .57857 | .02373 | 42.142 | .01373 | 72.839 | 24.491 | 55 |
| 60 | 1.8165 | .55049 | .02225 | 44.950 | .01225 | 81.655 | 26.520 | 60 |
| 65 | 1.9092 | .52378 | .02100 | 47.622 | .01100 | 90.920 | 28.508 | 65 |
| 70 | 2.0065 | .49836 | .01993 | 50.163 | .00993 | 100.65 | 30.457 | 70 |
| 75 | 2.1089 | .47418 | .01902 | 52.582 | .00902 | 110.89 | 32.366 | 75 |
| 80 | 2.2164 | .45117 | .01822 | 54.883 | .00822 | 121.64 | 34.236 | 80 |
| 85 | 2.3295 | .42927 | .01752 | 57.072 | .00752 | 132.95 | 36.067 | 85 |
| 90 | 2.4483 | .40844 | .01690 | 59.156 | .00690 | 144.83 | 37.859 | 90 |
| 95 | 2.5732 | .38862 | .01636 | 61.138 | .00636 | 157.32 | 39.614 | 95 |
| 100 | 2.7044 | .36976 | .01587 | 63.024 | .00587 | 170.44 | 41.330 | 100 |

## 1½% Interest Factors for Discrete Compounding Periods

| | SINGLE PAYMENT | | UNIFORM SERIES | | | | | |
| --- | --- | --- | --- | --- | --- | --- | --- | --- |
| | Compound Amount Factor | Present Worth Factor | Capital Recovery Factor | Present Worth Factor | Sinking Fund Factor | Compound Amount Factor | Gradient Factor | |
| $N$ | $(F/P, 1½, N)$ | $(P/F, 1½, N)$ | $(A/P, 1½, N)$ | $(P/A, 1½, N)$ | $(A/F, 1½, N)$ | $(F/A, 1½, N)$ | $(A/G, 1½, N)$ | $N$ |
| 1 | 1.0150 | .98522 | 1.0150 | .9852 | 1.0000 | 1.0000 | .0000 | 1 |
| 2 | 1.0302 | .97066 | .51131 | 1.9557 | .49631 | 2.0148 | .4917 | 2 |
| 3 | 1.0456 | .95632 | .34340 | 2.9120 | .32840 | 3.0450 | .9857 | 3 |
| 4 | 1.0613 | .94219 | .25946 | 3.8540 | .24446 | 4.0905 | 1.4760 | 4 |
| 5 | 1.0772 | .92827 | .20910 | 4.7823 | .19410 | 5.1518 | 1.9653 | 5 |
| 6 | 1.0934 | .91455 | .17554 | 5.6967 | .16054 | 6.2290 | 2.4511 | 6 |
| 7 | 1.1098 | .90103 | .15157 | 6.5977 | .13657 | 7.3223 | 2.9351 | 7 |
| 8 | 1.1264 | .88772 | .13359 | 7.4853 | .11859 | 8.4320 | 3.4161 | 8 |
| 9 | 1.1433 | .87460 | .11962 | 8.3598 | .10462 | 9.5585 | 3.8952 | 9 |
| 10 | 1.1605 | .86168 | .10844 | 9.2214 | .09344 | 10.701 | 4.3716 | 10 |
| 11 | 1.1779 | .84894 | .09930 | 10.070 | .08430 | 11.862 | 4.8456 | 11 |
| 12 | 1.1956 | .83640 | .09169 | 10.906 | .07669 | 13.039 | 5.3169 | 12 |
| 13 | 1.2135 | .82404 | .08525 | 11.730 | .07025 | 14.235 | 5.7863 | 13 |
| 14 | 1.2317 | .81186 | .07973 | 12.542 | .06473 | 15.448 | 6.2524 | 14 |
| 15 | 1.2502 | .79987 | .07495 | 13.342 | .05995 | 16.680 | 6.7165 | 15 |
| 16 | 1.2689 | .78805 | .07077 | 14.130 | .05577 | 17.930 | 7.1781 | 16 |
| 17 | 1.2879 | .77640 | .06708 | 14.906 | .05208 | 19.199 | 7.6374 | 17 |
| 18 | 1.3073 | .76493 | .06381 | 15.671 | .04881 | 20.487 | 8.0939 | 18 |
| 19 | 1.3269 | .75363 | .06088 | 16.424 | .04588 | 21.794 | 8.5482 | 19 |
| 20 | 1.3468 | .74249 | .05825 | 17.167 | .04325 | 23.121 | 8.9998 | 20 |
| 21 | 1.3670 | .73152 | .05587 | 17.898 | .04087 | 24.468 | 9.4493 | 21 |
| 22 | 1.3875 | .72071 | .05371 | 18.619 | .03871 | 25.834 | 9.8959 | 22 |
| 23 | 1.4083 | .71006 | .05173 | 19.329 | .03673 | 27.222 | 10.340 | 23 |
| 24 | 1.4294 | .69957 | .04993 | 20.028 | .03493 | 28.630 | 10.782 | 24 |
| 25 | 1.4509 | .68923 | .04827 | 20.718 | .03327 | 30.059 | 11.221 | 25 |
| 26 | 1.4726 | .67904 | .04674 | 21.397 | .03174 | 31.510 | 11.658 | 26 |
| 27 | 1.4947 | .66901 | .04532 | 22.066 | .03032 | 32.983 | 12.093 | 27 |
| 28 | 1.5171 | .65912 | .04400 | 22.725 | .02900 | 34.477 | 12.525 | 28 |
| 29 | 1.5399 | .64938 | .04278 | 23.374 | .02778 | 35.994 | 12.955 | 29 |
| 30 | 1.5630 | .63979 | .04164 | 24.014 | .02664 | 37.534 | 13.382 | 30 |
| 31 | 1.5864 | .63033 | .04058 | 24.644 | .02558 | 39.097 | 13.807 | 31 |
| 32 | 1.6102 | .62102 | .03958 | 25.265 | .02458 | 40.683 | 14.229 | 32 |
| 33 | 1.6344 | .61184 | .03864 | 25.877 | .02364 | 42.293 | 14.649 | 33 |
| 34 | 1.6589 | .60280 | .03776 | 26.479 | .02276 | 43.928 | 15.067 | 34 |
| 35 | 1.6838 | .59389 | .03694 | 27.073 | .02194 | 45.586 | 15.482 | 35 |
| 40 | 1.8139 | .55129 | .03343 | 29.913 | .01843 | 54.261 | 17.522 | 40 |
| 45 | 1.9541 | .51174 | .03072 | 32.550 | .01572 | 63.606 | 19.501 | 45 |
| 50 | 2.1051 | .47504 | .02857 | 34.997 | .01357 | 73.673 | 21.422 | 50 |
| 55 | 2.2677 | .44096 | .02683 | 37.269 | .01183 | 84.518 | 23.283 | 55 |
| 60 | 2.4430 | .40933 | .02539 | 39.378 | .01039 | 96.201 | 25.087 | 60 |
| 65 | 2.6318 | .37997 | .02419 | 41.335 | .00919 | 108.78 | 26.833 | 65 |
| 70 | 2.8351 | .35271 | .02317 | 43.152 | .00817 | 122.34 | 28.523 | 70 |
| 75 | 3.0542 | .32741 | .02230 | 44.839 | .00730 | 136.95 | 30.157 | 75 |
| 80 | 3.2903 | .30392 | .02155 | 46.405 | .00655 | 152.68 | 31.737 | 80 |
| 85 | 3.5445 | .28212 | .02089 | 47.858 | .00589 | 169.63 | 33.262 | 85 |
| 90 | 3.8185 | .26188 | .02032 | 49.207 | .00532 | 187.89 | 34.734 | 90 |
| 95 | 4.1135 | .24310 | .01982 | 50.460 | .00482 | 207.57 | 36.155 | 95 |
| 100 | 4.4314 | .22566 | .01937 | 51.622 | .00437 | 228.76 | 37.524 | 100 |

## 2% Interest Factors for Discrete Compounding Periods

| N | SINGLE PAYMENT | | UNIFORM SERIES | | | | | N |
|---|---|---|---|---|---|---|---|---|
| | Compound Amount Factor | Present Worth Factor | Capital Recovery Factor | Present Worth Factor | Sinking Fund Factor | Compound Amount Factor | Gradient Factor | |
| $N$ | $(F/P, 2, N)$ | $(P/F, 2, N)$ | $(A/P, 2, N)$ | $(P/A, 2, N)$ | $(A/F, 2, N)$ | $(F/A, 2, N)$ | $(A/G, 2, N)$ | $N$ |
| 1 | 1.0200 | .98039 | 1.0200 | .9804 | 1.0000 | 1.0000 | .0000 | 1 |
| 2 | 1.0404 | .96117 | .51507 | 1.9415 | .49507 | 2.0199 | .4934 | 2 |
| 3 | 1.0612 | .94232 | .34677 | 2.8837 | .32677 | 3.0603 | .9851 | 3 |
| 4 | 1.0824 | .92385 | .26263 | 3.8075 | .24263 | 4.1214 | 1.4733 | 4 |
| 5 | 1.1040 | .90573 | .21217 | 4.7132 | .19217 | 5.2038 | 1.9584 | 5 |
| 6 | 1.1261 | .88798 | .17853 | 5.6012 | .15853 | 6.3078 | 2.4401 | 6 |
| 7 | 1.1486 | .87056 | .15452 | 6.4717 | .13452 | 7.4339 | 2.9189 | 7 |
| 8 | 1.1716 | .85350 | .13651 | 7.3252 | .11651 | 8.5826 | 3.3940 | 8 |
| 9 | 1.1950 | .83676 | .12252 | 8.1619 | .10252 | 9.7541 | 3.8659 | 9 |
| 10 | 1.2189 | .82035 | .11133 | 8.9822 | .09133 | 10.949 | 4.3347 | 10 |
| 11 | 1.2433 | .80427 | .10218 | 9.7865 | .08218 | 12.168 | 4.8001 | 11 |
| 12 | 1.2682 | .78850 | .09456 | 10.574 | .07456 | 13.411 | 5.2622 | 12 |
| 13 | 1.2935 | .77304 | .08812 | 11.347 | .06812 | 14.679 | 5.7209 | 13 |
| 14 | 1.3194 | .75788 | .08261 | 12.105 | .06261 | 15.973 | 6.1764 | 14 |
| 15 | 1.3458 | .74302 | .07783 | 12.848 | .05783 | 17.292 | 6.6288 | 15 |
| 16 | 1.3727 | .72846 | .07365 | 13.577 | .05365 | 18.638 | 7.0778 | 16 |
| 17 | 1.4002 | .71417 | .06997 | 14.291 | .04997 | 20.011 | 7.5236 | 17 |
| 18 | 1.4282 | .70017 | .06670 | 14.991 | .04670 | 21.411 | 7.9660 | 18 |
| 19 | 1.4567 | .68644 | .06378 | 15.677 | .04378 | 22.839 | 8.4052 | 19 |
| 20 | 1.4859 | .67298 | .06116 | 16.350 | .04116 | 24.296 | 8.8412 | 20 |
| 21 | 1.5156 | .65979 | .05879 | 17.010 | .03879 | 25.781 | 9.2739 | 21 |
| 22 | 1.5459 | .64685 | .05663 | 17.657 | .03663 | 27.297 | 9.7033 | 22 |
| 23 | 1.5768 | .63417 | .05467 | 18.291 | .03467 | 28.843 | 10.129 | 23 |
| 24 | 1.6084 | .62173 | .05287 | 18.913 | .03287 | 30.420 | 10.552 | 24 |
| 25 | 1.6405 | .60954 | .05122 | 19.522 | .03122 | 32.028 | 10.972 | 25 |
| 26 | 1.6733 | .59759 | .04970 | 20.120 | .02970 | 33.669 | 11.388 | 26 |
| 27 | 1.7068 | .58588 | .04829 | 20.706 | .02829 | 35.342 | 11.802 | 27 |
| 28 | 1.7409 | .57439 | .04699 | 21.280 | .02699 | 37.049 | 12.212 | 28 |
| 29 | 1.7758 | .56313 | .04578 | 21.843 | .02578 | 38.790 | 12.619 | 29 |
| 30 | 1.8113 | .55208 | .04465 | 22.395 | .02465 | 40.565 | 13.023 | 30 |
| 31 | 1.8475 | .54126 | .04360 | 22.937 | .02360 | 42.377 | 13.423 | 31 |
| 32 | 1.8844 | .53065 | .04261 | 23.467 | .02261 | 44.224 | 13.821 | 32 |
| 33 | 1.9221 | .52024 | .04169 | 23.987 | .02169 | 46.108 | 14.215 | 33 |
| 34 | 1.9606 | .51004 | .04082 | 24.497 | .02082 | 48.031 | 14.606 | 34 |
| 35 | 1.9998 | .50004 | .04000 | 24.997 | .02000 | 49.991 | 14.994 | 35 |
| 40 | 2.2079 | .45291 | .03656 | 27.354 | .01656 | 60.398 | 16.886 | 40 |
| 45 | 2.4377 | .41021 | .03391 | 29.489 | .01391 | 71.888 | 18.701 | 45 |
| 50 | 2.6914 | .37154 | .03182 | 31.422 | .01182 | 84.573 | 20.440 | 50 |
| 55 | 2.9715 | .33652 | .03014 | 33.174 | .01014 | 98.579 | 22.103 | 55 |
| 60 | 3.2808 | .30480 | .02877 | 34.760 | .00877 | 114.04 | 23.694 | 60 |
| 65 | 3.6223 | .27607 | .02763 | 36.196 | .00763 | 131.11 | 25.212 | 65 |
| 70 | 3.9993 | .25004 | .02667 | 37.497 | .00667 | 149.96 | 26.661 | 70 |
| 75 | 4.4155 | .22647 | .02586 | 38.676 | .00586 | 170.77 | 28.041 | 75 |
| 80 | 4.8751 | .20512 | .02516 | 39.743 | .00516 | 193.75 | 29.355 | 80 |
| 85 | 5.3824 | .18579 | .02456 | 40.710 | .00456 | 219.12 | 30.604 | 85 |
| 90 | 5.9426 | .16827 | .02405 | 41.586 | .00405 | 247.13 | 31.791 | 90 |
| 95 | 6.5611 | .15241 | .02360 | 42.379 | .00360 | 278.05 | 32.917 | 95 |
| 100 | 7.2440 | .13804 | .02320 | 43.097 | .00320 | 312.20 | 33.984 | 100 |

## 2½% Interest Factors for Discrete Compounding Periods

| | SINGLE PAYMENT | | UNIFORM SERIES | | | | | |
|---|---|---|---|---|---|---|---|---|
| | Compound Amount Factor | Present Worth Factor | Capital Recovery Factor | Present Worth Factor | Sinking Fund Factor | Compound Amount Factor | Gradient Factor | |
| $N$ | $(F/P, 2\frac{1}{2}, N)$ | $(P/F, 2\frac{1}{2}, N)$ | $(A/P, 2\frac{1}{2}, N)$ | $(P/A, 2\frac{1}{2}, N)$ | $(A/F, 2\frac{1}{2}, N)$ | $(F/A, 2\frac{1}{2}, N)$ | $(A/G, 2\frac{1}{2}, N)$ | $N$ |
| 1 | 1.0250 | .97561 | 1.0250 | .9756 | 1.0000 | 1.0000 | .0000 | 1 |
| 2 | 1.0506 | .95182 | .51884 | 1.9273 | .49384 | 2.0243 | .4930 | 2 |
| 3 | 1.0768 | .92860 | .35014 | 2.8559 | .32514 | 3.0755 | .9827 | 3 |
| 4 | 1.1038 | .90595 | .26582 | 3.7618 | .24082 | 4.1524 | 1.4681 | 4 |
| 5 | 1.1314 | .88386 | .21525 | 4.6457 | .19025 | 5.2562 | 1.9496 | 5 |
| 6 | 1.1596 | .86230 | .18155 | 5.5079 | .15655 | 6.3875 | 2.4269 | 6 |
| 7 | 1.1886 | .84127 | .15750 | 6.3492 | .13250 | 7.5472 | 2.9002 | 7 |
| 8 | 1.2184 | .82075 | .13947 | 7.1699 | .11447 | 8.7358 | 3.3695 | 8 |
| 9 | 1.2488 | .80073 | .12546 | 7.9707 | .10046 | 9.9542 | 3.8346 | 9 |
| 10 | 1.2800 | .78120 | .11426 | 8.7518 | .08926 | 11.203 | 4.2955 | 10 |
| 11 | 1.3120 | .76215 | .10511 | 9.5140 | .08011 | 12.483 | 4.7524 | 11 |
| 12 | 1.3448 | .74356 | .09749 | 10.257 | .07249 | 13.795 | 5.2052 | 12 |
| 13 | 1.3785 | .72543 | .09105 | 10.982 | .06605 | 15.140 | 5.6539 | 13 |
| 14 | 1.4129 | .70773 | .08554 | 11.690 | .06054 | 16.518 | 6.0985 | 14 |
| 15 | 1.4482 | .69047 | .08077 | 12.381 | .05577 | 17.931 | 6.5391 | 15 |
| 16 | 1.4844 | .67363 | .07660 | 13.054 | .05160 | 19.379 | 6.9756 | 16 |
| 17 | 1.5216 | .65720 | .07293 | 13.711 | .04793 | 20.864 | 7.4081 | 17 |
| 18 | 1.5596 | .64117 | .06967 | 14.353 | .04467 | 22.385 | 7.8365 | 18 |
| 19 | 1.5986 | .62553 | .06676 | 14.978 | .04176 | 23.945 | 8.2609 | 19 |
| 20 | 1.6386 | .61028 | .06415 | 15.588 | .03915 | 25.543 | 8.6813 | 20 |
| 21 | 1.6795 | .59539 | .06179 | 16.184 | .03679 | 27.182 | 9.0976 | 21 |
| 22 | 1.7215 | .58087 | .05965 | 16.765 | .03465 | 28.861 | 9.5100 | 22 |
| 23 | 1.7645 | .56671 | .05770 | 17.331 | .03270 | 30.583 | 9.9183 | 23 |
| 24 | 1.8087 | .55288 | .05591 | 17.884 | .03091 | 32.347 | 10.322 | 24 |
| 25 | 1.8539 | .53940 | .05428 | 18.424 | .02928 | 34.156 | 10.723 | 25 |
| 26 | 1.9002 | .52624 | .05277 | 18.950 | .02777 | 36.010 | 11.119 | 26 |
| 27 | 1.9477 | .51341 | .05138 | 19.463 | .02638 | 37.910 | 11.512 | 27 |
| 28 | 1.9964 | .50089 | .05009 | 19.964 | .02509 | 39.858 | 11.900 | 28 |
| 29 | 2.0463 | .48867 | .04889 | 20.453 | .02389 | 41.854 | 12.285 | 29 |
| 30 | 2.0975 | .47675 | .04778 | 20.929 | .02278 | 43.901 | 12.665 | 30 |
| 31 | 2.1499 | .46512 | .04674 | 21.395 | .02174 | 45.998 | 13.042 | 31 |
| 32 | 2.2037 | .45378 | .04577 | 21.848 | .02077 | 48.148 | 13.415 | 32 |
| 33 | 2.2588 | .44271 | .04486 | 22.291 | .01986 | 50.352 | 13.784 | 33 |
| 34 | 2.3152 | .43191 | .04401 | 22.723 | .01901 | 52.610 | 14.149 | 34 |
| 35 | 2.3731 | .42138 | .04321 | 23.144 | .01821 | 54.926 | 14.511 | 35 |
| 40 | 2.6850 | .37244 | .03984 | 25.102 | .01484 | 67.399 | 16.261 | 40 |
| 45 | 3.0378 | .32918 | .03727 | 26.832 | .01227 | 81.512 | 17.917 | 45 |
| 50 | 3.4370 | .29095 | .03526 | 28.361 | .01026 | 97.480 | 19.483 | 50 |
| 55 | 3.8886 | .25716 | .03365 | 29.713 | .00865 | 115.54 | 20.959 | 55 |
| 60 | 4.3996 | .22729 | .03235 | 30.908 | .00735 | 135.98 | 22.351 | 60 |
| 65 | 4.9777 | .20089 | .03128 | 31.964 | .00628 | 159.11 | 23.659 | 65 |
| 70 | 5.6318 | .17756 | .03040 | 32.897 | .00540 | 185.27 | 24.887 | 70 |
| 75 | 6.3719 | .15694 | .02965 | 33.722 | .00465 | 214.87 | 26.038 | 75 |
| 80 | 7.2092 | .13871 | .02903 | 34.451 | .00403 | 248.36 | 27.115 | 80 |
| 85 | 8.1565 | .12260 | .02849 | 35.095 | .00349 | 286.26 | 28.122 | 85 |
| 90 | 9.2283 | .10836 | .02804 | 35.665 | .00304 | 329.13 | 29.062 | 90 |
| 95 | 10.441 | .09578 | .02765 | 36.168 | .00265 | 377.63 | 29.937 | 95 |
| 100 | 11.813 | .08465 | .02731 | 36.613 | .00231 | 432.51 | 30.751 | 100 |

**3% Interest Factors for Discrete Compounding Periods**

| | SINGLE PAYMENT | | UNIFORM SERIES | | | | | |
| | Compound Amount Factor | Present Worth Factor | Capital Recovery Factor | Present Worth Factor | Sinking Fund Factor | Compound Amount Factor | Gradient Factor | |
| $N$ | $(F/P, 3, N)$ | $(P/F, 3, N)$ | $(A/P, 3, N)$ | $(P/A, 3, N)$ | $(A/F, 3, N)$ | $(F/A, 3, N)$ | $(A/G, 3, N)$ | $N$ |
|---|---|---|---|---|---|---|---|---|
| 1 | 1.0300 | .97087 | 1.0300 | .9709 | 1.0000 | 1.0000 | .0000 | 1 |
| 2 | 1.0609 | .94260 | .52262 | 1.9134 | .49262 | 2.0299 | .4920 | 2 |
| 3 | 1.0927 | .91514 | .35354 | 2.8285 | .32354 | 3.0908 | .9795 | 3 |
| 4 | 1.1255 | .88849 | .26903 | 3.7170 | .23903 | 4.1835 | 1.4622 | 4 |
| 5 | 1.1592 | .86261 | .21836 | 4.5796 | .18836 | 5.3090 | 1.9401 | 5 |
| 6 | 1.1940 | .83749 | .18460 | 5.4170 | .15460 | 6.4682 | 2.4129 | 6 |
| 7 | 1.2298 | .81310 | .16051 | 6.2301 | .13051 | 7.6622 | 2.8809 | 7 |
| 8 | 1.2667 | .78941 | .14246 | 7.0195 | .11246 | 8.8920 | 3.3440 | 8 |
| 9 | 1.3047 | .76642 | .12844 | 7.7859 | .09844 | 10.158 | 3.8022 | 9 |
| 10 | 1.3439 | .74410 | .11723 | 8.5300 | .08723 | 11.463 | 4.2555 | 10 |
| 11 | 1.3842 | .72243 | .10808 | 9.2524 | .07808 | 12.807 | 4.7040 | 11 |
| 12 | 1.4257 | .70139 | .10046 | 9.9537 | .07046 | 14.191 | 5.1475 | 12 |
| 13 | 1.4685 | .68096 | .09403 | 10.634 | .06403 | 15.617 | 5.5863 | 13 |
| 14 | 1.5125 | .66113 | .08853 | 11.295 | .05853 | 17.085 | 6.0201 | 14 |
| 15 | 1.5579 | .64187 | .08377 | 11.937 | .05377 | 18.598 | 6.4491 | 15 |
| 16 | 1.6046 | .62318 | .07961 | 12.560 | .04961 | 20.156 | 6.8732 | 16 |
| 17 | 1.6528 | .60502 | .07595 | 13.165 | .04595 | 21.760 | 7.2926 | 17 |
| 18 | 1.7024 | .58740 | .07271 | 13.753 | .04271 | 23.413 | 7.7072 | 18 |
| 19 | 1.7534 | .57030 | .06982 | 14.323 | .03982 | 25.115 | 8.1169 | 19 |
| 20 | 1.8060 | .55369 | .06722 | 14.877 | .03722 | 26.869 | 8.5219 | 20 |
| 21 | 1.8602 | .53756 | .06487 | 15.414 | .03487 | 28.675 | 8.9221 | 21 |
| 22 | 1.9160 | .52190 | .06275 | 15.936 | .03275 | 30.535 | 9.3176 | 22 |
| 23 | 1.9735 | .50670 | .06082 | 16.443 | .03082 | 32.451 | 9.7084 | 23 |
| 24 | 2.0327 | .49194 | .05905 | 16.935 | .02905 | 34.425 | 10.094 | 24 |
| 25 | 2.0937 | .47762 | .05743 | 17.412 | .02743 | 36.457 | 10.475 | 25 |
| 26 | 2.1565 | .46370 | .05594 | 17.876 | .02594 | 38.551 | 10.852 | 26 |
| 27 | 2.2212 | .45020 | .05457 | 18.326 | .02457 | 40.707 | 11.224 | 27 |
| 28 | 2.2878 | .43709 | .05329 | 18.763 | .02329 | 42.929 | 11.592 | 28 |
| 29 | 2.3565 | .42436 | .05212 | 19.188 | .02212 | 45.217 | 11.954 | 29 |
| 30 | 2.4272 | .41200 | .05102 | 19.600 | .02102 | 47.573 | 12.313 | 30 |
| 31 | 2.5000 | .40000 | .05000 | 20.000 | .02000 | 50.000 | 12.666 | 31 |
| 32 | 2.5750 | .38835 | .04905 | 20.388 | .01905 | 52.500 | 13.016 | 32 |
| 33 | 2.6522 | .37704 | .04816 | 20.765 | .01816 | 55.075 | 13.360 | 33 |
| 34 | 2.7318 | .36606 | .04732 | 21.131 | .01732 | 57.727 | 13.700 | 34 |
| 35 | 2.8137 | .35539 | .04654 | 21.486 | .01654 | 60.459 | 14.036 | 35 |
| 40 | 3.2619 | .30657 | .04326 | 23.114 | .01326 | 75.397 | 15.649 | 40 |
| 45 | 3.7814 | .26445 | .04079 | 24.518 | .01079 | 92.715 | 17.154 | 45 |
| 50 | 4.3837 | .22812 | .03887 | 25.729 | .00887 | 112.79 | 18.556 | 50 |
| 55 | 5.0819 | .19678 | .03735 | 26.774 | .00735 | 136.06 | 19.859 | 55 |
| 60 | 5.8913 | .16974 | .03613 | 27.675 | .00613 | 163.04 | 21.066 | 60 |
| 65 | 6.8296 | .14642 | .03515 | 28.452 | .00515 | 194.32 | 22.183 | 65 |
| 70 | 7.9173 | .12630 | .03434 | 29.123 | .00434 | 230.57 | 23.213 | 70 |
| 75 | 9.1783 | .10895 | .03367 | 29.701 | .00367 | 272.61 | 24.162 | 75 |
| 80 | 10.640 | .09398 | .03311 | 30.200 | .00311 | 321.33 | 25.034 | 80 |
| 85 | 12.334 | .08107 | .03265 | 30.630 | .00265 | 377.82 | 25.834 | 85 |
| 90 | 14.299 | .06993 | .03226 | 31.002 | .00226 | 443.31 | 26.566 | 90 |
| 95 | 16.576 | .06033 | .03193 | 31.322 | .00193 | 519.22 | 27.234 | 95 |
| 100 | 19.217 | .05204 | .03165 | 31.598 | .00165 | 607.23 | 27.843 | 100 |

**4% Interest Factors for Discrete Compounding Periods**

| | SINGLE PAYMENT | | UNIFORM SERIES | | | | | |
|---|---|---|---|---|---|---|---|---|
| | Compound Amount Factor | Present Worth Factor | Capital Recovery Factor | Present Worth Factor | Sinking Fund Factor | Compound Amount Factor | Gradient Factor | |
| $N$ | $(F/P, 4, N)$ | $(P/F, 4, N)$ | $(A/P, 4, N)$ | $(P/A, 4, N)$ | $(A/F, 4, N)$ | $(F/A, 4, N)$ | $(A/G, 4, N)$ | $N$ |
| 1 | 1.0400 | .96154 | 1.0400 | .9615 | 1.0000 | 1.0000 | .0000 | 1 |
| 2 | 1.0816 | .92456 | .53020 | 1.8860 | .49020 | 2.0399 | .4900 | 2 |
| 3 | 1.1248 | .88900 | .36035 | 2.7750 | .32035 | 3.1215 | .9736 | 3 |
| 4 | 1.1698 | .85481 | .27549 | 3.6298 | .23549 | 4.2464 | 1.4506 | 4 |
| 5 | 1.2166 | .82193 | .22463 | 4.4517 | .18463 | 5.4162 | 1.9213 | 5 |
| 6 | 1.2653 | .79032 | .19076 | 5.2420 | .15076 | 6.6328 | 2.3853 | 6 |
| 7 | 1.3159 | .75992 | .16661 | 6.0019 | .12661 | 7.8981 | 2.8429 | 7 |
| 8 | 1.3685 | .73069 | .14853 | 6.7326 | .10853 | 9.2140 | 3.2940 | 8 |
| 9 | 1.4233 | .70259 | .13449 | 7.4352 | .09449 | 10.582 | 3.7387 | 9 |
| 10 | 1.4802 | .67557 | .12329 | 8.1108 | .08329 | 12.005 | 4.1769 | 10 |
| 11 | 1.5394 | .64958 | .11415 | 8.7603 | .07415 | 13.486 | 4.6086 | 11 |
| 12 | 1.6010 | .62460 | .10655 | 9.3849 | .06655 | 15.025 | 5.0339 | 12 |
| 13 | 1.6650 | .60058 | .10014 | 9.9855 | .06014 | 16.626 | 5.4529 | 13 |
| 14 | 1.7316 | .57748 | .09467 | 10.563 | .05467 | 18.291 | 5.8655 | 14 |
| 15 | 1.8009 | .55527 | .08994 | 11.118 | .04994 | 20.023 | 6.2717 | 15 |
| 16 | 1.8729 | .53391 | .08582 | 11.652 | .04582 | 21.824 | 6.6716 | 16 |
| 17 | 1.9478 | .51338 | .08220 | 12.165 | .04220 | 23.697 | 7.0652 | 17 |
| 18 | 2.0257 | .49363 | .07899 | 12.659 | .03899 | 25.644 | 7.4526 | 18 |
| 19 | 2.1068 | .47465 | .07614 | 13.133 | .03614 | 27.670 | 7.8338 | 19 |
| 20 | 2.1911 | .45639 | .07358 | 13.590 | .03358 | 29.777 | 8.2087 | 20 |
| 21 | 2.2787 | .43884 | .07128 | 14.029 | .03128 | 31.968 | 8.5775 | 21 |
| 22 | 2.3698 | .42196 | .06920 | 14.450 | .02920 | 34.247 | 8.9402 | 22 |
| 23 | 2.4646 | .40573 | .06731 | 14.856 | .02731 | 36.617 | 9.2969 | 23 |
| 24 | 2.5632 | .39013 | .06559 | 15.246 | .02559 | 39.081 | 9.6475 | 24 |
| 25 | 2.6658 | .37512 | .06401 | 15.621 | .02401 | 41.644 | 9.9921 | 25 |
| 26 | 2.7724 | .36069 | .06257 | 15.982 | .02257 | 44.310 | 10.330 | 26 |
| 27 | 2.8833 | .34682 | .06124 | 16.329 | .02124 | 47.083 | 10.663 | 27 |
| 28 | 2.9986 | .33348 | .06001 | 16.662 | .02001 | 49.966 | 10.990 | 28 |
| 29 | 3.1186 | .32066 | .05888 | 16.983 | .01888 | 52.964 | 11.311 | 29 |
| 30 | 3.2433 | .30832 | .05783 | 17.291 | .01783 | 56.083 | 11.627 | 30 |
| 31 | 3.3730 | .29647 | .05686 | 17.588 | .01686 | 59.326 | 11.936 | 31 |
| 32 | 3.5079 | .28506 | .05595 | 17.873 | .01595 | 62.699 | 12.240 | 32 |
| 33 | 3.6483 | .27410 | .05510 | 18.147 | .01510 | 66.207 | 12.539 | 33 |
| 34 | 3.7942 | .26356 | .05432 | 18.411 | .01432 | 69.855 | 12.832 | 34 |
| 35 | 3.9460 | .25342 | .05358 | 18.664 | .01358 | 73.650 | 13.119 | 35 |
| 40 | 4.8009 | .20829 | .05052 | 19.792 | .01052 | 95.022 | 14.476 | 40 |
| 45 | 5.8410 | .17120 | .04826 | 20.719 | .00826 | 121.02 | 15.704 | 45 |
| 50 | 7.1064 | .14072 | .04655 | 21.482 | .00655 | 152.66 | 16.811 | 50 |
| 55 | 8.6460 | .11566 | .04523 | 22.108 | .00523 | 191.15 | 17.806 | 55 |
| 60 | 10.519 | .09506 | .04420 | 22.623 | .00420 | 237.98 | 18.696 | 60 |
| 65 | 12.798 | .07814 | .04339 | 23.046 | .00339 | 294.95 | 19.490 | 65 |
| 70 | 15.570 | .06422 | .04275 | 23.394 | .00275 | 364.27 | 20.195 | 70 |
| 75 | 18.944 | .05279 | .04223 | 23.680 | .00223 | 448.60 | 20.820 | 75 |
| 80 | 23.048 | .04339 | .04181 | 23.915 | .00181 | 551.21 | 21.371 | 80 |
| 85 | 28.042 | .03566 | .04148 | 24.108 | .00148 | 676.05 | 21.856 | 85 |
| 90 | 34.117 | .02931 | .04121 | 24.267 | .00121 | 827.93 | 22.282 | 90 |
| 95 | 41.508 | .02409 | .04099 | 24.397 | .00099 | 1012.7 | 22.654 | 95 |
| 100 | 50.501 | .01980 | .04081 | 24.504 | .00081 | 1237.5 | 22.979 | 100 |

**5% Interest Factors for Discrete Compounding Periods**

| | SINGLE PAYMENT | | UNIFORM SERIES | | | | | |
|---|---|---|---|---|---|---|---|---|
| | Compound Amount Factor | Present Worth Factor | Capital Recovery Factor | Present Worth Factor | Sinking Fund Factor | Compound Amount Factor | Gradient Factor | |
| $N$ | $(F/P, 5, N)$ | $(P/F, 5, N)$ | $(A/P, 5, N)$ | $(P/A, 5, N)$ | $(A/F, 5, N)$ | $(F/A, 5, N)$ | $(A/G, 5, N)$ | $N$ |
| 1 | 1.0500 | .95238 | 1.0500 | .9524 | 1.0000 | 1.0000 | .0000 | 1 |
| 2 | 1.1025 | .90703 | .53781 | 1.8593 | .48781 | 2.0499 | .4874 | 2 |
| 3 | 1.1576 | .86384 | .36722 | 2.7231 | .31722 | 3.1524 | .9671 | 3 |
| 4 | 1.2155 | .82271 | .28202 | 3.5458 | .23202 | 4.3100 | 1.4386 | 4 |
| 5 | 1.2762 | .78353 | .23098 | 4.3294 | .18098 | 5.5255 | 1.9021 | 5 |
| 6 | 1.3400 | .74622 | .19702 | 5.0756 | .14702 | 6.8017 | 2.3575 | 6 |
| 7 | 1.4070 | .71069 | .17282 | 5.7862 | .12282 | 8.1418 | 2.8048 | 7 |
| 8 | 1.4774 | .67684 | .15472 | 6.4631 | .10472 | 9.5488 | 3.2441 | 8 |
| 9 | 1.5513 | .64461 | .14069 | 7.1077 | .09069 | 11.026 | 3.6753 | 9 |
| 10 | 1.6288 | .61392 | .12951 | 7.7216 | .07951 | 12.577 | 4.0986 | 10 |
| 11 | 1.7103 | .58469 | .12039 | 8.3062 | .07039 | 14.206 | 4.5140 | 11 |
| 12 | 1.7958 | .55684 | .11283 | 8.8631 | .06283 | 15.916 | 4.9214 | 12 |
| 13 | 1.8856 | .53033 | .10646 | 9.3934 | .05646 | 17.712 | 5.3211 | 13 |
| 14 | 1.9799 | .50507 | .10103 | 9.8985 | .05103 | 19.598 | 5.7128 | 14 |
| 15 | 2.0789 | .48102 | .09634 | 10.379 | .04634 | 21.577 | 6.0969 | 15 |
| 16 | 2.1828 | .45812 | .09227 | 10.837 | .04227 | 23.656 | 6.4732 | 16 |
| 17 | 2.2919 | .43630 | .08870 | 11.273 | .03870 | 25.839 | 6.8418 | 17 |
| 18 | 2.4065 | .41553 | .08555 | 11.689 | .03555 | 28.131 | 7.2029 | 18 |
| 19 | 2.5269 | .39574 | .08275 | 12.085 | .03275 | 30.538 | 7.5565 | 19 |
| 20 | 2.6532 | .37690 | .08024 | 12.462 | .03024 | 33.064 | 7.9025 | 20 |
| 21 | 2.7859 | .35895 | .07800 | 12.821 | .02800 | 35.718 | 8.2412 | 21 |
| 22 | 2.9252 | .34186 | .07597 | 13.162 | .02597 | 38.503 | 8.5725 | 22 |
| 23 | 3.0714 | .32558 | .07414 | 13.488 | .02414 | 41.429 | 8.8966 | 23 |
| 24 | 3.2250 | .31008 | .07247 | 13.798 | .02247 | 44.500 | 9.2135 | 24 |
| 25 | 3.3862 | .29531 | .07095 | 14.093 | .02095 | 47.725 | 9.5234 | 25 |
| 26 | 3.5555 | .28125 | .06956 | 14.375 | .01957 | 51.111 | 9.8261 | 26 |
| 27 | 3.7333 | .26786 | .06829 | 14.642 | .01829 | 54.667 | 10.122 | 27 |
| 28 | 3.9200 | .25510 | .06712 | 14.898 | .01712 | 58.400 | 10.411 | 28 |
| 29 | 4.1160 | .24295 | .06605 | 15.140 | .01605 | 62.320 | 10.693 | 29 |
| 30 | 4.3218 | .23138 | .06505 | 15.372 | .01505 | 66.436 | 10.968 | 30 |
| 31 | 4.5379 | .22037 | .06413 | 15.592 | .01413 | 70.757 | 11.237 | 31 |
| 32 | 4.7647 | .20987 | .06328 | 15.802 | .01328 | 75.295 | 11.500 | 32 |
| 33 | 5.0030 | .19988 | .06249 | 16.002 | .01249 | 80.060 | 11.756 | 33 |
| 34 | 5.2531 | .19036 | .06176 | 16.192 | .01176 | 85.063 | 12.005 | 34 |
| 35 | 5.5158 | .18130 | .06107 | 16.374 | .01107 | 90.316 | 12.249 | 35 |
| 40 | 7.0397 | .14205 | .05828 | 17.158 | .00828 | 120.79 | 13.277 | 40 |
| 45 | 8.9846 | .11130 | .05626 | 17.773 | .00626 | 159.69 | 14.364 | 45 |
| 50 | 11.466 | .08721 | .05478 | 18.255 | .00478 | 209.33 | 15.223 | 50 |
| 55 | 14.634 | .06833 | .05367 | 18.633 | .00367 | 272.69 | 15.966 | 55 |
| 60 | 18.678 | .05354 | .05283 | 18.929 | .00283 | 353.56 | 16.605 | 60 |
| 65 | 23.838 | .04195 | .05219 | 19.161 | .00219 | 456.76 | 17.153 | 65 |
| 70 | 30.424 | .03287 | .05170 | 19.342 | .00170 | 588.48 | 17.621 | 70 |
| 75 | 38.829 | .02575 | .05132 | 19.484 | .00132 | 756.59 | 18.017 | 75 |
| 80 | 49.557 | .02018 | .05103 | 19.596 | .00103 | 971.14 | 18.352 | 80 |
| 85 | 63.248 | .01581 | .05080 | 19.683 | .00080 | 1244.9 | 18.634 | 85 |
| 90 | 80.723 | .01239 | .05063 | 19.752 | .00063 | 1594.4 | 18.871 | 90 |
| 95 | 103.02 | .00971 | .05049 | 19.805 | .00049 | 2040.4 | 19.068 | 95 |
| 100 | 131.48 | .00761 | .05038 | 19.847 | .00038 | 2609.7 | 19.233 | 100 |

## 6% Interest Factors for Discrete Compounding Factors

| | SINGLE PAYMENT | | UNIFORM SERIES | | | | | |
|---|---|---|---|---|---|---|---|---|
| | Compound Amount Factor | Present Worth Factor | Capital Recovery Factor | Present Worth Factor | Sinking Fund Factor | Compound Amount Factor | Gradient Factor | |
| N | (F/P, 6, N) | (P/F, 6, N) | (A/P, 6, N) | (P/A, 6, N) | (A/F, 6, N) | (F/A, 6, N) | (A/G, 6, N) | N |
| 1 | 1.0600 | .94340 | 1.0600 | .9434 | 1.0000 | 1.0000 | .0000 | 1 |
| 2 | 1.1236 | .89000 | .54544 | 1.8333 | .48544 | 2.0599 | .4852 | 2 |
| 3 | 1.1910 | .83962 | .37411 | 2.6729 | .31411 | 3.1835 | .9610 | 3 |
| 4 | 1.2624 | .79210 | .28860 | 3.4650 | .22860 | 4.3745 | 1.4269 | 4 |
| 5 | 1.3382 | .74726 | .23740 | 4.2123 | .17740 | 5.6370 | 1.8833 | 5 |
| 6 | 1.4185 | .70496 | .20337 | 4.9172 | .14337 | 6.9751 | 2.3301 | 6 |
| 7 | 1.5036 | .66506 | .17914 | 5.5823 | .11914 | 8.3936 | 2.7673 | 7 |
| 8 | 1.5938 | .62742 | .16104 | 6.2097 | .10104 | 9.8972 | 3.1949 | 8 |
| 9 | 1.6894 | .59190 | .14702 | 6.8016 | .08702 | 11.491 | 3.6130 | 9 |
| 10 | 1.7908 | .55840 | .13587 | 7.3600 | .07587 | 13.180 | 4.0217 | 10 |
| 11 | 1.8982 | .52679 | .12679 | 7.8867 | .06679 | 14.971 | 4.4210 | 11 |
| 12 | 2.0121 | .49698 | .11928 | 8.3837 | .05928 | 16.869 | 4.8109 | 12 |
| 13 | 2.1329 | .46884 | .11296 | 8.8525 | .05296 | 18.881 | 5.1917 | 13 |
| 14 | 2.2608 | .44231 | .10759 | 9.2948 | .04759 | 21.014 | 5.5632 | 14 |
| 15 | 2.3965 | .41727 | .10296 | 9.7121 | .04296 | 23.275 | 5.9257 | 15 |
| 16 | 2.5403 | .39365 | .09895 | 10.105 | .03895 | 25.671 | 6.2791 | 16 |
| 17 | 2.6927 | .37137 | .09545 | 10.477 | .03545 | 28.212 | 6.6237 | 17 |
| 18 | 2.8542 | .35035 | .09236 | 10.827 | .03236 | 30.904 | 6.9594 | 18 |
| 19 | 3.0255 | .33052 | .08962 | 11.158 | .02962 | 33.759 | 7.2864 | 19 |
| 20 | 3.2070 | .31181 | .08719 | 11.469 | .02719 | 36.784 | 7.6048 | 20 |
| 21 | 3.3995 | .29416 | .08501 | 11.763 | .02501 | 39.991 | 7.9148 | 21 |
| 22 | 3.6034 | .27751 | .08305 | 12.041 | .02305 | 43.390 | 8.2163 | 22 |
| 23 | 3.8196 | .26180 | .08128 | 12.303 | .02128 | 46.994 | 8.5096 | 23 |
| 24 | 4.0488 | .24698 | .07968 | 12.550 | .01968 | 50.814 | 8.7948 | 24 |
| 25 | 4.2917 | .23300 | .07823 | 12.783 | .01823 | 54.862 | 9.0719 | 25 |
| 26 | 4.5492 | .21982 | .07690 | 13.003 | .01690 | 59.154 | 9.3412 | 26 |
| 27 | 4.8222 | .20737 | .07570 | 13.210 | .01570 | 63.703 | 9.6027 | 27 |
| 28 | 5.1115 | .19564 | .07459 | 13.406 | .01459 | 68.525 | 9.8565 | 28 |
| 29 | 5.4182 | .18456 | .07358 | 13.590 | .01358 | 73.637 | 10.102 | 29 |
| 30 | 5.7433 | .17412 | .07265 | 13.764 | .01265 | 79.055 | 10.341 | 30 |
| 31 | 6.0879 | .16426 | .07179 | 13.929 | .01179 | 84.798 | 10.573 | 31 |
| 32 | 6.4531 | .15496 | .07100 | 14.083 | .01100 | 90.886 | 10.798 | 32 |
| 33 | 6.8403 | .14619 | .07027 | 14.230 | .01027 | 97.339 | 11.016 | 33 |
| 34 | 7.2507 | .13792 | .06960 | 14.368 | .00960 | 104.17 | 11.227 | 34 |
| 35 | 7.6858 | .13011 | .06897 | 14.498 | .00897 | 111.43 | 11.431 | 35 |
| 40 | 10.285 | .09723 | .06646 | 15.046 | .00646 | 154.75 | 12.358 | 40 |
| 45 | 13.764 | .07265 | .06470 | 15.455 | .00470 | 212.73 | 13.141 | 45 |
| 50 | 18.419 | .05429 | .06344 | 15.761 | .00344 | 290.32 | 13.796 | 50 |
| 55 | 24.649 | .04057 | .06254 | 15.990 | .00254 | 394.14 | 14.340 | 55 |
| 60 | 32.985 | .03032 | .06188 | 16.161 | .00188 | 533.09 | 14.790 | 60 |
| 65 | 44.142 | .02265 | .06139 | 16.289 | .00139 | 719.03 | 15.160 | 65 |
| 70 | 59.071 | .01693 | .06103 | 16.384 | .00103 | 967.86 | 15.461 | 70 |
| 75 | 79.051 | .01265 | .06077 | 16.455 | .00077 | 1300.8 | 15.705 | 75 |
| 80 | 105.78 | .00945 | .06057 | 16.509 | .00057 | 1746.4 | 15.903 | 80 |
| 85 | 141.56 | .00706 | .06043 | 16.548 | .00043 | 2342.7 | 16.061 | 85 |
| 90 | 189.44 | .00528 | .06032 | 16.578 | .00032 | 3140.7 | 16.189 | 90 |
| 95 | 253.52 | .00394 | .06024 | 16.600 | .00024 | 4208.7 | 16.290 | 95 |
| 100 | 339.26 | .00295 | .06018 | 16.617 | .00018 | 5637.8 | 16.371 | 100 |

**7% Interest Factors for Discrete Compounding Periods**

| | SINGLE PAYMENT | | UNIFORM SERIES | | | | | |
|---|---|---|---|---|---|---|---|---|
| | Compound Amount Factor | Present Worth Factor | Capital Recovery Factor | Present Worth Factor | Sinking Fund Factor | Compound Amount Factor | Gradient Factor | |
| $N$ | $(F/P, 7, N)$ | $(P/F, 7, N)$ | $(A/P, 7, N)$ | $(P/A, 7, N)$ | $(A/F, 7, N)$ | $(F/A, 7, N)$ | $(A/G, 7, N)$ | $N$ |
| 1 | 1.0700 | .93458 | 1.0700 | .9346 | 1.0000 | 1.000 | .0000 | 1 |
| 2 | 1.1449 | .87344 | .55310 | 1.8080 | .48310 | 2.0699 | .4830 | 2 |
| 3 | 1.2250 | .81630 | .38105 | 2.6242 | .31105 | 3.2148 | .9548 | 3 |
| 4 | 1.3107 | .76290 | .29523 | 3.3871 | .22523 | 4.4398 | 1.4153 | 4 |
| 5 | 1.4025 | .71299 | .24389 | 4.1001 | .17389 | 5.7506 | 1.8648 | 5 |
| 6 | 1.5007 | .66635 | .20980 | 4.7665 | .13980 | 7.1531 | 2.3030 | 6 |
| 7 | 1.6057 | .62275 | .18555 | 5.3892 | .11555 | 8.6539 | 2.7302 | 7 |
| 8 | 1.7181 | .58201 | .16747 | 5.9712 | .09747 | 10.259 | 3.1463 | 8 |
| 9 | 1.8384 | .54394 | .15349 | 6.5151 | .08349 | 11.977 | 3.5515 | 9 |
| 10 | 1.9671 | .50835 | .14238 | 7.0235 | .07238 | 13.816 | 3.9459 | 10 |
| 11 | 2.1048 | .47510 | .13336 | 7.4986 | .06336 | 15.783 | 4.3294 | 11 |
| 12 | 2.2521 | .44402 | .12590 | 7.9426 | .05590 | 17.888 | 4.7023 | 12 |
| 13 | 2.4098 | .41497 | .11965 | 8.3576 | .04965 | 20.140 | 5.0647 | 13 |
| 14 | 2.5785 | .38782 | .11435 | 8.7454 | .04435 | 22.550 | 5.4165 | 14 |
| 15 | 2.7590 | .36245 | .10980 | 9.1078 | .03980 | 25.128 | 5.7581 | 15 |
| 16 | 2.9521 | .33874 | .10586 | 9.4466 | .03586 | 27.887 | 6.0895 | 16 |
| 17 | 3.1587 | .31658 | .10243 | 9.7631 | .03243 | 30.839 | 6.4108 | 17 |
| 18 | 3.3798 | .29587 | .09941 | 10.059 | .02941 | 33.998 | 6.7223 | 18 |
| 19 | 3.6164 | .27651 | .09675 | 10.335 | .02675 | 37.378 | 7.0240 | 19 |
| 20 | 3.8696 | .25842 | .09439 | 10.593 | .02439 | 40.994 | 7.3161 | 20 |
| 21 | 4.1404 | .24152 | .09229 | 10.835 | .02229 | 44.864 | 7.5988 | 21 |
| 22 | 4.4303 | .22572 | .09041 | 11.061 | .02041 | 49.004 | 7.8723 | 22 |
| 23 | 4.7404 | .21095 | .08871 | 11.272 | .01871 | 53.434 | 8.1367 | 23 |
| 24 | 5.0722 | .19715 | .08719 | 11.469 | .01719 | 58.175 | 8.3922 | 24 |
| 25 | 5.4273 | .18425 | .08581 | 11.653 | .01581 | 63.247 | 8.6389 | 25 |
| 26 | 5.8072 | .17220 | .08456 | 11.825 | .01456 | 68.674 | 8.8772 | 26 |
| 27 | 6.2137 | .16093 | .08343 | 11.986 | .01343 | 74.481 | 9.1070 | 27 |
| 28 | 6.6486 | .15041 | .08239 | 12.137 | .01239 | 80.695 | 9.3288 | 28 |
| 29 | 7.1140 | .14057 | .08145 | 12.277 | .01145 | 87.344 | 9.5425 | 29 |
| 30 | 7.6120 | .13137 | .08059 | 12.409 | .01059 | 94.458 | 9.7485 | 30 |
| 31 | 8.1449 | .12278 | .07980 | 12.531 | .00980 | 102.07 | 9.9469 | 31 |
| 32 | 8.7150 | .11474 | .07907 | 12.646 | .00907 | 110.21 | 10.137 | 32 |
| 33 | 9.3250 | .10724 | .07841 | 12.753 | .00841 | 118.92 | 10.321 | 33 |
| 34 | 9.9778 | .10022 | .07780 | 12.853 | .00780 | 128.25 | 10.498 | 34 |
| 35 | 10.676 | .09367 | .07723 | 12.947 | .00723 | 138.23 | 10.668 | 35 |
| 40 | 14.973 | .06678 | .07501 | 13.331 | .00501 | 199.62 | 11.423 | 40 |
| 45 | 21.001 | .04762 | .07350 | 13.605 | .00350 | 285.73 | 12.035 | 45 |
| 50 | 29.455 | .03395 | .07246 | 13.800 | .00246 | 406.51 | 12.528 | 50 |
| 55 | 41.313 | .02421 | .07174 | 13.939 | .00174 | 575.90 | 12.921 | 55 |
| 60 | 57.943 | .01726 | .07123 | 14.039 | .00123 | 813.47 | 13.232 | 60 |
| 65 | 81.268 | .01230 | .07087 | 14.109 | .00087 | 1146.6 | 13.475 | 65 |
| 70 | 113.98 | .00877 | .07062 | 14.160 | .00062 | 1614.0 | 13.666 | 70 |
| 75 | 159.86 | .00626 | .07044 | 14.196 | .00044 | 2269.5 | 13.813 | 75 |
| 80 | 224.21 | .00446 | .07031 | 14.222 | .00031 | 3188.8 | 13.927 | 80 |
| 85 | 314.47 | .00318 | .07022 | 14.240 | .00022 | 4478.2 | 14.014 | 85 |
| 90 | 441.06 | .00227 | .07016 | 14.253 | .00016 | 6286.7 | 14.081 | 90 |
| 95 | 618.62 | .00162 | .07011 | 14.262 | .00011 | 8823.1 | 14.131 | 95 |
| 100 | 867.64 | .00115 | .07008 | 14.269 | .00008 | 12381.7 | 14.170 | 100 |

## 8% Interest Factors for Discrete Compounding Periods

| | SINGLE PAYMENT | | UNIFORM SERIES | | | | | |
| | Compound Amount Factor | Present Worth Factor | Capital Recovery Factor | Present Worth Factor | Sinking Fund Factor | Compound Amount Factor | Gradient Factor | |
| $N$ | $(F/P, 8, N)$ | $(P/F, 8, N)$ | $(A/P, 8, N)$ | $(P/A, 8, N)$ | $(A/F, 8, N)$ | $(F/A, 8, N)$ | $(A/G, 8, N)$ | $N$ |
|---|---|---|---|---|---|---|---|---|
| 1 | 1.0800 | .92593 | 1.0800 | .9259 | 1.0000 | 1.0000 | .0000 | 1 |
| 2 | 1.1664 | .85734 | .56077 | 1.7832 | .48077 | 2.0799 | .4807 | 2 |
| 3 | 1.2597 | .79383 | .38803 | 2.5770 | .30804 | 3.2463 | .9487 | 3 |
| 4 | 1.3604 | .73503 | .30192 | 3.3121 | .22192 | 4.5060 | 1.4038 | 4 |
| 5 | 1.4693 | .68059 | .25046 | 3.9926 | .17046 | 5.8665 | 1.8463 | 5 |
| 6 | 1.5868 | .63017 | .21632 | 4.6228 | .13632 | 7.3358 | 2.2762 | 6 |
| 7 | 1.7138 | .58349 | .19207 | 5.2063 | .11207 | 8.9227 | 2.6935 | 7 |
| 8 | 1.8509 | .54027 | .17402 | 5.7466 | .09402 | 10.636 | 3.0984 | 8 |
| 9 | 1.9989 | .50025 | .16008 | 6.2468 | .08008 | 12.487 | 3.4909 | 9 |
| 10 | 2.1589 | .46320 | .14903 | 6.7100 | .06903 | 14.486 | 3.8712 | 10 |
| 11 | 2.3316 | .42889 | .14008 | 7.1389 | .06008 | 16.645 | 4.2394 | 11 |
| 12 | 2.5181 | .39712 | .13270 | 7.5360 | .05270 | 18.976 | 4.5956 | 12 |
| 13 | 2.7196 | .36770 | .12652 | 7.9037 | .04652 | 21.495 | 4.9401 | 13 |
| 14 | 2.9371 | .34046 | .12130 | 8.2442 | .04130 | 24.214 | 5.2729 | 14 |
| 15 | 3.1721 | .31524 | .11683 | 8.5594 | .03683 | 27.151 | 5.5943 | 15 |
| 16 | 3.4259 | .29189 | .11298 | 8.8513 | .03298 | 30.323 | 5.9045 | 16 |
| 17 | 3.6999 | .27027 | .10963 | 9.1216 | .02963 | 33.749 | 6.2036 | 17 |
| 18 | 3.9959 | .25025 | .10670 | 9.3718 | .02670 | 37.449 | 6.4919 | 18 |
| 19 | 4.3156 | .23171 | .10413 | 9.6035 | .02413 | 41.445 | 6.7696 | 19 |
| 20 | 4.6609 | .21455 | .10185 | 9.8181 | .02185 | 45.761 | 7.0368 | 20 |
| 21 | 5.0337 | .19866 | .09983 | 10.016 | .01983 | 50.422 | 7.2939 | 21 |
| 22 | 5.4364 | .18394 | .09803 | 10.200 | .01803 | 55.455 | 7.5411 | 22 |
| 23 | 5.8713 | .17032 | .09642 | 10.371 | .01642 | 60.892 | 7.7785 | 23 |
| 24 | 6.3410 | .15770 | .09498 | 10.528 | .01498 | 66.763 | 8.0065 | 24 |
| 25 | 6.8483 | .14602 | .09368 | 10.674 | .01368 | 73.104 | 8.2253 | 25 |
| 26 | 7.3962 | .13520 | .09251 | 10.809 | .01251 | 79.953 | 8.4351 | 26 |
| 27 | 7.9879 | .12519 | .09145 | 10.935 | .01145 | 87.349 | 8.6362 | 27 |
| 28 | 8.6269 | .11592 | .09049 | 11.051 | .01049 | 95.337 | 8.8288 | 28 |
| 29 | 9.3171 | .10733 | .08962 | 11.158 | .00962 | 103.96 | 9.0132 | 29 |
| 30 | 10.062 | .09938 | .08883 | 11.257 | .00883 | 113.28 | 9.1896 | 30 |
| 31 | 10.867 | .09202 | .08811 | 11.349 | .00811 | 123.34 | 9.3583 | 31 |
| 32 | 11.736 | .08520 | .08745 | 11.434 | .00745 | 134.21 | 9.5196 | 32 |
| 33 | 12.675 | .07889 | .08685 | 11.513 | .00685 | 145.94 | 9.6736 | 33 |
| 34 | 13.689 | .07305 | .08630 | 11.586 | .00630 | 158.62 | 9.8207 | 34 |
| 35 | 14.785 | .06764 | .08580 | 11.654 | .00580 | 172.31 | 9.9610 | 35 |
| 40 | 21.724 | .04603 | .08386 | 11.924 | .00386 | 259.05 | 10.569 | 40 |
| 45 | 31.919 | .03133 | .08259 | 12.108 | .00259 | 386.49 | 11.044 | 45 |
| 50 | 46.900 | .02132 | .08174 | 12.233 | .00174 | 573.75 | 11.410 | 50 |
| 55 | 68.911 | .01451 | .08118 | 12.318 | .00118 | 848.89 | 11.690 | 55 |
| 60 | 101.25 | .00988 | .08080 | 12.376 | .00080 | 1253.1 | 11.901 | 60 |
| 65 | 148.77 | .00672 | .08054 | 12.416 | .00054 | 1847.1 | 12.060 | 65 |
| 70 | 218.59 | .00457 | .08037 | 12.442 | .00037 | 2719.9 | 12.178 | 70 |
| 75 | 321.19 | .00311 | .08025 | 12.461 | .00025 | 4002.3 | 12.265 | 75 |
| 80 | 471.93 | .00212 | .08017 | 12.473 | .00017 | 5886.6 | 12.330 | 80 |
| 85 | 693.42 | .00144 | .08012 | 12.481 | .00012 | 8655.2 | 12.377 | 85 |
| 90 | 1018.8 | .00098 | .08008 | 12.487 | .00008 | 12723.9 | 12.411 | 90 |
| 95 | 1497.0 | .00067 | .08005 | 12.491 | .00005 | 18701.5 | 12.436 | 95 |
| 100 | 2199.6 | .00045 | .08004 | 12.494 | .00004 | 27484.5 | 12.454 | 100 |

**9% Interest Factors for Discrete Compounding Periods**

| | SINGLE PAYMENT | | UNIFORM SERIES | | | | | |
|---|---|---|---|---|---|---|---|---|
| | Compound Amount Factor | Present Worth Factor | Capital Recovery Factor | Present Worth Factor | Sinking Fund Factor | Compound Amount Factor | Gradient Factor | |
| $N$ | $(F/P, 9, N)$ | $(P/F, 9, N)$ | $(A/P, 9, N)$ | $(P/A, 9, N)$ | $(A/F, 9, N)$ | $(F/A, 9, N)$ | $(A/G, 9, N)$ | $N$ |
| 1 | 1.0900 | .91743 | 1.0900 | .9174 | 1.0000 | 1.0000 | .0000 | 1 |
| 2 | 1.1881 | .84168 | .56847 | 1.7591 | .47847 | 2.0899 | .4784 | 2 |
| 3 | 1.2950 | .77219 | .39506 | 2.5312 | .30506 | 3.2780 | .9425 | 3 |
| 4 | 1.4115 | .70843 | .30867 | 3.2396 | .21867 | 4.5730 | 1.3923 | 4 |
| 5 | 1.5386 | .64993 | .25709 | 3.8896 | .16709 | 5.9846 | 1.8280 | 5 |
| 6 | 1.6770 | .59627 | .22292 | 4.4858 | .13292 | 7.5232 | 2.2496 | 6 |
| 7 | 1.8280 | .54704 | .19869 | 5.0329 | .10869 | 9.2002 | 2.6572 | 7 |
| 8 | 1.9925 | .50187 | .18068 | 5.5347 | .09068 | 11.028 | 3.0510 | 8 |
| 9 | 2.1718 | .46043 | .16680 | 5.9952 | .07680 | 13.020 | 3.4311 | 9 |
| 10 | 2.3673 | .42241 | .15582 | 6.4176 | .06582 | 15.192 | 3.7976 | 10 |
| 11 | 2.5804 | .38754 | .14695 | 6.8051 | .05695 | 17.559 | 4.1508 | 11 |
| 12 | 2.8126 | .35554 | .13965 | 7.1606 | .04965 | 20.140 | 4.4909 | 12 |
| 13 | 3.0657 | .32618 | .13357 | 7.4868 | .04357 | 22.952 | 4.8180 | 13 |
| 14 | 3.3416 | .29925 | .12843 | 7.7861 | .03843 | 26.018 | 5.1325 | 14 |
| 15 | 3.6424 | .27454 | .12406 | 8.0606 | .03406 | 29.360 | 5.4345 | 15 |
| 16 | 3.9702 | .25187 | .12030 | 8.3125 | .03030 | 33.002 | 5.7243 | 16 |
| 17 | 4.3275 | .23108 | .11705 | 8.5435 | .02705 | 36.972 | 6.0022 | 17 |
| 18 | 4.7170 | .21200 | .11421 | 8.7555 | .02421 | 41.300 | 6.2685 | 18 |
| 19 | 5.1415 | .19449 | .11173 | 8.9500 | .02173 | 46.017 | 6.5234 | 19 |
| 20 | 5.6043 | .17843 | .10955 | 9.1285 | .01955 | 51.158 | 6.7673 | 20 |
| 21 | 6.1086 | .16370 | .10762 | 9.2922 | .01762 | 56.763 | 7.0004 | 21 |
| 22 | 6.6584 | .15018 | .10591 | 9.4423 | .01591 | 62.871 | 7.2231 | 22 |
| 23 | 7.2577 | .13778 | .10438 | 9.5801 | .01438 | 69.530 | 7.4356 | 23 |
| 24 | 7.9109 | .12641 | .10302 | 9.7065 | .01302 | 76.787 | 7.6383 | 24 |
| 25 | 8.6228 | .11597 | .10181 | 9.8225 | .01181 | 84.698 | 7.8315 | 25 |
| 26 | 9.3989 | .10640 | .10072 | 9.9289 | .01072 | 93.321 | 8.0154 | 26 |
| 27 | 10.244 | .09761 | .09974 | 10.026 | .00974 | 102.72 | 8.1905 | 27 |
| 28 | 11.166 | .08955 | .09885 | 10.116 | .00885 | 112.96 | 8.3570 | 28 |
| 29 | 12.171 | .08216 | .09806 | 10.198 | .00806 | 124.13 | 8.5153 | 29 |
| 30 | 13.267 | .07537 | .09734 | 10.273 | .00734 | 136.30 | 8.6655 | 30 |
| 31 | 14.461 | .06915 | .09669 | 10.342 | .00669 | 149.57 | 8.8082 | 31 |
| 32 | 15.762 | .06344 | .09610 | 10.406 | .00610 | 164.03 | 8.9435 | 32 |
| 33 | 17.181 | .05820 | .09556 | 10.464 | .00556 | 179.79 | 9.0717 | 33 |
| 34 | 18.727 | .05340 | .09508 | 10.517 | .00508 | 196.97 | 9.1932 | 34 |
| 35 | 20.413 | .04899 | .09464 | 10.566 | .00464 | 215.70 | 9.3082 | 35 |
| 40 | 31.408 | .03184 | .09296 | 10.757 | .00296 | 337.86 | 9.7956 | 40 |
| 45 | 48.325 | .02069 | .09190 | 10.881 | .00190 | 525.83 | 10.160 | 45 |
| 50 | 74.353 | .01345 | .09123 | 10.961 | .00123 | 815.04 | 10.429 | 50 |
| 55 | 114.40 | .00874 | .09079 | 11.014 | .00079 | 1260.0 | 10.626 | 55 |
| 60 | 176.02 | .00568 | .09051 | 11.047 | .00051 | 1944.6 | 10.768 | 60 |
| 65 | 270.82 | .00369 | .09033 | 11.070 | .00033 | 2998.0 | 10.870 | 65 |
| 70 | 416.70 | .00240 | .09022 | 11.084 | .00022 | 4618.9 | 10.942 | 70 |
| 75 | 641.14 | .00156 | .09014 | 11.093 | .00014 | 7112.7 | 10.993 | 75 |
| 80 | 986.47 | .00101 | .09009 | 11.099 | .00009 | 10950.6 | 11.029 | 80 |
| 85 | 1517.8 | .00066 | .09006 | 11.103 | .00006 | 16854.8 | 11.055 | 85 |
| 90 | 2335.3 | .00043 | .09004 | 11.106 | .00004 | 25939.2 | 11.072 | 90 |
| 95 | 3593.1 | .00028 | .09002 | 11.108 | .00003 | 39916.6 | 11.084 | 95 |
| 100 | 5528.4 | .00018 | .09002 | 11.109 | .00002 | 61422.7 | 11.093 | 100 |

## 10% Interest Factors for Discrete Compounding Periods

| | SINGLE PAYMENT | | UNIFORM SERIES | | | | | |
| | Compound Amount Factor | Present Worth Factor | Capital Recovery Factor | Present Worth Factor | Sinking Fund Factor | Compound Amount Factor | Gradient Factor | |
| $N$ | $(F/P, 10, N)$ | $(P/F, 10, N)$ | $(A/P, 10, N)$ | $(P/A, 10, N)$ | $(A/F, 10, N)$ | $(F/A, 10, N)$ | $(A/G, 10, N)$ | $N$ |
|---|---|---|---|---|---|---|---|---|
| 1 | 1.1000 | .90909 | 1.1000 | .9091 | 1.0000 | 1.000 | .0000 | 1 |
| 2 | 1.2100 | .82645 | .57619 | 1.7355 | .47619 | 2.0999 | .4761 | 2 |
| 3 | 1.3310 | .75132 | .40212 | 2.4868 | .30212 | 3.3099 | .9365 | 3 |
| 4 | 1.4641 | .68302 | .31547 | 3.1698 | .21547 | 4.6409 | 1.3810 | 4 |
| 5 | 1.6105 | .62092 | .26380 | 3.7907 | .16380 | 6.1050 | 1.8100 | 5 |
| 6 | 1.7715 | .56448 | .22961 | 4.3552 | .12961 | 7.7155 | 2.2234 | 6 |
| 7 | 1.9487 | .51316 | .20541 | 4.8683 | .10541 | 9.4870 | 2.6215 | 7 |
| 8 | 2.1435 | .46651 | .18745 | 5.3349 | .08745 | 11.435 | 3.0043 | 8 |
| 9 | 2.3579 | .42410 | .17364 | 5.7589 | .07364 | 13.579 | 3.3722 | 9 |
| 10 | 2.5937 | .38555 | .16275 | 6.1445 | .06275 | 15.937 | 3.7253 | 10 |
| 11 | 2.8530 | .35050 | .15396 | 6.4950 | .05396 | 18.530 | 4.0639 | 11 |
| 12 | 3.1384 | .31863 | .14676 | 6.8136 | .04676 | 21.383 | 4.3883 | 12 |
| 13 | 3.4522 | .28967 | .14078 | 7.1033 | .04078 | 24.522 | 4.6987 | 13 |
| 14 | 3.7974 | .26333 | .13575 | 7.3666 | .03575 | 27.974 | 4.9954 | 14 |
| 15 | 4.1771 | .23940 | .13147 | 7.6060 | .03147 | 31.771 | 5.2788 | 15 |
| 16 | 4.5949 | .21763 | .12782 | 7.8236 | .02782 | 35.949 | 5.5492 | 16 |
| 17 | 5.0544 | .19785 | .12466 | 8.0215 | .02466 | 40.543 | 5.8070 | 17 |
| 18 | 5.5598 | .17986 | .12193 | 8.2013 | .02193 | 45.598 | 6.0524 | 18 |
| 19 | 6.1158 | .16351 | .11955 | 8.3649 | .01955 | 61.158 | 6.2860 | 19 |
| 20 | 6.7273 | .14865 | .11746 | 8.5135 | .01746 | 57.273 | 6.5080 | 20 |
| 21 | 7.4001 | .13513 | .11562 | 8.6486 | .01562 | 64.001 | 6.7188 | 21 |
| 22 | 8.1401 | .12285 | .11401 | 8.7715 | .01401 | 71.401 | 6.9188 | 22 |
| 23 | 8.9541 | .11168 | .11257 | 8.8832 | .01257 | 79.541 | 7.1084 | 23 |
| 24 | 9.8495 | .10153 | .11130 | 8.9847 | .01130 | 88.495 | 7.2879 | 24 |
| 25 | 10.834 | .09230 | .11017 | 9.0770 | .01017 | 98.344 | 7.4579 | 25 |
| 26 | 11.917 | .08391 | .10916 | 9.1609 | .00916 | 109.17 | 7.6185 | 26 |
| 27 | 13.109 | .07628 | .10826 | 9.2372 | .00826 | 121.09 | 7.7703 | 27 |
| 28 | 14.420 | .06935 | .10745 | 9.3065 | .00745 | 134.20 | 7.9136 | 28 |
| 29 | 15.862 | .06304 | .10673 | 9.3696 | .00673 | 148.62 | 8.0488 | 29 |
| 30 | 17.448 | .05731 | .10608 | 9.4269 | .00608 | 164.48 | 8.1761 | 30 |
| 31 | 19.193 | .05210 | .10550 | 9.4790 | .00550 | 181.93 | 8.2961 | 31 |
| 32 | 21.113 | .04736 | .10497 | 9.5263 | .00497 | 201.13 | 8.4090 | 32 |
| 33 | 23.224 | .04306 | .10450 | 9.5694 | .00450 | 222.24 | 8.5151 | 33 |
| 34 | 25.546 | .03914 | .10407 | 9.6085 | .00407 | 245.46 | 8.6149 | 34 |
| 35 | 28.101 | .03559 | .10369 | 9.6441 | .00369 | 271.01 | 8.7085 | 35 |
| 40 | 45.257 | .02210 | .10226 | 9.7790 | .00226 | 442.57 | 9.0962 | 40 |
| 45 | 72.887 | .01372 | .10139 | 9.8628 | .00139 | 718.87 | 9.3740 | 45 |
| 50 | 117.38 | .00852 | .10086 | 9.9148 | .00086 | 1163.8 | 9.5704 | 50 |
| 55 | 189.04 | .00529 | .10053 | 9.9471 | .00053 | 1880.4 | 9.7075 | 55 |
| 60 | 304.46 | .00328 | .10033 | 9.9671 | .00033 | 3034.6 | 9.8022 | 60 |
| 65 | 490.34 | .00204 | .10020 | 9.9796 | .00020 | 4893.4 | 9.8671 | 65 |
| 70 | 789.69 | .00127 | .10013 | 9.9873 | .00013 | 7886.9 | 9.9112 | 70 |
| 75 | 1271.8 | .00079 | .10008 | 9.9921 | .00008 | 12709.0 | 9.9409 | 75 |
| 80 | 2048.2 | .00049 | .10005 | 9.9951 | .00005 | 20474.0 | 9.9609 | 80 |
| 85 | 3298.7 | .00030 | .10003 | 9.9969 | .00003 | 32979.7 | 9.9742 | 85 |
| 90 | 5312.5 | .00019 | .10002 | 9.9981 | .00002 | 53120.2 | 9.9830 | 90 |
| 95 | 8555.9 | .00012 | .10001 | 9.9988 | .00001 | 85556.8 | 9.9889 | 95 |
| 100 | 13780.6 | .00007 | .10001 | 9.9992 | .00001 | 137796.1 | 9.9927 | 100 |

**11% Interest Factors for Discrete Compounding Periods**

| | SINGLE PAYMENT | | UNIFORM SERIES | | | | | |
|---|---|---|---|---|---|---|---|---|
| | Compound Amount Factor | Present Worth Factor | Capital Recovery Factor | Present Worth Factor | Sinking Fund Factor | Compound Amount Factor | Gradient Factor | |
| $N$ | $(F/P, 11, N)$ | $(P/F, 11, N)$ | $(A/P, 11, N)$ | $(P/A, 11, N)$ | $(A/F, 11, N)$ | $(F/A, 11, N)$ | $(A/G, 11, N)$ | $N$ |
| 1 | 1.1100 | .90090 | 1.1100 | .9009 | 1.0000 | 1.000 | .0000 | 1 |
| 2 | 1.2321 | .81162 | .58394 | 1.7125 | .47394 | 2.1099 | .4739 | 2 |
| 3 | 1.3676 | .73119 | .40922 | 2.4437 | .29922 | 3.3420 | .9305 | 3 |
| 4 | 1.5180 | .65873 | .32233 | 3.1024 | .21233 | 4.7097 | 1.3698 | 4 |
| 5 | 1.6850 | .59345 | .27057 | 3.6958 | .16057 | 6.2277 | 1.7922 | 5 |
| 6 | 1.8704 | .53464 | .23638 | 4.2305 | .12638 | 7.9128 | 2.1975 | 6 |
| 7 | 2.0761 | .48166 | .21222 | 4.7121 | .10222 | 9.7831 | 2.5862 | 7 |
| 8 | 2.3045 | .43393 | .19432 | 5.1461 | .08432 | 11.859 | 2.9584 | 8 |
| 9 | 2.5580 | .39093 | .18060 | 5.5370 | .07060 | 14.163 | 3.3143 | 9 |
| 10 | 2.8394 | .35219 | .16980 | 5.8892 | .05980 | 16.721 | 3.6543 | 10 |
| 11 | 3.1517 | .31729 | .16112 | 6.2065 | .05112 | 19.561 | 3.9787 | 11 |
| 12 | 3.4984 | .28584 | .15403 | 6.4923 | .04403 | 22.712 | 4.2878 | 12 |
| 13 | 3.8832 | .25752 | .14815 | 6.7498 | .03815 | 26.211 | 4.5821 | 13 |
| 14 | 4.3104 | .23200 | .14323 | 6.9818 | .03323 | 30.094 | 4.8618 | 14 |
| 15 | 4.7845 | .20901 | .13907 | 7.1908 | .02907 | 34.404 | 5.1274 | 15 |
| 16 | 5.3108 | .18829 | .13552 | 7.3791 | .02552 | 39.189 | 5.3793 | 16 |
| 17 | 5.8950 | .16963 | .13247 | 7.5487 | .02247 | 44.500 | 5.6180 | 17 |
| 18 | 6.5434 | .15282 | .12984 | 7.7016 | .01984 | 50.395 | 5.8438 | 18 |
| 19 | 7.2632 | .13768 | .12756 | 7.8392 | .01756 | 56.938 | 6.0573 | 19 |
| 20 | 8.0622 | .12404 | .12558 | 7.9633 | .01558 | 64.201 | 6.2589 | 20 |
| 21 | 8.9490 | .11174 | .12384 | 8.0750 | .01384 | 72.264 | 6.4490 | 21 |
| 22 | 9.9334 | .10067 | .12231 | 8.1757 | .01231 | 81.213 | 6.6282 | 22 |
| 23 | 11.026 | .09069 | .12097 | 8.2664 | .01097 | 91.146 | 6.7969 | 23 |
| 24 | 12.238 | .08171 | .11979 | 8.3481 | .00979 | 102.17 | 6.9554 | 24 |
| 25 | 13.585 | .07361 | .11874 | 8.4217 | .00874 | 114.41 | 7.1044 | 25 |
| 26 | 15.079 | .06631 | .11781 | 8.4880 | .00781 | 127.99 | 7.2442 | 26 |
| 27 | 16.738 | .05974 | .11699 | 8.5478 | .00699 | 143.07 | 7.3753 | 27 |
| 28 | 18.579 | .05382 | .11626 | 8.6016 | .00626 | 159.81 | 7.4981 | 28 |
| 29 | 20.623 | .04849 | .11561 | 8.6501 | .00561 | 178.39 | 7.6130 | 29 |
| 30 | 22.891 | .04368 | .11502 | 8.6937 | .00502 | 199.01 | 7.7205 | 30 |
| 31 | 25.409 | .03935 | .11451 | 8.7331 | .00451 | 221.90 | 7.8209 | 31 |
| 32 | 28.204 | .03545 | .11404 | 8.7686 | .00404 | 247.31 | 7.9146 | 32 |
| 33 | 31.307 | .03194 | .11363 | 8.8005 | .00363 | 275.52 | 8.0020 | 33 |
| 34 | 34.751 | .02878 | .11326 | 8.8293 | .00326 | 306.83 | 8.0835 | 34 |
| 35 | 38.573 | .02592 | .11293 | 8.8552 | .00293 | 341.58 | 8.1594 | 35 |
| 40 | 64.999 | .01538 | .11172 | 8.9510 | .00172 | 581.81 | 8.4659 | 40 |
| 45 | 109.52 | .00913 | .11101 | 9.0079 | .00101 | 986.60 | 8.6762 | 45 |
| 50 | 184.55 | .00542 | .11060 | 9.0416 | .00060 | 1668.7 | 8.8185 | 50 |

## 12% Interest Factors for Discrete Compounding Periods

| | SINGLE PAYMENT | | UNIFORM SERIES | | | | | |
|---|---|---|---|---|---|---|---|---|
| $N$ | Compound Amount Factor | Present Worth Factor | Capital Recovery Factor | Present Worth Factor | Sinking Fund Factor | Compound Amount Factor | Gradient Factor | $N$ |
| | $(F/P, 12, N)$ | $(P/F, 12, N)$ | $(A/P, 12, N)$ | $(P/A, 12, N)$ | $(A/F, 12, N)$ | $(F/A, 12, N)$ | $(A/G, 12, N)$ | |
| 1 | 1.1200 | .89286 | 1.1200 | .8929 | 1.0000 | 1.0000 | .0000 | 1 |
| 2 | 1.2544 | .79719 | .59170 | 1.6900 | .47170 | 2.1200 | .4717 | 2 |
| 3 | 1.4049 | .71178 | .41635 | 2.4018 | .29635 | 3.3743 | .9246 | 3 |
| 4 | 1.5735 | .63552 | .32924 | 3.0373 | .20924 | 4.7793 | 1.3588 | 4 |
| 5 | 1.7623 | .56743 | .27741 | 3.6047 | .15741 | 6.3528 | 1.7745 | 5 |
| 6 | 1.9738 | .50663 | .24323 | 4.1114 | .12323 | 8.115 | 2.1720 | 6 |
| 7 | 2.2106 | .45235 | .21912 | 4.5637 | .09912 | 10.088 | 2.5514 | 7 |
| 8 | 2.4759 | .40388 | .20130 | 4.9676 | .08130 | 12.299 | 2.9131 | 8 |
| 9 | 2.7730 | .36061 | .18768 | 5.3282 | .06768 | 14.775 | 3.2573 | 9 |
| 10 | 3.1058 | .32197 | .17698 | 5.6502 | .05698 | 17.548 | 3.5846 | 10 |
| 11 | 3.4785 | .28748 | .16842 | 5.9376 | .04842 | 20.654 | 3.8952 | 11 |
| 12 | 3.8959 | .25668 | .16144 | 6.1943 | .04144 | 24.132 | 4.1896 | 12 |
| 13 | 4.3634 | .22918 | .15568 | 6.4235 | .03568 | 28.028 | 4.4682 | 13 |
| 14 | 4.8870 | .20462 | .15087 | 6.6281 | .03087 | 32.392 | 4.7316 | 14 |
| 15 | 5.4735 | .18270 | .14682 | 6.8108 | .02682 | 37.279 | 4.9802 | 15 |
| 16 | 6.1303 | .16312 | .14339 | 6.9739 | .02339 | 42.752 | 5.2146 | 16 |
| 17 | 6.8659 | .14565 | .14046 | 7.1196 | .02046 | 48.883 | 5.4352 | 17 |
| 18 | 7.6899 | .13004 | .13794 | 7.2496 | .01794 | 55.749 | 5.6427 | 18 |
| 19 | 8.6126 | .11611 | .13576 | 7.3657 | .01576 | 63.439 | 5.8375 | 19 |
| 20 | 9.6462 | .10367 | .13388 | 7.4694 | .01388 | 72.051 | 6.0201 | 20 |
| 21 | 10.803 | .09256 | .13224 | 7.5620 | .01224 | 81.698 | 6.1913 | 21 |
| 22 | 12.100 | .08264 | .13081 | 7.6446 | .01081 | 92.501 | 6.3513 | 22 |
| 23 | 13.552 | .07379 | .12956 | 7.7184 | .00956 | 104.60 | 6.5009 | 23 |
| 24 | 15.178 | .06588 | .12846 | 7.7843 | .00846 | 118.15 | 6.6406 | 24 |
| 25 | 16.999 | .05882 | .12750 | 7.8431 | .00750 | 133.33 | 6.7708 | 25 |
| 26 | 19.039 | .05252 | .12665 | 7.8956 | .00665 | 150.33 | 6.8920 | 26 |
| 27 | 21.324 | .04689 | .12590 | 7.9425 | .00590 | 169.37 | 7.0049 | 27 |
| 28 | 23.883 | .04187 | .12524 | 7.9844 | .00524 | 190.69 | 7.1097 | 28 |
| 29 | 26.749 | .03738 | .12466 | 8.0218 | .00466 | 214.58 | 7.2071 | 29 |
| 30 | 29.959 | .03338 | .12414 | 8.0551 | .00414 | 241.32 | 7.2974 | 30 |
| 31 | 33.554 | .02980 | .12369 | 8.0849 | .00369 | 271.28 | 7.3810 | 31 |
| 32 | 37.581 | .02661 | .12328 | 8.1116 | .00328 | 304.84 | 7.4585 | 32 |
| 33 | 42.090 | .02376 | .12292 | 8.1353 | .00292 | 342.42 | 7.5302 | 33 |
| 34 | 47.141 | .02121 | .12260 | 8.1565 | .00260 | 384.51 | 7.5964 | 34 |
| 35 | 52.798 | .01894 | .12232 | 8.1755 | .00232 | 431.65 | 7.6576 | 35 |
| 40 | 93.049 | .01075 | .12130 | 8.2437 | .00130 | 767.07 | 7.8987 | 40 |
| 45 | 163.98 | .00610 | .12074 | 8.2825 | .00074 | 1358.2 | 8.0572 | 45 |
| 50 | 288.99 | .00346 | .12042 | 8.3045 | .00042 | 2399.9 | 8.1597 | 50 |

**13% Interest Factors for Discrete Compounding Periods**

| | SINGLE PAYMENT | | UNIFORM SERIES | | | | | |
| --- | --- | --- | --- | --- | --- | --- | --- | --- |
| | Compound Amount Factor | Present Worth Factor | Capital Recovery Factor | Present Worth Factor | Sinking Fund Factor | Compound Amount Factor | Gradient Factor | |
| $N$ | $(F/P, 13, N)$ | $(P/F, 13, N)$ | $(A/P, 13, N)$ | $(P/A, 13, N)$ | $(A/F, 13, N)$ | $(F/A, 13, N)$ | $(A/G, 13, N)$ | $N$ |
| 1 | 1.1300 | .88496 | 1.1300 | .8850 | 1.0000 | 1.0000 | .0000 | 1 |
| 2 | 1.2769 | .78315 | .59949 | 1.6680 | .46949 | 2.1299 | .4694 | 2 |
| 3 | 1.4428 | .69305 | .42352 | 2.3611 | .29353 | 3.4068 | .9187 | 3 |
| 4 | 1.6304 | .61332 | .33620 | 2.9744 | .20620 | 4.8497 | 1.3478 | 4 |
| 5 | 1.8424 | .54276 | .28432 | 3.5172 | .15432 | 6.4802 | 1.7570 | 5 |
| 6 | 2.0819 | .48032 | .25015 | 3.9975 | .12015 | 8.3226 | 2.1467 | 6 |
| 7 | 2.3525 | .42506 | .22611 | 4.4225 | .09611 | 10.404 | 2.5170 | 7 |
| 8 | 2.6584 | .37616 | .20839 | 4.7987 | .07839 | 12.757 | 2.8684 | 8 |
| 9 | 3.0040 | .33289 | .19487 | 5.1316 | .06487 | 15.415 | 3.2013 | 9 |
| 10 | 3.3945 | .29459 | .18429 | 5.4262 | .05429 | 18.419 | 3.5161 | 10 |
| 11 | 3.8358 | .26070 | .17584 | 5.6869 | .04584 | 21.813 | 3.8133 | 11 |
| 12 | 4.3344 | .23071 | .16899 | 5.9176 | .03899 | 25.649 | 4.0935 | 12 |
| 13 | 4.8979 | .20417 | .16335 | 6.1217 | .03335 | 29.984 | 4.3572 | 13 |
| 14 | 5.5346 | .18068 | .15867 | 6.3024 | .02867 | 34.882 | 4.6049 | 14 |
| 15 | 6.2541 | .15989 | .15474 | 6.4623 | .02474 | 40.416 | 4.8374 | 15 |
| 16 | 7.0672 | .14150 | .15143 | 6.6038 | .02143 | 46.670 | 5.0551 | 16 |
| 17 | 7.9859 | .12522 | .14861 | 6.7290 | .01861 | 53.737 | 5.2588 | 17 |
| 18 | 9.0240 | .11081 | .14620 | 6.8399 | .01620 | 61.723 | 5.4490 | 18 |
| 19 | 10.197 | .09807 | .14413 | 6.9379 | .01413 | 70.747 | 5.6264 | 19 |
| 20 | 11.522 | .08678 | .14235 | 7.0247 | .01235 | 80.944 | 5.7916 | 20 |
| 21 | 13.020 | .07680 | .14081 | 7.1015 | .01081 | 92.467 | 5.9453 | 21 |
| 22 | 14.713 | .06796 | .13948 | 7.1695 | .00948 | 105.48 | 6.0880 | 22 |
| 23 | 16.626 | .06015 | .13832 | 7.2296 | .00832 | 120.20 | 6.2204 | 23 |
| 24 | 18.787 | .05323 | .13731 | 7.2828 | .00731 | 136.82 | 6.3430 | 24 |
| 25 | 21.229 | .04710 | .13643 | 7.3299 | .00643 | 155.61 | 6.4565 | 25 |
| 26 | 23.989 | .04168 | .13565 | 7.3716 | .00565 | 176.84 | 6.5613 | 26 |
| 27 | 27.108 | .03689 | .13498 | 7.4085 | .00498 | 200.83 | 6.6581 | 27 |
| 28 | 30.632 | .03265 | .13439 | 7.4412 | .00439 | 227.94 | 6.7474 | 28 |
| 29 | 34.614 | .02889 | .13387 | 7.4700 | .00387 | 258.57 | 6.8295 | 29 |
| 30 | 39.114 | .02557 | .13341 | 7.4956 | .00341 | 293.18 | 6.9052 | 30 |
| 31 | 44.199 | .02262 | .13301 | 7.5182 | .00301 | 332.30 | 6.9747 | 31 |
| 32 | 49.945 | .02002 | .13266 | 7.5383 | .00266 | 376.50 | 7.0385 | 32 |
| 33 | 56.438 | .01772 | .13234 | 7.5560 | .00234 | 426.44 | 7.0970 | 33 |
| 34 | 63.775 | .01568 | .13207 | 7.5717 | .00207 | 482.88 | 7.1506 | 34 |
| 35 | 72.065 | .01388 | .13183 | 7.5855 | .00183 | 546.65 | 7.1998 | 35 |
| 40 | 132.77 | .00753 | .13099 | 7.6343 | .00099 | 1013.6 | 7.3887 | 40 |
| 45 | 244.62 | .00409 | .13053 | 7.6608 | .00053 | 1874.0 | 7.5076 | 45 |
| 50 | 450.71 | .00222 | .13029 | 7.6752 | .00029 | 3459.3 | 7.5811 | 50 |

## 14% Interest Factors for Discrete Compounding Periods

| | SINGLE PAYMENT | | UNIFORM SERIES | | | | | |
|---|---|---|---|---|---|---|---|---|
| | Compound Amount Factor | Present Worth Factor | Capital Recovery Factor | Present Worth Factor | Sinking Fund Factor | Compound Amount Factor | Gradient Factor | |
| $N$ | $(F/P, 14, N)$ | $(P/F, 14, N)$ | $(A/P, 14, N)$ | $(P/A, 14, N)$ | $(A/F, 14, N)$ | $(F/A, 14, N)$ | $(A/G, 14, N)$ | $N$ |
| 1 | 1.1400 | .87719 | 1.1400 | .8772 | 1.0000 | 1.000 | .0000 | 1 |
| 2 | 1.2996 | .76947 | .60729 | 1.6466 | .46729 | 2.1399 | .4672 | 2 |
| 3 | 1.4815 | .67497 | .43073 | 2.3216 | .29073 | 3.4395 | .9129 | 3 |
| 4 | 1.6889 | .59208 | .34321 | 2.9137 | .20321 | 4.9211 | 1.3369 | 4 |
| 5 | 1.9254 | .51937 | .29128 | 3.4330 | .15128 | 6.6100 | 1.7398 | 5 |
| 6 | 2.1949 | .45559 | .25716 | 3.8886 | .11716 | 8.535 | 2.1217 | 6 |
| 7 | 2.5022 | .39964 | .23319 | 4.2882 | .09319 | 10.730 | 2.4831 | 7 |
| 8 | 2.8525 | .35056 | .21557 | 4.6388 | .07557 | 13.232 | 2.8245 | 8 |
| 9 | 3.2519 | .30751 | .20217 | 4.9463 | .06217 | 16.085 | 3.1462 | 9 |
| 10 | 3.7071 | .26975 | .19171 | 5.2161 | .05171 | 19.337 | 3.4489 | 10 |
| 11 | 4.2261 | .23662 | .18339 | 5.4527 | .04339 | 23.044 | 3.7332 | 11 |
| 12 | 4.8178 | .20756 | .17667 | 5.6602 | .03667 | 27.270 | 3.9997 | 12 |
| 13 | 5.4923 | .18207 | .17116 | 5.8423 | .03116 | 32.088 | 4.2490 | 13 |
| 14 | 6.2612 | .15971 | .16661 | 6.0020 | .02661 | 37.580 | 4.4819 | 14 |
| 15 | 7.1378 | .14010 | .16281 | 6.1421 | .02281 | 43.841 | 4.6990 | 15 |
| 16 | 8.1371 | .12289 | .15962 | 6.2650 | .01962 | 50.979 | 4.9010 | 16 |
| 17 | 9.2763 | .10780 | .15692 | 6.3728 | .01692 | 59.116 | 5.0888 | 17 |
| 18 | 10.574 | .09456 | .15462 | 6.4674 | .01462 | 68.392 | 5.2629 | 18 |
| 19 | 12.055 | .08295 | .15266 | 6.5503 | .01266 | 78.967 | 5.4242 | 19 |
| 20 | 13.743 | .07276 | .15099 | 6.6231 | .01099 | 91.022 | 5.5734 | 20 |
| 21 | 15.667 | .06383 | .14954 | 6.6869 | .00955 | 104.76 | 5.7111 | 21 |
| 22 | 17.860 | .05599 | .14830 | 6.7429 | .00830 | 120.43 | 5.8380 | 22 |
| 23 | 20.361 | .04911 | .14723 | 6.7920 | .00723 | 138.29 | 5.9549 | 23 |
| 24 | 23.211 | .04308 | .14630 | 6.8351 | .00630 | 158.65 | 6.0623 | 24 |
| 25 | 26.461 | .03779 | .14550 | 6.8729 | .00550 | 181.86 | 6.1609 | 25 |
| 26 | 30.165 | .03315 | .14480 | 6.9060 | .00480 | 208.32 | 6.2514 | 26 |
| 27 | 34.388 | .02908 | .14419 | 6.9351 | .00419 | 238.49 | 6.3342 | 27 |
| 28 | 39.203 | .02551 | .14366 | 6.9606 | .00366 | 272.88 | 6.4039 | 28 |
| 29 | 44.691 | .02238 | .14320 | 6.9830 | .00320 | 312.08 | 6.4791 | 29 |
| 30 | 50.948 | .01963 | .14280 | 7.0026 | .00280 | 356.77 | 6.5422 | 30 |
| 31 | 58.081 | .01722 | .14245 | 7.0198 | .00245 | 407.72 | 6.5997 | 31 |
| 32 | 66.212 | .01510 | .14215 | 7.0349 | .00215 | 465.80 | 6.6521 | 32 |
| 33 | 75.482 | .01325 | .14188 | 7.0482 | .00188 | 532.01 | 6.6998 | 33 |
| 34 | 86.049 | .01162 | .14165 | 7.0598 | .00165 | 607.49 | 6.7430 | 34 |
| 35 | 98.096 | .01019 | .14144 | 7.0700 | .00144 | 693.54 | 6.7824 | 35 |
| 40 | 188.87 | .00529 | .14075 | 7.1050 | .00075 | 1341.9 | 6.9299 | 40 |
| 45 | 363.66 | .00275 | .14039 | 7.1232 | .00039 | 2590.4 | 7.0187 | 45 |
| 50 | 700.19 | .00143 | .14020 | 7.1326 | .00020 | 4994.2 | 7.0713 | 50 |

**15% Interest Factors for Discrete Compounding Periods**

| | SINGLE PAYMENT | | UNIFORM SERIES | | | | | |
|---|---|---|---|---|---|---|---|---|
| | Compound Amount Factor | Present Worth Factor | Capital Recovery Factor | Present Worth Factor | Sinking Fund Factor | Compound Amount Factor | Gradient Factor | |
| $N$ | $(F/P, 15, N)$ | $(P/F, 15, N)$ | $(A/P, 15, N)$ | $(P/A, 15, N)$ | $(A/F, 15, N)$ | $(F/A, 15, N)$ | $(A/G, 15, N)$ | $N$ |
| 1 | 1.1500 | .86957 | 1.1500 | .8696 | 1.0000 | 1.000 | .0000 | 1 |
| 2 | 1.3225 | .75614 | .61512 | 1.6257 | .46512 | 2.1499 | .4651 | 2 |
| 3 | 1.5208 | .65752 | .43798 | 2.2832 | .28798 | 3.4724 | .9071 | 3 |
| 4 | 1.7490 | .57175 | .35027 | 2.8549 | .20027 | 4.9933 | 1.3262 | 4 |
| 5 | 2.0113 | .49718 | .29832 | 3.3521 | .14832 | 6.7423 | 1.7227 | 5 |
| 6 | 2.3130 | .43233 | .26424 | 3.7844 | .11424 | 8.7536 | 2.0971 | 6 |
| 7 | 2.6600 | .37594 | .24036 | 4.1604 | .09036 | 11.066 | 2.4498 | 7 |
| 8 | 3.0590 | .32690 | .22285 | 4.4873 | .07285 | 13.726 | 2.7813 | 8 |
| 9 | 3.5178 | .28426 | .20957 | 4.7715 | .05957 | 16.785 | 3.0922 | 9 |
| 10 | 4.0455 | .24719 | .19925 | 5.0187 | .04925 | 20.303 | 3.3831 | 10 |
| 11 | 4.6523 | .21494 | .19107 | 5.2337 | .04107 | 24.349 | 3.6549 | 11 |
| 12 | 5.3502 | .18691 | .18448 | 5.4206 | .03448 | 29.001 | 3.9081 | 12 |
| 13 | 6.1527 | .16253 | .17911 | 5.5831 | .02911 | 34.351 | 4.1437 | 13 |
| 14 | 7.0756 | .14133 | .17469 | 5.7244 | .02469 | 40.504 | 4.3623 | 14 |
| 15 | 8.1369 | .12290 | .17102 | 5.8473 | .02102 | 47.579 | 4.5649 | 15 |
| 16 | 9.3575 | .10687 | .16795 | 5.9542 | .01795 | 55.716 | 4.7522 | 16 |
| 17 | 10.761 | .09293 | .16537 | 6.0471 | .01537 | 65.074 | 4.9250 | 17 |
| 18 | 12.375 | .08081 | .16319 | 6.1279 | .01319 | 75.835 | 5.0842 | 18 |
| 19 | 14.231 | .07027 | .16134 | 6.1982 | .01134 | 88.210 | 5.2307 | 19 |
| 20 | 16.366 | .06110 | .15976 | 6.2593 | .00976 | 102.44 | 5.3651 | 20 |
| 21 | 18.821 | .05313 | .15842 | 6.3124 | .00842 | 118.80 | 5.4883 | 21 |
| 22 | 21.644 | .04620 | .15727 | 6.3586 | .00727 | 137.62 | 5.6010 | 22 |
| 23 | 24.891 | .04018 | .15628 | 6.3988 | .00628 | 159.27 | 5.7039 | 23 |
| 24 | 28.624 | .03493 | .15543 | 6.4337 | .00543 | 184.16 | 5.7978 | 24 |
| 25 | 32.918 | .03038 | .15470 | 6.4641 | .00470 | 212.78 | 5.8834 | 25 |
| 26 | 37.856 | .02642 | .15407 | 6.4905 | .00407 | 245.70 | 5.9612 | 26 |
| 27 | 43.534 | .02297 | .15353 | 6.5135 | .00353 | 283.56 | 6.0318 | 27 |
| 28 | 50.064 | .01997 | .15306 | 6.5335 | .00306 | 327.09 | 6.0959 | 28 |
| 29 | 57.574 | .01737 | .15265 | 6.5508 | .00265 | 377.16 | 6.1540 | 29 |
| 30 | 66.210 | .01510 | .15230 | 6.5659 | .00230 | 434.73 | 6.2066 | 30 |
| 31 | 76.141 | .01313 | .15200 | 6.5791 | .00200 | 500.94 | 6.2541 | 31 |
| 32 | 87.563 | .01142 | .15173 | 6.5905 | .00173 | 577.08 | 6.2970 | 32 |
| 33 | 100.69 | .00993 | .15150 | 6.6004 | .00150 | 664.65 | 6.3356 | 33 |
| 34 | 115.80 | .00864 | .15131 | 6.6091 | .00131 | 765.34 | 6.3705 | 34 |
| 35 | 133.17 | .00751 | .15113 | 6.6166 | .00113 | 881.14 | 6.4018 | 35 |
| 40 | 267.85 | .00373 | .15056 | 6.6417 | .00056 | 1779.0 | 6.5167 | 40 |
| 45 | 538.75 | .00186 | .15028 | 6.6543 | .00028 | 3585.0 | 6.5829 | 45 |
| 50 | 1083.6 | .00092 | .15014 | 6.6605 | .00014 | 7217.4 | 6.8204 | 50 |

**20% Interest Factors for Discrete Compounding Periods**

| N | SINGLE PAYMENT | | UNIFORM SERIES | | | | | N |
|---|---|---|---|---|---|---|---|---|
| | Compound Amount Factor | Present Worth Factor | Capital Recovery Factor | Present Worth Factor | Sinking Fund Factor | Compound Amount Factor | Gradient Factor | |
| $N$ | $(F/P, 20, N)$ | $(P/F, 20, N)$ | $(A/P, 20, N)$ | $(P/A, 20, N)$ | $(A/F, 20, N)$ | $(F/A, 20, N)$ | $(A/G, 20, N)$ | $N$ |
| 1 | 1.2000 | .83333 | 1.2000 | .8333 | 1.0000 | 1.0000 | .0000 | 1 |
| 2 | 1.4400 | .69445 | .65455 | 1.5277 | .45455 | 2.1999 | .4545 | 2 |
| 3 | 1.7280 | .57870 | .47473 | 2.1064 | .27473 | 3.6399 | .8791 | 3 |
| 4 | 2.0736 | .48225 | .38629 | 2.5887 | .18629 | 5.3679 | 1.2742 | 4 |
| 5 | 2.4883 | .40188 | .33438 | 2.9906 | .13438 | 7.4415 | 1.6405 | 5 |
| 6 | 2.9859 | .33490 | .30071 | 3.3255 | .10071 | 9.9298 | 1.9788 | 6 |
| 7 | 3.5831 | .27908 | .27742 | 3.6045 | .07742 | 12.915 | 2.2901 | 7 |
| 8 | 4.2998 | .23257 | .26061 | 3.8371 | .06061 | 16.498 | 2.5756 | 8 |
| 9 | 5.1597 | .19381 | .24808 | 4.0309 | .04808 | 20.798 | 2.8364 | 9 |
| 10 | 6.1917 | .16151 | .23852 | 4.1924 | .03852 | 25.958 | 3.0738 | 10 |
| 11 | 7.4300 | .13459 | .23110 | 4.3270 | .03110 | 32.150 | 3.2892 | 11 |
| 12 | 8.9160 | .11216 | .22527 | 4.4392 | .02527 | 39.580 | 3.4840 | 12 |
| 13 | 10.699 | .09346 | .22062 | 4.5326 | .02062 | 48.496 | 3.6596 | 13 |
| 14 | 12.839 | .07789 | .21689 | 4.6105 | .01689 | 59.195 | 3.8174 | 14 |
| 15 | 15.406 | .06491 | .21388 | 4.6754 | .01388 | 72.034 | 3.9588 | 15 |
| 16 | 18.488 | .05409 | .21144 | 4.7295 | .01144 | 87.441 | 4.0851 | 16 |
| 17 | 22.185 | .04507 | .20944 | 4.7746 | .00944 | 105.92 | 4.1975 | 17 |
| 18 | 26.623 | .03756 | .20781 | 4.8121 | .00781 | 128.11 | 4.2975 | 18 |
| 19 | 31.947 | .03130 | .20646 | 4.8435 | .00646 | 154.73 | 4.3860 | 19 |
| 20 | 38.337 | .02608 | .20536 | 4.8695 | .00536 | 186.68 | 4.4643 | 20 |
| 21 | 46.004 | .02174 | .20444 | 4.8913 | .00444 | 225.02 | 4.5333 | 21 |
| 22 | 55.205 | .01811 | .20369 | 4.9094 | .00369 | 271.02 | 4.5941 | 22 |
| 23 | 66.246 | .01510 | .20307 | 4.9245 | .00307 | 326.23 | 4.6474 | 23 |
| 24 | 79.495 | .01258 | .20255 | 4.9371 | .00255 | 392.47 | 4.6942 | 24 |
| 25 | 95.394 | .01048 | .20212 | 4.9475 | .00212 | 471.97 | 4.7351 | 25 |
| 26 | 114.47 | .00874 | .20176 | 4.9563 | .00176 | 567.36 | 4.7708 | 26 |
| 27 | 137.36 | .00728 | .20147 | 4.9636 | .00147 | 681.84 | 4.8020 | 27 |
| 28 | 164.84 | .00607 | .20122 | 4.9696 | .00122 | 819.21 | 4.8291 | 28 |
| 29 | 197.81 | .00506 | .20102 | 4.9747 | .00102 | 984.05 | 4.8526 | 29 |
| 30 | 237.37 | .00421 | .20085 | 4.9789 | .00085 | 1181.8 | 4.8730 | 30 |
| 31 | 284.84 | .00351 | .20070 | 4.9824 | .00070 | 1419.2 | 4.8907 | 31 |
| 32 | 341.81 | .00293 | .20059 | 4.9853 | .00059 | 1704.0 | 4.9061 | 32 |
| 33 | 410.17 | .00244 | .20049 | 4.9878 | .00049 | 2045.8 | 4.9193 | 33 |
| 34 | 492.21 | .00203 | .20041 | 4.9898 | .00041 | 2456.0 | 4.9307 | 34 |
| 35 | 590.65 | .00169 | .20034 | 4.9915 | .00034 | 2948.2 | 4.9406 | 35 |
| 40 | 1469.7 | .00068 | .20014 | 4.9966 | .00014 | 7343.6 | 4.9727 | 40 |
| 45 | 3657.1 | .00027 | .20005 | 4.9986 | .00005 | 18281.3 | 4.9876 | 45 |
| 50 | 9100.1 | .00011 | .20002 | 4.9994 | .00002 | 45497.2 | 4.9945 | 50 |

**25% Interest Factors for Discrete Compounding Periods**

| | SINGLE PAYMENT | | UNIFORM SERIES | | | | | |
|---|---|---|---|---|---|---|---|---|
| | Compound Amount Factor | Present Worth Factor | Capital Recovery Factor | Present Worth Factor | Sinking Fund Factor | Compound Amount Factor | Gradient Factor | |
| $N$ | $(F/P, 25, N)$ | $(P/F, 25, N)$ | $(A/P, 25, N)$ | $(P/A, 25, N)$ | $(A/F, 25, N)$ | $(F/A, 25, N)$ | $(A/G, 25, N)$ | $N$ |
| 1 | 1.2500 | .80000 | 1.2500 | .8000 | 1.0000 | 1.0000 | .00000 | 1 |
| 2 | 1.5625 | .64000 | .69444 | 1.4400 | .44444 | 2.2500 | .44444 | 2 |
| 3 | 1.9531 | .51200 | .51230 | 1.9520 | .26230 | 3.8125 | .85246 | 3 |
| 4 | 2.4414 | .40960 | .42344 | 2.3616 | .17344 | 5.7656 | 1.2249 | 4 |
| 5 | 3.0518 | .32768 | .37185 | 2.6893 | .12185 | 8.2070 | 1.5631 | 5 |
| 6 | 3.8147 | .26214 | .33882 | 2.9514 | .08882 | 11.259 | 1.8683 | 6 |
| 7 | 4.7684 | .20972 | .31634 | 3.1661 | .06634 | 15.073 | 2.1424 | 7 |
| 8 | 5.9605 | .16777 | .30040 | 3.3289 | .05040 | 19.842 | 2.3872 | 8 |
| 9 | 7.4506 | .13422 | .28876 | 3.4631 | .03876 | 25.802 | 2.6048 | 9 |
| 10 | 9.3132 | .10737 | .28007 | 3.5705 | .03007 | 33.253 | 2.7971 | 10 |
| 11 | 11.642 | .08590 | .27349 | 3.6564 | .02349 | 42.566 | 2.9663 | 11 |
| 12 | 14.552 | .06872 | .26845 | 3.7251 | .01845 | 54.208 | 3.1145 | 12 |
| 13 | 18.190 | .05498 | .26454 | 3.7801 | .01454 | 68.760 | 3.2437 | 13 |
| 14 | 22.737 | .04398 | .26150 | 3.8241 | .01150 | 86.949 | 3.3559 | 14 |
| 15 | 28.422 | .03518 | .25912 | 3.8593 | .00912 | 109.687 | 3.4530 | 15 |
| 16 | 35.527 | .02815 | .25724 | 3.8874 | .00724 | 138.109 | 3.5366 | 16 |
| 17 | 44.409 | .02252 | .25576 | 3.9099 | .00576 | 173.636 | 3.6084 | 17 |
| 18 | 55.511 | .01801 | .25459 | 3.9279 | .00459 | 218.045 | 3.6698 | 18 |
| 19 | 69.389 | .01441 | .25366 | 3.9424 | .00366 | 273.556 | 3.7222 | 19 |
| 20 | 86.736 | .01153 | .25292 | 3.9539 | .00292 | 342.945 | 3.7667 | 20 |
| 21 | 108.420 | .00922 | .25233 | 3.9631 | .00233 | 429.681 | 3.8045 | 21 |
| 22 | 135.525 | .00738 | .25186 | 3.9705 | .00186 | 538.101 | 3.8365 | 22 |
| 23 | 169.407 | .00590 | .25148 | 3.9764 | .00148 | 673.626 | 3.8634 | 23 |
| 24 | 211.758 | .00472 | .25119 | 3.9811 | .00119 | 843.033 | 3.8861 | 24 |
| 25 | 264.698 | .00378 | .25095 | 3.9849 | .00095 | 1054.791 | 3.9052 | 25 |
| 26 | 330.872 | .00302 | .25076 | 3.9879 | .00076 | 1319.489 | 3.9212 | 26 |
| 27 | 413.590 | .00242 | .25061 | 3.9903 | .00061 | 1650.361 | 3.9346 | 27 |
| 28 | 516.988 | .00193 | .25048 | 3.9923 | .00048 | 2063.952 | 3.9457 | 28 |
| 29 | 646.235 | .00155 | .25039 | 3.9938 | .00039 | 2580.939 | 3.9551 | 29 |
| 30 | 807.794 | .00124 | .25031 | 3.9950 | .00031 | 3227.174 | 3.9628 | 30 |
| 31 | 1009.742 | .00099 | .25025 | 3.9960 | .00025 | 4034.968 | 3.9693 | 31 |
| 32 | 1262.177 | .00079 | .25020 | 3.9968 | .00020 | 5044.710 | 3.9746 | 32 |
| 33 | 1577.722 | .00063 | .25016 | 3.9975 | .00016 | 6306.887 | 3.9791 | 33 |
| 34 | 1972.152 | .00051 | .25013 | 3.9980 | .00012 | 7884.609 | 3.9828 | 34 |
| 35 | 2465.190 | .00041 | .25010 | 3.9984 | .00010 | 9856.761 | 3.9858 | 35 |

### 30% Interest Factors for Discrete Compounding Periods

| N | SINGLE PAYMENT | | UNIFORM SERIES | | | | | N |
|---|---|---|---|---|---|---|---|---|
| | Compound Amount Factor | Present Worth Factor | Capital Recovery Factor | Present Worth Factor | Sinking Fund Factor | Compound Amount Factor | Gradient Factor | |
| | $(F/P, 30, N)$ | $(P/F, 30, N)$ | $(A/P, 30, N)$ | $(P/A, 30, N)$ | $(A/F, 30, N)$ | $(F/A, 30, N)$ | $(A/G, 30, N)$ | |
| 1 | 1.3000 | .76923 | 1.3000 | .7692 | 1.0000 | 1.000 | .0000 | 1 |
| 2 | 1.6900 | .59172 | .73478 | 1.3609 | .43478 | 2.2999 | .4348 | 2 |
| 3 | 2.1969 | .45517 | .55063 | 1.8161 | .25063 | 3.9899 | .8277 | 3 |
| 4 | 2.8560 | .35013 | .46163 | 2.1662 | .16163 | 6.1869 | 1.1782 | 4 |
| 5 | 3.7129 | .26933 | .41058 | 2.4355 | .11058 | 9.0430 | 1.4903 | 5 |
| 6 | 4.8267 | .20718 | .37839 | 2.6427 | .07839 | 12.755 | 1.7654 | 6 |
| 7 | 6.2748 | .15937 | .35687 | 2.8021 | .05687 | 17.582 | 2.0062 | 7 |
| 8 | 8.1572 | .12259 | .34192 | 2.9247 | .04192 | 23.857 | 2.2155 | 8 |
| 9 | 10.604 | .09430 | .33124 | 3.0190 | .03124 | 32.014 | 2.3962 | 9 |
| 10 | 13.785 | .07254 | .32346 | 3.0915 | .02346 | 42.619 | 2.5512 | 10 |
| 11 | 17.921 | .05580 | .31773 | 3.1473 | .01773 | 56.404 | 2.6832 | 11 |
| 12 | 23.297 | .04292 | .31345 | 3.1902 | .01345 | 74.326 | 2.7951 | 12 |
| 13 | 30.287 | .03302 | .31024 | 3.2232 | .01024 | 97.624 | 2.8894 | 13 |
| 14 | 39.373 | .02540 | .30782 | 3.2486 | .00782 | 127.91 | 2.9685 | 14 |
| 15 | 51.185 | .01954 | .30598 | 3.2682 | .00598 | 167.28 | 3.0344 | 15 |
| 16 | 66.540 | .01503 | .30458 | 3.2832 | .00458 | 218.46 | 3.0892 | 16 |
| 17 | 86.503 | .01156 | .30351 | 3.2948 | .00351 | 285.01 | 3.1345 | 17 |
| 18 | 112.45 | .00889 | .30269 | 3.3036 | .00269 | 371.51 | 3.1718 | 18 |
| 19 | 146.18 | .00684 | .30207 | 3.3105 | .00207 | 483.96 | 3.2024 | 19 |
| 20 | 190.04 | .00526 | .30159 | 3.3157 | .00159 | 630.15 | 3.2275 | 20 |
| 21 | 247.06 | .00405 | .30122 | 3.3198 | .00122 | 820.20 | 3.2479 | 21 |
| 22 | 321.17 | .00311 | .30094 | 3.3229 | .00094 | 1067.2 | 3.2646 | 22 |
| 23 | 417.53 | .00240 | .30072 | 3.3253 | .00072 | 1388.4 | 3.2781 | 23 |
| 24 | 542.79 | .00184 | .30055 | 3.3271 | .00055 | 1805.9 | 3.2890 | 24 |
| 25 | 705.62 | .00142 | .30043 | 3.3286 | .00043 | 2348.7 | 3.2978 | 25 |
| 26 | 917.31 | .00109 | .30033 | 3.3297 | .00033 | 3054.3 | 3.3049 | 26 |
| 27 | 1192.5 | .00084 | .30025 | 3.3305 | .00025 | 3971.6 | 3.3106 | 27 |
| 28 | 1550.2 | .00065 | .30019 | 3.3311 | .00019 | 5164.1 | 3.3152 | 28 |
| 29 | 2015.3 | .00050 | .30015 | 3.3316 | .00015 | 6714.4 | 3.3189 | 29 |
| 30 | 2619.9 | .00038 | .30011 | 3.3320 | .00011 | 8729.7 | 3.3218 | 30 |
| 31 | 3405.9 | .00029 | .30009 | 3.3323 | .00009 | 11350.0 | 3.3242 | 31 |
| 32 | 4427.6 | .00023 | .30007 | 3.3325 | .00007 | 14756.0 | 3.3261 | 32 |
| 33 | 5755.9 | .00017 | .30005 | 3.3327 | .00005 | 19184.0 | 3.3276 | 33 |
| 34 | 7482.7 | .00013 | .30004 | 3.3328 | .00004 | 24940.0 | 3.3287 | 34 |
| 35 | 9727.5 | .00010 | .30003 | 3.3329 | .00003 | 32423.0 | 3.3297 | 35 |

**40% Interest Factors for Discrete Compounding Periods**

| N | SINGLE PAYMENT | | UNIFORM SERIES | | | | | N |
|---|---|---|---|---|---|---|---|---|
| | Compound Amount Factor | Present Worth Factor | Capital Recovery Factor | Present Worth Factor | Sinking Fund Factor | Compound Amount Factor | Gradient Factor | |
| | $(F/P, 40, N)$ | $(P/F, 40, N)$ | $(A/P, 40, N)$ | $(P/A, 40, N)$ | $(A/F, 40, N)$ | $(F/A, 40, N)$ | $(A/G, 40, N)$ | |
| 1 | 1.4000 | .71429 | 1.40000 | .7143 | 1.00000 | 1.0000 | .0000 | 1 |
| 2 | 1.9600 | .51020 | .81667 | 1.2244 | .41667 | 2.3999 | .4167 | 2 |
| 3 | 2.7440 | .36443 | .62936 | 1.5889 | .22936 | 4.3599 | .7798 | 3 |
| 4 | 3.8415 | .26031 | .54077 | 1.8492 | .14077 | 7.1039 | 1.0923 | 4 |
| 5 | 5.3782 | .18593 | .49136 | 2.0351 | .09136 | 10.945 | 1.3579 | 5 |
| 6 | 7.5295 | .13281 | .46126 | 2.1679 | .06126 | 16.323 | 1.5810 | 6 |
| 7 | 10.541 | .09486 | .44192 | 2.2628 | .04192 | 23.853 | 1.7663 | 7 |
| 8 | 14.757 | .06776 | .42907 | 2.3306 | .02907 | 34.394 | 1.9185 | 8 |
| 9 | 20.660 | .04840 | .42034 | 2.3790 | .02034 | 49.152 | 2.0422 | 9 |
| 10 | 28.925 | .03457 | .41432 | 2.4135 | .01432 | 69.813 | 2.1419 | 10 |
| 11 | 40.495 | .02469 | .41013 | 2.4382 | .01013 | 98.738 | 2.2214 | 11 |
| 12 | 56.693 | .01764 | .40718 | 2.4559 | .00718 | 139.23 | 2.2845 | 12 |
| 13 | 79.370 | .01260 | .40510 | 2.4685 | .00510 | 195.92 | 2.3341 | 13 |
| 14 | 111.11 | .00900 | .40363 | 2.4775 | .00363 | 275.29 | 2.3728 | 14 |
| 15 | 155.56 | .00643 | .40259 | 2.4839 | .00259 | 386.41 | 2.4029 | 15 |
| 16 | 217.79 | .00459 | .40184 | 2.4885 | .00185 | 541.98 | 2.4262 | 16 |
| 17 | 304.91 | .00328 | .40132 | 2.4918 | .00132 | 759.77 | 2.4440 | 17 |
| 18 | 426.87 | .00234 | .40094 | 2.4941 | .00094 | 1064.6 | 2.4577 | 18 |
| 19 | 597.62 | .00167 | .40067 | 2.4958 | .00067 | 1491.5 | 2.4681 | 19 |
| 20 | 836.67 | .00120 | .40048 | 2.4970 | .00048 | 2089.1 | 2.4760 | 20 |
| 21 | 1171.3 | .00085 | .40034 | 2.4978 | .00034 | 2925.8 | 2.4820 | 21 |
| 22 | 1639.8 | .00061 | .40024 | 2.4984 | .00024 | 4097.1 | 2.4865 | 22 |
| 23 | 2295.8 | .00044 | .40017 | 2.4989 | .00017 | 5737.0 | 2.4899 | 23 |
| 24 | 3214.1 | .00031 | .40012 | 2.4992 | .00012 | 8032.8 | 2.4925 | 24 |
| 25 | 4499.8 | .00022 | .40009 | 2.4994 | .00009 | 11247.2 | 2.4944 | 25 |

## 50% Interest Factors for Discrete Compounding Periods

| | SINGLE PAYMENT | | UNIFORM SERIES | | | | | |
|---|---|---|---|---|---|---|---|---|
| | Compound Amount Factor | Present Worth Factor | Capital Recovery Factor | Present Worth Factor | Sinking Fund Factor | Compound Amount Factor | Gradient Factor | |
| $N$ | $(F/P, 50, N)$ | $(P/F, 50, N)$ | $(A/P, 50, N)$ | $(P/A, 50, N)$ | $(A/F, 50, N)$ | $(F/A, 50, N)$ | $(A/G, 50, N)$ | $N$ |
| 1 | 1.5000 | .66667 | 1.5000 | .6667 | 1.00000 | 1.000 | .0000 | 1 |
| 2 | 2.2500 | .44444 | .90000 | 1.1111 | .40000 | 2.500 | .4000 | 2 |
| 3 | 3.3750 | .29630 | .71053 | 1.4074 | .21053 | 4.750 | .7368 | 3 |
| 4 | 5.0625 | .19753 | .62308 | 1.6049 | .12308 | 8.125 | 1.0153 | 4 |
| 5 | 7.5937 | .13169 | .57583 | 1.7366 | .07583 | 13.187 | 1.2417 | 5 |
| 6 | 11.390 | .08779 | .54812 | 1.8244 | .04812 | 20.781 | 1.4225 | 6 |
| 7 | 17.085 | .05853 | .53108 | 1.8829 | .03108 | 32.171 | 1.5648 | 7 |
| 8 | 25.628 | .03902 | .52030 | 1.9219 | .02030 | 49.257 | 1.6751 | 8 |
| 9 | 38.443 | .02601 | .51335 | 1.9479 | .01335 | 74.886 | 1.7596 | 9 |
| 10 | 57.665 | .01734 | .50882 | 1.9653 | .00882 | 113.33 | 1.8235 | 10 |
| 11 | 86.497 | .01156 | .50585 | 1.9768 | .00585 | 170.99 | 1.8713 | 11 |
| 12 | 129.74 | .00771 | .50388 | 1.9845 | .00388 | 257.49 | 1.9067 | 12 |
| 13 | 194.61 | .00514 | .50258 | 1.9897 | .00258 | 387.23 | 1.9328 | 13 |
| 14 | 291.92 | .00343 | .50172 | 1.9931 | .00172 | 581.85 | 1.9518 | 14 |
| 15 | 437.89 | .00228 | .50114 | 1.9954 | .00114 | 873.78 | 1.9656 | 15 |
| 16 | 656.84 | .00152 | .50076 | 1.9969 | .00076 | 1311.6 | 1.9756 | 16 |
| 17 | 985.26 | .00101 | .50051 | 1.9979 | .00051 | 1968.5 | 1.9827 | 17 |
| 18 | 1477.8 | .00068 | .50034 | 1.9986 | .00034 | 2953.7 | 1.9878 | 18 |
| 19 | 2216.8 | .00045 | .50023 | 1.9991 | .00023 | 4431.6 | 1.9914 | 19 |
| 20 | 3325.2 | .00030 | .50015 | 1.9994 | .00015 | 6648.5 | 1.9939 | 20 |
| 21 | 4987.8 | .00020 | .50010 | 1.9996 | .00010 | 9973.7 | 1.9957 | 21 |
| 22 | 7481.8 | .00013 | .50007 | 1.9997 | .00007 | 14961.7 | 1.9970 | 22 |
| 23 | 11222.7 | .00009 | .50004 | 1.9998 | .00004 | 22443.5 | 1.9979 | 23 |
| 24 | 16834.1 | .00006 | .50003 | 1.9998 | .00003 | 33666.2 | 1.9985 | 24 |
| 25 | 25251.2 | .00004 | .50002 | 1.9999 | .00002 | 50500.3 | 1.9990 | 25 |

**60% Interest Factors for Discrete Compounding Periods**

| | SINGLE PAYMENT | | UNIFORM SERIES | | | | | |
| | Compound Amount Factor | Present Worth Factor | Capital Recovery Factor | Present Worth Factor | Sinking Fund Factor | Compound Amount Factor | Gradient Factor | |
| $N$ | $(F/P, 60, N)$ | $(P/F, 60, N)$ | $(A/P, 60, N)$ | $(P/A, 60, N)$ | $(A/F, 60, N)$ | $(F/A, 60, N)$ | $(A/G, 60, N)$ | $N$ |
|---|---|---|---|---|---|---|---|---|
| 1 | 1.6000 | .62500 | 1.6000 | .6250 | 1.0000 | 1.000 | .0000 | 1 |
| 2 | 2.5600 | .39063 | .98462 | 1.0156 | .38462 | 2.6000 | .3846 | 2 |
| 3 | 4.0959 | .24414 | .79380 | 1.2597 | .19380 | 5.1599 | .6977 | 3 |
| 4 | 6.5535 | .15259 | .70804 | 1.4123 | .10804 | 9.2559 | .9464 | 4 |
| 5 | 10.485 | .09537 | .66325 | 1.5077 | .06325 | 15.809 | 1.1395 | 5 |
| 6 | 16.777 | .05960 | .63803 | 1.5673 | .03803 | 26.295 | 1.2863 | 6 |
| 7 | 26.843 | .03725 | .62322 | 1.6045 | .02322 | 43.072 | 1.3958 | 7 |
| 8 | 42.949 | .02328 | .61430 | 1.6278 | .01430 | 69.915 | 1.4759 | 8 |
| 9 | 68.719 | .01455 | .60886 | 1.6424 | .00886 | 112.86 | 1.5337 | 9 |
| 10 | 109.95 | .00909 | .60551 | 1.6515 | .00551 | 181.58 | 1.5748 | 10 |
| 11 | 175.92 | .00568 | .60343 | 1.6571 | .00343 | 291.53 | 1.6037 | 11 |
| 12 | 281.47 | .00355 | .60214 | 1.6607 | .00214 | 467.45 | 1.6238 | 12 |
| 13 | 450.35 | .00222 | .60134 | 1.6629 | .00134 | 748.92 | 1.6377 | 13 |
| 14 | 720.57 | .00139 | .60083 | 1.6643 | .00083 | 1199.2 | 1.6472 | 14 |
| 15 | 1152.9 | .00087 | .60052 | 1.6652 | .00052 | 1919.8 | 1.6536 | 15 |
| 16 | 1844.6 | .00054 | .60033 | 1.6657 | .00033 | 3072.7 | 1.6579 | 16 |
| 17 | 2951.4 | .00034 | .60020 | 1.6661 | .00020 | 4917.4 | 1.6609 | 17 |
| 18 | 4722.3 | .00021 | .60013 | 1.6663 | .00013 | 7868.8 | 1.6628 | 18 |
| 19 | 7555.7 | .00013 | .60008 | 1.6664 | .00008 | 12591.0 | 1.6641 | 19 |
| 20 | 12089.0 | .00008 | .60005 | 1.6665 | .00005 | 20147.0 | 1.6650 | 20 |

**70% Interest Factors for Discrete Compounding Periods**

| | SINGLE PAYMENT | | UNIFORM SERIES | | | | | |
| | Compound Amount Factor | Present Worth Factor | Capital Recovery Factor | Present Worth Factor | Sinking Fund Factor | Compound Amount Factor | Gradient Factor | |
| $N$ | $(F/P, 70, N)$ | $(P/F, 70, N)$ | $(A/P, 70, N)$ | $(P/A, 70, N)$ | $(A/F, 70, N)$ | $(F/A, 70, N)$ | $(A/G, 70, N)$ | $N$ |
|---|---|---|---|---|---|---|---|---|
| 1 | 1.7000 | .58824 | 1.7000 | .5882 | 1.0000 | 1.000 | .0000 | 1 |
| 2 | 2.8900 | .34602 | 1.0703 | .9343 | .37037 | 2.700 | .3704 | 2 |
| 3 | 4.9130 | .20354 | .87889 | 1.1378 | .17889 | 5.590 | .6619 | 3 |
| 4 | 8.3520 | .11973 | .79521 | 1.2575 | .09521 | 10.502 | .8845 | 4 |
| 5 | 14.198 | .07043 | .75304 | 1.3279 | .05304 | 18.855 | 1.0497 | 5 |
| 6 | 24.137 | .04143 | .73025 | 1.3693 | .03025 | 33.053 | 1.1692 | 6 |
| 7 | 41.033 | .02437 | .71749 | 1.3937 | .01749 | 57.191 | 1.2537 | 7 |
| 8 | 69.757 | .01434 | .71018 | 1.4080 | .01018 | 98.224 | 1.3122 | 8 |
| 9 | 118.58 | .00843 | .70595 | 1.4165 | .00595 | 167.98 | 1.3520 | 9 |
| 10 | 201.59 | .00496 | .70349 | 1.4214 | .00349 | 286.56 | 1.3787 | 10 |
| 11 | 342.71 | .00292 | .70205 | 1.4244 | .00205 | 488.16 | 1.3963 | 11 |
| 12 | 582.62 | .00172 | .70120 | 1.4261 | .00120 | 830.88 | 1.4079 | 12 |
| 13 | 990.45 | .00101 | .70071 | 1.4271 | .00071 | 1413.5 | 1.4154 | 13 |
| 14 | 1683.7 | .00059 | .70042 | 1.4277 | .00042 | 2403.9 | 1.4202 | 14 |
| 15 | 2862.4 | .00035 | .70024 | 1.4280 | .00024 | 4087.7 | 1.4233 | 15 |
| 16 | 4866.0 | .00021 | .70014 | 1.4282 | .00014 | 6950.1 | 1.4252 | 16 |
| 17 | 8272.3 | .00012 | .70008 | 1.4284 | .00008 | 11816.0 | 1.4265 | 17 |
| 18 | 14063.0 | .00007 | .70005 | 1.4284 | .00005 | 20089.0 | 1.4272 | 18 |
| 19 | 23907.0 | .00004 | .70003 | 1.4285 | .00003 | 34152.0 | 1.4277 | 19 |
| 20 | 40642.0 | .00002 | .70002 | 1.4285 | .00002 | 58059.0 | 1.4280 | 20 |

**80% Interest Factors for Discrete Compounding Periods**

| | SINGLE PAYMENT | | UNIFORM SERIES | | | | | |
| | Compound Amount Factor | Present Worth Factor | Capital Recovery Factor | Present Worth Factor | Sinking Fund Factor | Compound Amount Factor | Gradient Factor | |
| $N$ | $(F/P, 80, N)$ | $(P/F, 80, N)$ | $(A/P, 80, N)$ | $(P/A, 80, N)$ | $(A/F, 80, N)$ | $(F/A, 80, N)$ | $(A/G, 80, N)$ | $N$ |
|---|---|---|---|---|---|---|---|---|
| 1 | 1.8000 | .55556 | 1.8000 | .5556 | 1.00000 | 1.0000 | .0000 | 1 |
| 2 | 3.2400 | .30864 | 1.1571 | .8642 | .35714 | 2.8000 | .3571 | 2 |
| 3 | 5.8319 | .17147 | .96556 | 1.0356 | .16556 | 6.0399 | .6291 | 3 |
| 4 | 10.497 | .09526 | .88423 | 1.1309 | .08423 | 11.871 | .8288 | 4 |
| 5 | 18.895 | .05292 | .84470 | 1.1838 | .04470 | 22.369 | .9706 | 5 |
| 6 | 34.012 | .02940 | .82423 | 1.2132 | .02423 | 41.265 | 1.0682 | 6 |
| 7 | 61.221 | .01633 | .81328 | 1.2295 | .01328 | 75.277 | 1.1337 | 7 |
| 8 | 110.19 | .00907 | .80733 | 1.2386 | .00733 | 136.49 | 1.1767 | 8 |
| 9 | 198.35 | .00504 | .80405 | 1.2437 | .00405 | 246.69 | 1.2044 | 9 |
| 10 | 357.04 | .00280 | .80225 | 1.2465 | .00225 | 445.05 | 1.2219 | 10 |
| 11 | 642.68 | .00156 | .80125 | 1.2480 | .00125 | 802.10 | 1.2328 | 11 |
| 12 | 1156.8 | .00086 | .80069 | 1.2489 | .00069 | 1444.7 | 1.2396 | 12 |
| 13 | 2082.2 | .00048 | .80038 | 1.2494 | .00038 | 2601.6 | 1.2437 | 13 |
| 14 | 3748.1 | .00027 | .80021 | 1.2496 | .00021 | 4683.8 | 1.2462 | 14 |
| 15 | 6746.5 | .00015 | .80012 | 1.2498 | .00012 | 8431.9 | 1.2477 | 15 |

**90% Interest Factors for Discrete Compounding Periods**

| | SINGLE PAYMENT | | UNIFORM SERIES | | | | | |
|---|---|---|---|---|---|---|---|---|
| | Compound Amount Factor | Present Worth Factor | Capital Recovery Factor | Present Worth Factor | Sinking Fund Factor | Compound Amount Factor | Gradient Factor | |
| $N$ | $(F/P, 90, N)$ | $(P/F, 90, N)$ | $(A/P, 90, N)$ | $(P/A, 90, N)$ | $(A/F, 90, N)$ | $(F/A, 90, N)$ | $(A/G, 90, N)$ | $N$ |
| 1 | 1.9000 | .52632 | 1.9000 | .52632 | 1.00000 | 1.0000 | .00000 | 1 |
| 2 | 3.6100 | .27701 | 1.2448 | .80332 | .34483 | 2.9000 | .34483 | 2 |
| 3 | 6.8589 | .14579 | 1.0536 | .94912 | .15361 | 6.5099 | .59908 | 3 |
| 4 | 13.032 | .07673 | .97480 | 1.0258 | .07480 | 13.368 | .77867 | 4 |
| 5 | 24.760 | .04039 | .93788 | 1.0662 | .03788 | 26.401 | .90068 | 5 |
| 6 | 47.045 | .02126 | .91955 | 1.0874 | .01955 | 51.161 | .98081 | 6 |
| 7 | 89.386 | .01119 | .91018 | 1.0986 | .01018 | 98.207 | 1.0319 | 7 |
| 8 | 169.83 | .00589 | .90533 | 1.1045 | .00533 | 187.59 | 1.0637 | 8 |
| 9 | 322.68 | .00310 | .90280 | 1.1076 | .00280 | 357.42 | 1.0831 | 9 |
| 10 | 613.10 | .00163 | .90147 | 1.1093 | .00147 | 680.11 | 1.0947 | 10 |

**100% Interest Factors for Discrete Compounding Periods**

| | SINGLE PAYMENT | | UNIFORM SERIES | | | | | |
|---|---|---|---|---|---|---|---|---|
| | Compound Amount Factor | Present Worth Factor | Capital Recovery Factor | Present Worth Factor | Sinking Fund Factor | Compound Amount Factor | Gradient Factor | |
| $N$ | $(F/P, 100, N)$ | $(P/F, 100, N)$ | $(A/P, 100, N)$ | $(P/A, 100, N)$ | $(A/F, 100, N)$ | $(F/A, 100, N)$ | $(A/G, 100, N)$ | $N$ |
| 1 | 2.000 | .50000 | 2.0000 | .50000 | 1.0000 | 1.000 | .00000 | 1 |
| 2 | 4.000 | .25000 | 1.3333 | .75000 | .33333 | 3.000 | .33333 | 2 |
| 3 | 8.000 | .12500 | 1.1428 | .87500 | .14286 | 7.000 | .57143 | 3 |
| 4 | 16.000 | .06250 | 1.0666 | .93750 | .06667 | 15.000 | .73333 | 4 |
| 5 | 32.000 | .03125 | 1.0322 | .96875 | .03226 | 31.000 | .83871 | 5 |
| 6 | 64.00 | .01562 | 1.0158 | .98438 | .01587 | 63.00 | .90476 | 6 |
| 7 | 128.00 | .00781 | 1.0078 | .99219 | .00787 | 127.00 | .94488 | 7 |
| 8 | 256.00 | .00391 | 1.0039 | .99609 | .00392 | 255.00 | .96863 | 8 |
| 9 | 512.00 | .00195 | 1.0019 | .99805 | .00196 | 511.00 | .98239 | 9 |
| 10 | 1024.0 | .00098 | 1.0009 | .99902 | .00098 | 1023.0 | .99022 | 10 |

# APPENDIX C

## CONTINUOUS-COMPOUNDING INTEREST FACTORS

**Continuous-Compounding, Continuous-Flow Interest Factors
at an Effective Interest Rate of 8%; r = 7.696%**

| N | SINGLE PAYMENT | | | UNIFORM SERIES | | | N |
|---|---|---|---|---|---|---|---|
| | $(F/\bar{P}, 7.696, N)$ | $(P/\bar{F}, 7.696, N)$ | $(\bar{A}/P, 7.696, N)$ | $(P/\bar{A}, 7.696, N)$ | $(\bar{A}/F, 7.696, N)$ | $(F/\bar{A}, 7.696, N)$ | |
| 1 | 1.039 | .9625 | 1.03897 | 962 | .96201 | 1.039 | 1 |
| 2 | 1.123 | .8912 | .53947 | 1.854 | .46251 | 2.162 | 2 |
| 3 | 1.212 | .8252 | .37329 | 2.679 | .29633 | 3.375 | 3 |
| 4 | 1.309 | .7641 | .29045 | 3.443 | .21349 | 4.684 | 4 |
| 5 | 1.414 | .7075 | .24094 | 4.150 | .16398 | 6.098 | 5 |
| 6 | 1.527 | .6551 | .20810 | 4.805 | .13114 | 7.626 | 6 |
| 7 | 1.650 | .6065 | .18478 | 5.412 | .10782 | 9.275 | 7 |
| 8 | 1.781 | .5616 | .16740 | 5.974 | .09044 | 11.057 | 8 |
| 9 | 1.924 | .5200 | .15400 | 6.494 | .07704 | 12.981 | 9 |
| 10 | 2.078 | .4815 | .14337 | 6.975 | .06641 | 15.059 | 10 |
| 11 | 2.244 | .4458 | .13476 | 7.421 | .05779 | 17.303 | 11 |
| 12 | 2.424 | .4128 | .12765 | 7.834 | .05069 | 19.726 | 12 |
| 13 | 2.618 | .3822 | .12172 | 8.216 | .04475 | 22.344 | 13 |
| 14 | 2.827 | .3539 | .11669 | 8.570 | .03973 | 25.171 | 14 |
| 15 | 3.053 | .3277 | .11239 | 8.897 | .03543 | 28.224 | 15 |
| 16 | 3.297 | .3034 | .10869 | 9.201 | .03172 | 31.522 | 16 |
| 17 | 3.561 | .2809 | .10546 | 9.482 | .02850 | 35.083 | 17 |
| 18 | 3.846 | .2601 | .10265 | 9.742 | .02569 | 38.929 | 18 |
| 19 | 4.154 | .2409 | .10017 | 9.983 | .02321 | 43.083 | 19 |
| 20 | 4.486 | .2230 | .09798 | 10.206 | .02102 | 47.569 | 20 |
| 21 | 4.845 | .2065 | .09604 | 10.412 | .01908 | 52.414 | 21 |
| 22 | 5.233 | .1912 | .09431 | 10.604 | .01735 | 57.647 | 22 |
| 23 | 5.651 | .1770 | .09276 | 10.781 | .01580 | 63.298 | 23 |
| 24 | 6.103 | .1639 | .09137 | 10.945 | .01441 | 69.401 | 24 |
| 25 | 6.592 | .1518 | .09012 | 11.096 | .01316 | 75.993 | 25 |
| 26 | 7.119 | .1405 | .08899 | 11.237 | .01203 | 83.112 | 26 |
| 27 | 7.688 | .1301 | .08797 | 11.367 | .01101 | 90.800 | 27 |
| 28 | 8.303 | .1205 | .08705 | 11.487 | .01009 | 99.103 | 28 |
| 29 | 8.968 | .1116 | .08621 | 11.599 | .00925 | 108.071 | 29 |
| 30 | 9.685 | .1033 | .08545 | 11.702 | .00849 | 117.756 | 30 |
| 31 | 10.460 | .0956 | .08476 | 11.798 | .00780 | 128.216 | 31 |
| 32 | 11.297 | .0886 | .08413 | 11.887 | .00717 | 139.513 | 32 |
| 33 | 12.201 | .0820 | .08355 | 11.969 | .00659 | 151.714 | 33 |
| 34 | 13.177 | .0759 | .08303 | 12.044 | .00606 | 164.890 | 34 |
| 35 | 14.231 | .0703 | .08254 | 12.115 | .00558 | 179.121 | 35 |
| 40 | 20.910 | .0478 | .08067 | 12.395 | .00371 | 269.286 | 40 |
| 45 | 30.723 | .0326 | .07945 | 12.587 | .00249 | 401.768 | 45 |
| 50 | 45.142 | .0222 | .07864 | 12.717 | .00168 | 596.427 | 50 |

**Continuous-Compounding, Continuous-Flow Interest Factors
at an Effective Interest Rate of 9%; r = 8.618%**

| N | SINGLE PAYMENT | | | UNIFORM SERIES | | | N |
|---|---|---|---|---|---|---|---|
| | $(F/\overline{P}, 8.618, N)$ | $(P/\overline{F}, 8.618, N)$ | $(\overline{A}/P, 8.618, N)$ | $(P/\overline{A}, 8.618, N)$ | $(\overline{A}/F, 8.618, N)$ | $(F/\overline{A}, 8.618, N)$ | |
| 1 | 1.044 | .9581 | 1.04371 | .958 | .95753 | 1.044 | 1 |
| 2 | 1.138 | .8790 | .54433 | 1.837 | .45815 | 2.183 | 2 |
| 3 | 1.241 | .8064 | .37828 | 2.644 | .29210 | 3.423 | 3 |
| 4 | 1.352 | .7398 | .29556 | 3.383 | .20938 | 4.776 | 4 |
| 5 | 1.474 | .6788 | .24617 | 4.062 | .16000 | 6.250 | 5 |
| 6 | 1.607 | .6227 | .21345 | 4.685 | .12727 | 7.857 | 6 |
| 7 | 1.751 | .5713 | .19025 | 5.256 | .10407 | 9.609 | 7 |
| 8 | 1.909 | .5241 | .17300 | 5.780 | .08682 | 11.518 | 8 |
| 9 | 2.081 | .4808 | .15971 | 6.261 | .07354 | 13.599 | 9 |
| 10 | 2.268 | .4411 | .14920 | 6.702 | .06302 | 15.867 | 10 |
| 11 | 2.472 | .4047 | .14071 | 7.107 | .05453 | 18.339 | 11 |
| 12 | 2.695 | .3713 | .13372 | 7.478 | .04754 | 21.034 | 12 |
| 13 | 2.937 | .3406 | .12789 | 7.819 | .04172 | 23.971 | 13 |
| 14 | 3.202 | .3125 | .12298 | 8.131 | .03680 | 27.173 | 14 |
| 15 | 3.490 | .2867 | .11879 | 8.418 | .03261 | 30.663 | 15 |
| 16 | 3.804 | .2630 | .11519 | 8.681 | .02901 | 34.467 | 16 |
| 17 | 4.146 | .2413 | .11208 | 8.923 | .02590 | 38.614 | 17 |
| 18 | 4.520 | .2214 | .10936 | 9.144 | .02318 | 43.133 | 18 |
| 19 | 4.926 | .2031 | .10699 | 9.347 | .02081 | 48.060 | 19 |
| 20 | 5.370 | .1863 | .10489 | 9.533 | .01872 | 53.429 | 20 |
| 21 | 5.853 | .1710 | .10305 | 9.704 | .01687 | 59.282 | 21 |
| 22 | 6.380 | .1568 | .10141 | 9.861 | .01523 | 65.002 | 22 |
| 23 | 6.954 | .1439 | .09995 | 10.005 | .01377 | 72.616 | 23 |
| 24 | 7.580 | .1320 | .09865 | 10.137 | .01247 | 80.196 | 24 |
| 25 | 8.262 | .1211 | .09748 | 10.258 | .01130 | 88.458 | 25 |
| 26 | 9.006 | .1111 | .09644 | 10.369 | .01026 | 97.463 | 26 |
| 27 | 9.816 | .1019 | .09550 | 10.471 | .00932 | 107.279 | 27 |
| 28 | 10.699 | .0935 | .09465 | 10.565 | .00848 | 117.979 | 28 |
| 29 | 11.662 | .0858 | .09389 | 10.651 | .00771 | 129.641 | 29 |
| 30 | 12.712 | .0787 | .09320 | 10.729 | .00702 | 142.353 | 30 |
| 31 | 13.856 | .0722 | .09258 | 10.802 | .00640 | 156.209 | 31 |
| 32 | 15.103 | .0663 | .09201 | 10.868 | .00584 | 171.313 | 32 |
| 33 | 16.462 | .0608 | .09150 | 10.929 | .00533 | 187.775 | 33 |
| 34 | 17.944 | .0558 | .09104 | 10.984 | .00486 | 205.719 | 34 |
| 35 | 19.559 | .0512 | .09062 | 11.035 | .00444 | 225.278 | 35 |
| 40 | 30.094 | .0332 | .08901 | 11.234 | .00283 | 352.869 | 40 |
| 45 | 46.303 | .0216 | .08800 | 11.364 | .00182 | 549.183 | 45 |
| 50 | 71.244 | .0140 | .08735 | 11.448 | .00117 | 851.236 | 50 |

**Continuous-Compounding, Continuous-Flow Interest Factors**
**At an Effective Interest Rate of 10%; r = 9.531%**

| N | SINGLE PAYMENT | | | UNIFORM SERIES | | | N |
|---|---|---|---|---|---|---|---|
| | $(F/\bar{P}, 9.531, N)$ | $(P/\bar{F}, 9.531, N)$ | $(\bar{A}/P, 9.531, N)$ | $(P/\bar{A}, 9.531, N)$ | $(\bar{A}/F, 9.531, N)$ | $(F/\bar{A}, 9.531, N)$ | |
| 1 | 1.049 | .9538 | 1.04841 | .954 | .95310 | 1.049 | 1 |
| 2 | 1.154 | .8671 | .54917 | 1.821 | .45386 | 2.203 | 2 |
| 3 | 1.270 | .7883 | .38326 | 2.609 | .28795 | 3.473 | 3 |
| 4 | 1.396 | .7166 | .30068 | 3.326 | .20537 | 4.869 | 4 |
| 5 | 1.536 | .6515 | .25143 | 3.977 | .15612 | 6.406 | 5 |
| 6 | 1.690 | .5922 | .21884 | 4.570 | .12353 | 8.095 | 6 |
| 7 | 1.859 | .5384 | .19577 | 5.108 | .10046 | 9.954 | 7 |
| 8 | 2.045 | .4895 | .17865 | 5.597 | .08334 | 11.999 | 8 |
| 9 | 2.249 | .4450 | .16550 | 6.042 | .07019 | 14.248 | 9 |
| 10 | 2.474 | .4045 | .15511 | 6.447 | .05980 | 16.722 | 10 |
| 11 | 2.721 | .3677 | .14674 | 6.815 | .05143 | 19.443 | 11 |
| 12 | 2.994 | .3343 | .13988 | 7.149 | .04457 | 22.437 | 12 |
| 13 | 3.293 | .3039 | .13418 | 7.453 | .03887 | 25.729 | 13 |
| 14 | 3.622 | .2763 | .12938 | 7.729 | .03407 | 29.352 | 14 |
| 15 | 3.984 | .2512 | .12531 | 7.980 | .03000 | 33.336 | 15 |
| 16 | 4.383 | .2283 | .12182 | 8.209 | .02651 | 37.719 | 16 |
| 17 | 4.821 | .2076 | .11882 | 8.416 | .02351 | 42.540 | 17 |
| 18 | 5.303 | .1887 | .11621 | 8.605 | .02090 | 47.843 | 18 |
| 19 | 5.833 | .1716 | .11394 | 8.777 | .01863 | 53.676 | 19 |
| 20 | 6.417 | .1560 | .11195 | 8.932 | .01664 | 60.093 | 20 |
| 21 | 7.059 | .1418 | .11020 | 9.074 | .01489 | 67.152 | 21 |
| 22 | 7.764 | .1289 | .10866 | 9.203 | .01335 | 74.916 | 22 |
| 23 | 8.541 | .1172 | .10729 | 9.320 | .01198 | 83.457 | 23 |
| 24 | 9.395 | .1065 | .10608 | 9.427 | .01077 | 92.852 | 24 |
| 25 | 10.334 | .0968 | .10500 | 9.524 | .00969 | 103.186 | 25 |
| 26 | 11.368 | .0880 | .10404 | 9.612 | .00873 | 114.554 | 26 |
| 27 | 12.505 | .0800 | .10318 | 9.692 | .00787 | 127.059 | 27 |
| 28 | 13.755 | .0728 | .10241 | 9.765 | .00710 | 140.814 | 28 |
| 29 | 15.131 | .0661 | .10172 | 9.831 | .00641 | 155.944 | 29 |
| 30 | 16.644 | .0601 | .10110 | 9.891 | .00579 | 172.588 | 30 |
| 31 | 18.308 | .0547 | .10055 | 9.945 | .00524 | 190.896 | 31 |
| 32 | 20.139 | .0497 | .10005 | 9.995 | .00474 | 211.035 | 32 |
| 33 | 22.153 | .0452 | .09960 | 10.040 | .00429 | 233.188 | 33 |
| 34 | 24.368 | .0411 | .09919 | 10.081 | .00388 | 257.556 | 34 |
| 35 | 26.805 | .0373 | .09883 | 10.119 | .00352 | 284.360 | 35 |
| 40 | 43.169 | .0232 | .09746 | 10.260 | .00215 | 464.371 | 40 |
| 45 | 69.525 | .0144 | .09664 | 10.348 | .00133 | 754.279 | 45 |
| 50 | 111.970 | .0089 | .09618 | 10.403 | .00082 | 1221.180 | 50 |

**Continuous-Compounding, Continuous-Flow Interest Factors
at an Effective Interest Rate of 11%; r = 10.436%**

| | SINGLE PAYMENT | | | UNIFORM SERIES | | | |
|---|---|---|---|---|---|---|---|
| $N$ | $(F/\overline{P}, 10.436, N)$ | $(P/\overline{F}, 10.436, N)$ | $(\overline{A}/P, 10.436, N)$ | $(P/\overline{A}, 10.436, N)$ | $(\overline{A}/F, 10.436, N)$ | $(F/\overline{A}, 10.436, N)$ | $N$ |
| 1 | 1.054 | .9496 | 1.05309 | .950 | .94873 | 1.054 | 1 |
| 2 | 1.170 | .8555 | .55399 | 1.805 | .44963 | 2.224 | 2 |
| 3 | 1.299 | .7707 | .38823 | 2.576 | .28387 | 3.523 | 3 |
| 4 | 1.442 | .6943 | .30580 | 3.270 | .20144 | 4.964 | 4 |
| 5 | 1.600 | .6255 | .25670 | 3.896 | .15234 | 6.564 | 5 |
| 6 | 1.776 | .5635 | .22426 | 4.459 | .11990 | 8.340 | 6 |
| 7 | 1.971 | .5077 | .20133 | 4.967 | .09697 | 10.312 | 7 |
| 8 | 2.188 | .4574 | .18436 | 5.424 | .08000 | 12.500 | 8 |
| 9 | 2.429 | .4121 | .17134 | 5.836 | .06698 | 14.929 | 9 |
| 10 | 2.696 | .3712 | .16110 | 6.208 | .05674 | 17.626 | 10 |
| 11 | 2.993 | .3344 | .15286 | 6.542 | .04850 | 20.619 | 11 |
| 12 | 3.322 | .3013 | .14613 | 6.843 | .04177 | 23.941 | 12 |
| 13 | 3.688 | .2714 | .14055 | 7.115 | .03619 | 27.628 | 13 |
| 14 | 4.093 | .2445 | .13588 | 7.359 | .03152 | 31.721 | 14 |
| 15 | 4.543 | .2203 | .13194 | 7.579 | .02757 | 36.265 | 15 |
| 16 | 5.043 | .1985 | .12857 | 7.778 | .02421 | 41.308 | 16 |
| 17 | 5.598 | .1788 | .12568 | 7.957 | .02132 | 46.906 | 17 |
| 18 | 6.214 | .1611 | .12319 | 8.118 | .01883 | 53.120 | 18 |
| 19 | 6.897 | .1451 | .12102 | 8.263 | .01666 | 60.017 | 19 |
| 20 | 7.656 | .1307 | .11914 | 8.394 | .01478 | 67.673 | 20 |
| 21 | 8.498 | .1178 | .11749 | 8.511 | .01313 | 76.171 | 21 |
| 22 | 9.433 | .1061 | .11604 | 8.618 | .01168 | 85.603 | 22 |
| 23 | 10.470 | .0956 | .11477 | 8.713 | .01041 | 96.074 | 23 |
| 24 | 11.622 | .0861 | .11365 | 8.799 | .00929 | 107.696 | 24 |
| 25 | 12.901 | .0776 | .11265 | 8.877 | .00829 | 120.597 | 25 |
| 26 | 14.320 | .0699 | .11177 | 8.947 | .00741 | 134.916 | 26 |
| 27 | 15.805 | .0630 | .11099 | 9.010 | .00663 | 150.811 | 27 |
| 28 | 17.643 | .0567 | .11030 | 9.066 | .00594 | 168.454 | 28 |
| 29 | 19.584 | .0511 | .10968 | 9.118 | .00532 | 188.038 | 29 |
| 30 | 21.738 | .0460 | .10913 | 9.164 | .00477 | 209.777 | 30 |
| 31 | 24.129 | .0415 | .10864 | 9.205 | .00428 | 233.906 | 31 |
| 32 | 26.784 | .0374 | .10820 | 9.242 | .00384 | 260.690 | 32 |
| 33 | 29.730 | .0337 | .10780 | 9.276 | .00344 | 290.420 | 33 |
| 34 | 33.000 | .0303 | .10745 | 9.306 | .00309 | 323.420 | 34 |
| 35 | 36.630 | .0273 | .10714 | 9.334 | .00278 | 360.050 | 35 |
| 40 | 61.724 | .0162 | .10599 | 9.435 | .00163 | 613.270 | 40 |
| 45 | 104.009 | .0096 | .10532 | 9.495 | .00096 | 1039.960 | 45 |
| 50 | 175.261 | .0057 | .10493 | 9.530 | .00057 | 1758.958 | 50 |

**Continuous-Compounding, Continuous-Flow Interest Factors
at an Effective Interest Rate of 12%; r = 11.333%**

| N | SINGLE PAYMENT | | | UNIFORM SERIES | | | N |
|---|---|---|---|---|---|---|---|
| | $(F/\bar{P}, 11.333, N)$ | $(P/\bar{F}, 11.333, N)$ | $(\bar{A}/P, 11.333, N)$ | $(P/\bar{A}, 11.333, N)$ | $(\bar{A}/F, 11.333, N)$ | $(F/\bar{A}, 11.333, N)$ | |
| 1 | 1.059 | .9454 | 1.05773 | .945 | .94441 | 1.059 | 1 |
| 2 | 1.186 | .8441 | .55880 | 1.790 | .44547 | 2.245 | 2 |
| 3 | 1.328 | .7537 | .39320 | 2.543 | .27987 | 3.573 | 3 |
| 4 | 1.488 | .6729 | .31093 | 3.216 | .19760 | 5.061 | 4 |
| 5 | 1.666 | .6008 | .26199 | 3.817 | .14866 | 6.727 | 5 |
| 6 | 1.866 | .5365 | .22970 | 4.353 | .11638 | 8.593 | 6 |
| 7 | 2.090 | .4790 | .20694 | 4.832 | .09361 | 10.683 | 7 |
| 8 | 2.341 | .4277 | .19011 | 5.260 | .07678 | 13.024 | 8 |
| 9 | 2.622 | .3818 | .17725 | 5.642 | .06392 | 15.645 | 9 |
| 10 | 2.936 | .3409 | .16714 | 5.983 | .05382 | 18.582 | 10 |
| 11 | 3.289 | .3044 | .15905 | 6.287 | .04572 | 21.870 | 11 |
| 12 | 3.683 | .2718 | .15246 | 6.559 | .03913 | 25.554 | 12 |
| 13 | 4.125 | .2427 | .14702 | 6.802 | .03369 | 29.679 | 13 |
| 14 | 4.620 | .2167 | .14248 | 7.018 | .02915 | 34.299 | 14 |
| 15 | 5.175 | .1935 | .13866 | 7.212 | .02533 | 39.474 | 15 |
| 16 | 5.796 | .1727 | .13542 | 7.385 | .02209 | 45.270 | 16 |
| 17 | 6.491 | .1542 | .13265 | 7.539 | .01932 | 51.761 | 17 |
| 18 | 7.270 | .1377 | .13027 | 7.676 | .01694 | 59.032 | 18 |
| 19 | 8.143 | .1229 | .12822 | 7.799 | .01489 | 67.174 | 19 |
| 20 | 9.120 | .1098 | .12644 | 7.909 | .01311 | 76.294 | 20 |
| 21 | 10.214 | .0980 | .12489 | 8.007 | .01156 | 86.508 | 21 |
| 22 | 11.440 | .0875 | .12354 | 8.095 | .01021 | 97.948 | 22 |
| 23 | 12.813 | .0781 | .12236 | 8.173 | .00903 | 110.761 | 23 |
| 24 | 14.350 | .0698 | .12132 | 8.243 | .00799 | 125.111 | 24 |
| 25 | 16.072 | .0623 | .12041 | 8.305 | .00708 | 141.183 | 25 |
| 26 | 18.001 | .0556 | .11961 | 8.360 | .00628 | 159.184 | 26 |
| 27 | 20.161 | .0497 | .11890 | 8.410 | .00558 | 179.345 | 27 |
| 28 | 22.580 | .0443 | .11828 | 8.454 | .00495 | 201.925 | 28 |
| 29 | 25.290 | .0396 | .11773 | 8.494 | .00440 | 227.215 | 29 |
| 30 | 28.325 | .0353 | .11724 | 8.529 | .00391 | 255.539 | 30 |
| 31 | 31.724 | .0316 | .11681 | 8.561 | .00348 | 287.263 | 31 |
| 32 | 35.530 | .0282 | .11643 | 8.589 | .00310 | 322.793 | 32 |
| 33 | 39.794 | .0252 | .11609 | 8.614 | .00276 | 362.587 | 33 |
| 34 | 44.569 | .0225 | .11578 | 8.637 | .00246 | 407.157 | 34 |
| 35 | 49.918 | .0201 | .11552 | 8.657 | .00219 | 457.074 | 35 |
| 40 | 87.972 | .0114 | .11456 | 8.729 | .00123 | 812.248 | 40 |
| 45 | 155.037 | .0065 | .11402 | 8.770 | .00070 | 1438.185 | 45 |
| 50 | 273.228 | .0037 | .11372 | 8.793 | .00039 | 2541.300 | 50 |

### Continuous-Compounding, Continuous-Flow Interest Factors at an Effective Interest Rate of 13%; r = 12.222%

| N | SINGLE PAYMENT | | UNIFORM SERIES | | | | N |
|---|---|---|---|---|---|---|---|
| | $(F/\bar{P}, 12.222, N)$ | $(P/\bar{F}, 12.222, N)$ | $(\bar{A}/P, 12.222, N)$ | $(P/\bar{A}, 12.222, N)$ | $(\bar{A}/F, 12.222, N)$ | $(F/\bar{A}, 12.222, N)$ | |
| 1 | 1.064 | .9413 | 1.06235 | .941 | .94014 | 1.064 | 1 |
| 2 | 1.202 | .8330 | .56360 | 1.774 | .44138 | 2.266 | 2 |
| 3 | 1.358 | .7372 | .39817 | 2.512 | .27595 | 3.624 | 3 |
| 4 | 1.535 | .6524 | .31607 | 3.164 | .19385 | 5.159 | 4 |
| 5 | 1.734 | .5773 | .26729 | 3.741 | .14508 | 6.893 | 5 |
| 6 | 1.960 | .5109 | .23518 | 4.252 | .11296 | 8.853 | 6 |
| 7 | 2.215 | .4521 | .21257 | 4.704 | .09036 | 11.067 | 7 |
| 8 | 2.502 | .4001 | .19591 | 5.104 | .07369 | 13.570 | 8 |
| 9 | 2.828 | .3541 | .18320 | 5.458 | .06099 | 16.397 | 9 |
| 10 | 3.195 | .3133 | .17326 | 5.772 | .05104 | 19.593 | 10 |
| 11 | 3.611 | .2773 | .16531 | 6.049 | .04310 | 23.203 | 11 |
| 12 | 4.080 | .2454 | .15887 | 6.294 | .03665 | 27.283 | 12 |
| 13 | 4.611 | .2172 | .15357 | 6.512 | .03135 | 31.894 | 13 |
| 14 | 5.210 | .1922 | .14917 | 6.704 | .02695 | 37.104 | 14 |
| 15 | 5.887 | .1701 | .14548 | 6.874 | .02326 | 42.991 | 15 |
| 16 | 6.653 | .1505 | .14236 | 7.024 | .02014 | 49.644 | 16 |
| 17 | 7.517 | .1332 | .13971 | 7.158 | .01749 | 57.161 | 17 |
| 18 | 8.495 | .1179 | .13745 | 7.275 | .01523 | 65.656 | 18 |
| 19 | 9.599 | .1043 | .13551 | 7.380 | .01329 | 75.254 | 19 |
| 20 | 10.847 | .0923 | .13383 | 7.472 | .01161 | 86.101 | 20 |
| 21 | 12.257 | .0817 | .13238 | 7.554 | .01017 | 90.358 | 21 |
| 22 | 13.850 | .0723 | .13113 | 7.626 | .00891 | 112.208 | 22 |
| 23 | 15.651 | .0640 | .13004 | 7.690 | .00782 | 127.859 | 23 |
| 24 | 17.685 | .0566 | .12909 | 7.747 | .00687 | 145.544 | 24 |
| 25 | 19.984 | .0501 | .12826 | 7.797 | .00604 | 165.529 | 25 |
| 26 | 22.582 | .0443 | .12753 | 7.841 | .00532 | 188.111 | 26 |
| 27 | 25.518 | .0392 | .12690 | 7.880 | .00468 | 213.629 | 27 |
| 28 | 28.835 | .0347 | .12634 | 7.915 | .00412 | 242.465 | 28 |
| 29 | 32.584 | .0307 | .12585 | 7.946 | .00364 | 275.049 | 29 |
| 30 | 36.820 | .0272 | .12542 | 7.973 | .00321 | 311.869 | 30 |
| 31 | 41.607 | .0241 | .12505 | 7.997 | .00283 | 353.476 | 31 |
| 32 | 47.016 | .0213 | .12471 | 8.018 | .00250 | 400.491 | 32 |
| 33 | 53.128 | .0188 | .12442 | 8.037 | .00220 | 453.619 | 33 |
| 34 | 60.034 | .0167 | .12416 | 8.054 | .00195 | 513.653 | 34 |
| 35 | 67.839 | .0148 | .12394 | 8.069 | .00172 | 581.491 | 35 |
| 40 | 124.988 | .0080 | .12315 | 8.121 | .00093 | 1078.253 | 40 |
| 45 | 230.283 | .0043 | .12272 | 8.149 | .00050 | 1993.505 | 45 |
| 50 | 424.281 | .0024 | .12249 | 8.164 | .00027 | 3679.796 | 50 |

**Continuous-Compounding, Continuous-Flow Interest Factors**
**at an Effective Interest Rate of 14%; r = 13.103%**

| N | SINGLE PAYMENT | | UNIFORM SERIES | | | | N |
|---|---|---|---|---|---|---|---|
| | $(F/\overline{P}, 13.103, N)$ | $(P/\overline{F}, 13.103, N)$ | $(\overline{A}/P, 13.103, N)$ | $(P/\overline{A}, 13.103, N)$ | $(\overline{A}/F, 13.103, N)$ | $(F/\overline{A}, 13.103, N)$ | |
| 1 | 1.068 | .9373 | 1.06694 | .937 | .93592 | 1.068 | 1 |
| 2 | 1.218 | .8222 | .56837 | 1.759 | .43734 | 2.287 | 2 |
| 3 | 1.389 | .7212 | .40313 | 2.481 | .27210 | 3.675 | 3 |
| 4 | 1.583 | .6326 | .32121 | 3.113 | .19018 | 5.258 | 4 |
| 5 | 1.805 | .5549 | .27262 | 3.668 | .14159 | 7.063 | 5 |
| 6 | 2.057 | .4868 | .24068 | 4.155 | .10965 | 9.120 | 6 |
| 7 | 2.345 | .4270 | .21825 | 4.582 | .08722 | 11.465 | 7 |
| 8 | 2.674 | .3746 | .20176 | 4.956 | .07073 | 14.139 | 8 |
| 9 | 3.048 | .3286 | .18921 | 5.285 | .05818 | 17.187 | 9 |
| 10 | 3.475 | .2882 | .17943 | 5.573 | .04840 | 20.661 | 10 |
| 11 | 3.961 | .2528 | .17164 | 5.826 | .04061 | 24.622 | 11 |
| 12 | 4.516 | .2218 | .16535 | 6.048 | .03432 | 29.138 | 12 |
| 13 | 5.148 | .1945 | .16019 | 6.242 | .02917 | 34.286 | 13 |
| 14 | 5.868 | .1706 | .15593 | 6.413 | .02490 | 40.154 | 14 |
| 15 | 6.690 | .1497 | .15238 | 6.563 | .02135 | 46.844 | 15 |
| 16 | 7.627 | .1313 | .14939 | 6.694 | .01836 | 54.471 | 16 |
| 17 | 8.694 | .1152 | .14686 | 6.809 | .01583 | 63.165 | 17 |
| 18 | 9.912 | .1010 | .14471 | 6.910 | .01368 | 73.077 | 18 |
| 19 | 11.299 | .0886 | .14288 | 6.999 | .01185 | 84.376 | 19 |
| 20 | 12.881 | .0777 | .14131 | 7.077 | .01028 | 97.258 | 20 |
| 21 | 14.685 | .0682 | .13996 | 7.145 | .00893 | 111.942 | 21 |
| 22 | 16.740 | .0598 | .13880 | 7.205 | .00777 | 128.682 | 22 |
| 23 | 19.084 | .0525 | .13780 | 7.257 | .00677 | 147.766 | 23 |
| 24 | 21.756 | .0460 | .13693 | 7.303 | .00590 | 169.522 | 24 |
| 25 | 24.802 | .0404 | .13617 | 7.344 | .00515 | 194.324 | 25 |
| 26 | 28.274 | .0354 | .13552 | 7.379 | .00449 | 222.598 | 26 |
| 27 | 32.232 | .0311 | .13495 | 7.410 | .00392 | 254.830 | 27 |
| 28 | 36.745 | .0273 | .13446 | 7.437 | .00343 | 291.574 | 28 |
| 29 | 41.889 | .0239 | .13403 | 7.461 | .00300 | 333.463 | 29 |
| 30 | 47.753 | .0210 | .13365 | 7.482 | .00262 | 381.217 | 30 |
| 31 | 54.439 | .0184 | .13332 | 7.501 | .00230 | 435.655 | 31 |
| 32 | 62.060 | .0161 | .13304 | 7.517 | .00201 | 497.716 | 32 |
| 33 | 70.749 | .0142 | .13279 | 7.531 | .00176 | 568.464 | 33 |
| 34 | 80.653 | .0124 | .13257 | 7.543 | .00154 | 649.118 | 34 |
| 35 | 91.945 | .0109 | .13238 | 7.554 | .00135 | 741.063 | 35 |
| 40 | 177.032 | .0057 | .13173 | 7.592 | .00070 | 1433.916 | 40 |
| 45 | 340.860 | .0029 | .13139 | 7.611 | .00036 | 2767.945 | 45 |
| 50 | 656.298 | .0015 | .13122 | 7.621 | .00019 | 5336.505 | 50 |

**Continuous-Compounding, Continuous-Flow Interest Factors
at an Effective Interest Rate of 15%; r = 13.976%**

| N | SINGLE PAYMENT | | | UNIFORM SERIES | | | N |
|---|---|---|---|---|---|---|---|
| | $(F/\bar{P}, 13.976, N)$ | $(P/\bar{F}, 13.976, N)$ | $(\bar{A}/P, 13.976, N)$ | $(P/\bar{A}, 13.976, N)$ | $(\bar{A}/F, 13.976, N)$ | $(F/\bar{A}, 13.976, N)$ | |
| 1 | 1.073 | .9333 | 1.07151 | .933 | .93175 | 1.073 | 1 |
| 2 | 1.234 | .8115 | .57313 | 1.745 | .43337 | 2.307 | 2 |
| 3 | 1.419 | .7057 | .40808 | 2.450 | .26832 | 3.727 | 3 |
| 4 | 1.632 | .6136 | .32636 | 3.064 | .18660 | 5.359 | 4 |
| 5 | 1.877 | .5336 | .27795 | 3.598 | .13819 | 7.236 | 5 |
| 6 | 2.159 | .4640 | .24620 | 4.062 | .10644 | 9.395 | 6 |
| 7 | 2.483 | .4035 | .22395 | 4.465 | .08419 | 11.877 | 7 |
| 8 | 2.855 | .3508 | .20764 | 4.816 | .06788 | 14.732 | 8 |
| 9 | 3.283 | .3051 | .19527 | 5.121 | .05551 | 18.015 | 9 |
| 10 | 3.776 | .2653 | .18565 | 5.386 | .04589 | 21.791 | 10 |
| 11 | 4.342 | .2307 | .17803 | 5.617 | .03827 | 26.133 | 11 |
| 12 | 4.993 | .2006 | .17189 | 5.818 | .03213 | 31.126 | 12 |
| 13 | 5.742 | .1744 | .16689 | 5.992 | .02712 | 36.868 | 13 |
| 14 | 6.604 | .1517 | .16277 | 6.144 | .02300 | 43.472 | 14 |
| 15 | 7.594 | .1319 | .15934 | 6.276 | .01958 | 51.066 | 15 |
| 16 | 8.733 | .1147 | .15648 | 6.390 | .01672 | 59.799 | 16 |
| 17 | 10.043 | .0997 | .15408 | 6.490 | .01432 | 69.842 | 17 |
| 18 | 11.550 | .0867 | .15205 | 6.577 | .01229 | 81.392 | 18 |
| 19 | 13.282 | .0754 | .15032 | 6.652 | .01056 | 94.674 | 19 |
| 20 | 15.274 | .0656 | .14886 | 6.718 | .00910 | 109.948 | 20 |
| 21 | 17.565 | .0570 | .14760 | 6.775 | .00784 | 127.513 | 21 |
| 22 | 20.200 | .0496 | .14653 | 6.824 | .00677 | 147.714 | 22 |
| 23 | 23.230 | .0431 | .14561 | 6.868 | .00585 | 170.944 | 23 |
| 24 | 26.715 | .0375 | .14482 | 6.905 | .00506 | 197.659 | 24 |
| 25 | 30.722 | .0326 | .14414 | 6.938 | .00438 | 228.381 | 25 |
| 26 | 35.330 | .0284 | .14355 | 6.966 | .00379 | 263.711 | 26 |
| 27 | 40.630 | .0247 | .14305 | 6.991 | .00329 | 304.341 | 27 |
| 28 | 46.724 | .0214 | .14261 | 7.012 | .00286 | 351.066 | 28 |
| 29 | 53.733 | .0186 | .14223 | 7.031 | .00247 | 404.799 | 29 |
| 30 | 61.793 | .0162 | .14191 | 7.047 | .00214 | 466.592 | 30 |
| 31 | 71.062 | .0141 | .14162 | 7.061 | .00186 | 537.654 | 31 |
| 32 | 81.721 | .0123 | .14138 | 7.073 | .00161 | 619.375 | 32 |
| 33 | 93.980 | .0107 | .14116 | 7.084 | .00140 | 713.355 | 33 |
| 34 | 108.076 | .0093 | .14098 | 7.093 | .00122 | 821.431 | 34 |
| 35 | 124.288 | .0081 | .14082 | 7.101 | .00106 | 945.719 | 35 |
| 40 | 249.987 | .0040 | .14029 | 7.128 | .00052 | 1909.415 | 40 |
| 45 | 502.814 | .0020 | .14002 | 7.142 | .00026 | 3847.752 | 45 |
| 50 | 1011.339 | .0010 | .13989 | 7.148 | .00013 | 7746.440 | 50 |

# GLOSSARY

Acceptable Investment Diagram (AID): graphic method of evaluation of investment alternatives which indicates the probability that a given rate of return will be surpassed. (*diagramme d'investissement acceptable (DIA)*).

Acid Test Ratio (quick ratio): current assets less inventories divided by current liabilities. (*ratio de liquidité immédiate*).

Amortization: retirement of a debt by periodic payments or reduction of the book value of an asset by periodic charges. (*amortissement*).

Annual Equivalent: annual amount which is equivalent to the present worth of a sequence of payments at a given rate of interest, or to a sequence of payments differently spaced in time and/or amount. (*équivalent annuel*).

Annuity: series of equal payments for a specified time. (*annuité*).

Annuity Factor: coefficient used to find the present (future) worth of an annuity if the amount of the payments is known. (*facteur d'annuité*).

Aspiration Level: minimum amount that will satisfy a decision maker. (*niveau d'aspiration*).

Assets: things of value owned and used to generate income. (*actif*).

Balance Sheet (statement of financial position): accounting report that indicates the financial position of an entity at a particular date. (*bilan*).

**Benefit-Cost Analysis:** method of evaluation of public sector investment projects which expressly considers all of the relevant benefits and costs. (*analyse coûts-avantages*).

**Bond:** long term debt instrument that promises to repay the principal at some future date (maturity) and pay interest in the meantime. (*obligation*).

**Book Value:** value of an asset on the accounting records. Equivalent to the original cost less accumulated depreciation to date. (*valeur comptable*).

**Breakeven Analysis:** method for determining the level of operations at which there is neither profit nor loss. (*analyse du seuil de rentabilité*).

**Capital Assets:** assets not ordinarily bought and sold in the normal course of business whose useful lives exceed one year. Also called fixed assets. (*immobilisations*).

**Capital Budgeting:** process of deciding which long term investment projects will be undertaken in a given time period. (*budgétisation des investissements*).

**Capital Cost Allowance (CCA):** amount allowed by the Income Tax Act of Canada for depreciation expense. (*amortissement du coût en capital (ACC)*).

**Capital Cost Tax Factor (CCTF):** coefficient used to calculate the present worth of tax savings (shields) due to the capital cost allowance. (*facteur de coût en capital*).

**Capital Gains (losses):** profits (losses) on the sale of capital assets. (*gains (pertes) en capital*).

**Capital Rationing:** constraint on the total amount which may be invested in a given time period. (*rationnement du capital*).

**Capital Recovery Factor:** coefficient used to calculate the sum required to recoup the first cost of a project plus compounded interest on the unrecovered balance. (*facteur de recouvrement du capital*).

**Capital Structure:** percentage of each type of permanent capital used by the firm — debt, preferred stock, and common stock. (*structure du capital*).

**Carrybacks (forwards):** amounts which can be carried back (forward) to other fiscal periods for tax purposes. (*reports retrospectifs (prospectifs)*).

**Challenger:** the new machine in replacement studies. (*opposant*).

**Common-Multiple Method:** method of replacement analysis used when the lives of the two alternatives are not the same. It assumes repeated investments for a period long enough to make the two alternatives comparable. (*méthode de multiple commun*).

**Compound Interest:** interest paid on the principal as well as the interest earned in previous periods. (*intérêt composé*).

**Continuous Compounding/Discounting:** situations in which the interest/discount is added continuously rather than discretely. (*capitalisation/actualisation continue*).

**Contribution:** difference between the selling price and variable cost of a product. (*contribution*).

Cost Accounting: process of determining the cost of products, services, etc. (*comptabilité des coûts*).

Cost of Capital: weighted average cost of all the components of the pool of capital which is available for investment. (*coût du capital*).

Criticality Index: measure of the significance of an event that incapacitates the system for normal operations. (*indice de criticalité*).

Critical Path Method: method of network analysis which identifies the shortest path through the network. (*méthode du chemin critique*).

Current Assets: assets that will normally be turned into cash within one year. (*actif à court terme*).

Current Liabilities: liabilities that will normally be paid within one year. (*passif à court terme*).

Current Ratio: current asets divided by current liabilities. (*ratio de liquidité générale*).

Debenture: long term debt which is not secured by any specific assets. (*débenture*).

Decision Tree: graphic method which shows the relationship between decisions and chance events. (*arbre de décision*).

Decisions Under Certainty: decision situations in which complete information is available to the decision maker. (*décisions dans un contexte certain*).

Decisions Under Risk: decision situations in which the probabilities of several future outcomes can be estimated objectively. (*décisions dans un contexte aléatoire*).

Decisions Under Uncertainty: decision situations in which the probabilities of several future outcomes can only be estimated subjectively. (*décisions dans un contexte incertain*).

Declining Balance Depreciation: method of depreciation in which a constant percentage is applied to the undepreciated book value of an asset each year to determine the annual depreciation charge. (*amortissement dégressif*).

Defender: existing machine in replacement studies. (*défenseur*).

Depletion: depreciation of extractable resource assets, such as coal, oil or timber. (*amortissement*).

Depreciation: reduction in value of fixed assets due to obsolescence, use, or accounting convention. (*amortissement*).

Discounted Cash Flow (DCF): the present worth of a series of cash inflows and outflows. (*flux de caisse actualisé (FCA)*).

Effective Interest Rate: true rate of interest computed by dividing the interest payment by the amount of money available to borrower. (*taux d'intérêt effectif*).

Effectiveness: doing the right things. (*efficacité*).

Efficiency: doing things right. (*efficience*).

Equity Ratio: ratio of equity capital (capital contributed by the owners) to total capital. (*ratio d'équité*).

Expected Value: sum of the products of all possible outcomes multiplied by their respective probabilities. (*valeur espérée*).

External Rate of Return: method of analysis of investment proposals which consists of applying the MARR to a limited portion of the cash flows so that sign reversals are eliminated. (*taux de rendement externe*).

Fault Tree: a graphic method for analyzing the reliability of a system. (*arbre de défaut*).

Financial Analysis: economic comparisons which consider both the expected returns from investment proposals as well as their financial costs. (*analyse financière*).

Financial Lease: lease which does not provide maintenance, is not cancellable, and is fully amortized over its life. (*bail financier*).

Financial Risk: that portion of total risk which results from using debt. (*risque financier*).

Financial Structure: the entire right hand side of the balance sheet. It indicates how a firm has been financed. A more all-inclusive concept than capital structure. (*structure financière*).

First Cost (initial outlay): the original cash outlay required for an investment project. (*coût initial*).

Fiscal Policy: government policy concerning its expenditures and revenues. (*politique fiscale*).

Fixed Cost: cost that does not vary with output. (*coût fixe*).

Future Worth: an equivalent worth at a future date, based on the time value of money, of one or more amounts at given earlier dates. (*valeur capitalisée*).

Going Concern Value: value of an asset as part of an operating whole. (*valeur d'usage*).

Gradient: amount of change per unit of time. (*gradient*).

Imputed Costs: costs which are allocated rather than incurred. (*coûts affectés*).

Income (profit and loss) Statement: a financial report that indicates the revenues and expenses of a particular period. (*état des résultats*).

Incremental: change in total results due to a new condition of comparison, such as producing one more batch. (*différentiel*).

Indifference Curve (isoquant): graphic representation of the various amounts of two items that will give equal satisfaction. (*courbe d'indifférence*).

Inflation: increase in the general price level. (*inflation*).

Interest Factor: coefficient used to find the present (future) worth of a payment to be received at some date other than the present. (*facteur d'intérêt*).

Internal Rate of Return (IRR): rate of interest at which the present worth of expected cash inflows from an investment project equals the present worth of the project's cash outflows. (*taux de rendement interne (TRI)*).

Inventory Turnover: ratio of sales to inventory, used to evaluate the management of inventories. (*rotation des stocks*).

Investment Risk Profile: measure of the probable worth of an investment proposal. (*profil de risque d'un investissement*).

Irreducibles: items in engineering economy studies that cannot be reduced to money flows so they must be evaluated qualitatively. (*irréductibles*).

Learning Curve: declining costs of repetitive operations due to experience. (*courbe d'apprentissage*).

Lessee: user of a leased asset. (*locataire*).

Lessor: owner of a leased asset. (*bailleur*).

Leverage: changes in profits (losses) resulting from the use of debt or other fixed costs. (*effet de levier*).

Liabilities: debts owed. (*passif*).

Life Cycle Costing (LCC): method of analysis using cash flows over the entire life of a project with the objective of minimizing the total cost, not just the first cost. (*coût de revient du cycle de vie*).

Life, Economic: period after which an asset should be replaced because of excessive costs of operation. (*vie économique*).

Life, Service: period during which an asset will satisfactorily perform its function without major overhaul. (*vie de service*).

Marginal: change in total results due to the addition (or subtraction) of one unit. (*marginal*).

Maximin: decision criterion that attempts to maximize the probability of achieving the minimum result. (*maximin*).

Maximax: decision criterion that attempts to maximize the probability of achieving the maximum result. (*maximax*).

Minimax-Regret: decision criterion that attempts to minimize the maximum regret. (*manque à gagner minimax*).

Minimum Acceptable Rate of Return (MARR): lower limit for investment acceptability. (*taux de rendement requis (TRR)*).

Monetary Policy: government program of control of the money supply and credit to achieve desired economic goals. (*politique monétaire*).

Most Probable Future: decision criterion that chooses the investment proposal with the greatest return for the future state of the world which has the highest probability. (*futur le plus probable*).

Multiple Rates of Return: situation which occurs when an investment project's expected future cash flows change sign more than once during the study period. It is mathematically impossible to identify which of the rates is economically correct. (*taux de rendement multiple*).

Net Cash Flow (NCF): cash inflows less cash outflows; before-tax cash flows less tax payments. (*flux de caisse net (FCN)*).

Net Worth (equity): capital provided by the owners, includes common and preferred share capital, retained earnings and any surplus accounts. Amount needed to make a balance sheet balance. Assets – Liabilities = Equity. (*capitaux propres, équité*).

Nominal Interest Rate: the contractual, or stated interest rate. (*taux d'intérêt nominal*).

Operating Lease: lease which is cancellable by the lessee on due notice to the lessor. (*bail d'exploitation*).

Operating Ratio: ratio of total expenses to net sales. (*ratio d'exploitation*).

Opportunity Cost: return on the best available alternative, which is foregone because another project was selected. (*coût d'opportunité*).

Payback: period required to recoup the first cost of an investment from the net cash flows generated by it. (*délai de récupération*).

Payoff Matrix: matrix indicating the expected result associated with each future state of nature. (*matrice des règlements*).

Present Worth: value found by discounting future cash flows by an appropriate discount rate, such as the cost of capital. (*valeur actualisée*).

Price Index: measure of the change in prices over some period of time. (*indice des prix*).

Profitability Index: present worth of expected returns divided by the first cost. (*indice de rentabilité*).

Public Goods: items available to all, such as public parks, air, water, defense, etc. (*biens publics*).

Replacement: situation in which one asset replaces another functionally. (*remplacement*).

Request For Expenditure (RFE): forms used by many firms so subordinate units will make investment proposals which are comparable. (*demande de dépense*).

Retained Earnings: portion of after-tax income not paid out in dividends. (*bénéfices réinvestis*).

Risk: probability that ex post returns will be less than ex ante. (*risque*).

Salvage Value: value of a capital asset at the end of a specified period. (*valeur de récupération*).

Sensitivity Analysis: analyses in which key variables are changed one at a time to see what is the effect on the total. (*analyse de sensibilité*).

Simple Interest: interest which is not compounded, paid only on the principal amount of the amount borrowed. (*intérêt simple*).

Sinking Fund: fund to which annual payments are made to amortize a bond or preferred share issue, or to accumulate funds with which to purchase a replacement asset. (*fonds d'amortissement*).

Social Discount Rate: discount rate which reflects the opportunity cost to society of resources used in public sector investment projects. (*taux d'escompte social*).

Spillovers (externalities): secondary effects of investment projects, such as in the increase in land values brought about by the construction of a new highway. (*externalités*).

Standard Operating Procedures (SOP): standardized procedures used by all divisions of a firm. (*normes d'exploitation*).

Straight Line Depreciation: method of depreciation in which the annual depreciation charge is the same each year; it is calculated by dividing the first cost (or the first cost less expected salvage value) by the expected economic life. (*amortissement linéaire*).

Study-Period Method: method of analysis in which a particular time period is assumed to be relevant for decision making. (*méthode de la période étudiée*).

Tax Incentives: reductions in taxes otherwise payable for certain kinds of government approved expenditures. (*incitations fiscales*).

Time Value of Money: effect of time on the money value of an event, taking into consideration the opportunity cost of money. (*valeur de l'argent dans le temps*).

Undepreciated Capital Cost (UCC): the book value of an asset, used as the basis for determining the annual depreciation deduction for tax purposes. (*coût en capital non amorti*).

Variable Cost: cost that varies with output. (*coût variable*).

VisiCalc: microcomputer software package for spreadsheet analyses. (*VisiCalc*).

Working Capital: current assets (gross) or current assets less current liabilities (net). (*fonds de roulement*).

Yield: ratio of return (profit) over investment expressed as a percentage, usually on an annual basis. (*rendement*).

# GLOSSAIRE

*actif*: assets
*actif à court terme*: current assets
*amortissement*: depreciation, depletion, or amortization
*amortissement dégressif*: declining balance depreciation
*amortissement du coût en capital (ACC)*: capital cost allowance (CCA)
*amortissement linéaire*: straight line depreciation
*analyse coûts-avantages*: benefit-cost analysis
*analyse de sensibilité*: sensitivity analysis
*analyse du seuil de rentabilité*: breakeven analysis
*analyse financière*: financial analysis
*annuité*: annuity
*arbre de décision*: decision tree
*arbre de défaut*: fault tree
*bail d'exploitation*: operating lease
*bail financier*: financial lease
*bailleur*: lessor
*bénéfices réinvestis*: retained earnings
*biens publics*: public goods
*bilan*: balance sheet (statement of financial position)
*budgétisation des investissements*: capital budgeting
*capitalisation/actualisation continue*: continuous compounding/discounting

*capitaux propres (équité)*: net worth (equity)
*comptabilité des coûts*: cost accounting
*contribution*: contribution
*courbe d'apprentissage*: learning curve
*courbe d'indifférence*: indifference curve (isoquant)
*coût d'opportunité*: opportunity cost
*coût du capital*: cost of capital
*coût du revient de cycle de vie*: life cycle costing (LCC)
*coût en capital non amorti*: undepreciated capital cost (UCC)
*coût fixe*: fixed cost
*coût initial*: first cost (initial outlay)
*coût variable*: variable cost
*coûts affectés*: imputed costs
*débenture*: debenture
*décisions dans un contexte aléatoire*: decisions under risk
*décisions dans un contexte certain*: decisions under certainty
*décisions dans un contexte incertain*: decisions under uncertainty
*défenseur*: defender
*délai de récupération*: payback
*demande de dépense*: request for expenditure (RFE)
*diagramme d'investissement acceptable (DIA)*: acceptable investment diagram (AID)
*différentiel*: incremental
*effet de levier*: leverage
*efficacité*: effectiveness
*efficience*: efficiency
*équivalent annuel*: annual equivalent
*état des résultats*: income (profit and loss) statement
*externalités*: spillovers (externalities)
*facteur d'annuité*: annuity factor
*facteur d'intérêt*: interest factor
*facteur de coût en capital*: capital cost tax factor (CCTF)
*facteur de recouvrement du capital*: capital recovery factor
*flux de caisse actualisé (FCA)*: net cash flow (DCF)
*flux de caisse net (FCN)*: net cash flow (NCF)
*fonds d'amortissement*: sinking fund
*fonds de roulement*: working capital
*futur le plus probable*: most probable future
*gains (pertes) en capital*: capital gains (losses)
*gradient*: gradient
*immobilisations*: capital assets
*incitations fiscales*: tax incentives
*indice de criticalité*: criticality index
*indice de rentabilité*: profitability index
*indice des prix*: price index
*inflation*: inflation
*intérêt composé*: compound interest
*intérêt simple*: simple interest
*irréductibles*: irreducibles

*locataire*: lessee
*manque à gagner minimax*: minimax-regret
*marginal*: marginal
*matrice des règlements*: payoff matrix
*maximax*: maximax
*maximin*: maximin
*méthode de multiple commun*: common-multiple method
*méthode de la période étudiée*: study-period method
*méthode du chemin critique*: critical path method
*niveau d'aspiration*: aspiration level
*normes d'exploitation*: standard operating procedures (SOP)
*obligation*: bond
*opposant*: challenger
*passif*: liabilities
*passif à court terme*: current liabilities
*politique fiscale*: fiscal policy
*politique monétaire*: monetary policy
*profil de risque d'un investissement*: investment risk profile
*ratio d'équité*: equity ratio
*ratio d'exploitation*: operating ratio
*ratio de liquidité générale*: current ratio
*ratio de liquidité immédiate*: acid test (quick) ratio
*rationnement du capital*: capital rationing
*rendement*: yield
*remplacement*: replacement
*reports rétrospectifs (prospectifs)*: carrybacks (forwards)
*risque*: risk
*risque financier*: financial risk
*rotation des stocks*: inventory turnover
*structure du capital*: capital structure
*structure financière*: financial structure
*taux de rendement externe*: external rate of return
*taux de rendement interne (TRI)*: internal rate of return (IRR)
*taux de rendement multiple*: multiple rates of return
*taux de rendement requis (TRR)*: minimum acceptable rate of return (MARR)
*taux d'escompte social*: social discount rate
*taux d'intérêt effectif*: effective interest rate
*taux d'intérêt nominal*: nominal interest rate
*valeur actualisée*: present worth
*valeur capitalisée*: future worth
*valeur comptable*: book value
*valeur de l'argent dans le temps*: time value of money
*valeur de récupération*: salvage value
*valeur d'usage*: going concern value
*valeur espérée*: expected value
*vie économique*: economic life
*vie de service*: service life
*VisiCalc*: VisiCalc

# SUBJECT INDEX

565

# NAME INDEX